Heinemann is an imprint of Pearson Education Limited, a
company incorporated in England and Wales, having its
registered office at Edinburgh Gate, Harlow, Essex, CM20 2JE.
Registered company number: 872828

www.heinemann.co.uk

Heinemann is the registered trademark of Pearson Education Limited

Text © 2007

First published 2007

12 11 10 09
10 9 8 7 6 5 4 3

British Library Cataloguing in Publication Data is available
from the British Library on request.

ISBN 978 0 435499 24 2

Edited by Susan Ross
Typeset by Tek-Art, Croydon, Surrey, UK
Illustrated by Tek-Art, Croydon, Surrey, UK
Cover design by Penacor Big
Cover photo © Getty Images/Science Faction
Original illustrations © Pearson Education Limited 2007
Picture research by Alison Prior
Printed and bound in China (SWTC/03)

**Websites**

The websites used in this book were correct and up-to-date at the time of publication. It is
essential for tutors to preview each website before using it in class so as to ensure that the URL
is still accurate, relevant and appropriate. We suggest that tutors bookmark useful websites and
consider enabling students to access them through the school/college intranet.

# BTEC national

# Construction
## Building Services Engineering & Civil Engineering

Simon Topliss

Mike Hurst

Skarratt

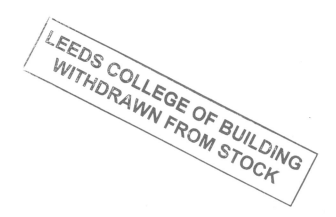

Heinemann

# Contents

# Acknowledgments

The authors and publisher would like to thank the following individuals and organisations for permission to reproduce photographs:

Alamy / Mark Hamilton – pages 2–3; Alamy / Rob Wilkinson – page 10; Corbis / Michael S; Yamashita – page 11;Photographers Direct / David Burton – page 15;Corbis / Jeremy Horner – page 16;Alamy / Nordicphotos – page 18; Alamy / Chris Selby – page 18; Alamy / Justin Kase – page 33;Corbis / James Emmerson – pages 42–43;Corbis/Roy Rainford – page 48;

Alamy / Dick Makin – page 59;iStockphoto.com / Rafa Irusta – page 68;Harcourt Ltd / Debbie Rowe – pages 74–75;Corbis / Loretta Steyn, Gallo Images – page 106;Science Photo Library – pages 144–145;Science Photo Library – page 177;Construction Photography – page 178;

Getty Images / Matthew Lewis – pages 184–185;iStockphoto.com / Tony Tremblay – pages 222–223;Alamy / Alan Oliver – page 225;Quantum Imaging – page 229;Construction Photography – page 234;Alamy / Leslie Garland – page 241;Alamy / Leslie Garland – page 243;Alamy / Gunter Marx – pages 270–271;Alamy/ Roger Bamber – page 274;

Photographers Direct / Stephen Hay – page 279;Alamy / David Hoffman – page 281;

Gary Moon, AIA Principal Designer for +BP / Architecture – page 283;Alamy / EnviroScene – page 291;Alamy / Wherrett.com – page 296;Photographers Direct / Ian Clowes / Goldy Solutions – 301;Construction Photography – pages 314–315;Harcourt Ltd / Gareth Boden – page 316/343;Alamy / Ace Stock Ltd – page 319;Photographers Direct / Cynthia Simmons – pages 360–361;Construction Photography / Damian Gillie – page 374;Corbis / Helmut Meyer zur Capellen / Zefa – page 378;Alamy / Mark Bolton Photography – page 379;Alamy / Chris Howes / Wild Places Photography – page 380;Alamy / Martin Mayer – page 381;Alamy / Roger Bamer – page 386;Alamy / John Bradshaw – pages 402–403;Photographers Direct / Paul Williams – page 407;York Survey – page 407;Photographers Direct / Paul Williams – page 417;Harcourt Ltd / Gareth Boden – page 417;Alamy / Geogphotos – page 419;

Construction Photography – pages 452–453;Science Photo Library – page 464;Supplied by the authors – page 465;Supplied by the authors – page 466;York Survey – page 467; Supplied by the authors – page 468

The authors and publishers would like to thank the following individuals and organisations for permission to reproduce the following copyrighted material:

Figures. 3.11, p126 Graph: Construction output percentage change, 3.17, p134 Example of a pie chart, 3.18, p134 Example of a multiple bar chart used to compare Construction Employment by Occupation in the UK compared to the East of England region in 2005 reproduced with kind permission of ConstructionSkills, Construction Skills Network (2006) East of England Labour Market Intelligence 2006 King's Lynn: ConstructionSkills;Fig. 6.10, p264 Typical scaffolding system courtesy of the Health & Safety Executive, www.hse.gov.uk/Reproduced under the terms of the Click-

Use Licence;. Fig. 8.14, p334 A red lined CAD drawing Image from http://www.graphisoft.com/Graphisoft, Virtual Building Solutions; Figures 8.17 p338, 8.19 P340, 8.20 P341, 8.21 P342, 8.25 P344, courtesy of Munday and Cramer; Figure 8.24 courtesy of Carillion; Table 4.1, P147 Typical heat output of an adult male; Table 4.2, P148 Clothing values;Table 4.3, P149 K value of materials are all adapted from CIBSE (Chartered Institution of Building Services Engineers) Guide A: Environmental design

**Edexcel endorsement**

This material has been endorsed by Edexcel and offers high quality support for the delivery of Edexcel qualifications.

Edexcel endorsement does not mean that this material is essential to achieve any Edexcel qualification, nor does it mean that this is the only suitable material available to support any Edexcel qualification. No endorsed material will be used verbatim in setting any Edexcel examination and any resource lists produced by Edexcel shall include this and other appropriate texts. While this material has been through an Edexcel quality assurance process, all responsibility for the content remains with the publisher.

Copies of official specifications for all Edexcel qualifications may be found on the Edexcel website – www.edexcel.org.uk

# Introduction

Welcome to this BTEC National Construction course book, specifically designed to support students on the following programmes:

- BTEC National Awards in Construction, Civil Engineering and Building Services
- BTEC National Certificate & Diploma in Construction
- BTEC National Certificate & Diploma in Civil Engineering
- BTEC National Certificate & Diploma in Building Services Engineering

For the BTEC National Award programmes, the book covers the four core units, that is:

- Health, Safety and Welfare in Construction and the Built Environment
- Construction and the Environment
- Science and Materials in Construction and the Built Environment
- Construction Technology and Design in Construction and Civil Engineering

It also provides five specialist units from which two units can be selected for this qualification. These are:

- Mathematics in Construction and the Built Environment
- Planning, Organisation and Control of Resources in Construction and the Built Environment
- Graphical Detailing in Construction and the Built Environment

- Measuring, Estimating and Tendering Processes in Construction and the Built Environment
- Surveying in Construction and Civil Engineering

For the BTEC National Certificate and Diploma programmes, this book covers all six core units for the National Certificate and Diploma in Construction namely:

- Health, Safety and Welfare in Construction and the Built Environment
- Construction and the Environment
- Mathematics in Construction and the Built Environment
- Science and Materials in Construction and the Built Environment
- Construction Technology and Design in Construction and Civil Engineering
- Building Technology in Construction

It also provides five specialist units from which you can complete the qualification. These units are the more common ones that have been selected and are:

- Planning, Organisation and Control of Resources in Construction and the Built Environment
- Measuring, Estimating and Tendering Processes in Construction and the Built Environment
- Surveying in Construction and Civil Engineering
- Building Surveying in Construction
- Graphical Detailing in Construction and the Built Environment

The aim of this book is to provide a comprehensive source of information for your course. It follows the BTEC specification closely, so that you can easily see what you have covered and quickly find the information you need.

A wide variety of case studies, diagrams and assessments are provided to help build your understanding of the construction industry. We hope the links between the book and the course specification will greatly assist you in your learning.

You will often be asked to carry out research for activities in the text, and this will develop your research skills and enable you to find many sources of interesting construction information, particularly on the Internet.

**Theory into practice**

These features allow you to consider theoretical knowledge and relate this to the construction industry.

**Grading tips**

There are valuable grading tips at the end of each chapter to help you attain a higher grade in the units you are studying.

**Assessment practice**

Activities are also provided throughout each unit. These are linked to real situations and case studies and they can be used for practice before tackling the preparation for assessment or completing your own actual assessment.

Your tutor should check that you have completed enough activities to meet all the assessment criteria for the unit.

Tutors and students should refer to the BTEC standards for the qualification for the full BTEC grading criteria for each unit (www.edexcel.org.uk).

**Key terms**

Issues and terms that you need to be aware of are summarised under these headings. They will help you check your knowledge as you learn, and will prove to be a useful quick-reference tool.

**Remember**

These highlight important points to help you focus on key issues and reflect on the wider context.

## 9.1 Recording dimensions and descriptions of construction work in a methodical way and processing these into final quantities for varying purposes

# Applications of measurement

### Detailed measurement and production of quantities and descriptions for bills of quantities

This is where the **SMM7** rule book comes into force. It consists of several chapters that cover aspects of the construction of a project, and the measurement rules that apply to each item. Detailed measurement is undertaken from the contract drawings and specification and, using dimension paper or a software program, quantities are **taken off** and calculated for each item. The descriptions for the items that are produced for the bill of quantities must follow the rules set out within SMM7. These should contain all the necessary information for the estimator to know what they are pricing, for example fixed with screws rather than nails is more expensive as it takes longer to do.

### Key term

**SMM7** This is the standard method of measurement (seventh edition) and is published by the Royal Institution of Chartered Surveyors (RICS).

**Taken off or taking off** The process of taking dimensions from drawings and producing a quantity.

### Remember!

The SMM7 provides a clear set of rules that can be applied fairly, so that all contractors bidding for work do so on an equal basis that is fair to all, that is, every contractor will be pricing the same set of items.

### Theory into practice

Find out more about the RICS by visiting their website, www.rics.org.

In general terms, the rules contained within SMM7 follow the following structure:

- the item's classification, e.g. excavation
- size restrictions, e.g. maximum depth less than 0.25 m
- the unit of measurement, e.g. cubic metres ($m^3$)
- the measurement rule for that item, e.g. quantities are measured in bulk before excavation
- the definition rule for that item, e.g. site vegetation includes hedges, scrub, trees and stumps
- the coverage rule for that item, e.g. works include removing tree roots
- any supplementary information, e.g. describe filling materials that will be used.

### Interim payments

Interim payments occur at a regular time intervals during a project's life – usually every 30 days. The client's quantity surveyor will, in agreement with the contractor's quantity surveyor, measure all the work accomplished on site to date. This is called the gross valuation and from this all the previous payments are deducted to give the net valuation, which represents the work achieved that month. The valuation is prepared using the percentage of work done against each item within the **bill of quantities**. Simple multiplication and summing up gives the value of the total amount of work achieved to date.

# Features of the book

This book has a number of features to help you relate theory to practice and reinforce your learning. It also aims to help you gather evidence for assessment. You will find the following features in each unit.

The author team has invested a great deal of effort to help and guide you through the core units and some of the more common specialist units. This book is an invaluable tool:, use it to learn effectively and independently to develop some individual and outstanding assessments within your studies

**Simon A Topliss**
**Greg Skarratt**
**Mike Hurst**

## Key term

**Bill of quantities** A document produced as a result of the taking off of dimensions. It represents the whole of the project measured as items, square metres, cubic metres, all broken down into the SMM7 sections, and is used to place prices in as rates against the quantity measured, then totalled.

### Final account work

A final account is the summation of all the variations that have occurred on a typical contract and this is adjusted against the original contract sum that was agreed at the commencement of the project. It is the final total that the client has to pay the contractor less the previous payments they have received.

In compiling the final account, an architect's instruction may require carrying out measurement on site and then valuing against the bills of quantities rates that the contractor entered within their **tender**. All the contract variations are worked through and the final account is then prepared for agreement by the contractor and the client.

## Key term

**Tender** The estimate that is submitted by the contractor to the client containing the price for the work.

### Variations

These are changes to the construction works on site as a result of, for example:

- errors in the design
- errors in the specification
- the expenditure of **provisional and prime cost sums**
- design changes by the client.

These may need to be measured in order to ascertain how much the client has to pay the contractor for

## Key term

**Provisional and prime cost sums** These are sums of money placed within a tender for unforeseen works or items that cannot as yet be measured. They are subsequently omitted and the agreed rate and price is put back when the work is completed. These can also be sums of money for nominated suppliers or subcontractors.

the variation. For example, if you have been asked to increase the length of a brick wall, then you would physically measure the length on site or from a revised drawing. This would establish the quantity of wall in square metres ($m^2$); looking up the bill of quantities' rate for this gives the value of the additional work.

### Claims and disputes

Claims and disputes items often arise on construction projects and are principally between the client and the contractor. They can lead to losses and expenses for the contractor and a delay to the project handover for the client. Many factors start disputes such as:

- adverse weather conditions
- late receipt of information from the designer
- a vast number of design changes
- cancellation of some part of the construction work.

Measurement may be needed to substantiate some of the claims and dispute items in order to provide evidence for an adjudicator to decide who is right in the dispute. Any record supplied in evidence will help to determine who is to blame and, ultimately, who will pay for the additional resources used.

### Thinking points

When the Wembley Stadium project ran into delays and additional costs associated with several design changes, the contractor and the Football Association eventually settled out of court.

### Case studies

These provide hands-on examples of how a situation could be handled within the construction industry.

### Knowledge check

At the end of each unit is a set of quick questions to test your knowledge of the information you have been studying. Use these to check your progress, and also as a revision tool.

### Preparation for assessment

Each unit concludes with a suggested full unit assessment which, taken as a whole, fulfils all the unit requirements from Pass to Distinction.

Each task is matched to the relevant criteria in the specification.

If you are aiming for a Pass, make sure you complete all the Pass **P** tasks

If you are aiming for a Merit, make sure you complete all the Pass **P** and Merit **M** tasks.

If you are aiming for a Distinction, you will also need to complete all the Distinction **D** tasks. **P1** means the first of the Pass criteria listed in the specification, **M1** the first of the Merit criteria, **D1** the first of the Distinction criteria, and so on.

### Thinking points

These are points relevant to the section of text you are reading and specific to the construction environment.

# Health, safety and welfare in construction and the built environment

## Introduction

The health, safety and welfare of the construction workforce are crucial within our industry, which contains many hazards and risks. Falls from height and incidents involving plant and machinery are the primary causes of accidents on construction sites.

In this unit, you will look at the employer's and employee's duties under current health, safety and welfare legislation, along with the identification of the risks and hazards in the workplace. The control of these hazards and risks will be investigated using the risk assessment process. You will learn how to undertake a typical construction risk assessment, using a site visit at your educational establishment or from a construction site visit. You will learn how accidents can be prevented by the use of risk control measures and how to meet legal requirements. Finally, you will look at what happens after an accident, the immediate processes and the legal reporting procedure.

### How you will be assessed

This unit is internally assessed by your tutor. A variety of activities is included in this chapter to help you understand all aspects of working safely in the construction industry.

After completing this unit you should be able to achieve the following outcomes:

1 Understand the general and specific responsibilities of both employers and employees under current health, safety and welfare legislation
2 Be able to identify workplace hazards, persons who may be affected by such hazards, and the potential consequences of accidents
3 Know how to use risk assessments in appropriate formats
4 Be able to use workplace health and safety policies to recommend control measures, reduce risk and meet legal requirements
5 Understand own role in accident recording and reporting procedures

# Thinking points

Health and safety is present every day of our lives and includes not just our home life but also our working life. The construction of buildings, roads, drainage, schools, factories and houses can be unique and complicated projects, each having different and varied risks and hazards associated with them. Multi-storey, high-rise buildings in major cities are now a normal occurrence and involve the risk of working at height to construct them.

Take a look at a local construction site that is near where you live – make sure you do not enter the site but observe from the outside. What are the hazards associated with this construction work? How are you going to control these hazards? How will you prevent major accidents occurring? As you work through this chapter, you will learn how to answer these vital health and safety questions, many of which require to be answered by law!

Whatever aspect of construction you choose for your future career, be it architecture, civil engineering or building services, health and safety will be of considerable importance, whether you work in a large or a small organisation. It is an aspect of construction that has to be considered daily.

In the UK, the majority of fatal and major accidents occurs within the construction industry. What do you consider is the major cause of these accidents? Can they be prevented with precautions and legislation?

# Roles and responsibilities

## The employer

**Employers** have a general duty under the Heath and Safety at Work Act (HASAWA) 1974 to ensure, so far as is reasonably practicable, your health, safety and welfare at work.

## Key Term

**Employer** This is a person who owns the company constructing the building or project; it may be the managing director or a multinational with shareholders and a chief executive officer.

### ■ Specific responsibilities

Specific responsibilities are listed in the HASAWA under the general duties to employees and are as follows:

- To ensure the health and safety of all employees.
- To provide safe systems of work, safe handling, storage and transport, information training and supervision, a safe place of work access and egress, and a safe environment.
- To provide a health and safety policy if there are five or more employees.
- To observe the regulations on union appointed safety representatives.
- To consult and cooperate with employees on safety measures.
- To observe the regulations on safety committees.
- Not to charge for anything provided for safety (Health & Safety Executive).

As you can see, this list is quite comprehensive and covers all the vital elements to provide a safe environment for employees.

## The employee

Under the HASAWA, **employees** have the following general duties:

- To act with due care for themselves and others, e.g. to walk rather than run down a corridor.
- To cooperate with the employer, e.g. taking part in **tool box talks**.
- To use correctly anything provided for health and safety in accordance with any instruction or training, e.g. safety glasses and ear protectors.
- Not to recklessly interfere or misuse anything provided for health and safety, e.g. letting off a fire extinguisher for fun.

## Key Terms

**Employees** Workers who receive wages for their skills from the employer.

**Tool box talks** Where everyone stops work to discuss a safety aspect of the job they are working on.

## The client

The **client**, whether a landlord, private individual or a company, has many health and safety responsibilities. They must demonstrate an acceptable standard of health and safety. Under the Construction (Design and Management) Regulations 1994 (usually referred to as the CDM Regulations), they have specific responsibilities:

- They have to appoint the planning supervisor.
- They must provide all health and safety information about the workplace where the work is to be carried out.
- They must appoint a competent, resourced, main contractor.

- They must ensure that the construction phase health and safety plan has been produced before commencement.
- They have to store the health and safety file on completion.

## Theory into practice

The CDM Regulations are currently under revision and may be changed in 2007. Look up the latest edition on the Office of Public Sector Information website: www.opsi.gov.uk.

## Key Term

**Client** The person who will ultimately own the constructed building or project and who pays for the work.

## Theory into practice

Look at sections 3 and 4 of the HASAWA 1974 for other duties that may be undertaken by a client.

### The main contractor

The **main contractor** is often referred to as the 'principal contractor' under the terms of the CDM Regulations 1994. The main contractor has general and specific duties as an employer under the HASAWA 1974, but the CDM Regulations place specific responsibilities upon them as follows:

- The principal contractor must ensure the cooperation of all contractors on site.

- They must ensure that any rules set out within the construction phase health and safety plan are passed on to everyone who will be working on the site.
- They must make sure that the only people allowed on the site have permission to be there.
- They must ensure that the Health & Safety Executive (HSE) is notified about the works and that the **F10** is displayed in a prominent position.
- They must ensure that they pass on any relevant health and safety information to the planning supervisor.
- They prepare the health and safety file. This may be the responsibility of the planning supervisor, but it often falls to the contractor to complete the file and hand it over to the client.

## Key Terms

**Main contractor** The company constructing the building or project. It may be a large or small organisation.

**F10** The official document that informs the HSE that a company is undertaking a project.

### Subcontractors

**Subcontractors** generally work under contract to the main or principal contractor. The principal contractor has to ensure that they are competent, provided with the relevant information, a site safety induction and ensure they provide **method statements** and risk assessments so that their work can be coordinated safely.

## Key Terms

**Subcontractors** Separate companies who work for the main contractor, e.g. a heating engineering company.

**Method statements** These outline in detail how the company is going to undertake the work, what it will use and what precautions it will take.

## Remember!

Subcontractors are employers in their own right and have to fulfil the duties of employers (see page 5).

## Health & Safety Executive

The **Health & Safety Executive (HSE)** was set up to regulate and control health and safety in the UK. The HSE has many divisions that cover industries from nuclear power, agriculture, railways to construction. The HSE has a wide role to play in controlling health and safety in construction. Its responsibilities are:

- to advise
- to inspect
- to enforce.

It also offers and promotes health and safety information.

## Key Term

**Health & Safety Executive (HSE)** A body set up by the Health and Safety Commission acting under the Health and Safety at Work Act. The HSE is responsible for inspecting, and enforcing health and safety.

## Theory into practice

Visit the website of the HSE, www.hse.gov.uk, and explore the depth of free information that is available.

If it wishes, the HSE has powers to inspect any construction site notified to it under the notification rules associated with the F10. The F10 is the official form that is completed by the contractor and sent to the HSE to advise it that works are about to commence. It contains a brief description of the work, where it is being carried out, for how long and who will be working on it.

The HSE can enforce health and safety legislation in two ways, either by an improvement notice or a prohibition notice. An improvement notice tells the person receiving it that an incident has been found during an inspection that requires correcting within a certain time as it has the potential to cause harm (although is not currently serious enough to cause immediate injury). A prohibition notice is served when there is a serious and imminent danger to persons who might be harmed. Work or activity is stopped immediately and cannot be restarted until the defect is corrected.

## Remember!

The HSE also carries out extensive inspections and investigations following an accident, especially if there has been a fatality. In the last 25 years, nearly 3000 people have been killed within the construction sector. These investigations may often lead to a conviction for failure of duties under the HASAWA, with either a fine or imprisonment or both.

## The local authority

**Local authorities'** responsibilities for safety mainly cover environmental health and other general duties such as highways and road safety. The environmental health officer may visit a site on grounds of noise, nuisance or environmental issues, for example if a contractor is disturbing surrounding residents with noise from a compressor, or excessive dust is blowing into people's homes.

## Key Term

**Local authority** The elected local council which runs the services within a geographical area.

## The planning supervisor

The planning supervisor has the following key responsibilities under the CDM Regulations.

- To ensure that the HSE is notified of the project – the F10. The client's and principal contractor's names also appear on the form. Indeed, the latter two have to sign it, which is then sent to the HSE.

- To ensure that there is cooperation between designers if there is more than one on the contract, e.g. a structural designer, an architect, an interior designer and a landscape architect. The planning supervisor must ensure that they cooperate with each other. This can be achieved with regular meetings.

- To ensure designers comply with their duties to:
  - make the client aware of their duties
  - assess the risks within the design
  - provide adequate information on the risks (assessments)
  - cooperate with the planning supervisor and other designers.

- To make sure that the pre-tender health and safety plan is prepared.

- To advise the client.

- To check a health and safety file is prepared and handed over to the client (Construction Information Sheets No 40 and No 41).

## Remember!

The planning supervisor is given specific roles and responsibilities on planning the health and safety before and after a contract under the Construction (Design and Management) Regulations 1994.

## Remember!

Everyone has a **duty of care** in law on a construction site and must act if they see something that would be considered dangerous and might harm a person.

## Key Term

**Duty of care** The duty placed upon everyone by the HASAWA to take care of themselves and others about them.

## Case study

Read the following newspaper article on an accident that occurred when a roofing contractor fell through a fragile roof covering. When you have fully read the article, answer the following questions.

# Roofer died in fall

Health and safety officials are considering a criminal prosecution after an experienced roofer fell through a roof panel to his death.

Graham Cartwright was checking for rain leaks on an asbestos roof at a local factory. Factory workers described at the inquest hearing the roof crack. They saw Mr Cartwright falling through the air then hitting his head on some machinery before landing. He received multiple injuries, including extensive head injuries.

Mr Cartwright had worked at the factory many times. The inquest heard that the factory had a detailed health and safety manual and inducted subcontractors on health and safety procedures. The factory's managing director told the inquest that repair and maintenance of the roof was carried out regularly by subcontractors.

An inspector from the Health & Safety Executive confirmed that the HSE had investigated Mr Cartwright's death. She explained that asbestos sheeting panels sometimes shattered to the touch and were the cause of several fatalities each year.

1  **Identify and describe the roles and responsibilities of the persons responsible for health, safety and welfare on a construction project.**

2  **Identify from the case study who was responsible for health and safety in this workplace? and describe their roles and responsibilities in this case.**

You have just started the external walls of a building in brickwork and have reached the first-floor level. The scaffolding has just been put into place. The front wall you are currently working on is next to a public footpath in a busy shopping centre To whom do you owe a duty of care? **P1**

After you have identified who was responsible for safety on this site, suggest suitable improvements that could be made to the workplace systems at this factory to avoid such a fatal accident again. **D2**

# Legislation

## The Health and Safety at Work Act 1974

The HASAWA 1974 is a very important piece of legislation. It is from this Act that many regulations have been developed. There are numerous sections in the Act that cover where the duty of care lies on a construction site. For example, manufacturers of materials used to construct a building must ensure they are safe; contractors must provide a safe means of access and egress from the place of work, such as scaffolding.

Legislation on health and safety is there for a reason and that is to protect *everyone* involved in and around the construction workplace. It also covers people who are not employees, such as delivery drivers and visitors, and places that are not necessarily the employer's, for example landlords or factory owners where part of the site may be let to another employer.

## Assessment practice

Identify three main pieces of health, safety and welfare legislation relevant to the construction and built environment sector and describe the legal duties of employees and employers in terms of such legislation. **P2**

# Theory into practice

Figure 1.1 contains a section of the Health and Safety at Work Act. Ask your tutor to print off the resource copy. You will notice that it is divided into several sections: employee's duties, and so on. The copy shown has several areas missing from it. You will have to undertake research on the Internet in order to complete all the missing sections and duties. Alternatively, you could find an original copy of the legislation within a library resource, or within a health and safety textbook.

| Obligations | Public | Premises | Emissions | Designers | Employee | Interfere | Charge |
|---|---|---|---|---|---|---|---|
| 2 | 3 | 4 | 5 | 6 | 7 | 8 | 9 |
| | General duties to persons other than employees | General duties of persons concerned with premises | Replaced by the Environmental Protection Act | General duties of designers, importers, manufacturers and installers of equipment | General duties of employees 1 To act with due care for H&S of ☐ 2 To observe ☐ 3 To ☐ with employer | Duty not ☐ or ☐ Anything provided in the interests of H&S at work | Duty of the employer Not to ☐ for anything needed to meet requirement of the Act |

**General duties of employers to employees**

(1) Duty to ensure H&S at work ☐ employees

(2) Should provide
(a) Safe ☐ & safe plant
(b) Safe handling, ☐
(c) Information, ☐ supervision
(d) Safe place of work, access & egress
(e) Safe ☐

(3) Safety Policy

(4) Safety Reps

(6) Consult and cooperate to develop

(7) Safety committees

▲ Figure 1.1 Health and Safety at Work Act 1974: sections 2–9

## Remember!

The HSE website has a lot of information that can help you. Visit www.hse.gov.uk for more details.

▶
**Safety boots have steel toe caps**

There has been a considerable amount of health and safety legislation since the HASAWA 1974. Listed below are just some of the primary pieces of legislation that are concerned with the construction industry.

## Remember!

Health and safety legislation continually evolves and changes. Look for updated laws and regulations.

### Construction (Design and Management) Regulations 1994

The Construction (Design and Management) Regulations were developed from a European directive that had looked at the principal cause of accidents. The research showed that nearly a third of accidents could be traced back to the design stage of a project. From this, the onus of a risk assessment had now to be undertaken by the designer, so that the contractor and

the client were aware of the inherent risks associated with constructing and maintaining a building. The regulations placed duties upon four main parties to the design and construction process:

- the client
- the designer
- the planning supervisor
- the principal contractor.

Specific duties concerning these four are covered later in the chapter.

### Work at Height Regulations 2005

These regulations were introduced to try to control the large number of fatalities each year in construction that result from falls from a height. They set out some basic rules that must be followed.

If you can fall off a chair and be injured, then this is classed as 'working at height' where there is risk of injury from that height. To control this, the regulations state that you must avoid working at height where an alternative method can be used. For example, cleaning first-floor windows to a building can be done using a specialist pole from outside, or if it is a new building, altering the design to install tilt and turn windows which can be cleaned from the inside.

Where there is no alternative and you have to work at height, then: 'Where work is carried out at height, every employer shall take suitable and sufficient measures to prevent, so far as is reasonably practicable, any person falling a distance liable to cause personal injury' (Work at Height Regulations, © Crown Copyright 2005). So how can this be achieved? All the following precautions would help prevent a person falling from height:

- using scaffolding instead of ladders
- mobile elevated platforms
- guard rails, barriers and handrails
- toe boards.

The third major item the regulations cover is to restrict the distance a person can fall. This can be done using:

- **PPE** suspension harnesses to secure a person to a solid structure and restrict the distance they fall, through a lanyard

▲ This is definitely not an acceptable method of working at height

## Key Term

**PPE** Personnel protective equipment. This is equipment provided for the individual to use to protect themselves against certain hazards where there is no alternative method, and it should always be the last resort as you should try to design out its use.

## Key Term

**Collective means of protection** A system of protection that protects the whole workforce and not just the individual. For example, a scaffold with guardrails, handrails, toe boards and netting protects everyone working on or using it.

- netting or airbags to catch a person falling.

The Work at Height Regulations also ask employers to check the competency of each individual asked to work at height. To do this, employers may provide suitable training, instruction and supervision and can check that employees are happy and feel confident at the height at which they are being asked to work. The regulations also require that the work is suitably planned and organised and has sufficient supervision. The schedules at the end of the regulations provide details of requirements for working platforms, ladders for risk-assessed, short duration work, access and egress, requirements for PPE and **collective means of protection**.

### Management of Health, Safety and Welfare Regulations 1999

These were introduced to reinforce the message of risk assessment through the five steps to risk assessment which we will cover later in the chapter. The employer's duties under these regulations are many. We have picked out some of the regulations that apply to construction work to illustrate the wide range of duties that an employer has under these regulations. The index for the regulations covers:

- health and safety arrangements, e.g. first aid provision

- the surveillance of employees' health, e.g. hearing tests
- informing employees on safety aspects
- judging the capabilities of employees, e.g. can a person work at height?
- risk assessment processes not to endanger employees
- the protection of people under 18 years of age
- provision for expectant mothers
- temporary workers.

## Theory into practice

You can find the index for the Management of Health, Safety and Welfare Regulations at the Office of Public Sector Information website: www.opsi.gov.uk.

The employee's duties under these regulations are to:
- use any plant or machinery provided in accordance with any training in its use
- to inform their employer of a work situation that poses a serious and imminent danger to employees
- to inform the employer of any safety protection measure or arrangement that may be defective (www.opsi.gov.uk: Management of Health, Safety and Welfare Regulations, © Crown Copyright).

## Construction (Health, Safety and Welfare) Regulations 1996

These regulations were introduced in 1996 specifically for the construction industry in order to try to reduce the high level of accidents that were occurring year on year.

The employer's duties under these regulations include the following:
- Ensuring that construction workplaces are safe – this is a broad statement that must be adhered to.
- Putting in place measures to prevent operatives falling.

- Providing toe boards, netting or a physical barrier to prevent objects from falling.
- Undertaking measures with regard to excavations, their support and prevention of people and plant from falling into the excavation.
- Putting in place special measures when working above water, to prevent an employee drowning.
- Considering the movement of traffic on construction sites, both on and off.
- Putting in place temporary emergency routes and procedures while the building is incomplete.
- Providing suitable welfare facilities for workers.
- Providing suitable lighting and fresh air to workplaces.
- Undertaking some specific safety inspections, e.g. scaffolds and excavations.

There are no specifically defined duties for employees within these regulations apart from Regulation 4:
- It is the duty of every employee to comply with these regulations.
- Employees should report to a supervisor any defect that could cause harm to themselves or colleagues.
- Every employee has to cooperate regarding health and safety.

## Assessment practice

Identify three main pieces of health, safety and welfare legislation relevant to the construction and built environment sector and describe the legal duties of employees and employers in terms of such legislation. **P2**

## Theory into practice

You have been asked to help set up the construction site for a new shopping complex outside the city centre. The contracts manager is unsure of the legal requirements, both documentary and physical resources, and asks you to look into this.

With regard to the legislation, identify what is required on site to be provided by the employer – you may find the HSE website useful as it contains summaries in leaflet form of many of the regulations below.

- A construction phase health and safety plan (CDM Regulations)
- Does an F10 have to be filled in? (CDM Regulations)
- Risk assessments required (Management of Health, Safety and Welfare Regulations)
- Checking competency of all workers on site (Management of Health, Safety and Welfare Regulations)
- The use of ladders to reach three storeys (Work at Height Regulations)
- A separate fresh drinking water supply (Construction (Health, Safety and Welfare) Regulations – look at the schedules at the back)
- Health and safety plans. Is one required to be in place on site before work commences? (summary of the CDM Regulations)
- The parties to CDM
- Regulation 3 in the Management of Health, Safety and Welfare Regulations
- There is a specific regulation that covers capabilities and training. Is this in the Management of Health, Safety and Welfare Regulations?
- Can you use ladders? (Work at Height Regulations – see Regulation 6 and Schedule no. 1.) What do the regulations not contain?
- Schedule 6 in the Construction (Health, Safety and Welfare) Regulations.

## Assessment practice

Explain how the members of the building team interact in terms of their health, safety and welfare roles and responsibilities.

Take a blank sheet of A4 paper and write into each corner one member of the design team:

- Designer
- Planning supervisor
- Principal contractor
- Client

Draw lines between each one vertically and horizontally, then join up the diagonals, so that you have a square with an 'x' in it . It should look like this:

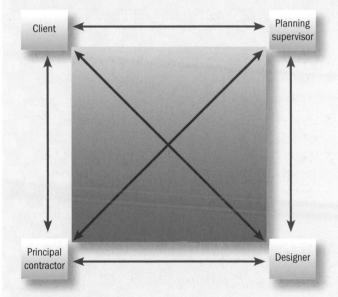

▲ Figure 1.2

You can now write on each arrowed line how team members interact with each other on health and safety matters. For example, the client would give the principal contractor any health and safety information on the site they are working on. **M1**

# Hazards and risks

## The difference between hazards and risks

A hazard is something that has the potential to cause harm, for example electricity, hot water, steam, noise. A risk is the potential of that hazard to actually cause someone injury. For example, steam contained within an insulated stainless steel pipe 4 metres in the air has very low potential to cause someone harm.

## Identification of hazards

Risk assessments are a vital part of a company's safety ethos and are a legal requirement. They have to be carried out for a number of reasons:

- Manual handling of loads – the risks with moving loads have to be assessed.
- Control of Substances Hazardous to Health (COSHH) – the risks of using chemicals.
- Personal protective equipment (PPE) – the risks of using PPE.
- Construction (Design and Management) Regulations – the risks and hazards on site.
- Management of Health, Safety and Welfare Regulations – the risks and hazards at work.

Construction work is continually evolving, from modular construction to one-off prestigious building projects. As such, the process and practices on site will be subject to change. This may be daily in some cases. Construction is not like a factory production line where there may be little change to the process each year. Risk assessment is used to identify these changes, and the safe system of work associated with it requires that these are reviewed. Factors might include the following:

- The workplace activity has changed.
- The processes used have changed.
- New materials are being used.
- Inexperienced new operatives.
- A change in safety legislation.

Risk assessments have to be reviewed and signed off with a date of review and any actions to be taken. Any actions instigated and put in place must be clearly recorded.

## Risk rating of hazards

The identification of hazards relies on training, knowledge and experience of construction. This is especially so when you have to identify hidden hazards that are not immediately obvious to the eye. For example, asbestos insulation had a hidden hazard – the asbestos fibres. Hazards have to be classified so you can understand which are the most important. To accomplish this, they can be classified high, medium or low.

Part of the risk assessment process asks you to assess the potential harm from the hazard. Risks can be rated by the likelihood that the hazard will cause harm and the severity of that harm were it to occur. The mathematical formula to do this is:

$$Risk = Likelihood \times Severity$$

Now you can use this to judge the likelihood and the severity of the risk and produce a risk matrix (see Figure 1.3). Employers often use numbers as they are much smaller to squeeze onto a risk assessment form, and have a key to reflect what the numbers mean. This calculation may place the risk rating into a $4 \times 4 = 16$, which means the likelihood of it occurring is certain and the severity is fatal, so would you continue with this?

| | | | | |
|---|---|---|---|---|
| **4** | Green | Yellow | Red | Red |
| **3** | Green | Yellow | Yellow | Red |
| **2** | Green | Green | Yellow | Yellow |
| **1** | Green | Green | Green | Green |
| | **1** | **2** | **3** | **4** |

Likelihood

Severity

▲ Figure 1.3 A risk matrix

You can work out the risk using the following scale:

*Likelihood:*
1 = slight
2 = possible
3 = very likely
4 = certainty

*Severity:*
1 = no injury
2 = minor injury
3 = major injury
4 = fatal

You have to rate the severity and likelihood from 1 to 4. You then multiply severity and likelihood to work out the potential risk  The table has been coloured from green for okay with existing controls; yellow requires further measures; to red which means that the work being risk assessed is too dangerous to continue with. The more complex the work, the bigger the matrix can become. High ratings must have further control measures placed upon them. These are then reassessed to check that the rating has been reduced to an acceptable level.

## Potential to cause harm

This refers to the possible dangers from the identified hazard and the likelihood that it may cause an injury. For example, gas contained within a gas pipe serving your home has the potential to explode if ignited and cause a fatal injury.

## Case study

Everywhere you look on a construction site, there may be a physical hazard. For example, a reinforcing bar sticking out of the ground has the potential to cause an injury to a worker by impaling them should they fall onto it.

Is it certain or unlikely that a worker could fall on the reinforcing bar? What would be the severity of the injury?

## Theory into practice

Look closely at the reinforcing rods sticking out of this slab that is ready to be cast. What do you notice? The rods have caps over them to protect operatives should they fall onto the rods. This is called a 'control measure' and is used to reduce the risk to an acceptable level.

## Assessment practice

Look at the photo below and list the hazards that you can see. Discuss these with your tutor once you have identified at least three hazards.

Look again at the photo and decide who might be harmed by the construction operations you can see – don't forget the people you cannot see. What would be the possible consequences for such individuals?

# Environmental aspects

## Hazards and risks in the workplace environment

Different workplaces present different potential dangers.

### ■ Working within hot and cold environments

Hot and cold environments can present many hazards. Hot environments create a drying-out environment which may affect operatives working within them. Individuals may suffer from dehydration, which can lead to unconsciousness and, ultimately, death. Similarly, cold environments cause the body to shiver, followed by hypothermia, eventually lowering the body's core temperature, which may result in death. Obviously, these extremes are only found when working outdoors or within cold stores or boiler rooms. Working alone in any of these environments could be considered dangerous.

## ■ Working over water

Working over water presents difficulties as there is the risk of drowning to be considered. There are additional control measures that must be used for this hazard. Contractors must make sure that anyone working above water has a stable platform with guardrails to work on. Secondly, operatives working above water must be able to swim, and wear lifejackets (a suitable PPE). Thirdly, there must be means of rescue – a boat with a trained operative.

### Confined spaces

'A "confined space" is any enclosed space that has restricted natural ventilation and is not intended for continual occupancy by people, and where by virtue of its enclosed nature there is a reasonably foreseeable risk of injury to workers.' (Confined Spaces Regulations 1997)

In construction, confined spaces might be basements, cellars or under-floor spaces. Manholes are also a confined space with the added hazard of gas. Under-floor ducts for services would also conform to the above definition.

When working in confined spaces, the following must always be considered:

- If there is no alternative and you have to work within the confined space, then you will have to undertake a risk assessment for the work you will carry out.

- A safe system of working. A **permit to work** system is an example of this, where all the requirements for working in a confined space would be listed so that none are missed.

- Emergency arrangements in the event of an accident in the confined space.

- If rescue is required, the risks to the people who will have to enter the confined space and carry out a rescue must be assessed.

- If unconscious operatives have been removed from the confined space, then trained personnel must be available to carry out resuscitation.

### Key Term

**A permit to work** This is a document that is issued by the person responsible for a particular work area. Such an area is usually one of high and complex activity; the permits detail who is working in that area. They also list any precautions that must be taken and any isolation of services that may be required.

### Access and egress

### Key Term

**Access and egress** Getting in and out of the workplace.

Construction sites are notoriously difficult to enter and exit as the permanent structure has not yet been completed. Temporary **access and egress** can be achieved through:

- mobile elevated platforms
- scissor lifts
- scaffolding
- scaffolding stairs
- ladders for short risk-assessed durations
- tower scaffolds
- lifts.

The most common way is by the safe use of scaffold, but stair towers must now be incorporated as it is not safe to use ladders with scaffolding. Access platforms with roll-over guards have to be provided for the safe lifting and placing of materials onto the scaffolding by a rough terrain forklift with telescopic boom.

### Assessment practice

You have been asked to provide the access and egress arrangements for a roof repair on a corrugated metal, pitched roof. What would you provide to safely gain access to work on the roof? **P5**

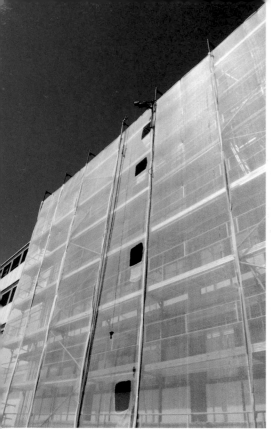

▲ Protected scaffolding  ▲ Working safely at height

## Working at height

The photo illustrates a typical scaffold that has protection covering it to prevent materials falling and injuring the general public. Mobile elevated platforms (MEPs) allow you to drive and rotate the guarded cage you work in 360 degrees. They provide a safe and secure means of access. Training to use one of these is essential.

Working at height is inherently dangerous as an accident can often be fatal. Connected with this is the danger of falling objects such as tools, plant and materials which can injure workers at ground level. Access and egress issues with working at height can be solved with MEPs and stair scaffolds. This enables plant and materials to be moved safely to the workplace.

Personal protective equipment for working at height takes the form of a harness, which is worn by the operative and contains a **lanyard**. This lanyard slows down the rate of descent should a fall occur. The lanyard must be secured to a physical fixing point that will support a fall. A rescue procedure must be in place because you need to be taken out of the harness within 10 minutes. This is because the harness interrupts the blood flow to the brain and you would gradually become unconscious if left dangling after a fall.

## Key Term

**Lanyard** An attachment that clips between the safety harness and the secure point and gradually slows the rate of descent.

Other prevention measures involve physical barriers. These are horizontal rails set at certain distances as specified in the Working at Height Regulations, so there is no unprotected gap of more than 470 mm that you could fall through. Toe boards must also be provided to stop objects being pushed off the working platform.

As mentioned earlier, the Working at Height Regulations state that you must not work at height unless it is reasonably practical to do so. If no such method can be employed, work at ground level. Examples of this would be external lighting columns where the bulb cluster can be winched down to ground level to maintain the bulbs.

## Case study

Look at the photograph of the worker on the edge of a building. As you can see, he is working at a considerable height.

1 **Would you be happy to carry out this work?**

2 **What are the risks in doing so?**

3 **Is there any other way this work could be undertaken by not working at height?**

4 **What precautions have to be taken to control the risks involved in undertaking this work?**

# Persons who may be affected by hazards and risks

On a construction site many people may be affected by the harm from a hazard, including:

- employees
- site visitors
- the general public.

The nature of the hazard, for example a gas escape from a site, will determine how many people will be harmed, whereas minor incidents may involve only one person.

## Employees

The employees are the people who will be directly undertaking the construction of the project. They are the most vulnerable when faced with potential hazards, as the majority are at the 'sharp end' of the process and not based within an office where they may be some distance away from the hazards. Employees may be very experienced or very new to the project. Each will require information, instruction and training about the potential site hazards.

## Site visitors

Visitors to a construction site should report first to the site manager's office. Here the manager will confirm that the visitor has signed in on a register (in the event of a fire everyone needs accounting for), has been given appropriate personal protective equipment and has been inducted on the site hazards. The visitor may be accompanied on their visit by a supervisor.

## General public

The main contractor has a duty to protect the general public. This is normally achieved by fencing off the construction site so that people cannot wander onto the site. In addition, signs are put up on the fencing to warn intruders of the inherent dangers of trespass.

## Case study

Your current employment is as an assistant site manager on an out-of-town supermarket shopping development. One of your responsibilities is to set up the site establishment before the main construction work commences. You have set up the site accommodation and site compound and have fenced in the site on three sides using 2.4-metre high temporary **panel fencing** bolted together on rubber feet. The fourth side is an existing farmer's fence that is 1.2 metres high and is topped with two strands of barbed wire. The site is on the outskirts of a town next to the local school.

1 **Have you taken all reasonable precautions to protect employees and the general public from the construction site activities?**

2 **What other measures would you undertake?**

## Key Term

**Panel fencing** This is constructed out of mesh squares welded to a framework. The fences sit into feet and are bolted together with clips; they are high enough so they cannot be climbed over.

# Methods of hazard identification on a construction site

## Observation of work environment

How can you identify the hazards on a construction site? The most useful method is by direct observation. This technique requires practice to spot the hazards that are not obvious and can be aided by the use of photographs. A photograph enables you to check the image later to identify or confirm a hazard in the workplace.

### Remember!

The most useful tool you have is your eyes. Directly observing a site should enable you to spot many potential hazards.

## The use of accident data

The statistical analysis of accident data is another tool to help you spot potential hazards. Looking at a pyramid of injuries, with the minor ones at the base and the major ones at the top, will soon enable you to identify the causes of the injuries and hence a control method. For example, if you were seeing a large volume of eye injuries due to cement mortar entering the eye on a windy day, then the control method must be to wear eye protection or cease work when the wind speed exceeds a certain number of kilometres per hour.

A large number of minor accidents can be a cause for concern as eventually there will be a major accident. If you can reduce the volume of minor accidents, then the statistical probability of a major one is reduced. For example, if there arc many injuries to the hands, then you could make it a site rule that everyone on site has to wear safety gloves while working.

The analysis of risk assessments is another method of hazard identification. By looking through a large number of risk assessments to locate a common hazard, this can be collectively dealt with by global control measures. In effect, you are using this data as a set of fresh eyes to assess the situation and to point out something you may have missed.

## Checklists and method statements

Checklists are a standard sheet produced for a particular workplace environment. The hazards are then identified by a safety audit or inspection, which involves walking around the environment and ticking off the hazards from the pre-set list. Checklists are useful for complex construction sites where a large number of processes and substances are utilised. When new hazards are identified, these can be added to the existing checklist to build up a more comprehensive checklist.

Method statements are produced as part of the CDM Regulations. They are a statement of the methods to be used to construct a particular item. For example, if you were going to drill through a wall for a toilet connection, the method statement would list how you were going to do this, the equipment you were going to use (hand or machine) and a list of safety precautions. Method statements enable you to analyse the correct and safest way to undertake a task.

## Safety inspections and audits

These get you out of the office environment and on to the site! It is a hands-on approach to safety. Inspecting plant and machinery to ensure all test certificates are up to date is essential. If operatives know they will be subject to inspection and checking, they will act more appropriately in their work environment. Coupled with this is close supervision by a competent supervisor, who can inspect as the work proceeds ensuring all control measures are in place and used.

Inspections by the HSE will, of course, have the most effect on health and safety on site, but sadly statistically there are just not enough inspectors to cover the tremendous workload the UK construction industry generates; only the major accidents appear to get investigated. Company-employed health and safety inspectors (appointed in accordance with the MHSW Regulations – see above) are an excellent resource that can be used to visit company construction sites. They provide experience, training and knowledge on all aspects of health and safety and will know the company's procedures that must be adopted on all sites.

## Assessment practice

1.2

You have been asked by the company health and safety officer to assist in compiling a health and safety checklist that will be used for an inspection of the current construction sites. This checklist will obviously cover a wide range of construction activity. List five important items you would include and expect to tick off during an inspection.

P4

# Accident data

## Principal major causes of accidents and fatalities

The construction industry employs around 2.2 million people each year and still accounts for over 50 fatalities every year. As we have previously seen, the most frequent cause of death is through falling, but there are other reasons why employees are killed while working in construction.

Figure 1.4 shows the four major causes plotted against time:

- Falls from height.
- Struck by a moving vehicle.
- Struck by a falling object.
- Trapped by collapse or overturning.

As you can see, falls from height have steadily decreased.

Figure 1.5 illustrates the current trend in fatalities over the past nine years.

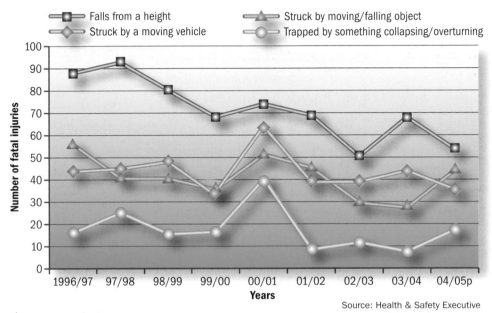

Source: Health & Safety Executive

▲ Figure 1.4 Number of fatal injuries to workers by kinds of accident, 1996/97–2004/5

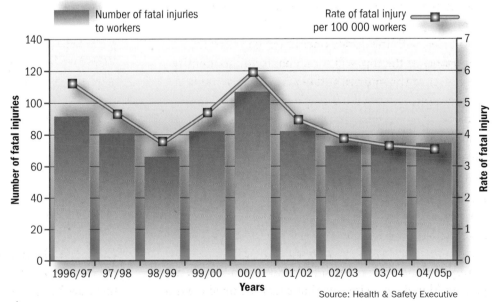

Source: Health & Safety Executive

▲ Figure 1.5 Number and rate of fatal injuries to workers, 1996/97–2004/5

## Demographics

The HSE publishes statistics classified by gender, location or age (see the HSE's website at www.hse.gov.uk). The **demographics** of statistics involves looking at the people involved in the accidents and their classification. We could look at the occupations of those involved in major accidents. Why? This would tell us where best to direct any legislation and to provide inspection themes by statutory bodies, for example the HSE. Demographics by gender may lead to removing one sex from a certain industry or occupation because of sharp rises in accident trends. A large number of accidents at age 64 may result in reducing the retirement age to 60. The government uses demographics to shape its policy and procedures through the Department of Environment and through safety legislation.

## Key Term

**Demographics** The characteristics of a population, e.g. age.

## UK and European safety statistics

Figure 1.6 illustrates how the UK compares with the rest of Europe. As you can see, the UK has the lowest rate of fatal injury. This may be due to several reasons: the UK may report all its accidents (see Observable trends below), it may have more inspectors touring the country, it introduces more health and safety legislation, it takes the forefront in safety campaigns.

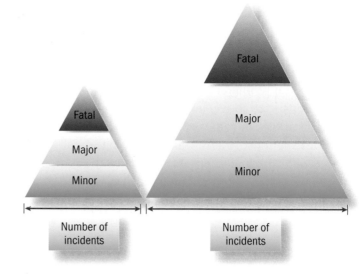

▲ Figure 1.7 The number of incidents that occur is represented by the width of the triangle at the base

## Observable trends

The UK keeps records of its accidents, which helps to prevent future accidents from occurring. For example, if the number of reported accidents increases in a certain area or location, then this would indicate the need for an investigation into why these are occurring. The accidents could be due to a change in the process or procedure. Accident trends formed at a minor level require acting upon so they do not increase into a major or fatal accident. A large number of trends in this pyramid diagram may cause a larger number of major accidents (see Figure 1.7). The wider the base, the more danger that a fatal accident may occur.

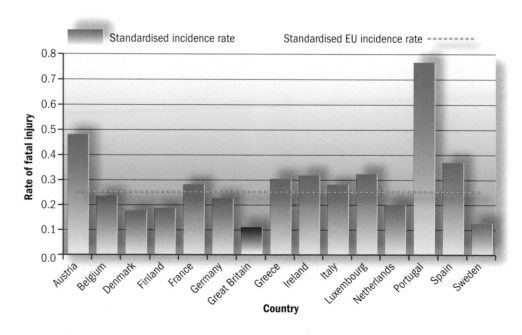

► Figure 1.6 Rate of fatal injuries in the UK and the rest of Europe

# Consequences of accidents

## Consequences to humans

The consequences of an accident to the human body can be devastating to both victims and their families. The disability caused by the fracture, breaking or amputation of a limb may leave an employee with no option but to leave their employment. Victims of workplace accidents may suffer with poor health for many years. Diseases of the lung caused by asbestos poisoning, for example, are just one long-term consequence of dealing with a product that had a hidden hazard.

### Case study

John Curtis had been working as a site engineer at a local construction firm. He started this job straight from university. He eventually settled down, married and had two children. His career was fast developing and he was rising quickly through the ranks to senior engineer and, eventually, project manager. One day, John was setting out some road kerb lines for a 250 housing unit development when he looked up from the surveying instrument and received a hot blast of sparks from a saw being used to cut road kerbs. This permanently damaged his eye sight.

What are the human consequences for John and his family?

## Moral consequences

A company that has a high accident rate and does nothing to control this will eventually have a demotivated workforce. The causes of accidents need to be brought into the open, not pushed aside. Managing directors and chief executives need to lead from the front. Safety before costs should be the ethical ethos of a business.

## Financial consequences

If you have had an accident at work, you may have to stay off work as a consequence. Your employer may only have within their conditions of contract two weeks' sick pay. Should you be off work longer than this period, then you are paid statutory sick pay which is a very small amount each week. Employees who are off work longer may have to endure short-term financial hardship, or have to make a claim against the company for their injury. The company itself may face a large financial fine as a result of a prosecution by the HSE, along with the unrecoverable costs that are explained below.

## The cost of an accident

The cost of an accident can be split into the insured costs that can be recovered from an insurance company and the uninsured costs that cannot. Look at the iceberg in Figure 1.8. Part of it can be seen above the water line – this represents the direct costs of the accident. Below the water line is two-thirds of the iceberg which represents the hidden costs, or uninsured costs, that the company cannot see at the time of the accident but eventually will have to pay for.

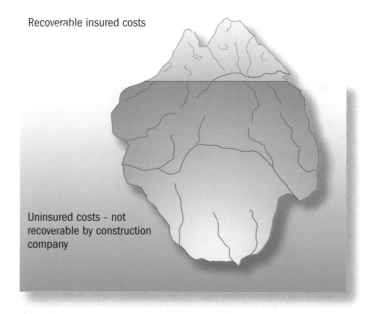

Recoverable insured costs

Uninsured costs – not recoverable by construction company

▲ Figure 1.8 Insured and uninsurable costs

All businesses have to carry employer's and public liability insurance to cover claims against their business from injury of a worker or a member of the public, but there are exclusions within these policies.

The following are the types of insurance cover that may be in place on a construction site and represent insured costs that can be recovered:

- Employer's liability insurance on its workers to insure against claims.
- Public liability insurance to the general public.
- Motor vehicle insurance to cover company transport.
- Product liability insurance from manufacturers and suppliers to cover defective products.

Uninsured costs cover the following that cannot be claimed back or recovered from an insurance policy:

- Court fines imposed as a result of a prosecution from the HSE.
- The cost of clearing up the accident.
- The loss of reputation.
- The resulting bad publicity and loss of business and sales.
- Loss of production and the damaged product.
- The demotivating effect on employees.
- The cost of the accident investigation.
- Any overtime or additional labour required.

None of these can be accounted for at the time of the initial accident; it is only afterwards that the unaccounted costs become apparent. Several major accidents can have a very detrimental effect on a company's performance and may put it out of business.

## Case study

The managing director of a housing construction company has asked you to calculate the cost of a recent accident from the following data that has been analysed from timesheets and invoices. The accident involved a joiner using a bench saw on site to cut roof timbers to length.

Calculate:

**a** the total cost of the accident

**b** which of the costs are insured or uninsured.

---

*Accident cost data:*

First aid treatment 1 hour at £30 per hour

Bandages and miscellaneous items £20

Transportation to hospital by ambulance: NHS cost 2 hours at £23.55 per hour

Loss of immediate staff working hours on site:

    Site manager 2 hours at £45 per hour

    General foreman 2 hours at £25 per hour

    Joiners (2) 2 hours at £18.50 per operative per hour

    Bricklayers (5) 2 hours at £18.50 per operative per hour

    Labourers (3) 2 hours at £12.50 per operative per hour

    Store person 2 hours at £10.50 per hour

Accident Investigation by C. M. 12 hours at £50 per hour

In-house meeting with three people 3 hours at £55 per person per hour

Agency joiner to replace injured worker 6 weeks at £250 per week

On-site cleaning by contract company £550

Disposal of old saw £120

Purchase of new site bench saw £2500

Hire charges temporary saw 3 weeks at £65.50 per week

Staff retraining on portable electric tools (4) 4 hours at £20 per operative per hour

Sick pay to injured person 12 weeks at £64.66 week

HSE prosecution and subsequent fine £35,000

Insurance premium increase £2500

## Principles of risk assessment

### Obligations under the Management of Health, Safety and Welfare Regulations

The principles of risk assessment are set out under Regulation 3 of the Management of Health, Safety and Welfare Regulations 1999, which is summarised as follows

- Every employer must make an assessment of the risk to their workers and non-employees at work.
- The risk assessment that is undertaken must be reviewed in the light of any changes.
- Specific risk assessments must be carried out on young persons employed at work.
- Where an employer employs five or more people, the assessment must be recorded in writing.

### The concept of what is 'reasonably practicable'

This is an expression that you may see in some of the legislation discussed at the beginning of the chapter. It means that a company should take all reasonable steps to protect workers against risks balanced against the cost and time of doing so. For example, the best solution in removing dust from a worker's environment may be to provide a mask rather than full-extract ventilation systems, because the dust is harmless. This is a judgement based upon knowledge and experience.

## The five steps to risk assessment

The procedure to be adopted in spotting hazards is called the risk assessment process and can be broken down into five main steps, as outlined by the HSE:

1 Identify the hazards.
2 Decide who might be harmed.
3 Evaluate the risks and precautions to be taken.
4 Record your findings.
5 Review your assessment and update.

### Remember!

Take the first letters of each of the steps – IDERR and use these as a prompt to remember each step.

### Evaluation of risks

The primary or principal hazards are the ones that you need to be fully aware of, but there may be hidden hazards that you cannot directly observe. During a site observation, everything may appear to be safe, but combining two hazards from two locations could produce a severe potential hazard. For example, there are electricity pylons running over the site. All appears fine on your visit. The next day a crane is brought on site. Now the hazard is the metal crane arm and the cables carrying electricity and the resultant electrocution. Looking back at the risk assessment matrix (Figure 1.3), a fatal injury means certain death as a result of an accident.

### Remember!

A fatal accident is reportable to the HSE even if the person concerned dies at a later date as a result of their injuries.

Now, the high score from the matrix requires you to look closely at the nature of the risk, and identify the existing control measures that you have in place to establish if they are sufficient to reduce the risk from the hazard to an acceptable level. You could do this by looking at the data sheets from a product construction workers might be using and checking the **control measures** against the manufacturer's recommendations. If your evaluation establishes that further controls are necessary, then you need to identify these and record what action is required until the risk is acceptable.

## Key Term

**Control measure** A method, system or product to reduce a high risk to an acceptable risk, for example using a fork-lift truck to lift a heavy object rather than trying to lift it by hand.

## Assessment practice

Look back at the photo on page 16 and the series of hazards that you identified, then describe the main principles and features of a typical risk assessment that would be used to control these hazards. One of these principles is to list the existing control measures you would apply to the hazards. **P4**

You have been asked to investigate a blocked manhole that is 4 metres deep. Upon investigation, you have found that it requires some work to its concrete base, which has broken away and is causing the obstruction.

Undertake a risk assessment for working within this confined space. Don't forget the main hazard with sewers is an explosive gas!

What is the definition for working within this type of environment called?

What is the principal hazard in working at the base of this manhole?

Can you work alone on this job?

What control measures will be required during the work?

Risk assessment forms

A risk assessment form should contain the following:

- Where is the work or activity going to be carried out? Undertake the same operation in two different places and the hazards will be different.

- Date of assessment – when did it take place? This will give you an indication of how old the risk assessment is. Does it need reviewing in the light of a change in conditions?

- Identify what the work activity is, e.g. using a pedestal drill to drill holes through some steelwork.

- Identify the hazards – the primary and most important hazards should be listed.

- Who might be harmed in this workplace? For example, visitors, employees, supervisors and members of the general public.

- Evaluation of the risk – what risk is there from the hazards you have identified?

- What are the existing control measures? Look closely and record what you are doing currently to control the risk from the hazards.

- Any further action/controls required – if the existing control measures are not effective, what further action must be taken to reduce the risk from the hazards to an acceptable level?

- Who will make sure additional controls are in place? Who will undertake the work on further controls and when will it be done? An accident could result if you fail to act quickly.

- Signed and dated – you may need to identify the person who undertook the risk assessment especially in an accident investigation.

- A review date – risk assessments will need reviewing periodically with any changes in systems of work, technology and further health and safety legislation.

## Remember!

The first step to risk assessment – identify the hazards!

## Theory into practice

Find a suitable risk assessment form either from a place of work or ask your tutor. The HSE website contains an example format you could download. If you have undertaken any research on risk assessments, you will find that there are several formats in existence. You should remember that these are all correct in their own right but have been tailored to more complex projects and hazards.

You are now ready to carry out a risk assessment. This can be undertaken on a site visit to a local construction site or within the educational establishment you are enrolled at or at your place of work, be it part time or full time. Locate an area that is a workplace and that contains a great deal of activity so that you have some principal hazards to identify. Fill in your risk assessment form until you have completed all the stages mentioned above. Taking a photograph is always an advantage as you can study this later in your own time.

## Assessment practice

Look closely at the risk assessment that you carried out and explain what precautions and control measures you selected. Are they 'reasonably practicable'? Could more be done, or would this be counterproductive? **P5**

### ■ Advantages of using a standard risk assessment form

- All the boxes have to be completed, so nothing can be missed during your assessment.
- The risk assessment can be continually reviewed to improve it.
- Health and safety policy can be written into the risk assessment format.
- It can be made as simple or as complex as necessary for the type of work being assessed.

# Workplace health and safety policies

## General workplace health and safety

These are required under the Health and Safety at Work Act 1974 which states that:

'Except in such cases as may be prescribed, it shall be the duty of every employer to prepare and as often as may be appropriate revise a written statement of his general policy with respect to the health and safety at work of his employees and the organisation and arrangements for the time being in force for carrying out that policy, and to bring the statement and any revision of it to the notice of all of his employees.' (www.health and safety.co.uk)

Employers now had to write down their health and safety arrangements if they employed five or more people. This is called a health and safety policy and is divided into three main sections:

1  A general statement – this is usually signed by the head of the organisation and dated, as it is an important statement giving a key outline as to how the employer will observe their duties under the Act. Specifically, the statement must:

   - demonstrate a company's commitment to health and safety
   - state how the company intends dealing with this
   - specify who is responsible for health and safety
   - contain a paragraph that all necessary resources will be provided in the pursuance of health and safety
   - inform all employees about the policy's contents
   - be signed and dated by a prominent person in charge.

2  Who has specific responsibilities, e.g. health and safety representative, employees' duties.

3  Health and safety administration, e.g. permit to work systems, accident reporting and risk assessment procedures.

### Remember!

As an employee, you have responsibilities. You must not ignore any unsafe acts and should bring these to the attention of a manager or supervisor.

## Other policies

As well as the health and safety policy that has to be produced as a requirement of the HASAWA 1974, companies may also produce their own safety policies. These cover many aspects such as:

- drugs – how the company will deal with employees found under the influence of drugs during their employment
- alcohol – how the company will deal with employees who are clearly under the influence of alcohol
- driving policy – all employees will hold a clean driving licence while using company vehicles
- smoking – now banned under recent UK legislation in many open access areas and within buildings.

## Thinking points

Look at a typical non-smoking policy below. Do you think that this smoking policy should apply to all construction sites? Give your reasons.

### COMPANY SMOKING POLICY

- This company operates a no-smoking policy within the company premises.
- No smoking is allowed within the company's buildings or construction sites.
- Facilities have been provided to enable you to smoke. These are designated as smoke rooms.
- Non-smokers use them at their risk.
- Any person found not to be utilising this facility will be dealt with under the company's disciplinary procedure.
- Would all employees please respect this policy.

# Procedures

### Monitoring, review and inspection

Health and safety must be monitored, checked and reviewed regularly. This is because changes in legislation are frequent and policies will need updating. There should be regular audits and inspections to ensure that employees are complying with the law, are not taking any unnecessary risks to their health and are acting in accordance with any training given. It is when these controls are relaxed and no one is looking that there might be a tendency to take a risk that results in a serious accident.

### Remember!

Monitoring and reviewing means taking time to look carefully through what has been produced in the past and improving it, often in line with new systems, procedures and legislation.

# Arrangements for implementation

### Allocation of roles and responsibilities

This section deals with who has the responsibility for the different aspects of the health and safety policy. This may be broken down into main roles and responsibilities for the following key people in a typical organisation:

- directors
- contracts managers
- site supervisors
- health and safety officer
- employees.

Often the roles are displayed on a chart which illustrates the management structure of the organisation from the top down.

### Arranging implementation of health and safety policies

The main part of a company's health and safety policy is where it states how it is going to carry out and implement the policy, and may contain any of the following:

- dealing with asbestos
- manual handling
- COSHH
- accident reporting procedure
- health surveillance
- permits to work
- lifting operations
- safety committees
- smoking policy.

## Remember!

This section is where many of the company's policies are placed, so this document must be available for all employees to read and be informed. It may contain the recent UK smoking regulations.

### Use of permits to work

These are documents used to safely control any activity on large projects and sites. They may tell a supervisor who is working in one particular area all the people and different trades that are working in the area under their control, so that they can plan safely. Large complex sites may have several levels and floors. For example, if there is one set of workers welding on one floor on some steel stairs, then it is essential to know who is working below them so they cannot be harmed by these workers. Similarly, this is true of workers working on roofs, confined spaces, and doing hot work such as welding, cutting, grinding. Permits make supervisors aware who is working, where they are working, what isolation may be required, when the work will be finished and what safety coordination is required. Permits may be required for the following work:

- working on roofs
- confined space working
- sewer works
- electrical installation works
- gas installation works.

These are all activities that are dangerous and need monitoring closely. Some permits may require that all operatives sign the permit so that supervisors know who is working on the site in the event of an emergency. The permit will list the control measures that will be required to be in place before the permit can be authorised. At the end of the working day the permit must be signed off by all who have been working on it. This can be either uncompleted or complete, so that the supervisor knows that the work is done. On large factory complexes there may be more than one permit station within definable boundaries of the factory. This is done so that adequate supervision can be assigned to each area. Too big an area and you lose control of it. Permits often are not issued without visible proof that a risk assessment and a method statement have been carried out. These will highlight the hazards and the control measures that are being used to reduce the risk to an acceptable level.

## Remember!

Some factory construction sites are vast, covering many square miles. If a supervisor knows who is working where on their permit, then all employees, visitors and workers can be accounted for should an emergency situation occur.

### Method statements

These analyse in detail the appropriate method to use in a work activity. They list whether it will be undertaken by hand or plant, the equipment to be used and the logical sequence of the work. This is good procedure as it makes the person writing the statements think in detail about the hazards and how they will control them.

### Induction and training

The induction introduces you to the construction site on which you will be working. It covers several aspects of the site and may include information about:

- hazards
- site rules
- transport movements
- first aid
- fire alarm
- evacuation procedures
- site accommodation facilities
- waste removal
- car parking
- site working hours.

An induction is essentially a comprehensive introduction to the rules and regulations of the particular site. All employees, visitors and workers on the site must have the induction. You cannot have non-informed workers moving around the site. They may cause a hazard in the event of an emergency.

Training is an essential element of health and safety. It helps to determine the competency of employees to undertake specific tasks on site such as driving a dumper truck. Highly qualified employees who have the correct training and equipment will result in a lower accident rate than a workforce who has not. Training can simply take the form of a tool box talk. This involves employees stopping work and gathering around a common meeting area to discuss the hazards of the day, control measures and any other high risk activity on site. These are very useful for passing on safety information to employees.

## Good site management procedures

These are procedures applied by supervisors and managers of the company. They can be as simple as signing in on a register on site, so you know how many people are on site. Site meetings are a procedure that helps to control health and safety on site. Setting up site rules and procedures is a vital health and safety tool, but to be effective it must be monitored and maintained, and obeyed by all without exception.

# Control measures

## Workplace procedures

These are safe systems of work and should be specifically designed for the workplace, for example separating delivery traffic from operatives on site, clear signage and pedestrian walkways such that neither can come into contact with each other.

Tool box talks are another example of a safe system of work; they identify daily or weekly hazards and keep all employees informed of site dangers. Safe systems of work take time to develop, implement, maintain and review to check that they are working. Advice and input from the workforce via safety committees act as a useful third set of eyes that can immediately see any problems with these systems. Corrective action can then be put in place.

## Hazardous substances

COSHH stands for the Control of Substances Hazardous to Health, and is a set of regulations. They mainly cover the chemicals used in any process such as adhesive glues to stick laminate onto kitchen worktops, or paint thinners in decorating. Every chemical that is used on a construction site has to be risk assessed under the COSHH Regulations for its harm potential. The regulations advise eight steps:

1 Undertake a risk assessment. You will need the manufacturer's data sheet on the substance.

2 Decide what precautions are needed – this may involve ventilation, PPE or isolation.

3 Prevent or adequately control exposure – gloves, dust masks, air flows.

4 Ensure that control measures are used and maintained.

5 Monitor exposure – this can be by measurement.

6 Carry out appropriate health surveillance – blood tests.

7 Prepare plans and procedures to deal with accidents, incidents and emergencies should a spillage occur of the substance in the workplace.

8 Ensure that employees are properly informed, trained and supervised (Health & Safety Executive).

It is worthwhile building up a COSHH library, where manufacturers' data sheets can be kept up to date with the necessary precautions for using that particular product. Dangerous chemicals are best substituted for less dangerous ones.

## Remember!

It is worthwhile substituting a chemical that harms the environment with a 'greener' version. Green chemicals also require fewer control measures as they have little effect on the environment and the person using them.

## Lifting and manual handling

There is a limit to how much a person can lift: for a man it is 25 kg close in to the body and properly lifted, for a woman it is 16 kg close in to the body. However, this is only a guide, and must be subject to a risk assessment which must take into account the weight to be lifted and how far it has to be moved and where is the centre of gravity.

## Working at height

This has already been discussed on page 18.

## Physical safeguards

Physical safeguards include secure fencing, barriers and guards that can be fitted to plant and machinery to reduce and prevent hands, feet, arm hair and any extremity from becoming entrapped and injured within a moving piece of equipment or plant.

Interlocking, where you have to switch off the machine before you can remove the guard, helps to prevent accidents.

## Working in excavations

There are several hazards that need controls when working in excavations. They are: falling into the excavation, drowning (should it fill with water), gas and collapse of the sides of the excavation. Control measures should include:

- the addition of secure fencing to the perimeter of an excavation
- a pumping system to remove any water that is building up within the excavation
- a physical barrier to prevent plant falling into the excavation
- a gas test to detect the presence of poisonous gas
- a support system for the sides to prevent collapse.

## Site traffic and plant

A large number of accidents are attributable to workers coming into contact with plant and machinery on a construction site. Construction sites can be noisy. Often you will not hear the plant operator in your vicinity. Control measures primarily involve segregation of workers and machinery. Clear traffic routes for each must be established on the site. Traffic lights and footpaths must be used to good effect. Reversing warning lights and pre-recorded voice warnings are very effective. Signage must be displayed to direct one-way traffic on a congested site. Operatives can assist the process by using high visibility clothing that reflects light.

## Contaminated ground

Construction regularly takes place on 'brown field sites'. These are development sites that tend to be in inner cities and have been cleared of the existing building structures. However, they are usually old and run-down sites where there has been a lot of work activity and hence soil contamination. Old petrol station sites are good examples. They contain spillages of detergents, petrol and diesel that can ignite and can also cause dermatitis and skin diseases if in contact with the skin. Inhalation of fuel fumes is also unpleasant.

The contamination can be treated in two ways: by removal to a licensed tip or by treatment within the ground. Soils must be tested to see what type of contamination is present.

## Case study

Look through the following case study and select a control. Taking each of the following in turn, identify a control measure from the list that would reduce the risk to an acceptable level. Discuss each with your tutor and peers.

A bricklayer's operative is using a diesel cement mixer to mix the ingredients for the bricklaying mortar. This requires that 25 kg bags of cement have to be opened and the correct quantities poured into the mixer by hand using a shovel. It is a windy day and every time the operative places the cement into the mixer, cement dust blows into their eyes. From the following list, pick the control measures you would use to avoid this occurring.

- Leave the task until a calm day.
- Replace the cement with an alternative.
- Provide the correct eye protection to the operative.
- If the contract is large enough, obtain cement in silos with a mortar plant.
- Form a shelter around the mixer.
- Obtain mortar in ready-mixed tubs.

▲ Bricklayer's operative mixing bricklaying mortar in a diesel cement mixer

## Remember!

The 'PIGSRISE' system can be employed when implementing control measures:

1 Remove the hazard – elimination.

2 Prevent exposure to the hazard by substituting it for another or guarding.

3 Provide safe systems of work, e.g. permit to work.

4 The use of PPE – this should always be the last resort.

PIGSRISE stands for the first letters of the following and is taken from HSG65 (Health & Safety Executive). You have to start with the last letter and work backwards.

**E** is for eliminate.
**S** is for substitute.
**I** is for isolate.
**R** is for reduce.
**S** is for safe systems of work.
**G** is for good housekeeping.
**I** is for information instruction and training.
**P** is for PPE.
This system can easily be applied to COSHH assessments. You can see the useful stages as you work through them.

# Legal issues

### The duty of everyone

Everyone has a duty of care. Negligence claims against individuals are fast becoming a normal event in the UK – no win, no fee. Individuals and employers cannot afford to ignore current health and safety legislation. Workplace policies are there for a reason. They prevent accidents occurring and diseases developing. You cannot just turn your back on an unsafe practice and walk away. The human, moral and legal consequences should outweigh this situation. Thinking 'It's not my job' is not the answer! Health and safety should be top driven by senior management so in itself it becomes the normal process in working safely.

## The consequences of non-compliance

### ■ Improvement and prohibition notices

These are issued by the HSE and can either state a time limit on when a safety defect should be corrected or a prohibition notice, in fact, stops work on site because of a serious and imminent danger to workers.

### ■ Financial penalties

The severity of an offence will decide which court – crown court or magistrates' court – deals with a health and safety prosecution. There are several outcomes to a conviction:

- A £5000 fine at a magistrates' court.
- A £20,000 fine or six months' imprisonment or both at a magistrates' court.
- Two years' imprisonment or an unlimited fine or both at a crown court. The type of penalty depends upon the scale of the breach.

The charge of corporate manslaughter, where a senior manager or the owner of the company is taken to court and charged with the death of an individual(s), has until recently been very difficult to prove and successfully prosecute, but the HSE will still take this line should it be warranted.

## Procedures after an accident or incident

Under the Reporting of Injuries, Diseases, Dangerous Occurrences Regulations 1995 (RIDDOR), you have a legal duty to report the following to the HSE:

- deaths
- major injuries
- accidents resulting in an **over-three-day injury**
- diseases
- dangerous occurrences
- gas incidents.

## Key Term

**Over-three-day injury** An injury which is not major but results in the person being away from work or unable to do the full range of their normal duties for more than three days.

After a serious accident, you might also have to contact the police to inform them of a fatality, as there might be suspicious circumstances to the death that may need to be investigated. The coroner also has to be informed that a death has occurred as they may also wish to hold an inquiry.

## Case study

Look at the following case study that is based on a real prosecution. This is just one example; there are many actual construction cases that you can view on the HSE website. After you have read the case study, answer the questions.

When XYZ Ltd decided to refurbish its office building in early 2002, it asked Builders Construction Ltd to take part in initial discussions, with a view to appointing the company as the principal contractor. The refurbishment was extensive, and included the removal of an asbestos ceiling. Before starting work, Builders Construction carried out a risk assessment. However, no control measures were put in place to protect

workers, and the general public, from the effects of asbestos fibres. Operatives who had no training in handling asbestos or the correct PPE removed the ceiling in a few days. Builders Construction Ltd was taken to court and found guilty of two breaches of the Control of Asbestos Regulations 2006 and one breach of the Health and Safety at Work Act 1974. The company was fined £20,000.

1   What breaches of the health and safety legislation was the defendant prosecuted on?

2   What was the nature of the offence and who was harmed?

## Principles – why keep safety records of accidents?

Let's look at the dangerous occurrences that often are not reported because no one has been injured. If you keep a record of these and find that a pattern is emerging, it is advisable to act on this occurrence. Why? Because soon enough one of these may result in a fatal or serious injury. This is a primary reason for keeping accident statistics. They are a historical record that can be used for future prevention. For example, accident black spots are used on highway safety schemes to locate speed restrictions to prevent further accidents. A second reason for employers keeping accident records is to provide evidence in the event of a claim against the company. Thirdly, all accidents have to be recorded within an accident book, which must be kept secure and the correct procedure followed in filling in the forms.

## Recording and reporting

We have already looked at the reporting of fatal injuries under the RIDDOR Regulations. There are additional conditions that require the reporting of fatal or major injuries. If a member of the public is killed or taken to hospital, you must immediately notify the enforcing authority (HSE) by telephone. Within ten days, you must follow this up with a completed accident report form (F2508). Over-three-day injuries must also be reported to the HSE.

The RIDDOR Regulations give some guidance on the classification of injuries. Major injuries are:

- 'fracture other than to fingers, thumbs or toes
- amputation
- dislocation of the shoulder, hip, knee or spine

- loss of sight (temporary or permanent)
- chemical or hot metal burn to the eye or any penetrating injury to the eye
- injury resulting from an electric shock or electrical burn leading to unconsciousness or requiring resuscitation or admittance to hospital for more than 24 hours
- any other injury: leading to hypothermia, heat-induced illness or unconsciousness; or requiring resuscitation; or requiring admittance to hospital for more than 24 hours
- unconsciousness caused by asphyxia or exposure to harmful substance or biological agent
- acute illness requiring medical treatment, or loss of consciousness arising from absorption of any substance by inhalation, ingestion or through the skin
- acute illness requiring medical treatment where there is reason to believe that this resulted from exposure to a biological agent or its toxins or infected material' (RIDDOR 1995).

Minor injuries are those that keep an employee off work for more than three days.

You will need to record the following

- date and time of injury
- a brief description of what happened
- the name and address of the person injured
- the date and method of reporting.

### Remember!

If a person is off work from normal duties for a period of over three days (excluding the day of the injury, but including weekends where they might not be at work), then this has to be reported under the regulations.

## Reporting dangerous occurrences

The HSE publishes a list of dangerous occurrences. The following are specific to construction:

- collapse, overturning or failure of load-bearing parts of lifts and lifting equipment
- plant or equipment coming into contact with overhead power lines
- electrical short circuit or overload causing fire or explosion
- collapse or partial collapse of a scaffold over 5 metres high, or erected near water where there could be a risk of drowning after a fall.

## Assessment practice

An accident has occurred on your construction site. An employee has hurt their fingers. While using a compressed air breaker, their fingers became trapped within the mechanism and on pulling the trigger to break out some concrete, the two fingers on the left hand were broken. This accident happens at 3.00 pm on a Friday afternoon; the employee is sent home that day and returns to work on Tuesday with their hand strapped to undertake light duties in the site office with paperwork.

What action will you take?

**P6**

## The role of the individual in accident recording and reporting procedures

The following procedure outlines what you should do following an accident:

1 A trained first aider should administer first aid to the casualty.
2 If required, an ambulance must be called to take the casualty to hospital or an on site facility.
3 Rescue teams may be on site to assist if it is too dangerous to approach the casualty.
4 The accident scene must be left intact if at all possible.

5 The casualty's immediate supervisor must be informed.
6 The company's health and safety department must be informed.
7 The HSE must be informed by phone if it is a fatal accident or within 10 days by filling in the correct form.
8 A full accident investigation must be carried out.

### Remember!

Only qualified first aiders should administer first aid – it could be dangerous for an untrained person to do so.

## The accident investigation

This is the process of analysing what went wrong. The process must be thorough and methodical. If the accident is a fatality or major, it may be conducted by the HSE. So why do we have to do this?

- So that the accident may not reoccur in the future injuring another person.
- Because it is a legal requirement under RIDDOR.
- To provide defensive evidence in a civil claim from the injured party.

The process may take the following form:

1 The accident location is photographed to record the area.
2 A statement is taken from the person who had the accident.
3 The accident report form is filled in and sent off if it is reportable under RIDDOR.
4 Witnesses are interviewed to provide further evidence as to the cause of the incident.
5 An analysis of the accident is undertaken to establish the primary cause, as there may be more than one.
6 New control measures are devised to establish if the existing system of working can be revised.
7 Any changes to the system of working or control measures are then implemented.

8 These changes are then reviewed periodically to see if they are working.

9 If the changes are not, then the process is reviewed until a successful outcome is established.

10 The new safe system of working is monitored periodically.

When a hazard cannot be adequately controlled, then the potential for it to cause an accident is raised. Can accidents be completely avoided? Well, no, because we are only human!

If an accident occurs at work, then the correct procedure must be followed to ensure that it is dealt with effectively and efficiently so that any investigation of the accident can ensure that the same occurrence will not happen in the future.

### Case study

So how should you report an accident? You must follow any company procedure that is in place; you will find this outlined in the company's health and safety policy. Now, imagine that a rough terrain fork truck on your construction site has just hit a worker. Write out the procedure you would follow from the point of giving first aid to the casualty.

## ■ The importance of collecting accurate accident data

A construction company for many reasons should collect accident data. First, it can be used to prevent future accidents and, second, many clients require to see your accident data. Why? Because part of the tendering procedure and applying to work for a client involves the client checking the contractor for competency. This can be done by looking at the number of accidents that a company has had over the last three years.

### Case study

The company you are working for is conducting a review of its health and safety policy. You have been asked to look over the past three years' accident statistics to identify if there are any trends. When you look through the data, you find that there are a large number of foot injuries to one set of workers manufacturing concrete lintels in the construction yard.

1 **Explain how your collection of data could contribute to a reduction of injuries to these workers.**

2 **What could you do to improve this situation?**

3 **How would you monitor improvements?**

## Assessment practice

The contracts manager has approached you, as the assistant health and safety manager, to report an accident that occurred yesterday on one of the company's construction sites. The accident involved a collision between an employee and a rough terrain forklift, where the rear wheel ran over the employee's foot.

What recording and reporting procedure would you undertake as an individual from the point of the accident just occurring to the employee's return to work? **P6**

# Preparation for assessment

Read through some of the construction trade papers or national papers and identify a construction-related accident. After reading the article, identify, either by name or job description, the person you think is responsible for health and safety in this instance. Try to explain their roles and responsibilities in their workplace. If you are having trouble locating a suitable article, ask your tutor to assist you.

Alternatively, visit a construction site on an educational site visit. Interview and ask the site supervisor to identify who is responsible for health and safety on the construction site and what their safety role is. **P1**

Identify at least two pieces of health and safety legislation that would be applicable to your job role as a supervisor on a typical construction site. When you have identified two, explain the employees' roles and responsibilities under one of these pieces of legislation. **P2**

Identify some potential hazards that are present in a workplace of your choosing (you could look at the workplace where you have a part-time job or at the educational establishment where you are undertaking your BTEC National course, or from a site visit to a local construction site). When you have identified at least four hazards, evaluate the existing control measures that are present to reduce the harm from the hazard. Identify who might be harmed and to what extent. **P3**

You have just started your first trainee position as an assistant site manager on a construction site. You keep hearing the term 'risk assessment'. Not wanting to appear foolish as you do not totally understand the meaning, you ask a fellow trainee on another site for help. Place yourself in the informed trainee's shoes and describe to the colleague what are the main principles of a risk assessment? What does it contain? **P4**

The following hazards have been identified on a risk assessment on the installation of a drainage sewer connection into a main road:

- Buried services – electric shock.
- Injection – from burst hydraulic pipe on excavator.
- Crushing injury from excavation collapse.
- Road traffic accident – collision with road traffic.
- Cuts and scrapes from hand excavation.
- Noise – from road saw.

Classify each of these hazards as low, medium or high risk, and evaluate what control measures you would put in place to reduce the high-risk hazards to an acceptable and legal level. **P5**

Your manager has asked you to evaluate the company's accident reporting and recording procedures. The information you find will be used to develop a training manual for all employees entitled 'The Company Accident Reporting Procedure'. Highlight what actions will be listed in this manual. **P6**

The managing director has asked you to review how well the company implements the values of the Construction (Design and Management) Regulations, namely cooperation and coordination of the safety issues involving the building team. Identify and explain how the building team interacts between each other in terms of their health and safety roles and responsibilities. **M1**

The construction project you are working on has just commenced. The current activity on site is the installation of the drainage and, specifically, the concrete manholes. These consist of chamber rings that stack one on top of another. The bottom ring sits on a bed of concrete and has the channel running through it. The chamber has a top with a manhole cover and frame secured to it. The rings are normally covered with poured concrete on the outside and are lifted in by the excavator.

Produce in a suitable format a risk assessment for this work. **M2**

You have been assigned to the health and safety department of your construction company to gain some experience as a health and safety practitioner. You notice that there is quite a rigorous procedure in place to collect and analyse the company's accident data and wonder why. You ask the senior health and safety adviser why. Produce the answer you received. **M3**

Look again at the risk assessment you produced for M2 and at the following current year's accident data obtained from the health and safety department on injuries caused by drainage operations:

- Hand injuries as a result of trapping between chamber rings 5 nr
- Chemical burns from cement 6 nr

Justify the contents of your risk assessment in light of the accident data and say whether you have taken all reasonably practicable steps in your control measures. **D1**

You have been handed the following accident report:

### Accident Report

Date: _____

Employee: J Smith

Location: Construction Site A

Description of what happened:

At about 4.30 pm on 26 January of this year I was locking up the construction site compound and walking towards the site entrance gate when I fell into an excavation and injured myself on some reinforcing bars. I was on my own and had to wait till the visiting security guard found me and helped me out of the excavation. I was taken by ambulance to the hospital to have a cut to my leg stitched and dressed. I reported for work the next day as normal.

Signed _____

Suggest improvements to this workplace to avoid a reoccurrence. **D2**

## Grading tips

The content refers to three members of the building team – the employer, the main contractor and the planning supervisor. You need to research the roles and responsibilities of the team including the designer. Looking at the CDM Regulations should help. You have to explain, that is, give details and make clear, how the members of the building team *interact*. This means the communication and cooperation between them. **M1**

This calls for you to perform a typical risk assessment for a given workplace. You need to identify the hazards, decide who might be affected, list the existing control measures, assess the risk, see if further action is required, then monitor and review. You could develop a standard form or simply write down the process in a logical sequence. **M2**

This calls for an explanation. You will need to provide a description of how the collection of accident data and incidents can be used to help improve safety and welfare in the workplace. **M3**

'Justify' is the key word here. A full reason supported by facts is required. Why is a control measure suitable and reasonably practicable in that work situation? You need to state the reasons why, with supporting evidence. **D1**

This involves evaluating the accident report, which means assess from the supplied document what could be done to improve the situation. Look through the report and identify with explanation which items you consider are defective or missing and require improvement. **D2**

## Knowledge check

1 Does the client have to appoint a planning supervisor?

2 Several employees are deliberately setting off fire extinguishers in your workplace. Can you prosecute them?

3 Does the main contractor feature in the Construction (Design and Management) Regulations?

4 What is the difference between a hazard and a risk?

5 What precautions must you take for working within a confined space?

6 What is the major cause of fatal accidents?

7 Name four hidden costs of an accident that cannot be recovered from insurances?

8 List the five steps to risk assessment.

9 What three penalties can the HSE impose for a failure in health and safety?

10 What does RIDDOR stand for?

11 You have had an accident on site and have fractured two fingers. Must this accident be reported to the safety authorities?

12 The following control measure is being used – the use of a mobile elevated platform to change a light bulb on the ground floor ceiling. Is this reasonably practicable?

13 An accident occurs on Thursday night and the injured person returns to work on Monday morning. Is the accident reportable if the person was unfit over the weekend?

14 What four essential items need to be on an accident report?

15 It is 11 days before you report a major accident to the HSE. It is not happy about this – why?

## Grading criteria: Unit 1

| To achieve a pass grade the evidence must show that the learner is able to: | To achieve a merit grade the evidence must show that, in addition to the pass criteria, the learner is able to: | To achieve a distinction grade the evidence must show that, in addition to the pass and merit criteria, the learner is able to: |
|---|---|---|
| **P1** identify and describe the roles and responsibilities of the persons responsible for health, safety and welfare on a construction project **Assessment practice pages 8, 38** | **M1** explain how the members of the building team interact in terms of their health, safety and welfare roles and responsibilities **Assessment practice pages 13, 38** | |
| **P2** identify three main pieces of health, safety and welfare legislation relevant to the construction and built environment sector and describe the legal duties of employees and employers in terms of such legislation **Assessment practice pages 8, 12, 38** | | |
| **P3** identify and describe a range of hazards present in a given workplace situation, the persons who may be at risk, and the possible consequences for such persons **Assessment practice pages 16, 38** | **M2** perform a typical risk assessment for a given workplace situation using a suitable format **Assessment practice pages 26, 38** | **D1** justify the contents of a risk assessment, in terms of available accident data and what is 'reasonably practicable' **Assessment practice page 39** |
| **P4** identify and describe the main principles and features of a typical risk assessment for a given workplace situation **Assessment practice pages 21, 24, 26, 38** | | |
| **P5** select control measures for a given workplace situation to reduce risks and meet legal requirements **Assessment practice pages 17, 27, 38** | **M3** explain how collecting accurate data and information on accidents and incidents contributes to improvements in health, safety and welfare in the workplace **Assessment practice page 39** | **D2** evaluate a provided accident report and suggest improvements that could be made to workplace systems in the future to avoid a recurrence **Assessment practice pages 8, 38, 39** |
| **P6** identify and describe the role of the individual in accident recording and reporting procedures **Assessment practice pages 36, 37, 38** | | |

# Construction and the environment

## Introduction

Global warming is changing our environment. To reduce its effects, environment legislation in the UK – including current Building Regulations – is changing too. Domestic and commercial construction has now to be much more thermally efficient in order to save energy in the long term.

For thousands of years, we have exploited the natural resources of the world – coal, oil, gas, metals, gypsum and aggregate, to name but a few. All of these are used to produce construction materials for consumption. Today, there are many measures in place to protect the natural environment, from National Parks, to Acts of Parliament to environmentally protected green belts of land, and the efficient use of recycling techniques that save on further development of resources.

The government's recent initiative to redevelop brownfield sites (areas of land with existing buildings on them that have exceeded their life span) has reduced the need to develop greenfield sites.

The current emphasis is on the sustainable use of construction materials, so that they can be manufactured and used without having an effect on the resources required for future generations to enjoy. This may be as simple as buying materials manufactured locally, therefore saving on transport costs.

### How you will be assessed

This unit is internally assessed by your tutor. A variety of activities is included in this unit to help you understand all aspects of construction and the environment.

After completing this unit you should be able to achieve the following outcomes:

1 Know the important features of the natural environment that need to be protected
2 Understand how the activities of the construction and built environment sector impact on the natural environment
3 Understand how the natural environment can be protected against the activities of the construction and built environment sector
4 Be able to select sustainable construction techniques that are fit for purpose

# Thinking points

Why is it important to protect our natural environment, including the Earth's resources?

How can we protect the natural environment and still develop construction activities, while saving valuable resources for future generations?

## Features

### Air quality

During the Industrial Revolution, first water then coal was the main source of fuel used to power pulleys and belts driving industrial machinery. There was no control over growth and pollution became a serious problem as the phenomenon known as smog developed over the large industrial cities of the UK.

Smog brought with it poor visibility as well as breathing difficulties for the cities' inhabitants as there was no clean air – smog depleted oxygen levels. Deaths from asthma, bronchitis and other lung diseases became common. The development of the petrol engine led to a further rise in pollution caused by lead-based petrol emissions. The governments of the day passed Acts to control waste emissions into the atmosphere. The first Clean Air Act of 1956 was one such form of legislation and its effect was to reduce the smog over large population centres.

Good air quality is vital for life and is an essential part of a healthy environment. Large factories tend to be sited away from population centres in order to prevent pollution entering the breathable atmosphere over towns and cities; indeed, large chimneys push the pollution further up into the atmosphere avoiding any fallout to local inhabitants. Today, emissions are strictly controlled to reduce the level of carbon dioxide ($CO_2$) that we now know adds to the effects of global warming. Tree and landscape planting improves the quality of air and is considered to be a sustainable part of any housing development.

Air quality obviously differs with geographical location. The centre of London or Birmingham compared to sparsely populated areas of Scotland or Wales will have different air qualities. Generally, the more population and industry in an area, the poorer the air quality.

### Ozone quality

Ozone is a gas that occurs naturally in the Earth's upper atmosphere. It shields the Earth from harmful ultraviolet (UV) radiation. Without this ozone layer, there would be no life on Earth as we know it.

Over the past 60 years, chemicals such as chlorofluorocarbons (CFCs) have been used as a cooling gas in fridges and freezers and as a propellant in aerosols. When scientists spotted a hole opening up in the ozone layer above the Antarctic, they realised it was caused by ozone-destroying chemicals like CFCs. Since 1987, many of the world's governments have signed up to the Montreal Protocol on Substances that Deplete the Ozone Layer. As a result, CFCs have been steadily replaced with less harmful chemicals. Scientists now believe that the hole in the ozone layer is getting smaller.

### Soil quality and natural drainage

The benchmark for soil quality is a difficult one to define. No two soils are the same and therefore there is no British Standard for a soil to be compared against, although recently, two environmental committees formulated up to 67 measured variables for soil quality. The **Soil Association** grades soils against a certain standard but this is for the organic growing of fruit and vegetables. Below are just a few of the categories against which soils may be measured:

- drainage properties
- texture
- acidity
- **pH** balance (see Figure 2.1)
- use
- level of contamination
- fertility
- mineral content
- organic content
- structural properties.

| | |
|---|---|
| Extremely acid | 4.3 or lower |
| Highly acid | 4.3 – 4.8 |
| Moderately acid | 4.8 – 5.5 |
| Mildly acid | 5.5 – 7.0 |
| Mildly alkaline | 7.0 – 7.7 |
| Moderately alkaline | 7.7 – 8.5 |
| Highly alkaline | 8.5 or higher |

▲ Figure 2.1 pH range of soil

but recent government planning policy has been to allow developments within flood plains. Overburden on a river's **levees** causes them to break and localised flooding to occur.

Soil drainage depends greatly on the structure of the soil, that is, how many pores or open voids are contained within it. The voids allow water to penetrate through the soil, eventually ending up within an **aquifer** below ground. Clay soils tend to resist the passage of moisture, whereas limestone rock allows the percolation of water through it. Therefore, geography and location play an important part in soil quality and drainage, along with the substrata of the rocks below the surface soils.

## Key Terms

**Soil Association** Organisation promoting healthy soils via a certification scheme that enables a producer to use the term 'organic' produce.

**pH** The measure of chemical balance that is acidic or alkaline. Remember litmus paper that changes colour with acids or alkalis? An ideal soil is somewhere in the mid range between red and blue.

## Key Terms

**Levees** Natural banks of silt deposits which are left after a river floods. These are shaped into higher banks to control flood waters. In 2005, some of the levees protecting New Orleans in the USA broke and flooded the city.

**Aquifer** An underground storage area created naturally within the Earth's rock strata.

In terms of construction, it could be said that a quality soil is one that will sustain life. We use soil to provide attractive and environmentally landscaped areas for the community to interact with. New housing schemes always include these areas as part of the government's sustainability policy.

The drainage of soils is a vital environmental consideration. One of the effects of global warming is flash floods. In poorer and underdeveloped countries, where trees have been cut down for use as fuel, there is no capture and absorption of water into the soil and it just runs off, with devastating consequences. Indeed, there are many parts of the UK that have been deforested since the Middle Ages. This leaves the soil unbound, as tree roots bind the soil together, and exposed to high levels of moisture that eventually runs off and sits on the surface. In small amounts this does not cause a problem,

### Landscape

The natural landscape of the British Isles is a valuable resource within easy reach of major towns and cities. From the highlands of Scotland to the Cotswolds, Cornwall, the Lake District and the Pennines, these are just some of the unique and diverse landscapes that are protected today. Local landscapes involve forests, rivers, streams, hills, topography and the unspoilt countryside.

Urban landscapes also carry a unique signature, for example the slate-built houses of the Lake District to the sandstone buildings of Edinburgh. Inner cities can have a vertical landscape; London is becoming a rival to the buildings of New York with many multi-storey constructions such as the Swiss Re Gherkin. Leeds city centre is also developing vertically.

Our landscape is a valuable resource. Tourists travel to the UK to see its ancient history, which is reflected in the landscape. An attractive view with open spaces allows the use of the landscape for recreation purposes such as horse riding, fishing and hill walking. The coastal landscape is one that continually changes over time with erosion taking place by the action of the waves, as parts of the coastline move steadily inward. The different coastal rocks produce different landscapes, from the clay boulder slopes of the Yorkshire coastline to the chalk white cliffs of Dover.

The natural landscape of the UK has been changed by the ice ages that pushed millions of tons of ice southwards across half of Britain. This moulded and shaped the landscape beneath it, often leaving behind boulder clay and rocks.

## Natural amenities

The facilities and services afforded by the natural environment cover a wide range of activities:

- Rivers – used for a variety of water-based sports such as fishing, angling and canoeing. Fishing is regulated under licence by the Waterways Environment Agency.
- Lakes – the Lake District, for example, is enjoyed by boating enthusiasts; a ferry service and pleasure craft attract a healthy tourist industry.
- Fenlands – the naturally occurring seasonal flooding areas of the fenlands and the Norfolk Broads produce large areas for migrating birds to feed upon during their annual migration from other climates. This enables the development of protected areas for wildlife conservation and the hobby of bird watching to flourish.
- Moors – the natural moors of the Yorkshire and Pennine regions are unique, although it may be said that humans have developed this environment by burning large areas for the promotion of grouse shooting as a sport. Large areas of the moors tend to be managed estates.
- Mountains – the Scottish and Welsh mountain areas offer hill walking and mountain climbing. Scotland also offers skiing facilities in winter.
- Natural forests – used to cover most of Britain during the Middle Ages, but they have been gradually cut down and used for fuel and ship building. There

are small areas of natural woodland that are now protected from felling. Natural woodlands provide a landscape that can be used for mountain biking, dog walking and exercise.

- The sea and beaches – Britain's coastal areas are unique and diverse. From the pebble beaches of the south coast to the sandy beaches of Norfolk and the rugged granite cliffs of parts of Cornwall and Scotland, beaches attract tourists during the summer months. Many are protected under an SSSI (site of special scientific interest). The sea is a valuable source of food, although stocks of fish are protected by European Union quotas.

## Land use

The use of the land has been defined over hundreds of years and has been largely governed by the local population and the resources that were available at the time. Villages developed into towns and then major cities; expansion generally took place into the surrounding land. In order to feed the population, farming and agriculture developed in the fields surrounding the villages.

When the Industrial Revolution took off, resources of coal, oil, water and wood were developed and the industrial use of plots of land was born. The waterway network developed with a canal system that was later superseded by the railway network. Planning control eventually gave the community more selection in the choice of land use and limited development where it was considered inappropriate. For example, the expansion of out-of-town shopping developments has been reversed through government policy on strategic planning.

Land use can therefore be broadly categorised into:

- agricultural
- heavy industrial
- housing
- commercial
- natural landscape.

## Green belts

These are areas of green land that surround communities and provide open parkland for the community to enjoy away from the industrial use of the land. Green belt land is protected and no development is permitted. It provides an attractive and aesthetic area that breaks up the large conurbations which formed as villages, grew into towns and cities, swallowing up all the available surrounding land. The green belt provides a buffer zone between different land uses and maintains a clean, fresh and naturally growing land use that all of the community can experience and enjoy.

## Thinking points

In 2006, over 300 applications were made to develop on areas of green belt. The Office of the Deputy Prime Minister (now Communities and Local Government) approved 150 of these!

## Agriculture

This is the use of land that has been developed to produce food. It can be classified into two broad areas:

- Arable – the growing of crops.
- Livestock – the raising of animals.

Arable farming in the UK includes cereal crops such as wheat and barley and horticulture, which is the growing of fruit and vegetables. There has recently been a drive for organically grown crops which are produced without the use of chemicals. Livestock includes the production of meat and milk from cattle, and sheep and pigs for meat production.

Agriculture plays a significant part in developing the fertile regions of the landscape by ploughing the land and adding fertilisers to grow crops. This alters the natural landscape from its raw state into a condition that can be used for food production. Large areas each side of a major river are the most fertile for this use, as the river floods depositing minerals and materials that feed nutrients into the soils.

## Assessment practice

A large plot of land has come on to the market and has obtained outline planning consent for housing development. You live in a local village adjacent to this land and are a parish councillor. The community is outraged at the decision to allow development on this piece of unspoilt, green landscape. In order to help fight an objection to full planning consent, you have been asked to identify and describe the features of the natural environment that must be considered at the planning stage, which could be used to defend development.

List five features of the natural environment with descriptions against each.

## Forestry

The use of land for forestry can be divided into:

- naturally occurring, established woodlands which are hundreds of years old and are carefully managed
- plantations which are areas of land that have been deliberately planted for the growth and harvesting of timber resources.

In Britain, natural woodlands are limited to small pockets. There is a national forest at Nottingham, but a lot of woodland was cleared for industrial development, ship building and to use as fuel. Forests also provide an opportunity for recreation, offering an ideal environment for walking, bird watching, horse riding and biking.

The UK government's Forestry Commission looks after many of the forests and protects them as well as developing and expanding the use of timber as a resource. Timber, unlike oil, gas and coal, is a renewable resource that is not finite.

## Countryside

The British countryside tends to be the region that is not developed in strong concentrations, unlike the major towns and cities and high conurbation areas such as

London and Manchester. Small villages and settlements such as farms are surrounded by green areas of farming or natural landscape which we call 'the countryside'. These areas are green due to high concentrations of rainfall; in hotter climates they would be brown.

There are very distinctive areas of countryside, for example the Wolds of Lincolnshire, the Lowlands of Scotland and the South Downs of Dorset.

It is vital that these are taken care of for future generations to enjoy. They are part of our culture and stand out as distinctive structures, for example the stone circle of Stonehenge. A system of **listing** important buildings has protected many of them, as has the National Trust which owns and runs some of the historic locations in the UK.

## Remember!

The countryside is an area of green scenery that is clean, attractive and unique within easy reach of major living areas.

## Key Term

**Listed building** A building of special architectural or historic interest in the UK. Alterations to these buildings must be carefully considered before they are made.

## Heritage

Britain has been inhabited by humans for thousands of years. Over this period, we have developed an enviable and unique heritage that has required protection. Heritage encompasses not just the land but the structures created upon it and could include the following:

- battlefields
- ancient monuments and icons
- castles
- manor houses
- streets
- archaeological sites
- bridges
- parks and gardens.

## Theory into practice

Find out more about listed buildings in England at English Heritage's website, www.english-heritage.org.uk; for information on listing in Scotland, see Historic Scotland's website, historic-scotland.gov.uk.

Castles are an important part of British heritage ▶

## Water resources

Over the past 100 years, we have developed the need for water as a resource. It is used not just for drinking but for washing, flushing toilets, cleaning and bathing. A dishwasher and washing machine are now considered essential items in many homes. Indeed, the growth in hot tubs now puts even more strain on the distribution systems that supply the water.

Water resources include the extraction of water above and below ground. Above ground, water is captured in reservoirs or by damming a river supply, extracting from rivers, or in hot climates by desalination plants from seawater. Below ground, boreholes are sunk within permeable rocks to extract the water by pumping. Water is a valuable commodity – a licence is needed to extract it and it must be protected from contamination through pollution leaking into the soils and rocks.

## Water quality

Water for human consumption is extracted from reservoirs, rivers and boreholes. It then has to be treated to enable it to be classified as drinking water. Water is distributed around the UK using a system of pipework, which is then rated or metered as the consumer uses it.

Water cannot contain any harmful elements such as bacteria, as this would affect our health and safety. Pure, fresh and clean water is often extracted at source and bottled as a mineral water. Non-drinking water supplies tend to be used in European countries where water is in short supply; we, for example, use drinking water to flush toilets in the UK.

Water quality is often determined by the material through which it percolates during its journey to the aquifer, which is an underground storage area created naturally within the Earth's rock strata, for example limestone.

## Marine environment

The marine environment covers many aspects, including:

- harbours
- the sea
- estuaries
- marshes
- beaches
- cliffs.

The marine environment differs from the river environment in that it is salt-water based and not fresh water, but it is worth noting that several rivers are tidal. The tides are a gravitational effect caused by the moon's influence on the Earth. Along the coast there will be high-tide and low-tide marks. It is said that global warming is steadily adding to the rise in sea levels through the melting of polar ice, which is threatening many cities of the world, for example London and Venice. Hurricanes and the storm surges that arrive with them are a real threat, as the flooding and devastation of New Orleans in 2005 shows.

Marine wildlife is extensive in its range and biodiversity; indeed, the surface of the Earth is covered with a great deal of salt water, much of which has not been explored, and there is still a great deal to discover about this environment. Britain's coastline differs depending on the surrounding rock structures that meet the sea – soft rocks and clays are easily washed away by the action of the waves, whereas igneous rocks take longer to be broken down into fine sands.

## Wildlife

Wildlife is the native life that exists within a geographical location, but wildlife does migrate with the seasons, for example the swallows of North Africa that visit Britain each year. Wildlife, as the name suggests, is *wild* in that it has not been tamed by human interference, for example horses, pigs and sheep.

We have a wide range of wildlife in Britain, from birds, seals, whales, fish, snakes to otters, all of which is left alone to develop and establish itself within the landscape. Our agriculture industry does have an effect on wildlife. The crops that we grow and the land that we clear for cattle have an effect on wildlife diversity and its location.

Native wildlife tends to be unique to its area, for example the colonies of birds that congregate in certain areas, like the Dartford warbler, or ospreys in Scotland. Humans have to be very careful to avoid disturbing wildlife or this may tragically mean extinction for some species.

## Biodiversity

This can be defined as the range of biological species that is present within the environment. It can span from micro-organisms to wildlife such as ducks and swans. It is the amount of living biological matter present within a geographical area. Biodiversity is an essential item for our eco-systems; if an imbalance develops, then one species takes over predominantly, for example rats and mice infestation.

Any activity humans undertake has an effect on biodiversity. For example, if you purchase a plot of green belt land and construct a building upon it, you have taken away the area of the footprint of the building, although it can be traded off with the external landscaping that can be undertaken with a new building.

## Natural habitat

Habitat may be defined as the place where any living thing lives. Natural means that it is naturally occurring. Some people say that there are no areas of natural habitat left in Britain. Most of our country was originally covered in woodlands, which have been removed for the construction of buildings and as a fuel source.

Natural habitats are some of the heaths, meadows, limestone pavements and moorlands, as these are areas that have not been interfered with by humans. For example, grazing sheep on land destroys the natural habitat. We have lost so much of the natural habitat that there is now a move by environmentalists to restore many of the natural habitats in Britain. For example, we have lost nearly half of our ancient woodlands, and almost three-quarters of our ponds; this has a detrimental effect on biodiversity with some species already extinct. Humans have had a considerable impact on British natural habitats, which now require more protection than ever, so those that remain can be enjoyed in the future.

## Assessment practice

A small area of green belt land has unexpectedly come on to the market and is expected to be granted outline planning permission with the sale. Many members of the local community have voiced their opposition to the development. To assist with fighting this cause, undertake an assessment of the potential environmental impact a proposed construction project will have on such a piece of land and on the local natural environment. **M1**

# Globally

## Greenhouse gases and global warming

Everyone in the world needs a roof over their heads to protect them from the environment they inhabit. In the UK, the winter is colder than in the warmer climates and so more substantial buildings are required, instead of simply using locally growing resources such as palms.

The construction industry uses raw materials, for example limestone and clays for cement and brick manufacture. Both these and many other processes require energy. The energy can be in the form of gas or electricity supplies. The process of turning the raw materials into a construction product releases carbon emissions into the atmosphere, which is a greenhouse gas. Similarly, we have cut down many trees in order to process the timber from them for construction. Trees absorb carbon and through photosynthesis produce oxygen as a by-product.

The construction industry cannot be blamed solely for global warming. The production of cars and the fuels they burn along with air conditioning and several other sources add to the problem.

## Theory into practice

The consequences of global warming are now a reality that is affecting all of us. Undertake a web-based search on the effects of global warming on the Earth and list three of the major causes and three consequences of this.

## Remember!

A natural layer of greenhouse gases – water vapour, carbon dioxide, methane, nitrous oxide and ozone – surrounds the Earth and keeps it warm. Without this layer, temperatures on our planet would be much cooler and life on Earth, as we know it, would not exist.

In recent times, manmade greenhouse gases – nitrous oxide, sulphur hexafluoride, hydrofluorocarbons, perfluorocarbons and chlorofluorocarbons (CFCs) – have been released into the atmosphere as a result of human activity and added to the natural greenhouse gas layer. The result has been global warming – heat which would normally excape through the greenhouse gas layer into space remains trapped, causing the temperature on Earth to rise. Scientists predict that the increase in temperature will have serious consequences for the environment, including a change in rainfall patterns and a rise in sea levels.

There are two sides to any discussion on global warming. Some scientists disagree that the Earth is entering a warmer phase; they point to the fact that the Earth was warmer in medieval times than it is now. Other factors influencing the Earth's climate could be:

- The sun's activity goes in cycles. During the last ice age, the sun was less active.
- The tilt of the earth is off centre and does move about this axis, which means that at certain times of the year some of the Earth is nearer the sun than other parts, which affects temperatures.
- A volcanic eruption on Earth throws dust into the atmosphere, which blocks sunlight. This can cause the Earth's climate to cool, sometimes for several years after the eruption.
- The Earth's orbit around the sun is elliptical, which means that it is sometimes closer to the sun than at others.

## Acid rain

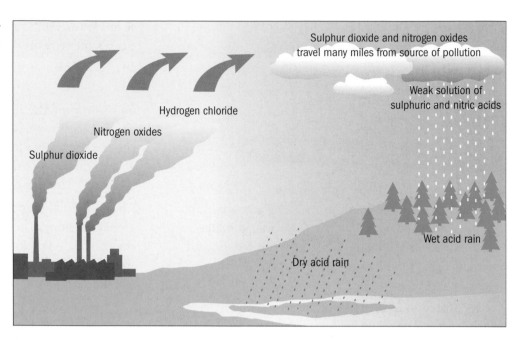

Figure 2.2 The acid rain cycle ▶

Sulphur dioxide and nitrogen oxides travel many miles from source of pollution

Weak solution of sulphuric and nitric acids

Hydrogen chloride

Nitrogen oxides

Sulphur dioxide

Wet acid rain

Dry acid rain

Acid rain has an unusually high pH value. When the gases sulphur dioxide, nitrogen oxides and hydrogen chloride combine with water droplets in the atmosphere, weak solutions of sulphuric and nitric acids are formed (see Figure 2.2). The gases come from two main sources: from hot magma ejected into the atmosphere during volcanic activity and from the burning of fossil fuels, namely oil, gas and coal. Sulphur dioxide and nitrogen oxides may not combine with water droplets until they are many miles from the initial source of pollution. They are carried by the prevailing winds, so the pollution of one country can seriously affect the environment of another.

The acid pollution can fall to the ground in two forms: wet and dry.

- Wet acid rain refers to precipitation, rain, fog and snow. It then affects plants, wildlife, trees and the area's biodiversity by upsetting the chemical balance of soils and the environment.
- Dry acid rain falls as a dust or a smoke that coats the ground, buildings, plants and the land. When it rains, these combine with the surface water to produce an acid water that has serious effects where it collects, especially in lakes and ponds and where it is taken up by tree roots.

### ■ Effects of acid rain

Acid rain can concentrate in thin soils and be extracted by trees and plants, causing slow growth and eventually death. It affects the water environment of lakes and rivers, killing fish and other aquatic life. Acid rain also causes damage to buildings where it destroys and reacts with some types of stone gradually removing the surface over time.

## Remember!

Because acid pollution is carried by the wind, there is nothing the receiving country can do about the acid rain that falls upon its lands. Only a global agreement can try to prevent future contamination.

## Ozone depletion due to CFCs

Chlorofluorocarbons (CFCs) are man-made chemicals that until recently were used in the following appliances:

- air conditioning units
- refrigerators
- cold stores
- freezers
- aerosols
- cleaning solvents
- foam products.

As mentioned on page 44, CFCs released into the atmosphere have damaged part of the protective ozone layer surrounding the Earth, increasing the amount of UV radiation reaching the Earth. UV radiation can:

- cause sunburn and lead to skin cancer
- affect the biodiversity and ecosystems of marine environments by killing certain micro-organisms
- lead to eye disorders such as blindness and cataracts.

## Remember!

According to scientists, a single CFC molecule can destroy over 100,000 ozone molecules, so it does not take much of this product to have an effect. Despite the reduction in use of CFCs, they are still affecting the atmosphere as they gradually decay.

## Over-extraction of water

The rise in the UK population has taken place over hundreds of years, and in order to house this growth we have expanded outwards turning villages into towns and towns into cities. This expansion is reflected in the increased demand for water resources. As we have seen, these are extracted by water companies from several sources. The growth in demand requires increased extraction. There are several ways to increase supply:

- Create more reservoirs.
- Reduce the level of wastage from distribution supply pipes.
- Install water meters.
- Increase pumping rates from boreholes.
- Increase extraction from rivers.

All these methods have a detrimental effect on the environment. Creating more reservoirs means turning suitable river valleys into lakes by damming, which floods valuable fertile agricultural land and any buildings in the area. Reducing the level of wastage by the distribution network is a sensible alternative. Water is wasted through leakage due to broken pipes and connections which have outlived their service life. Reduce this leakage and you increase the supply to consumers. Installing water meters has an immediate effect on consumption once end users realise that every

drop not used efficiently increases costs not only for the supply but also the disposal.

Increasing pumping rates from boreholes drops the level of water contained within the aquifer. Although this has no visible effect on the surface, the depth of the boreholes may have to be increased and the reduction in water level has to be replaced by rainfall or the borehole could run dry. Over-extraction of water from rivers can lead to environmental damage in the areas of wetlands within the UK. They dry out and their biodiversity and ecosystems change with the reduction in water levels. Indeed, during hot summers, rivers can run dry, which kills off all aquatic life.

## Fossil fuels and raw materials

Oil, gas and coal are the fossil fuels that were produced by the compression, that is, the force exerted from tons of plants piled on top of each other and then layers of rocks, of the detritus materials (plants) from forests over millions of years. They have to be extracted from below ground which has had a detrimental effect on the environment not only local to their source but also during transportation, for example the Torrey Canyon oil disaster of 1967 when the supertanker leaked thousands of gallons of oil onto the coast of Cornwall, and open cast mining of coal. All of these resources are *finite*, that is, when they run out they cannot be replaced. Only timber can be regrown and used again.

Oil extraction in the UK is mainly in small areas on land but is much more prevalent in the North Sea, for example the Brent oilfields off the coast of Scotland. The impact that oil has on construction and the environment is the distribution and storage facilities that are required to move it from the oilfield into tanks and then for processing into a range of products such as fuel oils and petrol. Heavier oils are imported using cargo ships that require docks and harbours for berthing and unloading.

It is a similar situation with natural gas, which is extracted from the North Sea gasfields and, more recently, delivered by pipeline from Russia and Norway. Large areas are required to store gas and pump up to pressure for distribution using underground pipelines.

The coal industry has recently undergone a decline in extraction of coal. This was due to industrial disputes and the pollution that is emitted from the burning of coal. There are two methods of coal extraction: underground mines and open cast. The first produces a substantial amount of waste that is landscaped into heaps and which alter the surrounding environment. The second involves the stripping of the overlying areas, the coal is excavated, the removed spoil is replaced and the land can be restored to a new use.

## Case study

The UK coal industry in its era of maximum production produced many thousands of tons of coal each year. Most of this was extracted by underground mining. As part of the extraction process large areas of land had to be filled with the waste product that was removed with the coal, which ended up in slag heaps. This used large areas of land. The coal product was produced mainly for the UK electric generation industry where it was burnt to produce steam that drove turbines which generated electric current. This also has consequences for the environment.

Divide yourselves into teams and undertake research into the two areas identified above which are:

- the land use associated with coal extraction
- the environmental effects of burning coal.

(*Hint*: There are many coalfields present within the South Yorkshire region.)

## Increased energy consumption and electricity generation

Since the reliance on fossil fuels, such as coal, that have been used to produce electricity has declined, there has been a net increase in burning gas, a cleaner fuel, to produce electrical energy. Energy consumption has increased with the modern consumer market that requires electricity to power the variety of electrical items we buy, from flat screen TVs to microwave ovens, all of which may be left on stand-by, using energy. Nuclear power still exists and produces energy in the UK, but public opinion on its use is influenced by green issues.

The problem with increasing energy consumption to supply this demand is the balance that has to be maintained between the limit on fossil fuels and the increase in greenhouse gases. In order to start to address this issue, energy is now being generated from renewable sources. The current sources used in the UK are:

- Wind power developed from wind turbines sited on land or at sea.
- Wave power produced from the action of the waves which forces air to drive a turbine.
- Hydro-electric power produced by damming rivers and directing water into turbines.
- Landfill gas that is tapped and burnt to produce heat, steam and electric turbine energy.
- Sewage sludge digestion that produces a flammable gas which is combusted to produce steam.
- Combustion of waste to produce gas which is converted into steam.
- The growing of crops to produce biofuels.
- Solar heating where the sun's rays warm water in coils of pipes.
- Geothermal aquifers, where the magma energy of the Earth's crust is used to produce steam.
- Solar voltaic, which is the production of electricity using photo cell panels that convert the sun's energy to electricity.

More and more of these renewable energy sources will have to be used to produce electricity if we are to reduce the effect of global warming. The reduction of energy using energy saving technology, for example low voltage light bulbs, also contributes to saving valuable energy that would be wasted and extends the life of the fossil fuels that we have.

## Deforestation

The tropical areas of the world are hot and humid and provide ideal conditions for the growth of natural rain forests. These have developed over thousands of years. The location of the rain forests coincides with countries whose infrastructure and therefore economic wealth is only just developing. The rain forests are disappearing for a number of reasons.

- Slash and burn agriculture where trees are cleared and the land used for the growing of crops until its natural fertility dies and the area is left to recover slowly.
- Hardwood timber is important to economic wealth and therefore the forest is seen as a resource to help the government.
- Expansion of towns and cities.
- Trees are used for firewood.
- Illegal logging.
- Clearing for cattle production.
- Forest fires.

The UK was once covered in deciduous forests which have nearly all been cleared and the timber used for fuel, house building and ship building.

So what impact will deforestation have on the natural environment?

- The water cycle may be affected as the tropical areas absorb a large volume of moisture and water which will be reduced with the loss of the trees that absorb it.
- The amount of carbon within the atmosphere will increase as trees absorb this and give out oxygen via photosynthesis.
- As the trees and ground covering are stripped, rainfall can now erode the surface of the soil.
- Following this erosion, soil is deposited in rivers, lakes and ponds which may eventually silt up.
- The change in environment may result in a desert being formed from the lower moisture levels.
- With the loss of this habitat, species contained within it become extinct.

## Loss of natural habitat

Some people say that Britain has lost all of its natural habitats as humans have touched every part of the country from the infrastructure of roads, railways, canals, airports, buildings and agriculture to name a few. Try to name a few unspoilt natural habitats and you will struggle. As our population has expanded, so

has the industry to provide wages and agriculture to supply food. The balance has favoured humans until recently.

The loss of natural habitat also includes the loss of biodiversity and the species associated with it. These are not recoverable. The loss of natural habitat in one area may also have an effect on another with mammals and animals that migrate between habitats finding that they no longer have a migrational home to complete the natural cycle between environments.

## Reduction in biodiversity

The process of natural selection, the way different species rely on one another, the predator and the prey, are all examples of how biodiversity is linked between species. Take one out and the result could be a plague of a more dominant species. For example, rats are now becoming resistant to the poisons used to control them; this will affect other species populations.

Biodiversity provides many natural resources from clean air to clean water allowing crops to propagate and fruit. To damage such an environment always has a reaction somewhere in the food chain.

## Remember!

Interfering in a biodiverse environment could lead to the creation of a virus that could kill humans.

## Assessment practice

The managing director of your construction company wants the company to have a green policy that relates to all its activities. You have been tasked with research on this topic and have initially to identify the forms of global pollution and describe how each may harm the local environment of the UK where the company operates. **P2**

# Locally

Air pollution by combustion products and volatile organic compounds

Combustible pollutants are compounds produced by burning a fuel. For example, petrol or diesel engines combust to produce exhaust gases that pollute and affect the quality of air. Smoking also burns a compound that gives off pollutants such as nicotine, which is addictive, and tar, which causes cancer. The harmful combustions are carbon monoxide, nitrogen dioxide, carbon dioxide and water vapour.

Combustion products can be dangerous to our health and in concentrated doses can damage respiratory tissue which leads to lung diseases and death through asphyxiation. Local combustion products can enter your home and affect you via several sources:

- gas boilers
- gas fires
- leaving a car engines running beside an open window
- through ventilation from traffic on busy roads
- smoking indoors.

Volatile organic compounds (VOCs) are given off by certain solids or liquids. Take a look at some of the products stored under your kitchen sink. Many will contain VOCs. Spirit-based paints contained VOCs; these are now gradually being replaced by water-based paints which do not contain the harmful compound. VOCs are more concentrated indoors due to the lack of ventilation within most homes. At work, VOCs are still present in photocopiers, inks, cleaning materials, and many other products. Local exhaust ventilation (LEV) in offices and workshops removes these to the atmosphere.

## Polluting discharges to water by communities

Whatever water we use for drinking or an industrial process exits the building as a waste product. The sewer system of the UK is either combined or separate. If it is a separate system, then the surface rainwater and foul are separate drains. In this way, the rainwater does not have to be treated. Foul drainage requires treatment before its discharge into rivers or sea outlets, or landfill, to remove solids and to bring the discharge water up to a quality standard. The alternative to connecting to the main sewer is a septic tank which contains the solids with the water draining into a ditch or reed bed.

## Thinking point

Some of London's water supply has passed through the human body three times!

So what are the problems with our ageing nineteenth-century sewer system? Capacity is the main problem as the system was not designed for today's large towns and cities. When there is heavy rainfall the sewer system is unable to hold all of the sudden water input. The water then backs up and floods the area where it escapes with the environmental health consequences associated with raw sewage.

The other modern problem has been hard landscaping for off road parking. Before the increase in personal transport, many of our driveways were grassed and unpaved areas. Since the boom in the motor car, many of these areas have been paved over to provide parking. Any rainfall therefore does not soak into the ground but runs off the driveway and into the road gullies, thus entering the sewer system. Further contamination occurs from car washing detergents, petrol and coolant liquid leaks which are washed into the drainage system, all of which add to the pollution problem.

Industrial pollution also takes several forms. The first is the heavy metals that have been used in the past such as cadmium and mercury; these collect in lakes and can sometimes affect drinking water supplies. The other pollution is through micro-organisms such as cryptosporidiosis in water that can cause sickness and upset stomach problems. These enter via back syphonage into the system and from water leaks, and if the conditions are right, grow and multiply. The only remedy is to boil the drinking water supply. In developing countries, where water supply is from wells only, then cholera and typhoid diseases can easily spread.

## Industry and agriculture

Industry and agriculture impact greatly, both locally and globally, on the built environment. Both require land for their processes, for example the conversion of sugar beet into sugar granules or the conversion of crude oil into petrol requires factories to be built. These factories then have other environmental links to global warming, energy usage and pollution.

Agriculture takes up vast areas of land and has changed our natural landscape through ploughing, the use of fertilisers and so on. Industry has tended to concentrate within certain areas and regions, from the steel industry of Sheffield to the Humber estuary, where a number of factories use the river for export and import of goods. Industry tends to be located where there is a workforce available along with easy access to raw materials.

## Contaminated land

Our past human activity has often been unregulated and uncontrolled. The Industrial Revolution of the eighteenth and nineteenth centuries led to rapid expansion where natural resources, power and transportation could be connected. Industry set up next to the raw materials, using whatever method was needed to produce a finished product. This often involved using chemicals to process the raw material. At the time no one realised that chemicals used in the petro-chemical, oil, paint and iron and steel industries would contaminate the soil and environment. The contamination took the form of arsenic, cyanide, acids, alkalis and various other toxins.

These sites of previous use have been classified as brownfield sites by the government and developers are encouraged to use these rather than take large areas of **greenfield land**. When we build on a brownfield site the soil below has to be tested for contamination and suitable action taken to prevent the contamination coming into contact with the occupants, which could eventually cause ill health. This may involve removing the pollutants to licensed tips or treating the contamination in the ground by adding another chemical to it till the pH of the soil is balanced. Soil

barriers can be inserted to prevent the contamination spreading causing problems for local residents.

## Key Term

**Greenfield land** Area which is undisturbed by previous construction – in effect, a green field.

## Waste disposal

As the population of the UK has grown and expanded, so has the demand for consumables. These generate waste in the form of packaging, food, paper, cardboard and plastics. There are only a few methods of dealing with this waste, which is collected by the local council.

- Disposal to landfill sites – this is now subject to a landfill tax levied to prevent waste and encourage recycling.
- Incineration – waste is managed as a fuel and burnt to produce electricity.
- Reduction by recycling valuable components such as cardboard, newspaper, metals, plastics and glass.
- Composting into mulch – this involves composting green waste from gardens into a useful compost.

Suitable sites for waste disposal are becoming increasingly difficult to find. We must try to reduce the amount of wastage produced by using recycling. Current local authority levels of recycling are at 40 per cent; European legislation will further increase this percentage. New technology is also helping with plants now capable of recycling fridges and freezers.

## Remember!

The more we recycle and conserve, the fewer finite resources we will need to use, and the more beneficial it will be for the construction and built environment and global warming.

## Existing site dereliction

Many old buildings become derelict. This may be because:

- The cost of refurbishing the building is too high.
- The building has exceeded its life expectancy.
- The building has been damaged by fire and/or vandalism.
- The occupier has gone bankrupt or ceased trading.
- The economy of the local area is in decline.

Often these buildings are listed and have to be preserved in the condition in which they were built. This prohibits any change of use and alteration to the exteriors; they have a recognised English Heritage status.

Empty buildings are a sitting target for vandalism and destruction. Any valuable item is removed and the exteriors are boarded up to prevent entry. When a derelict building becomes a dangerous structure the local authority building control officers become involved in making the structure safe so that it does not injure any member of the public

## Comfort disturbance

Your comfort within your home or working environment can be disturbed by:

- too little or excessive heat
- poor ventilation
- noise
- unpleasant smells
- lack of cleanliness.

Disturbance from traffic relates not only to noise but also to nuisance from vibration, which can severely shake buildings causing cracking and structural damage. The exhaust from traffic congestion has an environmental impact in developing countries when it mixes with the midday heat plus other combustion products to form a smog over large city areas. This affects the respiratory system causing breathing problems such as asthma.

While many people like to live in cities, city life has its downside. Uncollected refuse on the streets is

unsightly and can be smelly. Sewer systems may not be able to cope with the large demand. Noise is another disturbance associated with a densely populated area. Noise emanates from human occupation, not just from people playing music, or arguing but also from the large volume of traffic that the city has to cope with during rush hours.

The industrial part of any city often causes a dust and dirt problem. This does, to a certain degree, depend on the local climate, for example a hot climate is dustier than a wetter climate which washes down areas of the local environment.

## Thinking points

Litter is a common sight in our towns and cities. Think of ways to keep our streets and environment cleaner.

## Increased pressure upon existing services and infrastructure

With 60 million people now living in the UK, many of our towns and cities have expanded into huge conurbations. With this expansion has come increased pressure on the following types of infrastructure:

- The road network – for example, the M25 was built with four lanes in some places, but is now full to capacity at times.
- The railway network – increasingly passengers have to stand for their journey due to the sheer volume of people using the network services.
- Air traffic numbers – these have increased dramatically with the rise of low cost airlines offering budget fares.
- The water supply network – some areas of London struggle with inadequate supplies and water pressure.
- Gas supply – more demand has meant obtaining supplies from continental Europe and Russia.

## Specification of hazardous materials

Lead and asbestos are two harmful materials that were historically installed in a building's structure without determining the possible causes to the health of the occupants. Lead is present in old water pipes, some gas pipes and in paint and can be absorbed into the blood stream through ingestion from the drinking water supply. It can also be inhaled through burning off old paint during redecoration. Lead was also a constituent in petrol as a lubricant and entered the atmosphere as a result of combustion.

Asbestos is present in old vinyl tiles, pipe lagging, roof sheeting, latex and many other materials. Asbestos causes lung disorders and can lead to cancers and eventual death. As a result of this, asbestos is steadily undergoing a removal process during alterations and refurbishments where it is taken to licensed tips and disposed of safely in controlled conditions.

## Extraction of raw materials

There are many raw materials that are mined, quarried or extracted by drilling in the UK, including:

- coal, e.g. the Selby coalfield in Yorkshire
- oil and gas from the North Sea and some inland sites
- gold – there is still a small gold mine in Wales
- gypsum to form plasterboard and plasters
- various rocks for crushing into hardcore
- roofing materials such as slates
- various minerals.

The effect on the environment depends on the method of extraction used to obtain the raw product. Coal mining where seams of coal are taken out of the ground can cause long-term settlement to the ground above, along with the disposal issue of the unwanted material that is brought to the surface and tipped. Open cast mining requires the **overburden** to be removed so the raw material can be mass excavated and removed, and when the mine is exhausted the overburden is replaced. Ground levels are subsequently a lot lower than originally and the environment has to recover from this change.

## Key term

**Overburden** The worthless layer of material that has to be removed to get at the minerals beneath.

## Electromagnetic radiation from overhead power lines

We transport electricity using pylons as this is the cheapest method rather than burying the cables across miles of countryside. Electromagnetic radiation is formed from the conduction of electricity along the power line. There have been several studies published that may prove a link between an increased risk of childhood leukaemia and the proximity to power lines, but this is subject to confirmation from long-term studies as there may be other factors involved.

The electricity companies tend to try to site pylons away from high centres of population or bury them beneath the surface once the pylon nears a town or city, as they are also an eyesore.

▲ **Pylons transport electricity across the countryside**

## Sick building syndrome

This refers to a building that is causing the occupants to feel ill. It can take the form of headaches, flu-like symptoms, ear, nose and throat problems, nausea and tiredness. When the occupants leave the building their health improves so that the building then carries the stigma of 'sick building syndrome'. There could be several factors causing the syndrome:

- Lack of cleaning causing a build-up of dust particles.
- Chemicals that have been released through use into the atmosphere, e.g. photocopier toner.
- Pollution entering the office spaces from outside.
- Damp, dark conditions causing the growth of mould and bacteria that release spores into the atmosphere.
- Lack of the natural light needed for normal active health.
- Lack of fresh air from inadequate ventilation.
- Poor, dirty conditions.

- High humidity which can cause breathing problems.
- High temperatures that cause discomfort.

Good design and appreciation of the importance of the health of the occupants go together. If staff become sick through ill health caused by the structure that houses them, then this will have a detrimental effect on the financial side of the business, through sickness benefit and potential claims for ill health.

## Assessment practice

Residents of a local housing association have complained about some local pollution issues. You are asked to visit the site and establish what their concerns are. Identify some forms of local pollution that could be affecting them and describe how each may harm the local environment around the housing development.  **P3**

## Legislation

The Environmental Protection Act 1990 was a powerful, single piece of legislation introduced to protect the environment of the UK. In 1995, the Environment Agency was set up (see below). These are the main Acts of Parliament that protect the environment:

- Water Act 1989
- Control of Pollution (Amendment) Act 1989
- Environmental Protection Act 1990
- Land Drainage Act 1991
- Water Resources Act 1991
- Environment Act 1995.

### Theory into practice

Find out more about the legislation above at the Office of Public Sector Information website: www.opsi.gov.uk.

The following is a list of legislation types that has been taken from the Environment Agency's website (2007) – www.environment-agency.gov.uk (follow the links to the English legislation section):

- air
- chemicals
- conservation
- energy
- land
- noise and statutory nuisance
- pollution prevention and control (PPC)
- plant protection
- radioactive substances
- waste
- water.

Environmental regulations developed from Acts of Parliament include the End of Life Vehicle Regulations 2003 and Agricultural Waste Regulations 2006. European directives stem from the European Parliament and there are hundreds of these concerning the environment. Each member country then has to develop regulations from these directives.

### Thinking points

Legislation protects the environment by allowing people and individuals to be brought to court and prosecuted when they have caused damage to the environment. Is this too late?

## Control

### Health & Safety Executive

The Health & Safety Executive (HSE) has powers to enforce the legislation produced by the government. Its role is primarily to look after safety and it is this particular aspect that the HSE would investigate in environmental issues, for example are you wearing the correct personal protective equipment (PPE) to clean up a spillage and have you completed a risk assessment for that work? Should a breach of a safety regulation occur, then the HSE has the power of prosecution. The HSE has very little input into the environmental side of the law apart from the nuclear directive that governs releases of radiation into the environment.

### Environment Agency

The Environment Agency (EA) is a public body whose role is to protect the environment. Its chairman, John

Harman, says: 'We are the leading public body for protecting and improving the environment in England and Wales. It's our job to make sure that air, land and water are looked after by everyone in today's society, so that tomorrow's generations inherit a cleaner, healthier world' (Environment Agency website, 2007). The EA also prosecutes offenders and gathers evidence in support of cases going to court. It undertakes many checks including air and water quality monitoring.

## Local authorities

Local authorities have many powers under the departments listed below.

### ■ Planning

The planning department establishes the **local plan** under planning legislation. This enables the control of the erection and alteration of buildings, the removal of trees and hedges and the construction of roads and other hard landscaped areas. Development is restricted to areas earmarked for category developments which are contained within the local plan, for example industrial, residential, commercial, so that much of the environment can be protected and maintained.

### ■ Environmental services

It is the responsibility of local authorities to provide the local community with the following environmental services:

- municipal waste collection and disposal
- recycling
- pollution control
- noise control
- clean air
- public health
- commercial waste
- food safety.

All of the above can be legally enforced through prosecution and fines.

### ■ Building control

This department controls the demolition, alteration and erection of both commercial and domestic buildings. The environmental aspects covered by building control include drainage, the thermal properties of a dwelling and hence carbon emissions and reduction, heating, power and lighting and ventilation. Building control is often enforced through the checking of plans on conformity and by visual site inspections. Again, this department can legally enforce the regulations.

## Key Term

**Local plan** The document that sets out and controls the planning policy for the local authority's area. It sets out where the authority wants industry and housing to grow.

## Theory into practice

Visit your local authority's website to find out the local plan.

## Assessment practice

A new housing developer has purchased the field next to your row of houses. Development work has started on site and there have been several complaints by you and your neighbours. These have been about the size of the properties being constructed, how near they are to your boundary and the noise levels during construction. Describe how legislation and control may be used to reduce the environmental impact of the construction of these houses. **P4**

# Design and specification

Good design is essential to protect the local and global environment. The orientation of buildings, for example, can harness the sun's energy, providing natural light instead of artificial, thereby saving energy. Good quality design to a high standard, using sustainable construction techniques, will pay dividends for the environment. Sourcing local materials reduces transport effects and using low carbon footprint materials and renewable resources are just some of the ways in which designers can help to protect the environment.

Time spent on thermal design will save energy in the long term and hence reduce the effects of global warming. This has been further backed up with changes to Part L of the **Building Regulations** which deals with the thermal efficiency of buildings. If you specify better quality materials and spend more initially, in the long term you save resources on the building maintenance.

## Key Term

**Building Regulations** These are produced under the Building Act 1974 and control many aspects of construction so as to ensure that energy saving measures are built into new and existing designs.

### Reduction in energy usage

The longer we can extend the life of our finite resources, the better for all. To accomplish this, we need to save energy. This can be achieved through:

- energy saving measures
- renewable energy measures.

We can save energy in a building in many ways. Switching off appliances on standby, using grade A appliances, using low energy light bulbs, only filling a kettle with enough water for its use – these are just the tip of the iceberg. All rely on the education of the UK population and their willingness to accomplish these measures against the cost involved. For example, solar panels on a new house have a heavy initial cost on the

selling price and a long payback period.

Renewable energy sources are a rapidly developing technology. Examples in the UK include wind turbines, wave power, geothermal, and hydroelectric power. These harness renewable aspects of the environment but do have an effect upon it, for example hydroelectric reservoirs require large areas of land to be taken up with water; similarly, wind farms require large areas of land exposed to the strong winds with enough distance between the wind turbines.

## Case study

You live in the countryside region of the east coast, which is an area that receives a high and constant wind speed from the North Sea. The village where you have lived for the past 20 years is an area of natural beauty and has unspoilt views of the Lincolnshire Wolds. You are a member of the local parish council. It has just received an application for outline planning permission for ten wind turbines to be built in a field just outside the village. The council is outraged and plans to object strongly.

Discuss on what grounds the council could object to this electricity production development.

### Minimisation of pollution

Pollution has a marked effect upon the environment and on our health and well-being. Pollution can be reduced in several ways. Fume scrubbers fitted to chimney outputs from factories and power stations and any other discharge to air process remove solids and any pollutant chemicals that would be released into the air. Water treatment of foul drainage before it is discharged into sea outfalls reduces the effects on the marine environment. Minimising wastage by recycling construction products such as timber, metal and bricks reduces pollution dumped into landfill sites. Developments in technology such as biofuels and low sulphur fuels provide cleaner emissions released during combustion of engines.

## Reduction in embedded energy

There is a close relationship between the energy we use and the effects on global warming by utilising it. We can therefore try to reduce the amount of energy we use in construction by specifying materials that have lower **embedded energy** within them. Natural timber products are excellent examples as they take in carbon during growth and cost little in conversion into a useable construction product. Cement-based products, on the other hand, contain high levels of energy in their manufacture and careful consideration should be given to their use or replacing them with alternatives.

## Key Term

**Embedded energy** This is the amount of energy used to produce the material or product and is often expressed in terms of how much carbon has been released into the atmosphere during its manufacture and transport.

## Environmentally friendly, renewable materials

Sustainability has become the normal approach to specifying materials as architects, designers and clients consider the effect that their development will have on the environment. Green issues are an essential environmental consideration in selecting the materials to incorporate into a building. Products need to be environmentally friendly, in that they will reduce the amount of damage that is caused to the environment.

An example would be timber cedar boarding which lasts a long time, requires no treatment and is environmentally friendly in its use. Natural insulation products developed from newspaper and sheep wool are examples of green products used in a unique way to reduce energy consumption.

## Reuse of existing buildings and sites

Earlier in this unit, we mentioned the term brownfield site. This is a site for development that has had a previous commercial use and where the buildings may have been left standing or demolished. Often the ground is contaminated with pollutants that will require cleaning up to provide a safe environment for any future use. The question that must be asked before considering a development opportunity would be, is it better to reuse a plot of land than to develop on virgin land?

Reuse of buildings is often called refurbishment or adaptation. This is a useful technique and will save energy and materials in the long run. Buildings of any merit are conserved under English Heritage's listing scheme.

## Assessment practice

Select a material that is low in embedded energy, contains some elements of recycling and contains low carbon. Assess, evaluate and judge how well it achieves these objectives. Select a material by searching for the term 'green building materials' on the Internet.

## Management

### Simple environmental impact assessments

If the management of an organisation takes a strategic view on the environmental impact of its business, a simple environmental impact assessment (EIA) will enable a clear picture to be produced of the effect the organisation is having on the environment. An EIA is normally a checklist of items to be considered. For example:

- waste disposal
- thermal efficiency
- water discharges
- heat discharges
- water vapour discharges

would need careful assessment.

## Remember!

Once completed, environmental impact assessments need to become part of an action plan. Left in a file, there will be no benefit to the environment.

There are now a large number of companies that can undertake EIAs on more complicated projects such as wind farm locations where the EIA may stretch into many volumes of paperwork.

## Improved management of construction sites

The site manager is instrumental in protecting the environment. It is illegal for spillages to be released into the soil or for silts to be pumped into drainage. Double bunded tanks for fuel oils, spillage kits and silt tanks can be deployed by an effective site manager.

Waste should be sorted during the construction process to ensure materials can be recycled, for example:

- a metal skip where all waste metals can be melted down and reused in steel products
- a wood skip where the waste timber can be manufactured into mdf or chipboard products
- the use of plasterboard skips to recycle off-cuts back to the manufacturer
- cardboard and paper skips.

Avoiding the double handling of a material, that is, only moving it once, reduces fuel costs. The purchasing of raw materials locally such as gravels for drainage helps to reduce the effects of transport on the environment.

As you can see, there are many ways for an able, environmentally aware, site manager to provide added value on a construction project to the local and global environment.

## Clear policies and objectives

A construction company that has clear policies and objectives on reduction of wastage, increase in recycling, noise management and dust and dirt control makes a statement to all its employees and customers that it cares about the environment. For example, a large UK oil producer and fuel manufacturer actively promoting a greener fuel through its activities and advertising will send a clear message to its customers and helps the environment.

Local authorities' environmental services departments have a clear mandate from the government and the European Union (EU) to increase the percentage of municipal waste that is recycled so that there is a reduction of waste going to landfill sites. The EU has also taken steps to encourage car manufacturers to recycle 70 per cent of a car at the end of its life.

As with any policy, continual monitoring and review is necessary to ensure that there is a marked positive effect on the environment.

## Sharing of good practice

Good practice on one site or within one organisation must be shared among the others for an even greater impact to be felt on the environment. Ignorance must be a thing of the past with all employees taking environmental considerations into account when undertaking the duties of the company. A good idea must be rewarded with recognition as to what has been saved so that it advertises this to the rest of the sites and other companies. Fresh innovative ideas must be shared freely and not sold for profit, for it is only through the individual efforts of everyone that the possible effects of global climate change can be reduced or halted.

## Raising of awareness

Education of the people involved in the construction process is the first thing that must be accomplished in order to put into place the policies described earlier. If people are unaware of the effect they are having locally on a construction site with regard to protecting the environment, they are unlikely to participate in any policy or activity that you put into place. Companies can extend this further into local communities so everyone can be involved in the whole process, through school visits and organising activities at community centres, and through advertising green issues relating to the company's activities.

## Communication of information

Communication as a protective environmental measure can be verbal and written. Inductions held on site for all employees can make them aware of any environmental considerations related to the project they are working on. **Tool box talks** can reinforce this message during the construction phase of any project. Communication must be top driven, that is, from the managing director downwards, and must be two-way so that all levels of operatives and management are aware.

## Key Term

**Tool box talks** A brief discussion of key issues with supervisors who then inform the rest of the workers.

## Assessment practice

The board of directors of the design and build company you work for has revised its mission statement and strategy to move into green, environmentally friendly based projects. You have been asked to look at how good practice in:

- design
- specifying materials
- management of the sites

can greatly reduce environmental impact on the company's building projects.  **P5**

Select three methods that can be used to protect the natural environment and undertake a comparison of these. Look at each method in terms of financial cost, its effectiveness (how well it achieves protection) and its impact on the public (do people believe that the method achieves its goals?). You could do this by interviewing learners within your environment, or members of the local community.  **M2**

# Fit for purpose

Sustainability is now a very real need. In the life of this planet, human beings have existed the equivalent of no more than two seconds of time compared to the billions of years Earth has existed. Yet what a statement we have created on the Earth in so short a time. We have been prolific in our gorging of the environment – clearing the natural landscape, extracting wantonly its resources, developing uncontrolled communities and not restricting our growth.

So now the Earth has awoken from its undisturbed slumber and is fast gaining momentum to fight back. Polar ice caps are receding, temperatures and sea levels are rising, hurricanes are increasing in numbers, flooding is increasing and areas are experiencing drought.

Do we, the human inhabitants, sit back and just watch? You have that choice and you alone can make it, but you must consider the present needs against the needs of future generations – this is sustainability.

Just look at it this way: go into your living room before you go to bed – is the TV on standby? What about the DVD player, the video and the digital TV box? And when you get ready to go out in the morning, are there thousands of cars on our roads and motorways driving somewhere with just one occupant? The answer is 'yes'. The list of how we are using up the resources of our planet is endless. So, it's now time to take a long, hard look at the protection of the environment. It must be fit for the current diverse economic, political and social needs of every country.

# Techniques

## Energy-based techniques

### ■ Reduction in energy consumption

This is the easy one to tackle. Reduce the amount of energy that we use by employing more efficient technology, reducing waste and utilising alternative energy sources. This will make the finite resources we have last a lot longer with a reduced reliance and consumption. Electrical technology is now producing grade A appliances that require less electricity to run them. The cost of manufacturing low energy light bulbs has fallen and they are now available in a wide range of fittings. New buildings are subject to air leakage tests which reduces the amount of energy lost through unwanted ventilation.

### ■ Improved energy efficiency

Energy efficiency can be improved by the use of efficient boilers that take the heat out of exhaust gases, and by improved thermal insulation in housing that reduces the heat losses. Combined heat and power plants that produce electricity and heat are a third more efficient and are a growing technology that reduces our energy consumption. Heat pumps that extract waste heat from systems and harness it to heat water are a steadily developing technology.

### ■ Use of renewable energy and alternative sources of energy

Alternative sources of energy and renewable energy are the newer breed of energy sources that are starting to come on line. Examples include:

- wind turbines for home use – a leading DIY store is now providing a fixing service
- solar panels built into roof tiles format – so they look attractive and fit into the roof's profile
- geothermal energy using heat within the soil – a trench is dug in your garden to capture latent heat
- biofuels – crops can now be grown to produce fuels when distilled
- wave turbines
- hydroelectric schemes
- hydrogen fuel cells.

▲ Wind turbines offer an alternative source of renewable energy

All these energy sources save the Earth's finite resources and can be used over and over again – with maintenance and repair, they never run out.

## ■ Specification of renewable materials

This technology in construction is slowly developing. Sheep's wool insulation is a natural product that is renewable, is very efficient at thermal insulation and breathes with humidity. Recycled newspaper and paper products can be used to form cellulose loose fill insulation for lofts. Cedar timber cladding is a renewable material that can be used on the exterior of houses, with excellent green properties. Green roofs that are manufactured from selected plants can now be used as a weatherproof covering that is natural and renewable. Timber engineering is taking strides in maximising the use of timber products to develop joists of the same depth, but using smaller sections of timber built up, that can cover large spans so replacing the use of concrete beams (see Figure 2.3). Timber beams using recycled timber boarding cores can now be used instead of solid

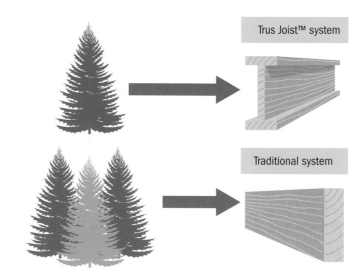

▲ Figure 2.3 Timber engineering replaces the use of concrete beams

timber joists. These use less timber in their manufacture and are considerably stronger.

## ■ Embodied energy consideration

Anything that can be used twice halves the amount of embodied energy used in its manufacture. Therefore, concrete and brickwork from demolition can be crushed onsite and used as a hardcore base for buildings, which also saves transport costs.

Using high-performance, hardwood windows instead of upvc saves energy and oil in the long term, and timber is a renewable source. Steelwork can be recycled and used to produce new structures which reduces the amount of energy consumed in the production of the raw materials.

Designers must be the principal driver of low embodied energy materials by specifying these materials within their designs and convincing clients of the benefit to the Earth of their inclusion.

## Assessment practice

Look closely at your home. If you could rebuild it, what sustainable construction techniques could you use within it and its surroundings. Identify three techniques. Look at each of these techniques in turn and evaluate with justification if it would work. **D2**

## ■ Low energy manufacture of materials and components

Any manufacturer of construction materials that can reduce the energy usage in the manufacturing process will save embodied energy within the product. This could be achieved in several ways. Waste heat can be recycled and taken out of exhaust gases and used to produce electrical energy which can be recycled back into the product. Many producers are starting up combined heat and power plants to gain the maximum benefit from their energy usage on site.

### Waste-based techniques

## ■ Reduction of waste

Waste costs money, as it has to be dealt with, the only disposal being incineration or landfill. Waste can be reduced by several methods, including:

- recycling the materials back into the process, e.g. steelwork

- finding a processor for the waste product to use in their manufacturing process
- ordering the correct amounts of material and managing the use of raw materials efficiently
- using the waste as fuel for energy production
- careful packaging to prevent breakages
- training in the use of a material
- educating that waste costs the environment
- modular coordination of dimensions to standard lengths.

A reduction in wastage can often be brought about by education of the people using the materials into the environmental costs of wasting these materials. Incentive schemes could help along with a top-down management approach to reducing the effects of construction on the environment, for example the manager using a smaller company car, leading by example.

### Recycling

In construction this has to be undertaken in certain ways; clients still want a brand new building, not one with certain reused elements within it. However, there are materials that can be reused as follows:

- Crushed concrete – this can be used as a fill material to raise levels.
- Facing bricks – when cleaned and reused in housing gives an aged appearance.
- Slates – these can be redressed or crushed and combined with an adhesive to form a reconstituted slate tile.
- Brick hardcore fill – this uses crushed bricks as a fill material.
- Glass – this can be melted and reformed.
- Structural steel – this uses recycled steel in its production.
- Plastics – these are used as timber-like products.
- Gabions – these are steel cages used as earth retainers which are filled with crushed concrete or brick.
- Timber – this can be engineered and recycled into structural products.
- Packaging of materials – suppliers can be encouraged to reduce the amount of packaging.

The possibilities are fast developing with new technologies and new products continually coming into the marketplace; recycling waste into materials is starting to take hold.

## ■ Offsite fabrication

This is recent development by UK manufacturers where a timber-framed house kit can be assembled offsite and delivered by lorries and site assembled using a crane to form the insulated internal skin of a complete house including the roof panels. The only additional elements are the cladding external finish, which can be in a brick skin or a timber-cladded product, and the roof tile installation. This type of construction is very thermally efficient, saves time and energy, uses timber renewable products and has relatively low carbon emissions in manufacture.

Offsite fabrication has been tried with house construction using modules that bolt together to form a house, but this has had limited success in domestic construction. Fast-food chains have taken this concept on board with modular units produced for site assembly.

## ■ Modern methods of production

Offsite fabrication of structural elements of commercial and domestic construction are the new approach to the production of houses and offices. Modules that simply bolt together are fast and efficient methods of producing a structure that is factory produced with minimal resulting wastage. This method is very efficient and is aimed at producing affordable social homes in the current economic climate.

Just in time (JIT) construction is where all the materials for incorporation into the structure are delivered just at the point they are needed in the construction process. This avoids the need to store materials onsite for long periods, where they could be damaged, or moved around the site.

Precast concrete is returning as a modern method of construction enabling benefits from factory-produced concrete members that are site assembled with no waste or secondary support systems like formwork.

## Assessment practice

The construction and built environment manager on a local housing development has asked your consultancy firm to assist in the selection of key sustainable construction techniques that could be incorporated into the new designs. Select and describe a fit for purpose sustainable construction technique to fit each of the following key issues from the company's strategic environmental policy:

- energy use
- materials recycling
- reduction of wastage.   **P6**

Compare the three techniques you selected above in terms of cost and performance in use. Use the Internet to help you in your research.    **M3**

# Preparation for assessment

The local authority planning department has undertaken a revision to its local planning strategy policy, involving identifying potential sites that could be considered for light industrial and housing development. You have been recruited as a consultant to identify and describe the features of the natural environment that must be considered at the planning stage. Identify the environmental features that should be considered on these areas of land. **P1**

Your local authority is becoming increasingly conscious of the amount of pollution that is affecting the local environment from global sources. Identify some forms of global pollution that could be causing this disturbance and describe how each may harm the local environment within the region. **P2**

Staff in a construction head office have complained to the office manager about the local environment surrounding the office. Identify forms of local pollution that could be affecting the office environment, externally and internally, and describe how each may harm the local environment. **P3**

A new construction site for a community centre has started next door to a local school. Several of the parents have complained about the effect this is having on the built environment surrounding the development. Describe how legislation and control can be used to reduce the environmental impact of the construction development. **P4**

The local community is increasingly concerned about the new dual carriageway proposed to be built as a bypass around their village. They have called for a public meeting to discuss and raise their concerns. They wish to know how good highway design, specification and management of the project will reduce the local environmental impact. Produce discussion points for the local authority to allay their fears. **P5**

The local authority in partnership with a housing association has commissioned the demolition and rebuilding of 300 houses. The policy for this prestigious project is sustainability, which has to be built into the new construction techniques that will be used. You have been asked to select a fit for purpose construction technique under each of the following headings:

- Energy
- Material
- Wastage.

Describe how each will assist the goals of the project. **P6**

A large retail chain has been given outline permission to undertake a feasibility study on an area of 'out of town land'. This will be a large development with several retail units and the proposed site is 'greenfield' in its classification. The local authority has asked for an environmental audit to assess the potential impact of the proposed construction project.

Produce a short report in no more than 300 words identifying and describing the environmental features that may need considering at this stage. **M1**

The following are three methods currently being used to protect the natural environment. Compare each in terms of cost, effectiveness and how the public perceives them.

- Legislation
- Landfill taxation
- Low sulphur fuels **M2**

Your company is proposing to use the following sustainable construction techniques in its current building programme:

- The use of recycled bricks
- Timber-framed construction
- Cedar cladding the first floor external walls.

Compare each of the techniques in terms of relative cost and performance in use. **M3**

The following are three methods proposed to protect the natural environment from a property development.

- Sites of special scientific interest (SSSIs)
- Tree preservation orders (TPOs)
- The construction of a reed-bed lake within the development to contain water run-off from rainwater goods and driveways.

Appraise the above methods used to protect the natural environment against the potential environmental impact of the proposed property development.  **D1**

Consider each of the examples in D1 above, and analyse it by justifying how well it achieves the protection of the natural environment. **D2**

## Grading tips

You are required to assess the potential environmental impact of a development. A real-life local area could be used to provide evidence for this. Important environmental points need to be identified, described and assessed. You should state what effect they will have on the local environment. Can they be measured, gauged, weighed up or calculated? **M1**

You should make some comparison between the methods of protecting the environment, that is, how effective one method is over another, which you consider is the most expensive, which the general public likes or prefers. You can source methods from the Internet or local newspapers. **M2**

You have to undertake a comparison between some selected sustainable methods. This means comparing one against another. You need to look at the costs

associated with them by undertaking some research. Finally, a comparison of their performance in use must be established. This could be aesthetics, thermal properties or maintenance. **M3**

You should look at the potential environmental impact of the sustainable methods when used on a real or virtual construction project. Appraise (i.e. evaluate, assess, judge) what effect these methods have on this project. How well do they protect the environment when applied to your construction project? **D1**

You will need to justify (i.e. evaluate, judge, defend, give a reason for) the selection of appropriate sustainable construction techniques for use in the 'real or virtual' construction project. You have to answer: does this technique work on this particular project? **D2**

## Knowledge check

1 Name three sources of drinking water.

2 What are the consequences of burning fossil fuels?

3 Identify three forms of air pollution.

4 What is SBS?

5 What does EPA mean in legislation?

6 What is embedded energy in a material?

7 How can we reduce the amount of construction waste produced during a project?

8 Identify five techniques that can be used within domestic housing to reduce energy consumption.

9 What is an EIA?

10 Name three products that can be recycled back into building materials.

11 What is sustainability?

12 How can we generate electricity using environmentally friendly techniques?

## Grading criteria~: Unit 2

| To achieve a pass grade the evidence must show that the learner is able to: | To achieve a merit grade the evidence must show that, in addition to the pass criteria, the learner is able to: | To achieve a distinction grade the evidence must show that, in addition to the pass and merit criteria, the learner is able to: |
|---|---|---|
| **P1** identify and describe four different features of the natural environment that must be considered at the planning stage **Assessment practice pages 47, 71** | **M1** assess the potential environmental impact of a proposed construction project, either real or virtual, on the local natural environment **Assessment practice pages 50, 71** | |
| **P2** identify two different forms of global pollution and describe how each may harm the local environment **Assessment practice pages 55, 71** | | |
| **P3** identify two different forms of local pollution and describe how each may harm the local environment **Assessment practice pages 60, 71** | | |
| **P4** describe how legislation and control are used to reduce the environmental impact of the construction and built environment sector **Assessment practice pages 62, 71** | **M2** compare the four key methods used to protect the natural environment in terms of cost, effectiveness and public perception of the construction and built environment sector **Assessment practice pages 66, 71** | **D1** evaluate methods used to protect the natural environment against the potential environmental impacts of a tutor specified 'real or virtual' construction project **Assessment practice pages 64, 72** |
| **P5** describe how good practice in design, specification and management can reduce the environmental impact of the construction and built environment sector **Assessment practice pages 66, 71** | | |
| **P6** select and describe a fit-for-purpose sustainable construction technique for each of the following issues: energy, materials, and waste **Assessment practice pages 70, 71** | **M3** compare selected sustainable construction techniques in terms of relative cost and performance-in-use **Assessment practice pages 70, 71** | **D2** justify their selection of appropriate sustainable construction techniques for a tutor-specified construction project **Assessment practice pages 69, 72** |

# Mathematics in construction and the built environment

## Introduction

Builders and contractors use a variety of manual and powered tools to construct buildings. Similarly, mathematics is simply another tool to assist construction craftspeople and professionals in doing their job. The mathematical knowledge and skills that you will learn here will help you to solve numerical problems and queries that you will certainly come across in your working life.

This unit will take you through the basic maths that you will need to deal with a range of problems faced by designers, surveyors, cost controllers and contractors in the construction industry. It will show you how to work with numbers and formulae using standard techniques and methods. You will learn how to apply theory to practical examples involving perimeters, area and volumes, as well as understand the properties of different shapes, and how to handle calculations involving angles. Finally, you will explore the use of graphs and statistics and see how they can be used to help solve and understand construction-related problems.

### How you will be assessed

This unit is internally assessed by your tutor. A variety of activities is included in this unit to help you understand all aspects of applying mathematics to the construction industry.

After completing this unit you should be able to achieve the following outcomes:

1 Know the basic underpinning mathematical techniques and methods used to manipulate and/or solve formulae, equations and algebraic expressions

2 Be able to select and correctly apply mathematical techniques to solve practical construction problems involving perimeters, areas and volumes

3 Be able to select and correctly apply a variety of geometric and trigonometric techniques to solve practical construction problems

4 Be able to select and correctly apply a variety of graphical and statistical techniques to solve practical construction problems

# Thinking points

Construction, civil engineering and building services engineering are technical disciplines which, in their normal day-to-day routines, require the collection, processing and use of numbers. For example, surveyors and engineers, who peg out the positions of walls and columns so that they can be built on site, could not do their job without a thorough understanding of how to calculate distances and angles from the architect's plans.

All professionals in the construction industry need to have a range of methods to calculate and check numerical information, for not only must the answer be right but the working out must also be clearly presented so anyone can check that a mistake has not been made. Accuracy and attention to detail are critical – it's much easier to rub out a wrong answer on a calculation sheet than it is to correct a partly constructed building!

Think of some famous large structures or buildings and write them down. It is likely that your list would include the London Eye, for example. Could you calculate the height of the highest viewing capsule, or the time it takes to make one complete revolution, or the size of its foundations? After learning some basic mathematical techniques and given some relevant data you should be able to calculate information just like this.

Take a look at London Eye website – www.londoneye. com – to see how mathematical calculations were used to design the Eye and keep it running.

# Mathematical techniques and methods

## Using your calculator

It is important that you have a good scientific calculator while you are studying this unit. Your tutor may advise you on which one to purchase, but there is no need to buy an expensive model – a basic scientific model is all you will need.

As well as the standard functions of ADD, SUBTRACT, DIVIDE and MULTIPY, the common scientific functions your calculator must have are:

| | |
|---|---|
| $\sqrt{}$ | Calculates the square root of a number |
| $\sqrt[3]{}$ | Calculates the cube root of a number |
| $X^2$ | Use this key to determine the square of a number |
| $X^3$ | Use this key to determine the cube of a number |
| $X^y$ | A number can be raised to any power by pressing this key |
| $\pi$ | Use this key wherever $\pi$ occurs in a formula |
| sin cos tan | Use the appropriate key to determine the sine/cosine/tangent of an angle |
| $\sin^{-1}$ $\cos^{-1}$ $\tan^{-1}$ | If the sin/cos/tan of an angle is given use the appropriate key to determine the angle |
| log | Use this key if the calculation involves logarithm to the base 10 |
| $10^x$ | This key is used to calculate antilogarithms, i.e. the reverse of log |
| EXP | Use this key to raise 10 to the power of a given number |
| $M^+$ | This key is used to input values into memory |
| $\circ$''' | This key is used to convert an angle into degrees, minutes and seconds |

| | |
|---|---|
| ( ) | These keys will insert brackets in the calculations involving complicated formulae |
| DEL | Press this key to delete the number at the current cursor position |
| MR | This button brings into the current display the number that has previously been stored in the memory |
| 1/x | This button divides the required number into the value 1 to give its reciprocal value |
| $a_{b/c}$ | This button enables you to put fractions directly into your calculations such as $\frac{1}{2}$ or $\frac{3}{8}$, etc |
| ENG | This button allows you to toggle through an answer in standard form in multiples of $10^3$ or $10^{-3}$. e.g. $0.53635 \times 10^6 = 536.350 \times 10^3 = 536350$ |
| R->P P->R | These buttons convert rectangular co-ordinates to polar co-ordinates and vice versa. They are a very useful tool for the setting out surveyor or site engineer. |

Your calculator will also need to perform a range of statistical functions which will be very useful for checking your statistical work in the final section of this chapter.

It will need to be able to switch MODES so that it can calculate angles in decimals or degrees/minutes/seconds or in a special measurement known as radians.

Finally, your calculator must have at least one storage area or MEMORY; most modern calculators provide more than one. Learn how to store and recall numbers with the memory – you will find this very useful when working out complicated sums where you need to hold part of the calculation safe while working on other parts.

## ■ 'Mental checks'

It's a good idea to do a mental check on the calculation just to make sure the answer that the calculator gives is what you were expecting! To do this, you need to know your multiplication tables – reciting and remembering these basic number relationships will help you with your mental arithmetic. Practise the use of the calculator's keys on simple calculations, and always keep the calculator's instruction book handy so that you can follow the examples it provides!

## Basic calculations

The order in which you carry out the separate parts of calculations is important. Look at the following two examples featuring the same numbers in which both answers are right but different:

$46 - 3 \times 11 = 46 - 33 = 13$

$(46 - 3) \times 11 = 43 \times 11 = 473$

In the first example, we multiplied 3 by 11 and then subtracted the answer from 46 because the multiplication part took precedence over the subtraction part, but in the second example, the subtraction took precedence because it was within brackets.

There is a simple acronym – BODMAS – that can help you remember the order in which to do the separate parts of the calculation:

**B**racketed calculations are done first.

**O**rder or powers are calculated next (e.g. $4^2$, where 2 is the power; $4^2 = 4 \times 4 = 16$)

**D**ivision and

**M**ultiplication take equal priority and are done next.

**A**ddition and

**S**ubtraction are done last and are of equal priority.

## Worked example

Calculate the value of R, where

$$R = 5000 - \left( \frac{25 \times 3}{2} + \frac{3}{2} \right)^2$$

Whatever is inside the brackets must be done first. This means carrying out the multiplication first as this takes precedence over the addition:

$$R = 5000 - \left( \frac{75}{2} + \frac{3}{2} \right)^2$$

Now the division parts inside the brackets need to be done. Once again, these operations take precedence over the addition to give:

$R = 5000 - (37.50 + 1.50)^2$

Then we carry out the addition that is within the brackets:

$R = 5000 - (39)^2$

Next, we square the value in the brackets, as this order or power operation must come before subtraction:

$R = 5000 - 1521$

Finally, we do the subtraction to give the answer required:

$R = 3479$

## Remember!

In a scientific calculator, the sequence in which you press the keys will be the same as the sequence in which a calculation is written down, provided you have remembered to include the brackets that are needed according to BODMAS.

## Remember!

You could have worked out this calculation on your calculator exactly as it was written, but you would still need to remember to insert brackets to make sure that you keep the correct sequence. So the keys to be pressed would be:

$5\ 0\ 0\ 0\ -\ (\ (\ (\ 2\ 5\ \times\ 3\ \div\ 2\ )\ +\ ($
$3\ \div\ 2\ )\ )\ y^x\ 2\ = 3479$

## Worked examples

**1** Calculate:

$$52.3 \times \frac{27.4}{91.8}$$

The solution on your calculator (rounded to 2 decimal places) would be:

$5\ 2\ .\ 3\ \times\ 2\ 7\ .\ 4\ \div\ 9\ 1\ .\ 8\ =$
15.61

and your mental check could be:

$$\frac{5\emptyset \times 3\emptyset}{1\emptyset\emptyset} \approx 15$$

Both answers are similar, so you can be sure that your calculated answer is right.

**2** Find the value of:

$$\frac{(3.2 \times 5.6) + (9.8 \times 2.7)}{5.4}$$

The solution on your calculator (rounded to 2 decimal places) would be:

$(\ 3\ .\ 2\ \times\ 5\ .\ 6\ )\ +\ (\ 9\ .\ 8\ \times\ 2\ .\ 7\ )\ =$ 44.38 $\div\ 5\ .\ 4\ =$ 8.22

and your mental check could be:

$$\frac{(3 \times 6) + (10 \times 3)}{5} = \frac{18 + 30}{5} = \frac{50}{5} = 10$$

Again, both answers are roughly the same.

*Note:* You must completely work out the top line before dividing the top line by the bottom.

**3** Calculate:

$$\frac{78.2 \times 67.3}{31.7 \times 42.5}$$

The solution on your calculator (rounded to 2 decimal places) could be:

$7\ 8\ .\ 2\ \times\ 6\ 7\ .\ 3\ \div\ (\ 3\ 1\ .\ 7\ \times\ 4\ 2\ .\ 5\ )\ =$ 3.90

*Note:* Brackets have been used to keep the bottom line separate from the top. It is always important to remember this.

Your mental check could be:

$$\frac{8\emptyset \times 7\emptyset}{3\emptyset \times 4\emptyset} \approx \frac{56}{12} \approx 4\tfrac{1}{2}$$

So we can be confident that our answer is right.

---

## Theory into practice

Find the answer to the following:

$$\frac{\sqrt{55 + 31.7 - 7.8}}{2}$$

(*Hint:* As the square root applies to the entire top row, remember to put it in brackets.)

Carry out a mental check to confirm your answer.

## Key term

**International System of Units (SI)** The International System of Units, which is abbreviated to SI units from the French *Système International d'unités*, is the modern form of the metric system. It was developed in 1960 to promote a worldwide measurement system based on the standard properties of metres, kilogrammes and seconds. It is the world's most commonly used system of units and is used in everyday business, science and technology.

## ■ Calculation units

### Metric

In all our calculations of physical properties within the construction industry we use units that are derived from the **International System of Units**, known as **SI**.

The most common units used in our calculations are shown in Table 3.1.

| Physical property | Unit name | Unit symbol | Conversion |
|---|---|---|---|
| Length | metre | m | 1 m = 1000 mm |
| | millimetre | mm | |
| Area | square metres | m² | 1 m² = 1000 mm x 1000 mm = 1,000,000 mm² |
| | square millimetres | mm² | |
| | hectare | ha | 1 ha = 100 m x 100 m = 10,000 m² |
| Volume | cubic metres | m³ | 1 m³ = 1000 mm x 1000 mm x 1000 mm = 1,000,000,000 m³ |
| | cubic millimetres | mm³ | 1 l = 100 cl = 1000 ml |
| Capacity | litre | l | (also 1 m³ = 1000 l) |
| | centilitre | cl | |
| | millilitre | ml | |
| Mass | kilogram | kg | 1 kg = 1000g |
| Force | Newton | N | 1 kN = 1000 N |
| | kilo-Newton | kN | |
| | tonne | t | 1 t = 10 kN |
| | stress | N/mm² or kN/m² | |
| Pressure | Pascal | Pa | where 1 Pa = 1 N/mm² |
| Time | seconds | s | |
| Temperature | degrees Celsius or | °C | |
| | degrees Kelvin | °K | |
| Luminous intensity | candela | cd | |

**Table 3.1 Common SI units of measurement**

## Imperial

Customers at builders' merchants still often ask for 'a 3-metre length of 2 by 4 inch timber'! In the UK, you will need to be aware that imperial units of measurement are sometimes quoted. The ones that you might still come across in construction are shown in Table 3.2, with their metric conversions.

| Unit | Imperial name | Conversion to metric |
|---|---|---|
| Length | inch | 1 inch = 25.4 mm |
| Area | 1 foot = 12 inches | |
| | 1 yard = 36 inches | |
| | 1 mile = 1760 yards | (also 1 mile ≈ 1609.344 m) |
| | 1 square yard = 9 square feet | 1 square foot = 0.0929 m² |
| | 1 acre = 4840 square yards | 1 acre = 0.4047 hectares |
| | 1 square mile = 640 acres | |
| Mass (weight) | ounce | 1 ounce = 28 g |
| | 1 pound = 16 ounces | |
| | 1 stone = 14 pounds | |
| Capacity | pint | |
| | 1 gallon = 8 pints | 1 gallon = 4.5 l |

**Table 3.2 Common imperial units of measurement and conversion to metric**

## Remember!

It is important that you are consistant in the units that you use within a calculation. This means if you are using metres cubed ($m^3$), then all the data must be in metres (m), not in millimetres (mm) or centimetres (cm). Simple but often costly mistakes can occur if we mix up metres and millimetres, for example, within one calculation! We cannot hope to work out the volume of concrete required for a strip foundation if we take its depth as 1 m, its length of 8 m and its width as 450 mm!

## Worked example

An old floor plan is being used to find the width of a new roller shutter door. The plan shows that the existing opening is 18 feet 5 inches wide. Convert this dimension to millimetres.

**Step 1:** Find the conversion factor, which in this case is 1 inch = 25.4 mm (see Table 3.2).

**Step 2:** Find how many inches are in the total distances needed.

18 feet 5 inches = 18 × 12 inches + 5 inches = 221 inches

**Step 3:** Convert into millimetres by applying the conversion factor.

Therefore the distance in millimetres is:

221 × 25.4 mm = 5613.4 mm

## Remember!

Many websites on the Internet can convert units from imperial to metric and vice-versa. Some offer lists of conversion tables while others provide automatic conversion calculators. Try searching the web for these sites or try this one at www.convert-it.co.uk/frindex.htm.

## Rounding and estimation

### ■ Significant figures

In the above worked example, quoting the answer to the nearest 1 mm may be far too accurate and indeed unnecessary. If the tolerance of the new door to be supplied is to the nearest 10 mm, then we could 'round' the answer to a more convenient value, which would be 5610 mm.

To help you to round up numbers to convenient and useable values we use the rules for significant figures (s.f.). The basic rules are as follows:

- Figures ending in 5 and above are rounded up and the next figure to the left increases by 1
- Figures ending in 4 and below are rounded down and the next figure to the left remains the same.

For example:

$$14.6539 = 14.654 \text{ (rounded to 5 s.f.)}$$
$$= 14.65 \text{ (rounded to 4 s.f.)}$$
$$= 14.7 \text{ (rounded to 3 s.f.)}$$
$$= 15 \text{ (rounded to 2 s.f.)}$$

Using significant figures is good for doing rough mental checks and estimations in all types of calculations. However, you must be careful to select the most appropriate significant figures to round to. The choice will depend upon the required accuracy of the calculation, as in the door example above where we rounded to 4 s.f.

In some situations it is more sensible to round down, even when the answer has a remainder of 0.5. For example, how many 2-metre lengths can be cut from a 7-metre long copper pipe? The answer is 7 m ÷ 2 m = 3.5. However, you can only cut three 2-metre lengths; the rest (0.5 of a 2-metre length) is wasted. So in this case you should round down.

### Decimal places

Significant figures should not be confused with quoting numbers to so many decimal places (d.p.). Decimal places are the numbers appearing to the right of the decimal point. So, in the above example:

$$14.6539 = 14.654 \text{ (rounded to 3 d.p.)}$$
$$= 14.65 \text{ (rounded to 2 d.p.)}$$
$$= 14.7 \text{ (rounded to 1 d.p.)}$$

Decimal places are useful when dealing with distance. In construction we measure distances in metres (m) or millimetres (mm), where 1000 mm = 1 m. This often requires us to quote measurements in metres to 3

decimal places so that our accuracy is to the nearest 1 mm. For example, 23647 mm is equivalent to 23.647 m, i.e. the distance is quoted in metres to 3 d.p. to ensure we are working to the nearest 1 mm.

## Knowledge check:
### significant figures, decimal places, conversions and basic calculations

1  Round the following numbers to 5 and then 3 significant figures:

  **a** 983.5246
  **b** 652881.0
  **c** 1519.72
  **d** 556187
  **e** 55.4515

2  Round the following numbers to 1 and then 2 significant figures:

  **a** 0.000142
  **b** 0.5498
  **c** 0.06429
  **d** 0.00000035
  **e** 1.94521

3  Write the following numbers to 1 and then 3 decimal places:

  **a** 12.87654
  **b** 93.6131
  **c** 1.59691
  **d** 465.4565
  **e** 0.0717
  **f** 0.1057

4  Convert the following physical properties from imperial units to metric units using the information supplied previously:

  **a** a distance of 8 feet 4 inches to millimetres
  **b** a length of 12 feet 7½ inches to metres to 3 d.p.
  **c** an area of 2.5 square yards to square metres to 1 d.p.
  **d** an area of 4 acres to hectares to 2 s.f.
  **e** a capacity of 5½ gallons to litres to 3 s.f.
  **f** a capacity of 2 gallons and 6 pints to litres to 4 s.f.
  **g** a capacity of 45 gallons to $m^3$ to 1 s.f.

5  For the following questions do a mental check first using pencil and paper by rounding the numbers to 1 or 2 significant figures, then work out your answer with your calculator:

  **a** $\dfrac{72.5 - 4.5}{3 \times 12 + 32}$
  **b** $\dfrac{\sqrt{46.6 + 17.4}}{½}$
  **c** $\dfrac{(9 - 3)^2 + 3}{6}$
  **d** $\sqrt{6.8} \times 3 - 5$
  **e** $1.4(23.5 \times 2.8 - 12.6)^2$

Did your mental check answers tie up with your calculated results?

## Standard form

In technical calculations you sometimes have to deal with very large or very small numbers. There is a very convenient way of writing and using very large or very small numbers and that is using **standard form**. It is important as it is the method used by scientific calculators to display very large or very small numbers, and it is how you need to input such numbers into your

calculator when doing construction calculations. Some scientific calculators only have 12 or so digits in their displays, so any number bigger than this could not be shown without using standard form!

In standard form a number is split into two parts: a decimal number (N) multiplied by the number 10 raised to a power (n) that can be positive for numbers greater than 1 or negative for numbers smaller than 1. Such that:

$N \times 10^n$

For example:

$78531 = 7.8531 \times 10^4$

where $10^4 = 10 \times 10 \times 10 \times 10 = 10{,}000$

and $7.8531 \times 10{,}000 = 78531$ (the original number!)

Standard form works like an equation, where the left-hand side (LHS) is equal to the right-hand side (RHS).

A simple way to remember this is that the decimal point for big numbers (i.e. much greater than 1) moves to the left and the power to which 10 is raised is always positive. For example:

Decimal point moves 11 places left

$235000000000.0 = 2.35 \times 10^{11}$    Positive power of 11

## Remember!

Powers or indices can be dealt with according to the 'Laws of Indices', i.e.

$a^r \times a^s = a^{r+s}$ and $\dfrac{a^r}{a^s} = a^r \div a^s = a^{r-s}$ and, finally, $(a^r)^s = a^{rs}$.

For example:

$2^3 \times 2^2 = 2^{3+2} = 2^5 = 32$

$\dfrac{2^3}{2^2} = 2^3 \div 2^2 = 2^{3-2} = 2^1 = 2$

$(2^3)^2 = 2^{3 \times 2} = 2^6 = 64$

Powers which are fractions refer to roots, e.g. 3 is the 'square' root of 9, written as $9^{1/2}$. These can be combined. For example:

$2^{4/3} = (2^4)^{1/3} = 16^{1/3} = \sqrt[3]{16} = 2.519$ (3 d.p.)

Explore the use of the 'power' key on your calculator – repeat the examples above and check that you get the same answers!

Standard form also works with small numbers which are less than 1 by using negative powers, because negative powers of 10 mean dividing by 10.

For example a very small number is: 0.0000000541 which in standard form is written

$5.41 \times 10^{-8}$

because

$$10^{-8} = \frac{1}{10^8} = \frac{1}{10 \times 10 \times 10 \times 10 \times 10 \times 10 \times 10 \times 10}$$

and

$$5.41 \times \frac{1}{10 \times 10 \times 10 \times 10 \times 10 \times 10 \times 10 \times 10} = 0.0000000541$$

Again, a simple way to remember this is that the decimal point for small numbers (i.e. much less than 1) moves to the right and the power to which 10 is raised is always negative. For example:

Decimal point moves 8 places right

$0.0000000541 = 5.41 \times 10^{-8}$    Negative power of $^{-8}$

## Remember!

Most scientific calculators allow you to toggle through standard form in powers of multiples of 3. This is often called 'engineering' standard form because we often quote physical properties in kilos, where kilo is 1000 or $10^3$.

## ■ Loading calculations

The unit that we use to measure load is the Newton (N), but for large numbers we often work in multiples of 1000 Newtons, called kilo-Newtons (kN), or when loads get really huge we use mega-Newtons (mN), where 1 mM is equal to 1,000,000 Newtons. Thus:

$500{,}000$ Newtons $= 500 \times 10^3$ Newtons or

500 kilo-Newtons

$= 0.5 \times 10^6$ Newtons or

0.5 mega-Newtons

**1** Write down the following numbers in standard form:

   **a** 875

   **b** 175113

   **c** 0.00221

   **d** 0.0000079

   **e** 3

**2** Write down the following standard forms as ordinary numbers:

   **a** $8.642 \times 10^3$

   **b** $5.8 \times 10^{-3}$

   **c** $2.5875 \times 10^2$

   **d** $9.11 \times 10^{-1}$

   **e** $9.11 \times 10^0$

**3** Write each of the following 'loads' in kilo-Newtons to 2 decimal places or fewer:

   **a** 860000 N

   **b** 167500 N

   **c** 50021.5 N

   **d** 0.00467 mN

   **e** 0.0005 mN

# Formulae, equations and algebraic expressions

## Algebraic expressions and equations

In algebra, letters are used together with numbers, where letters can represent things such as volume, load, time or temperature. Using algebraic notation you can form equations that can be used to solve many construction maths problems. Letters or algebraic terms are dealt with using straightforward rules similar to those used for ordinary numbers and fractions.

### ■ Addition and subtraction

Only terms that are alike can be added or subtracted. For example, the expression 30d + 20w − 10d + 30w relates to the number of doors (d) and windows (w) on a

particular housing development. Because the doors and windows are different, they have to be treated separately, thus:

$$30d + 20w - 10d + 30w = 30d - 10d + 20w + 30w$$
$$= 20d + 50w$$

Therefore, on the housing development there are 20 doors and 50 windows.

### ■ Multiplication and division

As with addition and subtraction, you can only multiply or divide 'like' terms. For example:

$8 \times 8 = 8^2$    Similarly,

$d \times d = d^2$

and

$$6 \times 6 \times \frac{6}{6} = 6^2 \quad \text{Similarly,}$$

$$d \times d \times \frac{d}{d} = d^2$$

### ■ Brackets and factors

Brackets are generally used when you are multiplying two terms together, and also avoid having to write an '$\times$', meaning multiply, which could be confused with an algebraic term $x$ representing a physical number or property.

Brackets are used in algebra to simplify expressions, or to change an expression which has terms added together to terms multiplied together. For example, the number 24 can be written as $3 \times 2 \times 4$. Therefore, 24 can be expressed as a sum of numbers such as 14 + 10 or as a product of numbers $3 \times 2 \times 4$.

$14 + 10 = \underline{3 \times 2 \times 4}$

            3, 2 and 4 are known as 'factors' of 24

The same can be done with algebraic expressions as well. For example, the expression $6x + 2y$ can be written as two factors $2(3x + y)$.

$6x + 2y = \underline{2(3x + y)}$

         2 and $3x + y$ are 'factors' of $6x + 2y$

Given the expression $6x + 2y$, we can find the factors because 2 is common to both $6x$ and $2y$ and it can be divided out of the expression, leaving $3x + y$ in brackets.

It is important that you can identify factors in

expressions. Look at this example and find the factors of the algebraic expression:

$8x + 4y$

We see that 4 is common to both terms. Therefore, we can divide it out of the expression, leaving the 'remainder' in brackets:

$8x + 4y = \underline{4(2x + y)}$

4 and $2x + y$ are 'factors' of $8x + 4y$

We can always get back to the original expression by multiplying out the factors. For example:

$4(2x + y) = 4(2x) + 4(y) = 8x + 4y$

Sometimes both factors can be bracketed, and to multiply them out we use the FOIL rule:

**F**irst terms multiplied
**O**utside terms multiplied
**I**nside terms multiplied
**L**ast terms multiplied

$(a + b)(c + d) = ac + ad + bc + bd$

For example, multiply out the following factors using the FOIL rule:

$(x + 2)(2x + 3)$

First $= x(2x) = 2x^2$
Outside $= 3(x) = 3x$
Inside $= 2(2x) = 4x$
Last $= 2(3) = 6$

Therefore, putting them all together:

$(x + 2)(2x + 3) = 2x^2 + 3x + 4x + 6$
$$= 2x^2 + 7x + 6$$

This expression is a quadratic expression because it has a term which is squared (see page 00). We shall be covering this in more detail later.

Finally, if you have an expression with three factors such as:

$x(5x + 2)(2x - 3)$

then a cubic equation will be formed when the brackets are multiplied out. The way to tackle this expression is to multiply out the two brackets to get a quadratic equation, then multiply each of the quadratic terms by $x$.

$x(5x + 2)(2x - 3) = x(10x^2 + 4x - 15x - 6)$
$$= x(10x^2 - 11x - 6)$$
$$= 10x^3 - 11x^2 - 6x$$

## Knowledge check:
### brackets and factors

1   Multiply out the brackets and then write down the following expressions in their simplest form:

   a   $5x(3x - 8) - 2x^2$
   b   $2(x + 3y - z) - 3(x + y - z) + 4(x - y)$
   c   $2x(y + 3z) - 2y(3z + x) - 3z(2x - 2y)$
   d   $(2x - 1)(3x^2 - x - 3)$
   e   $3(y^4 - y^2 - 2) - 2y(y^3 + 2y - 1) - y^2(y^2 + 1)$
   f   Add $(a + 4b)$ to $(3a - 2b)$ and $2a$, then subtract the result from $(8a - 5b)$.

2   Multiply out the following factors

   a   $3(2 + 5b)$
   b   $2x(1 - \frac{1}{2}x)$
   c   $(3x + 2)(x + 1)$
   d   $(x - 2)(5 + x)$
   e   $(x - 1)(4x - 2)$

3   Find the factors for the following expressions

   a   $7y + 49$
   b   $9 - 3a$
   c   $12x^2 - 6x$
   d   $5c^2 - 25c$

## Formulae and equations

Formulae and equations are used in construction calculations to calculate physical properties. There are many formulae used depending on the physical property being sought. Later in this chapter, you will discover several very important formulae used in construction calculations. One of the most common is the formula for the area of a triangle, where:

Area $= \frac{1}{2} \times$ base $\times$ height

which is abbreviated to $A = \frac{1}{2}$ bh, where the letters A, b and h can represent the area, base length and height of *any* triangle.

The equation in the form above puts the Area A as its 'subject', i.e. the actual values of the base length and height must be known and entered into the equation to find the triangle's actual area. It is also important that the units of both b and h are the same, for example both metres (m). This will then give the value of the Area A in square metres (m²).

## Remember!

The equation A = ½ bh is a **linear equation**. Linear equations have only one unknown. So, to work out the area A, we would need to substitute values for b and h.

The 'equals' sign (=) in an equation makes sure that the left-hand side (LHS) of the equation balances the right-hand side (RHS). Both sides must always balance, like the beam of a seesaw with equal weights – if you load up one side, then you must load the other side by the same amount if the beam is to remain balanced and level.

## ■ Transposition of formulae

We learned above that the area A of any triangle can be found from the following formula:

A = ½ bh

However, you could also use this formula to work out height (h) if you already know the Area (A) and the base length (b). This can be done by re-arranging the formula using simple rules of transposition to make h the subject, such that

$$h = \frac{2(Area)}{base} = \frac{2A}{b}$$

To transpose or re-arrange a formula you need to change the subject so that the item you want to find is:

- on the LHS of the formula
- on the top of the line as the numerator
- by itself.

## Remember!

If you have a fraction like $\frac{4}{5}$, the top of the fraction is the **numerator** and the bottom of the fraction is the **denominator**.

## Worked example

A rectangular swimming pool, shown below, is s metres wide and t metres long, and is surrounded by timber decking area, s metres wide. Find an equation in its simplest form for the area of decking in terms of s and t.

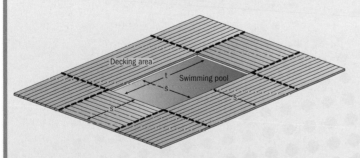

The decking area is made of a series of rectangles and squares. At the corners of the decking there are 4 squares, s by s m². Next to the longest sides the decking has dimensions t metres long by s metres wide, and the shortest sides have decking next to them of s metres long by s metres wide. Therefore the equation for the area can be constructed:

Total area of decking = 4(s × s) + 2(s × t) + 2(s × s)
                      = 4s² + 2st + 2s²
                      = 6s² + 2st

This is an equation that can now be used to calculate the area of decking, for *any* values of y, s and t.

If, say, we are given that s = 5.5 m, t = 12.5 m and y = 2 m, we can substitute these values into the equation to work out the area.

Therefore, total area of decking
 = 6s² + 2st
 = 6(5.5 m)² + 2 × 5.5 m × 12.5 m
 = 181.5 m² + 137.5 m²
 = 319 m²

## Addition and subtraction

With addition or subtraction, when a number or a term is moved across the equals sign from one side of the equation to the other, it always changes its sign to make sure that the equation remains balanced. For example:

$$25 + 10 = 41 - 6$$
$$35 = 35$$

is a balanced equation.

Moving the 6 across from the RHS to the LHS changes its sign to '+' and the equation still balances:

$$25 + 10 + 6 = 41$$
$$41 = 41$$

The same is also true for terms or letters, for example:

$$R + S = T + U$$
$$R = T + U - S$$

The equation is still balanced because we changed the sign of '+S' to '−S' as it moved across the equals sign from one side to the other.

## Multiplication, division and powers

When dealing with equations which have parts that include multiplication, division, powers or roots, whatever you do to one side you must do to the other. If you want to move a term from one side of the equation to the other, you must do the **opposite** of the operation that it is currently performing.

Let's look more closely at how we arrived at the equation for the height (h) of a triangle given its base (b) and area (A) above.

$$A = \frac{1}{2} \times b \times h$$

We want to get h on its own on the LHS of the equation. First, we switch *both sides* over – the equation remains balanced and the *signs do not change.*

$$\frac{1}{2} \times b \times h = A$$

We now want to remove the b which is at the moment multiplying the h value. The opposite of multiply is divide. So we divide *both* sides by b.

$$\frac{1 \times b \times h}{2 \times b} = \frac{A}{b}$$

Next, we can cancel out the bs on the LHS because b into b goes once, and note that the 2 is also on the bottom. Therefore, we have:

$$\frac{h}{2} = \frac{A}{b}$$

Now, we want to move the 2 to the other side of the equation and as it is *dividing* into h we need to *multiply* both sides by 2 to balance out the equation.

$$\frac{2 \times h}{2} = \frac{2 \times A}{b}$$

Finally, 2 goes into 2 once and so it cancels out, leaving the equation that we want:

$$h = \frac{2 \times A}{b} = \frac{2A}{b}$$

## Remember!

I have included an '×' in this equation to make it clear what is being multiplied. Normally, with transposition we do not need to write '×' in algebra. Two separate letters written next to each other implies that we multiply them together.

## Worked example

Transpose $r = \sqrt{\dfrac{V}{\pi h}}$ to make h the subject.

Here we have a square root sign, so to remove that we have to do the operation which is opposite to 'square root' which is 'square'. But again we must do this operation to both sides of the equation for it to remain balanced.

**Step 1:** Square both sides to get rid of the square root sign on the RHS.

$$r^2 = \frac{V}{\pi h}$$

**Step 2:** Multiply both sides by h so that h appears in the top line on the LHS line.

$$hr^2 = \frac{V}{\pi}$$

**Step 3:** Move $r^2$ to the RHS by dividing both sides by $r^2$, leaving h as the subject on the LHS.

$$h = \frac{V}{\pi r^2}$$

## Simultaneous equations

So far we have learned about simple linear equations, where we substituted values for all the given data to find the unknown subject. Sometimes, we had to re-arrange the formula by transposing the subject, but they all involved only one unknown.

However, we also need to deal with equations where we have two unknowns, and to solve this we need to have two equations. These two equations are known as **simultaneous equations**.

For example, find the values of x and y that make *both* of these equations correct, i.e. they are simultaneous equations.

$x + 2y = 8$
$5x - 3y = 1$

You could work out the values of *x* and y by 'trial and error' by guessing values of *x* and y which fitted both equations – for straightforward equations this may not be too difficult. However, it is best to use a method which can be used systematically for all types of simultaneous equation, no matter how difficult they appear to be. The worked example on page 88 shows you the method for working out simultaneous equations.

## Knowledge check:
### transposition of formulae and equations

1  Transpose the following equations to make a new subject of the equation as indicated:

  **a**   $v = u + at$            Make a the subject.

  **b**   $a^2 = b^2 + c^2$       Make b the subject.

  **c**   $C = \dfrac{N - n}{2\pi}$       Make n the subject.

  **d**   $v = \pi r^2 h$           Make r the subject.

  **e**   $T = 2\pi\sqrt{\dfrac{L}{g}}$      Make g the subject.

  **f**   $a = b + \sqrt{(b^2 + c^2)}$   Make c the subject.

2  A rectangular concrete block has edge dimensions of x, y and z measured in metres. Write down an expression for the total surface area (A) of the block in terms of x, y and z. (*Hint:* Draw a rough three-dimensional sketch of the block showing dimensions x, y and z.)

3  The total surface area of the block in 2 above is 7.5 m² and x is 1 m and y is 1.2 m. Transpose the formula for its area to make z the subject, and so calculate the length of dimension z in metres to 2 d.p.

Find the value of $x$ any $y$ to solve the following simultaneous equations.

$x + 2y = 8$ [equation 1]
$5x - 3y = 1$ [equation 2]

**Step 1:** Re-arrange both equations to get $x$ on its own.

$x = 8 - 2y$ [equation 1a]

$x = \dfrac{1 + 3y}{5}$ [equation 2a]

**Step 2:** As both equations equal $x$, they must equal each other:

$8 - 2y = \dfrac{1 + 3y}{5}$

**Step 3:** We now have one equation and one unknown called $y$, and we can solve this by transposing and simplifying its terms. First, bring the denominator 5 to the top of the LHS by multiplying both sides by 5, then multiply out the brackets, simplify and collect up all the $y$ terms and all the other numbers:

$5(8 - 2y) = 1 + 3y$
$40 - 10y = 1 + 3y$
$40 - 1 = 3y + 10y$
$39 = 13y$
$y = \dfrac{39}{13} = 3$

**Step 4:** Put the value that you have found for $y$ back into either equation 1 or 2 to find the other 'unknown' $x$.

Using equation 1:

$x + 2y = 8$
$x + 2(3) = 8$
$x + 6 = 8$
$x = 8 - 6$
$x = 2$

**Step 5:** Finally, put the values into equation 2 to check your answers!

$5x - 3y = 1$
$5(2) - 3(3) = 10 - 9 = 1$

Therefore, our answers must be right!

Solve the following equations for $x$ and y.

**a** $3x + 2y = 7$ and $4x - y = 2$

**b** $x - 4y = 7$ and $4x + y = 11$

**c** $5x - 3y = 5$ and $x - y = 3$

**d** $3x + 4y + 6 = 0$ and $x + 6y + 16 = 0$

**e** $3x - 3y + 2 = -2$ and $5x - 4y + 4 = -4$

## Quadratic equations

Quadratic equations are used in more complex calculations, often where maximum or minimum values are wanted. These equations take the form of:

$ax^2 + bx + c = 0$

where a, b and c are all numbers, called coefficients, and $x$ can usually have two values. Quadratic equations can be solved for $x$ in four ways, by:

- factors
- completing the squares
- formula
- drawing graphs.

### ■ Factors

We saw in the last section how we can multiply out factors to get a quadratic expression. Now, we will see how, given a quadratic equation, we can find its factors. This operation is know as **factorisation**.

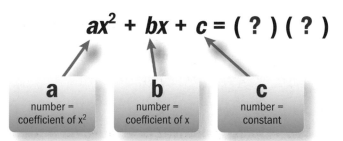

$$ax^2 + bx + c = (\ ?\ )(\ ?\ )$$

| a | b | c |
|---|---|---|
| number = coefficient of x² | number = coefficient of x | number = constant |

Some quadratic expressions can be factorised.

Factorising means rewriting the expression as the product of two brackets.

We can use factorisation to help us solve quadratic equations for $x$ provided we always re-arrange them to equal zero.

Consider the following quadratic equation that needs to be factorised:

$x^2 - 2x - 3 = 0$

Start by identifying the coefficients. In this example, they are a = 1, b = −2 and c = −3. The method for factorising them is as follows:

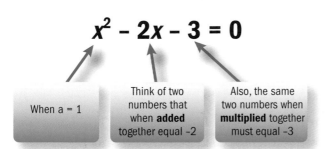

$x^2 - 2x - 3 = (x + ?)(x + ?)$

Now, −3 and +1 seem to fit because:

$-3 + 1 = -2$ and $-3 \times 1 = -3$

So let's try −3 and +1 to see if we get what we want when we multiply out the factors:

$(x - 3)(x + 1) = x^2 - 3x + x - 3$
$= x^2 - 2x - 3$

which is the quadratic expression that we need! Therefore, we can write:

$x^2 - 2x - 3 = (x - 3)(x + 1) = 0$
$(x - 3)(x + 1) = 0$

where the factors are $(x - 3)$ and $(x + 1)$.

Now, if the expression $(x - 3)(x + 1) = 0$, it must be true that either:

$(x - 3) = 0$ or $(x + 1) = 0$

which means that:

$x = 3$ or $x = -1$.

To check if this is right, substitute these answers for $x$ in the original quadratic equation. Let's first try $x = 3$ to see if the answer we get is zero.

$x^2 - 2x - 3 = (3)^2 - 2(3) - 3$
$= 9 - 6 - 3$
$= 0$

Let's now try $x = -1$.

$x^2 - 2x - 3 = (-1)^2 - 2(-1) - 3$
$= 1 + 2 - 3$
$= 0$

Both of these make the quadratic equation balance, so the solution to the quadratic equation $x^2 - 2x - 3 = 0$ is $x = 3$, $x = -1$.

## ■ Completing the squares

Take the standard format for a quadratic equation that we know, i.e. $ax^2 + bx + c = 0$

The method of completing the squares converts a quadratic equation to two equal factors or sides of a 'square'.

To find the values of $x$ that solve the equation $2x^2 + 8x - 10 = 0$, first move the numerical constant c to the RHS of the equation.

$2x^2 + 8x = 10$

Make a = 1 by dividing through both sides by a. In this example, divide by 2:

$x^2 + 4x = 5$

Now, add $\left(\dfrac{b}{2}\right)^2$ to both sides of the equation, where b in this example is 4.

$x^2 + 4x + \left(\dfrac{4}{2}\right)^2 = 5 + \left(\dfrac{4}{2}\right)^2 = 5 + \dfrac{16}{4} = 9$

Therefore:

$x^2 + 4x + \left(\dfrac{4}{2}\right)^2 = 9$

$x^2 + 4x + 2^2 = 9$

Next, 'complete the square' by factorising the LHS.

$x^2 + 4x + 2^2 = 9$
$(x + 2)(x + 2) = 9$
$(x + 2)^2 = 9$

## Remember!

If you expand $(x + 2)^2 = 9$, you get back to the original quadratic equation! Give it a try!

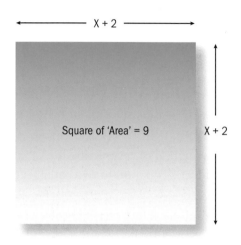

← X + 2 →

Square of 'Area' = 9        X + 2

This can be pictured as a square with sides $x + 2$, as illustrated.

Finally, rearrange and solve the linear equation for $x$ by finding the square root of both sides of the equation.

$(x + 2)^2 = 9$

$x + 2 = \sqrt{9}$

$x + 2 = \pm 3$

Therefore, $x = 3 - 2 = 1$ or
$\qquad x = -3 - 2 = -5$.

These values can be substituted into the original equation to check that your answers are correct.

$2x^2 + 8x - 10 = 0$

For $x = 1$

$2(1)^2 + 8(1) - 10 = 2 + 8 - 10 = 0$

And for $x = -5$

$2(-5)^2 + 8(-5) - 10 = 2(25) - 40 - 10 = 50 - 40 - 10 = 0$

## ■ Formula

The formula for working out the solution to the quadratic equation $ax^2 + bx + c = 0$ is given by substituting the values into the following equation:

$$x = \frac{-b \pm \sqrt{(b^2 - 4ac)}}{2a}$$

So using the example that we used above for solving by factors:

$x^2 - 2x - 3 = 0$

we see that $a = 1$, $b = -2$, $c = -3$.

Substituting these into the formula, we get:

$$x = \frac{-(-2) \pm \sqrt{((-2)^2 - 4(1)(-3))}}{2(1)}$$

$$x = \frac{2 \pm \sqrt{(4 + 12)}}{2} = \frac{2 \pm \sqrt{16}}{2} = \frac{2 \pm 4}{2}$$

Therefore, $x = \frac{6}{2} = 3$ or

$$x = \frac{-2}{2} = -1$$

which are the same answers that we had before.

## ■ Drawing graphs

This method is explained on page 00.

## Simultaneous linear and quadratic equations

Earlier, we came across linear simultaneous equations which dealt with finding the solutions to two linked straight line or linear equations. We can take this a step further and use it to solve for unknowns when one or both of the equations are in a quadratic form, i.e. they have an $x^2$ term included in them. We must remember that a quadratic equation always has two solutions for $x$. Therefore, in this situation there will also be two solutions for $y$. This can be solved graphically, as can be seen on page 61, or algebraically as shown on page 91

## Worked example

Find the values of $x$ and $y$ that satisfy the following two equations:

$y = 3x + 1$
$y = x^2 + 2x - 1$

**Step 1:** As both equations in this case equal $y$, they must both equal each other:

$\therefore 3x + 1 = x^2 + 2x - 1$

**Step 2:** We now have one quadratic equation which we can simplify and solve. Rearranging it into the standard quadratic form of

$ax^2 + bx + c = 0$

we have:

$0 = x^2 + 2x - 1 - 3x - 1$

$\therefore x^2 - x - 2 = 0$

**Step 3:** We can now solve this quadratic equation by any of the three methods previously studied. This particular one can be easily factorised thus:

$x^2 - x - 2 = ?$
$\qquad = (x + 1)(x - 2) = 0$

Therefore, either

$(x + 1) = 0$ or $(x - 2) = 0$

which means

$x = -1 \quad$ or $\quad x = 2$

**Step 4:** Because we are solving for simultaneous equations we need to find the corresponding values of $y$ to complete the solution. Therefore, we can substitute the values of $x$ back into one of the original equations to find its $y$ value, and it will be simpler to use the linear equation $y = 3x + 1$. Hence:

For $x = -1$, $y = 3 (-1) + 1 = -2$ and

For $x = 2$, $y = 3 (2) + 1 = 7$

Therefore, the solutions to the equations are:

$x = -1, y = -2$ and also $x = 2, y = 7$

## Knowledge check:
### solving quadratic equations

1 Solve the following quadratic equations for $x$ by the factors method:

  **a** $x^2 - x - 12 = 0$

  **b** $x^2 - 7x + 10 = 0$

  **c** $x^2 - 2x - 63 = 0$

2 Solve the following quadratic equations for $x$ by the completing the square method, giving your answers as fractions:

  **a** $4x^2 - 3x - 1 = 0$

  **b** $6x^2 + x - 35 = 0$

  **c** $12x^2 + 8x = 7$

3 Solve the following quadratic equations for $x$ by the formula method. Give your answers to 2 decimal places:

  **a** $x^2 - 6x - 10 = 0$

  **b** $2x^2 + 6x + 3 = 0$

  **c** $4x^2 - 5x = 4$

## The binomial theorem

This is a mathematical method which allows two terms held within a bracket to be expanded to any power. So far you have learned that $(a + b)^2$ can be expanded to become:

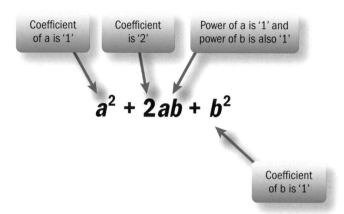

Coefficient of a is '1'

Coefficient is '2'

Power of a is '1' and power of b is also '1'

$$a^2 + 2ab + b^2$$

Coefficient of b is '1'

but, by using the binomial series, brackets can be expanded to any power giving the following coefficients in what is commonly known as Pascal's triangle.

| *Binomial expression:* | *Pascal's triangle (coefficients in the expansion):* |
|---|---|
| $(a + b)^0$ | 1 |
| $(a + b)^1$ | 1　1 |
| $(a + b)^2$ | 1　2　1 |
| $(a + b)^3$ | 1　3　3　1 |
| $(a + b)^4$ | 1　4　6　4　1 |
| $(a + b)^5$ | 1　5　10　10　5　1 |
| $(a + b)^6$ | 1　6　15　20　15　6　1 |
| $(a + b)^7$ | 1　7　21　35　35　21　7　1 |

We can see that:

- the number of terms in each expansion is one more than the index, e.g. the expansion of $(a + b)^9$ will have ten terms
- the arrangement of coefficients is symmetrical
- the coefficients of the first and last terms are both always one
- each coefficient in the triangle is obtained by adding together the two coefficients in the line above that lie on either side of it
- that the individual powers of a and b increase or decrease, but their total always equals the value of the original expansion power, e.g.

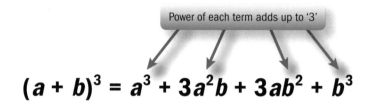

Power of each term adds up to '3'

$$(a + b)^3 = a^3 + 3a^2b + 3ab^2 + b^3$$

## Remember!

Any number or letter by itself is raised to the power of 1, but we do not usually write this, e.g. $3^1 = 3$ and $b^1 = b$.

Using Pascal's triangle, we can expand higher powers. For example:

Expand $(2x + 3y)^4$

Comparing $(2x + 3y)^4$ with $(a + b)^4$ we have '$2x$' in place of a, and '$3y$' in place of b. Substituting into Pascal's triangle and following the rules above, we get:

$$[(2x) + (3y)]^4 = (2x)^4 + 4(2x)^3(3y) + 6(2x)^2(3y)^2 + 4(2x)(3y)^3 + (3y)^4$$
$$= 16x^4 + 4(8x^3)(3y) + 6(4x^2)(9y^2) + 4(2x)(27y^3) + 81y^4$$
$$= 16x^4 + 96x^3y + 216x^2y^2 + 216xy^3 + 81y^4$$

This cannot be simplified any further as none of the terms in $x$ and y have identical powers.

## ■ Uses of the binomial theorem

In industry, the binomial expansion is useful when estimating the errors in, say, working out a volume where you have overestimated the lengths used to calculate that volume by a certain percentage. Consider $(1 + x)^n$ when $x$ is very small compared to 1, just like measuring a distance of say 10 m with an error of 5 mm. The binomial expansion for $(1 + x)^n$ where n is a power can be approximated to

$$(1 + x)^n \approx 1 + (n)(x)$$

## Worked examples

1  In measuring the area of a square glass cladding panel, the measurement was 1% too large. If this measurement is used to calculate the area of the glass, find the resulting error in the area.

Let the length of the side of the square be L and the area of the square glass panel be A. Let the error in the measured length be δL. Also let δA be the error in the area, then:

$$A = L^2 \text{ and } \delta L = \frac{L}{100}$$

### Remember!

When writing a percentage, it must be expressed as a fraction of 100, e.g. $7\% = \frac{7}{100}$.

$$A = L^2$$
$$A + \delta A = (L + \delta L)^2$$

Substituting in for δL from above

$$= \left(L + \frac{L}{100}\right)^2$$

Taking the L out of the brackets and remembering that it must remain squared,

$$A + \delta A = L^2\left(1 + \frac{1}{100}\right)^2$$

Since the error is small when compared to the length measured, we can approximate using binomial theory that:

$$A + \delta A \approx L^2\left(1 + \frac{2}{100}\right)$$

But $A = L^2$

$$A + \delta A = A\left(1 + \frac{2}{100}\right)$$

$$A + \delta A = A + A\frac{2}{100}$$

$$\delta A = A\frac{2}{100}$$

$$\delta A \approx 2\% \text{ of } A$$

Therefore, we can see that if the measurement of the length of the square, glass cladding panel is 1% too large, the resulting area calculation will be approximately 2% too large.

2  Find the approximate percentage error in the calculated volume of a **right circular cone** if the radius is taken as 2% too small and the height as 3% too large.

## Key term

**Right circular cone**  Cone where the top vertex or point of the cone is vertically above the centre of the circular base.

Volume (V) of a right cone $= \frac{1}{3}(\pi r^2 h)$

The error in height $(\delta h) = h\frac{3}{100}$ and

the error in the radius $(\delta r) = -r\frac{2}{100}$

$$V + \delta V = \frac{1}{3}\left(\pi\left(r - r\frac{2}{100}\right)^2\left(h + h\frac{3}{100}\right)\right)$$

$$V + \delta V = \frac{1}{3}\left(\pi r^2 h\left(1 - \frac{2}{100}\right)^2\left(1 - \frac{3}{100}\right)\right)$$

Since the errors in height and radius are small when compared to the original lengths, we can approximate using binomial theory that:

$$V + \delta V = \frac{1}{3}\pi r^2 h \left(1 - 2\frac{2}{100}\right)\left(1 + \frac{3}{100}\right)$$

Multiplying out the brackets:

$$V + \delta V = \frac{1}{3}\pi r^2 h \left(1 - \frac{1}{100}\right) \text{ approximately, ignoring the last small term}$$

$$V + \delta V = V\left(1 - \frac{1}{100}\right)$$

$$\therefore \delta V = -V\left(\frac{1}{100}\right)$$

Therefore, for a right circular cone with a radius taken as 2% too small and a height taken as 3% too large, the calculated volume will be 1% too small.

## Knowledge check:
### using binomial theorem

1  Using Pascal's triangle, expand the following bracketed expressions:

   a  $(x + 5y)^3$

   b  $(2 - y)^5$

   c  $(x - 2y)^4$

2  In measuring the internal radius of a circular sewer the measurement is 3% too large. If this measurement is then used to calculate the circular cross-sectional area of the pipe:

   a  calculate the percentage error that will occur compared to the true area

   b  calculate the true area of the pipe when the incorrect measured radius was recorded as 958 mm. Give your answer in m² to 6 decimal places.

   Take the cross-sectional area (A) of the pipe to be $A = 3.14r^2$

## Assessment practice

A waste management company Easidump has been contracted by Bestend Properties plc to remove construction waste from three of its local construction sites. The charges for each site include a standard charge (S) of £300 for removing the waste, together with additional labour costs (L) of £80 per operative (for sorting the waste ready for recycling) and a hire cost for the number of site bins (B) they supply at £10 per bin.

a  Write down an algebraic formula for the total cost (T) incurred for all 3 sites taking into account the standard charge (S), number of labourers (L) and number of bins (B).

b  Calculate the total cost for all 3 Bestend Properties sites if 3 Easidump operators supply 12 site bins for each site.

c  If the standing charge is increased to £390 and the labour cost increases to £90 per operator, rewrite the formula that you wrote for (a) to show these changes. Using this revised formula, find out the new total cost that Bestend Properties plc will have to pay assuming all other information stays the same.

d  Bestend Properties plc cannot afford these increased charges – the most its waste budget will stretch to is £2160. Therefore, rearrange the formula that you wrote for (c) making the cost of the bins (B) the subject of the formula, then using this new formula calculate the total number of site bins that can be supplied to each site by Easidump for £2160 assuming that they will still be using 3 operatives.

**e** Comment on the results and advise Bestend Properties plc on what it could do next. `P1` `P2`

Bestend properties plc is undertaking a cost comparison of windows and doors for its three luxury house types: the Asprey, the Barnhurst, the Clarendon. Each has the following specification of external windows and doors:

| | External doors (d) | Small windows (s) | Big windows (b) | Garage doors (g) |
|---|---|---|---|---|
| Asprey (A) | 3 | 3 | 8 | 2 |
| Barnhurst (B) | 2 | 6 | 10 | 1 |
| Clarendon (C) | 3 | 5 | 9 | 1 |

**a** The windows and doors required for the the Asprey can be expressed as:

A = 3d + 3s + 8b + 2g

Write down expressions for the doors and windows for the Barnhurst and the Clarendon.

**b** On one particular development site there are to be two of the the Asprey house types, one of the Barnhurst and three of the Clarendon. Using the expressions from **a** above, write down a simplified expression for the total number of windows and doors for the whole development.

**c** If the costs of the individual doors and windows are as shown below, calculate from your expression in **b** the total cost for the whole development.

- External doors = £160, Small windows = £115, Big windows = £180, Garage doors = £260.

**d** If Bestend's budget for the windows and doors for the development is only £17,000, how many garage doors could not be purchased for this sum? `P1` `P2`

The area of roof-top garden for one of Bestend Properties' new penthouse apartments is shown below. The local planning department has specified that the minimum area for the roof garden should be 126.75 m². As can be seen from the diagram, the design team has already allocated an area of 8 m x 5 m for lifts, service ducts and stairwell.

You are required to work out the dimension 'x', as shown on the diagram, to ensure that the planners' minimum requirements for the roof-top garden are met.

**a** Write down a quadratic equation for the area of the roof garden in terms of $x$ and the current dimensions of the lift shaft, etc.

**b** Solve the quadratic equation giving your answer in metres to 1 decimal place.

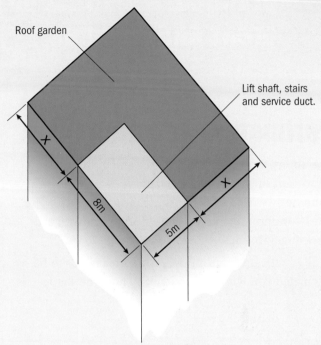

Roof garden

Lift shaft, stairs and service duct.

8m

5m

x

x

**c** Carry out two alternative methods to solve the equation and hence check your answer to (b). `M1` `D1`

Bestend Properties is refurbishing an old hospital that was built in the early 1950s. The building's main structure is a steel frame. The company's structural engineers are trying to determine the strength of the existing floor beams by loading them up and measuring the deflection.

The formula that relates deflection to the strength and loadings on the beam is:

$$E = \frac{5wL^4}{384Iy}$$

where:

E is Young's Modulus (strength of the material)
w is the measured uniformly distributed load on the beam
I is the moment of inertia of the beam (a constant due to the cross-sectional shape )
L is the measured span of the beam
y is the deflection of the loaded beam.

After the on-site testing was done, it was discovered that some of the measuring equipment was wrongly calibrated. The errors that were discovered were as follows:

The span L was 5% too long.
The load w was 3% too low.

Using your knowledge of binomial theory, produce a formula to show the net percentage effect of these calibration errors on the value of E (Young's Modulus). `D2`

# Perimeters and areas

The ability to find perimeter, area and volumes is important in all construction activities, and to work them out we need to know some basic formulae. The most common formulae for area and perimeter are shown in Table 3.3.

In all practical situations, where an area needs to be calculated you will need to identify how the shape that you have can be broken down into one or more of these standard cases. Sometimes assumptions will need to be made, for example that sides are at right angles to each other or are parallel or that the object can be approximated to a circle. You are making the area formula fit the given situation, but you must be aware how these approximations affect the accuracy of your final result.

| Shape | Area (A) | Perimeter (P) |
|---|---|---|
| i) Square | $A = L \times L$<br>$= L^2$ | $P = 4L$ |
| ii) Rectangle | $A = a \times b$<br>$= ab$ | $P = 2a + 2b = 2(a + b)$ |
| iii) Triangle 1 – Standard formula<br><br>Note: h is the perpendicular height | $A = \frac{1}{2} \times b \times h$<br>$= \frac{1}{2} bh$ | $P = a + b + c$ |
| iv) Triangle 2 – Half perimeter formula | $A = \sqrt{s(s - a)(s - b)(s - c)}$<br>Where $s = \dfrac{a + b + c}{2}$ | $P = a + b + c$ |

| Shape | Area (A) | Perimeter (P) |
|---|---|---|
| v) Trapezium | $A = h\dfrac{(a + b)}{2}$ | |
| vi) Parallelogram | $A = b \times h$<br>$= bh$ | |
| vii) Circle<br>r = radius<br>d = diameter | $A = \pi r^2$ or $A = \dfrac{\pi d^2}{4}$ | Circumference $= 2\pi r$<br>$= \pi d$<br>Where d = diameter<br>$= 2r$ |
| viii) Ellipse<br>a = half-major axis length<br>b = half-minor axis length | $A = \pi ab$ | $P = 2\pi \sqrt{\dfrac{(a^2 + b^2)}{2}}$ |

**Table 3.3 Area and perimeter formulae**

## Worked examples

1 The cross-section of a symmetrical precast concrete bridge beam is shown below with dimensions in millimetres. Calculate the cross-sectional area in metres squared to 4 d.p.

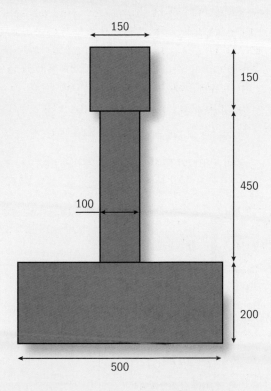

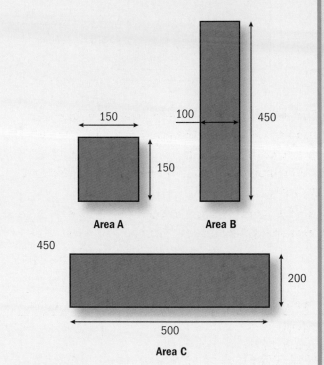

Area A

Area B

Area C

We can assume that the beam is rectilinear, that is, all the sides are parallel and all angles are right angles. Some concrete beams are made with curved corners to prevent damage to the edges, so always check whether this information is given. Here, we can assume that all edges meet at right angles; therefore, the beam can be split up into three parts: one square and two rectangles.

Area of precast concrete beam
= Area A + Area B + Area C

= 150 × 150 + 100 × 450 + 200 × 500
= 22,500 + 45,000 + 100,000
= 167,500 mm²

Converting into square metres, we have:

$$167{,}500 \text{ mm}^2 = \frac{167{,}500}{1{,}000{,}000} = 0.1675 \text{ m}^2$$

## Remember!

To convert square millimetres to square metres, apply the conversion factor 1/1,000,000 because:

1 m = 1000 mm and
1 m² = 1000 × 1000 mm² = 1,000,000 mm²

2 When constructing domestic cavity walls bricklayers need to estimate how many bricks and concrete blocks they will need to build a given area of wall. The coordinating sizes of a brick and blocks are shown below which includes a 10 mm bedding and perpendicular mortar joints.

a To assist the bricklayers in finding how many bricks and blocks they will need, determine the approximate number of bricks and blocks required to build a 1 m by 1 m area of cavity wall.

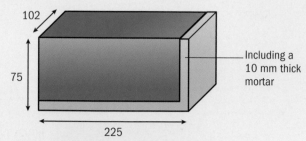

Coordinating dimensions for a brick

Including a 10 mm thick mortar

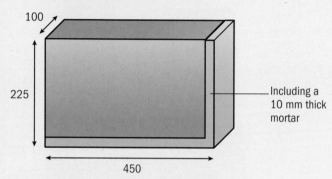

Coordinating dimensions for a concrete block

Including a 10 mm thick mortar

The area of the face of one coordinated brick = 225 × 75 = 16,875 mm²

and the area of the face of one coordinated block = 450 × 225 = 101,250 mm²

Therefore, the number of bricks that could fit into

$1 \text{ m}^2 = \dfrac{1000 \times 1000 \text{ mm}^2}{16,875 \text{ mm}^2}$

= 59.259 bricks, say, 60 bricks

The number of blocks that could fit into

$1 \text{ m}^2 = \dfrac{1000 \times 1000 \text{ mm}^2}{101,250 \text{ mm}^2}$

= 9.877 blocks, say, 10 blocks

## Remember!

For practical purposes, blocks and bricks have to be cut to fit the given dimensions of the required area and often there is wastage, which has to be allowed for in the estimation calculations. Typically, up to 5% is allowed.

These are very useful approximations for estimating the number of bricks and block required per metre squared for any cavity wall.

**b** Calculate the number of bricks and blocks to build a wall measuring 6.3 m long by 2.7 m high allowing for wastage of 5%.

Area of wall = 6.3 m × 2.7 m = 17.01 m²

Number of blocks = 10 × 17.01 = 170.1

Wastage at 5% = $\dfrac{170.1 \times 5}{100}$ = 8.505

Total number of blocks = 170.1 + 8.505 = 178.606, say, 179 blocks

Number of bricks = 60 × 17.01 = 1020.6

Wastage at 5% = $\dfrac{1020.6 \times 5}{100}$ = 51.03

Total number of bricks = 1020.6 + 51.03 = 1071.63, say, 1072 bricks

## Remember!

The extra allowance for wastage could be included within the overall calculation in one line using brackets in the formula. For example:

Total no. of bricks = $60 \times 17.01 \left(1 + \dfrac{5}{100}\right)$ = 1071.63, say, 1072 bricks

**3** The layout of a proposed modern stained-glass window is shown below made up from a semi-circle and a triangle. In order to price the job the glazier needs to calculate both the length of the lead **cames** and the area of glass. By applying the basic formula provided above, calculate this information. Give the area of glazing in mm², and allow 5% wastage for the length of lead came.

## Key term

**Cames** Slender, grooved lead bars used to hold together the panes in stained-glass or latticework windows.

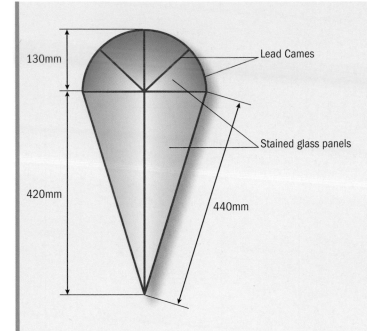

130mm

Lead Cames

Stained glass panels

420mm

440mm

**a** First, we can calculate the length of cames that is required. It may at first appear that we have not got enough information about the size of the panel. However, the top part of the panel is a semi-circle and the radius of the circle is 130 mm. This now allows us to add up all the separate cames that radiate out from the centre of the semi-circles as the length of each of these is the same as the radius.

Length of internal cames in the semi-circle
= 5 × 130 mm = 650 mm

Length of internal came in the lower triangle
= 420 mm

Length of external cames for lower triangle
= 2 × 440 mm = 880 mm

Length of curved came for semi-circle
= (½)2πr
= ½ × 2 × π × 130 mm = 408 mm

Adding up length of lead cames = 2358 mm

Allowing for 5% wastage

$$= 2358 \times \frac{5}{100}$$

= 118mm

Total length of lead came

= 2358 + 118

= 2476 mm

**b** The calculation of the whole area can be worked out by splitting up the window into a semi-circle and a triangle. The area of a semi-circle is half the area of a circle, and the lower triangle can be found by either the standard formula of ½ base multiplied by height or the half perimeter rule. We shall do both.

The area of the semi-circle
= π r² × ½ = π × 130² × ½ = 26,546 mm²

The area of the triangle by standard formula
= ½ bh = ½ × 260 × 420 = 54,600 mm²

Total area = 26,546 + 54,600 = 81,146 mm²

Alternatively, using the half-perimeter formula:

where the area of the triangle by

$$\sqrt{s(s-a)(s-b)(s-c)}$$

$$\text{where } s = \frac{a+b+c}{2}$$

Hence, $s = \dfrac{440 + 440 + 260}{2} = 570$ mm

and area, A =

$$= \sqrt{570(570-440)(570-440)(570-260)}$$

$$= \sqrt{570(130)(130)(310)}$$

$$= \sqrt{2.986 \times 10^9}$$

= 54646.4 mm² ≈ 54,600 mm²

This small rounding error occurs because of the tiny error within the original triangle lengths – the true length of the external came is actually 439.659 mm, not 440 mm!

## Knowledge check:
### area

1 Calculate the areas of the following triangles in m² to 3 d.p. where:

   a base = 12.56 m, height = 5.39 m
   b base length is 2855 mm and height is 3870 mm
   c the lengths of the side are 21.30 m, 14.95 m and 18.45 m.

2 Calculate the cross-sectional area of an elliptical steel duct that fits snugly through a rectangular service hole measuring 0.6 m x 0.4 mm. Give your answer to the nearest 10 mm².

3 Calculate the cross-sectional areas of the gravity retaining walls shown opposite in m³ to 2 s.f.

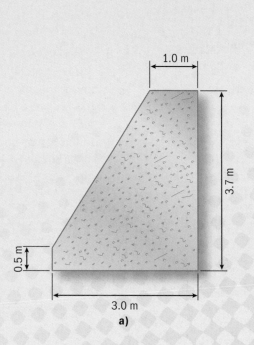

a)

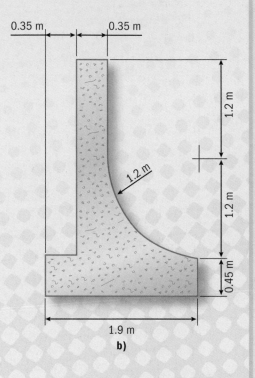

b)

# Volumes

Volumes can be understood as the space inside a three-dimensional (3D) object. In order to calculate the volume, we need to know the dimensions of the object in three directions which are at right angles to each other. The simplest object to picture is a cube, where its volume has been formed by extruding (pulling out) a flat square to a height equal to the length of its square side.

The common name for a 3D object that has been created by extruding a shape from a flat surface area is a prism, where the

Volume of prism = Cross-sectional area × Length

This can be applied to a whole range of rectilinear objects where a cross-sectional area can be calculated and multiplied by a perpendicular length, as can be seen from Figure 3.1.

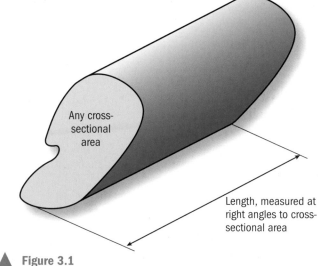

▲ Figure 3.1

Similarly, the surface area of such an object can be found from knowing the perimeter length of the cross-sectional area and its length.

Surface area = (Perimeter of cross-section × Length) + (Area of the two ends)

## Cones and pyramids

Cones and pyramids are common forms found in construction, particularly in roofs and glazed atriums. They can be called 'oblique' or 'right' according to if they are symmetrical about a vertical centre line.

### Remember!

A right cone is where the top vertex or point of the cone is vertically above the centre of the base; an oblique cone is where it's not! Their volumes are unaffected by whether they are 'oblique' or 'right' in shape.

The calculation of the volume of pyramids and cones is similar to that of prisms, but because their cross-sectional areas taper down with their height, the volume is reduced to a third of the equivalent prism volume. Therefore, in general for cones and pyramids:

Volume = $\frac{1}{3}$ × (area of base) × (perpendicular height)

Other standard volume formulae are given in Table 3.4.

In all practical situations, where a volume needs to be calculated, you will need to identify how the shape that you have can be broken down into one or more of these standard cases. Just as with areas, you will need to

| Object | Cross-sectional area (CA) | Volume | Surface area (SA) |
|---|---|---|---|
| i) Rectangular prism<br>Length L, Height h, Width w | $CA = wh$ | $V = whL$ | $SA = 2(hL + wL + hw)$ |
| ii) Triangular prism<br>c, h, a, Length L, b | $CA = \frac{1}{2}bh$ | $V = \frac{1}{2}bhL$ | $SA = L(a + b + c) + 2(CA)$ |
| iii) Cylinder<br>r, L<br>r = radius | $CA = \pi r^2$ | $V = \pi r^2 L$ | $SA = 2\pi rL + 2\,(CA)$ |
| iv) Oblique or right cone<br>vertex, h = height, r<br>r = radius of base | $CA = \pi r^2$<br>r varies according to height of horizontal cross-sections | $V = \frac{1}{3}\pi r^2 h$ | For cone only:<br>$SA = \pi r\sqrt{(r^2 + h^2)}$ |
| v) Square oblique or right pyramid<br>h = height, a, a<br>The base can be any rectilinear shape | Base area rectangular pyramid = $a^2$ | $V = \frac{1}{3}a^2 h$ | For sloping sides only:<br>$SA = 2a\sqrt{\left(\left(\frac{a}{2}\right)^2 + h^2\right)}$ |
| vi) Sphere<br>r, d | $CA = \pi r^2$<br>r varies according to height of horizontal cross-section | $V = \frac{4}{3}\pi r^3$ | $SA = 4\pi r^2$ |

**Table 3.4 Volumes and surface area formulae**

make reasonable assumptions, for example that sides are at right-angles to each other or are parallel or that the object can be approximated to a sphere. You are making the area formula fit the given situation, but you must be aware how these approximations affect the accuracy of your final result.

Let's look at some simple examples involving the calculation of volumes:

## Worked examples

1   A drainage ditch is 2.3 m deep and has a trapezoidal cross-section 6 m wide at ground level and 3.4 m wide at the bottom. The ditch is being dug between two existing drainage ditches that are 1.2 km apart. The spoil is to be transported from the site by barge, where each barge has a loaded capacity of 480 m³. Determine the number of barge loads that will be required to move the spoil material if the soil bulks by 10%.

First, we need to collate all the information that we have and the best way is to draw a diagram and add all the given dimensions in the units in which the answer is required, in this case metres (m). You must be consistent in the use of the units.

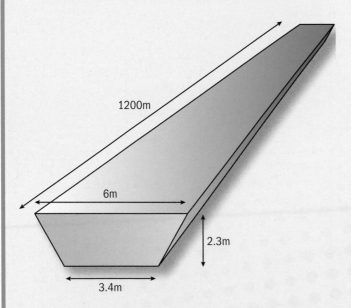

The drainage ditch can be seen as a prism with a trapezium for its cross-section. Therefore, we can work out the volume of this shape based on the standard formula, where:

$$\text{Cross-sectional area} = h\frac{a + b}{2}$$

where h is 2.3 m, a and b are the parallel sides of 6 m and 3.4 m respectively. Then, to find the volume all that is needed is to multiply the cross-sectional area by the length of the prism, which is 1.2 km or to be consistent, 1200 m. Thus:

$$\text{Volume of ditch} = h\frac{a + b}{2}L$$

$$= 2.3 \text{ m} \times \tfrac{1}{2} (6 \text{ m} + 3.4 \text{ m}) \times 1200 \text{ m}$$

$$= 2.3 \text{ m} \times 4.7 \text{ m} \times 1200 \text{ m}$$

$$= 12{,}972 \text{ m}^3$$

This volume is the size of the drainage trench, but we have been told that the soil bulks by 10%. This means that when soil is excavated from the ground its mass is packed and compressed tightly together. After the soil is dug out, it expands into large clods with air gaps in between to such an extent that the bulk of material excavated has increased, sometimes up to 15%–20% depending on the type of soil. Therefore, the spoil lorries need to cart away the net bulked volume, not just the theoretical value that we have just worked out. So, in our example, we need to increase the volume calculated by 10%.

$$\therefore 10\% \text{ of ditch volume} = \left(\frac{10}{100}\right) \times 12{,}972 \text{ m}^3$$

$$= 1297.2 \text{ m}^3$$

$$\therefore \text{Total net bulked volume} = 12{,}972 \text{ m}^3 + 1297.2 \text{ m}^3$$
$$= 14{,}269 \text{ m}^3$$

Finally, we can work out the number of barge loads

$$\text{required} = \frac{14{,}269 \text{m}^3}{480 \text{m}^3} = 29.7 \approx 30 \text{ loads}$$

Therefore, 30 barge loads are required to transport the excavated soil material in the construction of the drainage ditch.

2  A copper, hot-water tank is in the shape of a cylinder with a hemispherical top. The height of the tank is 1200 mm in total and it has a diameter of 450 mm. Calculate:

   a  the capacity of the hot-water cylinder in litres

   b  the surface area of the whole tank in square metres to 3 d.p.

   a  Any calculation involving volumes needs a good diagram so that you can collate all the information that you need. If you are not provided with one, read the description carefully and sketch out the object roughly to scale, and if you can, sketch it in 3D. On the sketch write in all the dimensions that you are given in a consistent set of units and start thinking how it can be split up into some of the 'standard' shapes that we have already seen in Table 3.4.
Here's a sketch of the hot-water tank and you will note that we have split the tank into two parts: the bottom cylinder and the top hemisphere.

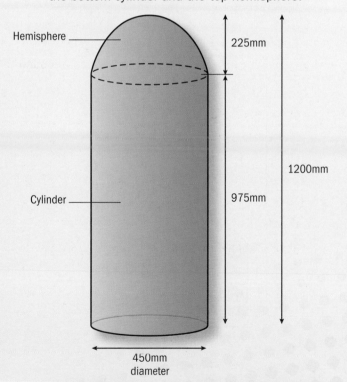

Hemisphere

225mm

1200mm

975mm

Cylinder

450mm
diameter

We have put in the dimensions of 1200 mm for the height and 450 mm for the diameter, but we have also jotted down 225 mm as the radius of the hemisphere as it's got to be half of the diameter of the cylinder, and this also allows us to find the height of the cylinder which is:

1200 – 225 = 975 mm

Thus, the volume can be calculated by working out the volume of the cylinder and hemisphere separately and adding together for the total volume. We need to bear in mind that the final answer should be given as a 'capacity' in litres, but if we work out the volume in metres cubed first, we can convert it to litres from our knowledge of conversion factors – see page 00.

Volume of cylinder

$$V_{cylinder} = \pi r^2 L$$
$$= \pi (0.225 \text{ m})^2 \times 0.975 \text{ m}$$
$$= 0.155 \text{ m}^3 \text{ to 3 d.p.}$$

Volume of a sphere

$$V = \frac{4}{3}\pi r^3$$

Therefore, the volume of a hemisphere will be half that of the sphere, hence:

Volume of hemisphere

$$V_{hemisphere} = \frac{1}{2} \times \frac{4}{3}\pi (0.225 \text{m})^3$$
$$= 0.024 \text{ m}^3 \text{ to 3 d.p.}$$

Therefore, Total volume of tank

$$= V_{cylinder} + V_{hemisphere}$$
$$= 0.155 \text{ m}^3 + 0.024 \text{ m}^3$$
$$= 0.179 \text{ m}^3$$

This is the volume in metres cubed, but when dealing with liquids such as water that would fill

## Remember!

It is always good practice when substituting known values into a formula that you also include the symbols that indicate what unit they are measured in, such as 'm' or 'm²'. This will help you to remember the units your final answer should be stated in. It is also handy in complicated formulae because you can divide or multiply out these 'embedded units' to give you the right units for your final answer.

Look closely at this example converting metres cubed into litres. The metres³ on the bottom cancel out the metres³ on top to leave the correct units of litres!

this tank, we need to quote the answer in litres. From the conversion table on page 00 we see that 1 m³ = 1000 litres, i.e. there are 1000 litres for every metre cubed capacity that you have.

Therefore,

$$0.179 \text{ m}^3 = 1000 \ \frac{\text{litres}}{\text{metres}^3} \times 0.179 \text{ m}^3$$
$$= 179 \text{ l}$$

b Surface area calculations can be treated in the same way as before by calculating the surface areas for the cylinder and hemisphere separately. However, don't get confused when including 'end' or 'base' areas.

Surface area of curved side of cylinder

$$= 2\pi rh$$
$$= 2\pi(0.225)(0.975)\text{m}^2$$
$$= 1.378 \text{ m}^2$$

Surface area of bottom of cylinder

$$= \pi r^2$$
$$= \pi(0.225\text{m})^2$$
$$= 0.159 \text{ m}^2$$

Surface area of hemispherical top

$$= \tfrac{1}{2} \text{ surface area of sphere} = \tfrac{1}{2} \times 4\pi r^2$$
$$= 2\pi r^2$$
$$= 2\pi(0.225 \text{ m})^2$$
$$= 0.318 \text{ m}^2$$

Therefore, the total surface area of tank can be found by adding up these three separate areas.

Total surface area

$$= 1.378 \text{ m}^2 + 0.159 \text{ m}^2 + 0.318 \text{ m}^2$$
$$= 1.855 \text{ m}^2$$

3 A diagram of a brick boundary wall is shown below. Calculate the volume of the brick work in cubic metres to 3 d.p. and hence find the weight of the wall to 3 s.f., if the unit weight of brickwork is 22 kN/m³ – that is, one cubic metre has a weight of 22 kN.

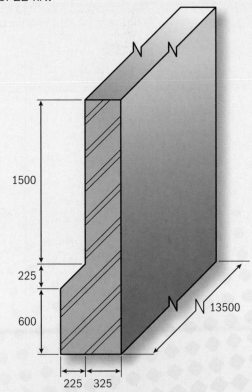

The cross-section of the wall is not as straightforward as it seems – there is a wider plinth at the base of the wall. We need to think about how to split up the wall cross-section into easy and manageable areas. It could be done by splitting into three parts, another way would be to divide into two parts by considering the plinth as a trapezium.

## Remember!

Always set out your calculations line by line, just like the examples above. It is important that you use a clear presentation style so that the work can be checked and people can see what assumptions you have made, and how you have approached solving the problem.

Always write down the formula you are using and explain what you are doing. Then substitute in the given values together with their proper units – identify clearly the units that you are using and be consistent – check what the answer requires and the accuracy needed.

When you have got an answer always try to think of an alternative way of checking your result. Just because the calculator gives you an answer does not mean it's correct. Since you put the values in, if you key in the figures wrongly or miss out a bracket, the calculator won't know.

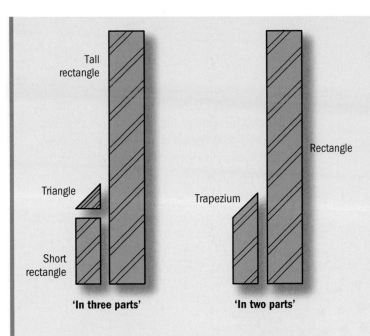

Tall rectangle

Triangle

Short rectangle

Rectangle

Trapezium

'In three parts'

'In two parts'

Total cross-sectional area of wall

= Area of trapezium plinth + Area of rectangle

= 0.160 m² + 0.756 m²

= 0.916 m²

Therefore, the volume of the wall

= Cross-sectional area × Length of wall

= 0.916 m² × 13.5 m

= 12.366 m³

And the weight of the wall

= Volume × Unit weight of brickwork

= 12.366 m³ × 22 $\frac{kN}{m^3}$

= 272.052 kN

≈ 272 kN to 3 s.f.

Therefore, considering the wall cross-section split into two parts we have:

Cross-sectional area of trapezium plinth

= ½(a + b)h

= ½(0.6 m + (0.6 + 0.225)m) × 0.225 m

= 0.160 m²

Cross-sectional area of rectangle

= (1.5 + 0.225 + 0.6)m × 0.325 m

= 0.756 m²

## Remember!

The m³ cancel each other out, leaving you with the weight of the wall in kilo-Newtons (kN).

# Knowledge check:
## volumes

1 Sketch the following precast concrete **dolos units** described in parts **a–c** below.

## Key term

**Dolos units** Man-made sea defence blocks, which are piled against quaysides and jetties to protect them from being eroded by wave action.

Calculate the volumes of each dolos unit in m³ and hence find out the weight of each one in kilo-Newtons to 1 d.p. Assume that the weight of 1 m³ of concrete is 24 kN.

**a** This dolos has a triangular cross-sectional base of 250 mm, a height of 350 mm and a length of 2.5 m.

**b** This dolos has a parallelogram-shaped cross-section with parallel sides of 325 mm separated by a distance of 200 mm. It is 3 m long.

**c** A dumb-bell shaped dolos comprises two different diameter spheres joined by a cylindrical connector. The radii of the largest and smallest spheres are 450 mm and 300 mm respectively. The length and diameter of the cylindrical connector is 1200 mm and 300 mm respectively.

2 The internal dimensions of a village hall are shown below with an open couple roof, that is, the pitched rafters of the roof form the fixing of the ceiling materials. In order to check ventilation calculations, find the volume of air contained in the hall.

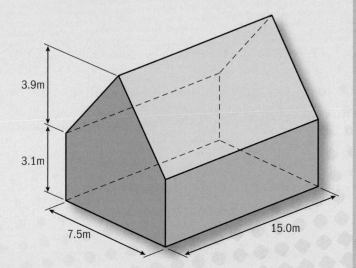

3 A large, circular, reinforced concrete sewer pipe has an internal diameter of 1500 mm and an external diameter of 1800 mm, and is 9.5 m long.

**a** Calculate the volume of the walls of one pipe in m³ to 2 d.p .

**b** Calculate the amount of concrete required to make 20 of these pipes, allowing for the fact that the steel reinforcement within the pipe wall will take up around 10% of the volume.

**Figure 3.2 Numerical integration terms** ▶

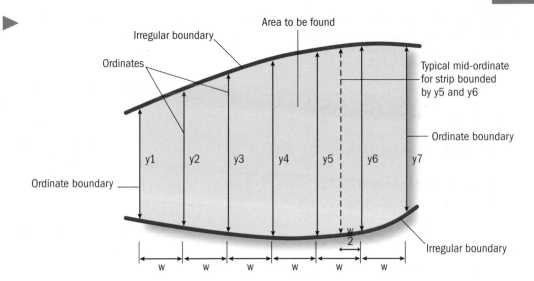

# Numerical integration methods

**Areas**

So far, when calculating areas and volumes, we have used standard formulae and applied them to regular, geometric patterns that formed the boundaries of the given object. However, when shapes and objects have irregular boundaries we have to use another technique known as numerical integration. This involves the area being split into thin, equal-width strips where the lengths on either side of the strip are called ordinates (see Figure 3.2).

Three useful techniques for carrying out numerical integration are:

- Trapezoidal rule – simple to use and can deal with any number of ordinates.

Trapezoidal rule

= Width of strip × {½ (sum of the 1st & last ordinate) + (sum of the remaining ordinates)}

$= w\{½(y_1 + y_7) + (y_2 + y_3 + y_4 + y_5 + y_6)\}$

- Mid-ordinate rule – again simple to use and can deal with any number of ordinates, provided you are given all the mid-ordinate lengths.

   Area = Width of strip × (sum of all mid-ordinates)

- Simpson's rule – more accurate than previous rules but can only be used when the total ordinates are an odd number.

Simpson's rule

= 1 × Width of strip × {(1st + last ordinate) + 4(sum of even ordinates) + 2(sum of remaining odd ordinates)}

$= \dfrac{w}{3}\{(y_1 + y_7) + 4(y_2 + y_4 + y_6) + 2(y_3 + y_5)\}$

# Worked example

The cross-section through a river is shown below. Regular depths across the river were recorded at 2.5 m intervals. Determine the cross-sectional area of water in the river in metres squared to 2 d.p. using:

a  trapezoidal rule

b  Simpson's rule.

c  Comment on the accuracy of the results.

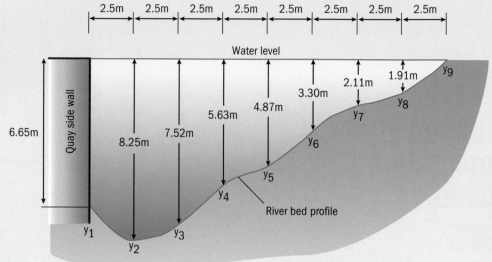

In this example, there are 9 ordinates separated by equal distances of 2.5 m. It is always good practice to draw a good diagram roughly to scale and mark up the ordinates in sequential order starting at $y_1$ and working through to the last ordinate. In this way, you can clearly see what ordinates are 'odd' and which ones are 'even'.

We can then take the formula for both techniques and adapt them for use here.

a  Using the trapezoidal rule:

Cross-sectional area = $w\{½ (y_1 + y_9) + (y_2 + y_3 + y_4 + y_5 + y_6 + y_7 + y_8)\}$

= 2.5m x $\{½(6.65m + 0) + ( 8.25m + 7.52m + 5.63m + 4.87m + 3.30m + 2.11m + 1.91m)\}$

Working out the ordinate totals within the brackets gives:

= 2.5m × {3.325 + 33.590}m
= 2.5m × 36.915m
= 92.2875 m²
= 92.29 m² (to 2 d.p.)

b  Using Simpson's rule:

Cross-sectional area

= $\dfrac{w}{3}\{(y_1 + y_9) + 4(y_2 + y_4 + y_6 + y_8) + 2(y_3 + y_5 + y_7)\}$

= $\dfrac{2.5m}{3}$ {(6.65m + 0m) + 4(8.25m + 5.63m + 3.30m + 1.91m) + 2(7.52m + 4.87m + 2.11m)}

Work out all the figures in the brackets:

= $\dfrac{2.5m}{3}$ {(6.65m) + 4(19.09m) + 2(14.5m)}

= $\dfrac{2.5m}{3}$ (112.01 m)

= 93.3416 m²
= 93.34 m² to 2 d.p.

c  Both results are of the same order of size, which is a useful check on our calculations. The Simpson's rule result of 93.34 m² is the more accurate answer because it assumes a curved line for the profile of the bed, while the trapezoidal rule always assumes a straight line between each of the ordinates, which is not the case as can be seen from the diagram above. So Simpson's rule is the best one to use when the boundaries are curving. However, if there are straight lines joining the ordinates, then the trapezoidal rule will give just as good a result – and the formula is quicker and easier to use!

## Remember!

If you are going to use Simpson's rule, check to see that there is an odd number of ordinates – in this example, there are 9, so this is fine.

## Volumes

We can develop the techniques of numerical integration to deal with irregular volumes as well as irregular areas. The only difference is that rather then using ordinates which are distances, if we use ordinates which themselves are cross-sectional areas, then we can use the trapezoidal rule or Simpson's rule to find volumes.

## Worked example

Look at the diagram below of a large spoil heap. Calculate the volume of the spoil heap to the nearest m³ by using numerical integration techniques. We have already determined the cross-sections at regular positions along its length.

These values such as 8.5 m², 10.3 m², 15.8 m², etc. could have been worked out using the normal Simpson's rule, and the width between each of these area ordinates is 3 m.

We shall use Simpson's rule because the soil heap has an irregular curved surface. Now, if we replace the 'y' symbol for length of the ordinate to 'a' to represent the 'area' of each 'area ordinate', we can apply Simpson's rule. Start by noting up these values from $a_1$ to $a_7$ on the diagram and we have a Simpson's rule for the volume of the spoil heap as:

a7
a6   6.0 m²
a5   9.2 m²
a4   16.7 m²
a3   22.6 m²
a2   15.8 m²
a1   10.3 m²
8.5 m²

3 m (×7)

Volume of spoil heap $= \dfrac{w}{3}\{(a_1 + a_7) + 4(a_2 + a_4 + a_6) + 2(a_3 + a_5)\}$

$$= \dfrac{3m}{3}\{(8.5m^2 + 6.0m^2) + 4(10.3m^2 + 22.6m^2 + 9.2m^2) + 2(15.8m^2 + 16.7m^2)\}$$

$$= \dfrac{3m}{3}\{(14.5m^2) + 4(42.1m^2) + 2(32.5m^2)\}$$

$$= \dfrac{3m}{3}\{247.9m^2\}$$

$$= 247.9m^3$$

$$\approx 248\ m^3$$

# Knowledge check:
## numerical integration methods

1   A plan view of a greenfield site for a development of 4 houses is shown below together with a set of measurements in metres taken with a measuring tape. Using this sketch, estimate the area of land of the site and hence the possible plot size in square metres to 1 d.p. for each house.

2   A main sewer is to be excavated as shown in the cross-section drawing below. If the trench width is 600 mm and the soil bulks by 7%, calculate the volume of spoil in m³ to be carted away to 1 d.p. between points A and B.

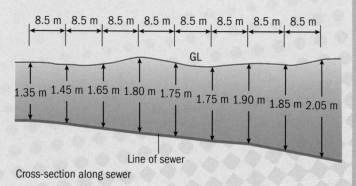

Cross-section along sewer

Plan view of greenfield site

# Assessment practice

A proposed new garden layout is shown for an old house below. The new design is for a landscaped lawn and elliptical pond, secured by new vertical boarded timber fencing. Currently, the entire triangular area is used as a car park and has concrete/hardcore surfacing to an approximate depth of 300 mm over the whole site.

From the dimensions of the initial site survey shown, estimate the following:

a   The length of new timber fencing required.
b   The amount of concrete/hardcore to be broken up and carted off site.
c   The area of new turf required to cover the garden allowing for the new pond.   **P4**

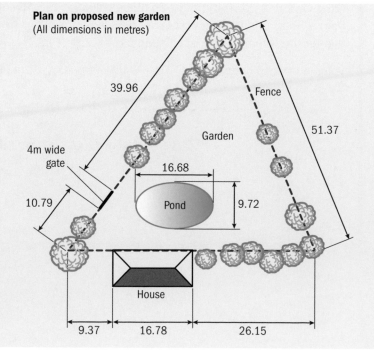

Plan on proposed new garden
(All dimensions in metres)

A swimming pool with a cross-section as shown below is to be built for an important client. A preliminary costing is to be undertaken and you are to provide the information as noted below. Take the width of the pool to be 5 m.

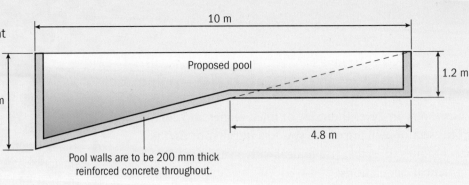

10 m

Proposed pool

1.2 m

2.5 m

4.8 m

Pool walls are to be 200 mm thick reinforced concrete throughout.

a Find the amount of excavated soil to be removed from the site to the nearest 0.1 of a m³ assuming that the soil removed bulks by 20%.

b Calculate the volume of concrete and reinforcing steel required, given that the thickness of the pool walls is 200 mm and assuming 10% of the volume of the pool walls is reinforcing steel. State your answer for the concrete to the nearest m³ and for the steel to the nearest 100 mm³.

c Clearly show how you arrived at your answer to (b), including any assumptions and estimations that you made. How confident do you feel that your answer is correct allowing for these rough estimations?

**M**2 **D**2

In a highways contract a road embankment is currently under construction. Part of the monitoring process as the embankment is built up is regular measurement of the cross-sectional areas at regular chainages along the length of the road. A diagram of a typical cross-section of the embankment is shown opposite.

The results of the most recent survey are as follows:

| Chainage (m) (distance along road) | Recorded value of height of embankment H (m) | Area of cross-section (m²) |
| --- | --- | --- |
| 0 | 8.6 | |
| 12 | 9.4 | |
| 24 | 10.7 | |
| 36 | 8.9 | |
| 48 | 9.9 | |
| 60 | 11.2 | |

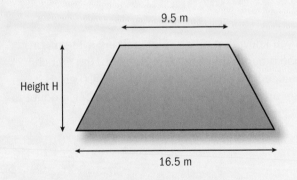

9.5 m

Height H

16.5 m

a Complete the table by working out the cross-sectional areas at each chainage.

b Calculate the volume of the embankment using a suitable numerical method. Give your answer in m³ to the nearest 0.5 m³.

c How might future improvements to the method of carrying out the survey improve the accuracy of the results?

**M**2 **D**2

# Geometric techniques

Geometry involves the study of lines, angles and curves. This section will introduce you to a number of useful techniques to enable you to deal with a variety of practical calculations.

## Properties of angles

When two lines intersect, an angle is formed between them. The typical types of different angles can be seen in Figure 3.3 where two parallel lines are intersected by other lines as shown:

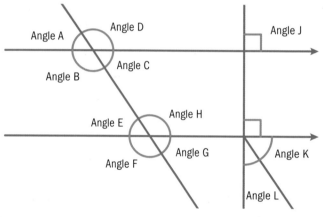

 **Figure 3.3**

Angles are categorised as shown in Table 3.5:

### Theory into practice

Using Figure 3.3, look for other angles that can be similarly categorised besides the examples already given in Table 3.5. There are many, so look carefully!

### ■ Degrees and radians

There are two basic mathematical methods for measuring the size of angles; one uses degrees, the other radians:

- Degrees – used by surveyors and construction professionals.
- Radians – mostly used for complex civil engineering analysis.

### Remember!

Did you know that different measuring systems are in use around the world? For example, the French developed the gradian system where 400 grads made up a whole circle, making a right angle equal to 100 grads.

| Types of angles | Degrees | Example |
| --- | --- | --- |
| Acute | less than 90° | Angle A |
| Right | equal 90° | Angle J |
| Obtuse | between 90° and 180° | Angle D |
| Reflex | between 180° and 360° | Angle B + Angle C + Angle D |
| Complementary | when added equal 90° | Angle K and Angle L |
| Supplementary | when added equal 180° | Angle A and B |
| Alternate or 'Z' | equal | Angle C and Angle E |
| Opposite | equal | Angle E and Angle G |

**Table 3.5 Types of angles**

Let's see how these systems of measurement work.

Angles in the UK are measured using the sexagesimal system where there are 360 degrees in a whole circle. This system is very common in both land and setting-out surveys where a high degree of accuracy is needed in setting out buildings on site.

The sexagesimal system splits up parts of a degree into fractions of a degree as follows:

1 whole circle = 360 degrees, written as 360°

1° = 60 minutes, written as 60'

1' = 60 seconds written as 60"

So, for example, an angle could be quoted as 46° 30' 45".

In simple calculations, where high accuracy is not required, angles can be quoted in decimal degrees to one or two places of decimal, for example 72.5° is equivalent to 72° 30' because 30' is half a degree.

## Theory into practice

Most scientific calculators allow you to input angles in degrees, minutes and seconds and to convert from one to another. Look at your calculator's instruction booklet to see how it is done.

The method of using radians to measure angles is very useful for more complex trigonometry. A radian is the angle made at the centre of a circle when a length, equal to the radius, is traced out around its circumference (see Figure 3.4).

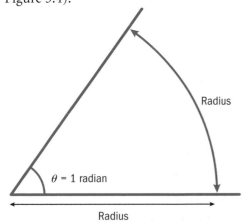

$\theta = 1$ radian

Radius

Radius

▲ **Figure 3.4**

We know that the circumference of a circle = $2\pi r$

Therefore, the number of radians contained within one whole circle of $360° = \dfrac{2\pi r}{r}$

Therefore, $360° = 2\pi$ radians, or $180° = \pi$ radians

which means that:

$1 \text{ radian} = \dfrac{180°}{\pi} \approx 57°$ and

$1 \text{ degree} = \dfrac{\pi}{180°} \approx 0.01745$ radians

## ■ Internal angles in polygons

A polygon is a two-dimensional shape made up from straight lines. We have already examined a range of regular polygons in the previous section on areas, but in terms of angles, it is sometimes useful to know something about the size of angles that define a polygon's shape.

A useful formula that relates the sum of the internal angles of polygon to the number of its sides is:

Sum of internal angles of a polygon = $(2n - 4) \times 90°$

where n is the number of sides of the polygon.

For example, we know that all the angles in a triangle add up to 180°. Let's try using the internal angle formula.

For a triangle, n = 3 as there are three sides to every triangle.

Therefore, the sum of the internal angles of a triangle
$= (2 \times 3 - 4) \times 90°$
$= (6 - 4) \times 90°$
$= 2 \times 90°$
$= 180°$

which is correct!

This formula is very useful when setting up a control network of survey stations as part of a **closed traverse** survey.

## Key term

**Closed traverse** An irregular ring of survey stations linked by measured distances and internal angles which can provide 'eastings' and 'northing' coordinates to help set out large structures.

## Worked example

In a closed traverse with seven survey stations, the following internal angles were measured with a surveyor's **theodolite**. If the results are to be satisfactory, they must be within +/−1° of what the sum of internal angles should be. Check to see if the results are within that tolerance.

**Plan on closed traverse survey**

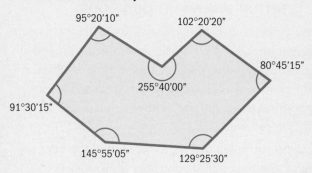

The true value of internal angles
= (2n − 4) × 90°
= (2 × 7 − 4) × 90°
= 10 × 90°
= 900°

The sum of the measured values on site = 91° 30' 15" + 95° 20' 10" + 255° 40'+ 102° 20' 20" + 80° 45' 15" + 129° 25' 30" + 145° 55' 05"

= 900° 56' 35"

which is within the allowed tolerance of +/−1° for this survey, so the angular results are within tolerance.

## Key term

**Theodolite** A highly accurate instrument for measuring horizontal and vertical angles for undertaking land surveying and setting out surveys (see Chapter 10 Surveying for Construction, page 00).

## ■ Similar triangles

The use of similar triangles is very common in construction calculations. It involves applying ratios to find unknown lengths. Similar triangles contain the same internal angles, but their sides are different lengths. Look at the figure below, which shows two triangles, ABC and ADE. They are similar because all their internal angles are the same. Therefore, their sides are in the same ratio.

$$\frac{AB}{EC} = \frac{AD}{DE}$$

## Theory into practice

Draw any two similar triangles just like the ones below to a size that conveniently fits on your paper. Measure the four lengths as indicated.

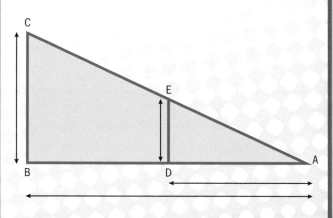

Apply the formula above, and you should find that they equal each other.

## Worked example

A monopitch roof is like the ABC triangle shown on page 114. The height of the roof BC = 2.8 m and the span of the roof AB is 5 m. Calculate the height of the vertical post DE, if the distance from the eaves AD is 2 m.

By similar triangles $\dfrac{AB}{BC} = \dfrac{AD}{DE}$

$$\dfrac{5.0m}{2.8m} = \dfrac{2.0m}{DE}$$

Re-arranging the formula by cross multiplying by DE, cross multiplying by 2.8 m and, finally, cross dividing by 5.0 m, we get:

$$DE = \dfrac{2.0m}{5.0m} \times 2.8m$$

DE = 1.12 m

## Remember!

Watch out to see where similar triangles may occur. They are very useful in helping you find unknown lengths and distances.

## ■ Pythagoras' rule

In the right-angled triangle shown in Figure 3.5 the longest side – the hypotenuse – is opposite the right angle and is labelled 'c'. The two other sides forming the triangle are 'b' and 'a'.

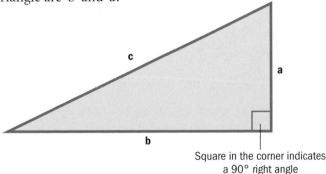

Square in the corner indicates a 90° right angle

▲ Figure 3.5

Pythagoras' rule relates these three sides together such that:

$$c^2 = a^2 + b^2$$

This can be seen graphically in Figure 3.6 where:

$$c \times c = (a \times a) + (b \times b)$$

Area 3 = Area 1 + Area 2

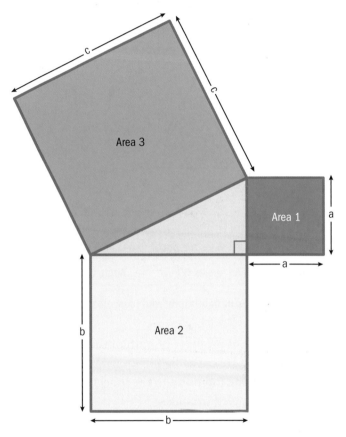

▲ Figure 3.6

The most important practical application of Pythagoras' rule is that the sides a and b will always meet at a right angle and the right angle will be located opposite the longest side c. This formula is used regularly by surveyors when setting out walls and other features that need to be built at right angles to one another.

Also, given any two of the three sides, the third unknown can always be found by transposing Pythagoras' rule. For example:

$$a^2 = c^2 - b^2$$

Then take the square root of both sides to get a by itself:

$$a = \sqrt{(c^2 - b^2)}$$

## ■ Special triangles

Apart from the right-angle triangle, there are two other triangles that are commonly used in construction calculations:

- the equilateral triangle
- the isosceles triangle

The properties of these two triangles are shown in Table 3.6.

| Property | Equilateral triangle | Isosceles triangle |
|---|---|---|
| Basic shape | 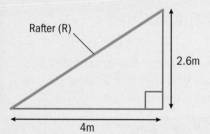 | |
| Sides | All sides are equal | Length AC = Length AB |
| Internal angles | All angles 60° | Angle C = Angle B |

**Table 3.6 Properties of equilateral and isosceles triangles**

Another important property of both of these triangles is that when they are cut in half by drawing a vertical line down from the top point to the base, they form two identical right-angled triangles.

The cross-section through a timber scissor truss is shown below. Estimate the length of both the rafter and ceiling tie in metres using Pythagoras' rule.

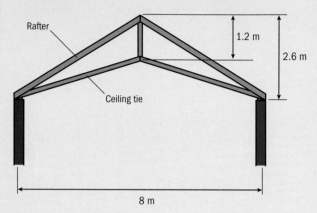

If you study the diagram closely, you can identify two separate right-angled triangles that feature the lengths that we need to find.

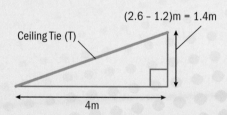

For the length of the rafter (R), we have:

$R^2 = 2.6^2 + 4^2$
$R^2 = 6.76 + 16$
$R = \sqrt{22.76}$
$R = 4.77$ m

And for the length of the ceiling tie (T) we also have

$T^2 = 1.4^2 + 4^2$
$T^2 = 1.96 + 16$
$T = \sqrt{17.96}$
$T = 4.24$ m

## Properties of circles

Circles have a number of important geometric properties and terms which occur regularly in construction problems. The basic ones are as follows:

Circumference of circle $= 2\pi r$

Perimeter of sector $=$ Circumference of circle $\times \dfrac{\theta°}{360°}$

Area of circle $= \pi r^2$

Area of sector $=$ Area of circle $\times \dfrac{\theta°}{360°}$

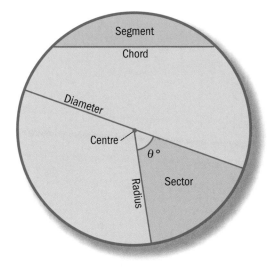

▲ **Figure 3.7 Properties of a circle**

### Worked example

Calculate the area of a sector of a circle whose subtended angle at the centre is 34°and with a radius of 350 mm. Give your answer in mm².

Area of sector $= 2\pi r^2$

$= 2\pi r^2 \dfrac{\theta°}{360°}$

$= 2\pi (350)^2 \times \dfrac{34°}{360°}$

$= 72693 \text{ mm}^2$

## Knowledge check:
### geometric techniques

1  In the following five-station survey traverse as shown below, the measured angles W, X, Y and Z are unrecognisable in the assistant surveyor's booking sheets.

   **a**  What are these missing angles?
   **b**  What is the sum of all the measured internal angles in the survey traverse?
   **c**  Are the measured angles within +/−2° of the theoretical value?

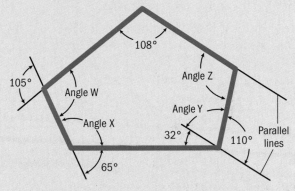

2  A cross-section through a church spire is an isosceles triangle as shown below. Using Pythagoras' rule, calculate the vertical height of the spire in metres to 2 d.p.

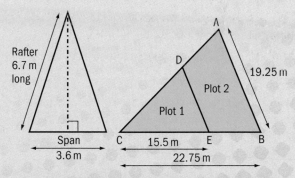

3  An area of land in the shape of triangle ABC is to be split into two separate building plots as shown above so that the new fence line DE is parallel to AB. Using the dimensions given and the technique of similar triangles, find:

   **a**  the length of the new fence DE in metres to nearest $^1/_{10}$ of a metre.
   **b**  the whole number of 1.2 m long timber fence panels needed to build the fence.

# Trigonometric techniques

## Right-angle trigonometry

So far we have dealt with a lot of triangles as they are very common in all branches of construction. We have looked at their areas and how their side lengths can be found by using Pythagoras' rule or using similar triangles. We have also studied the internal angles that make up a triangle. However, the next step is to look more closely at how angles in triangles affect the lengths of their sides. This technique is the study of trigonometry.

Let's look at some basic definitions. In a right-angled triangle:

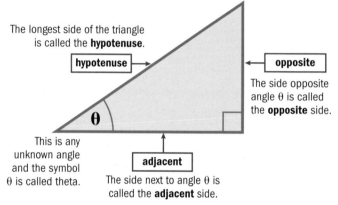

The longest side of the triangle is called the **hypotenuse**.

**hypotenuse**

**opposite**

The side opposite angle θ is called the **opposite** side.

θ

This is any unknown angle and the symbol θ is called theta.

**adjacent**

The side next to angle θ is called the **adjacent** side.

The sine (sin), cosine (cos) and tangent (tan) of angle θ are defined by the lengths of the sides of the triangle:

- $\sin \theta = \dfrac{\text{Opposite}}{\text{Hypotenuse}}$

- $\cos \theta = \dfrac{\text{Adjacent}}{\text{Hypotenuse}}$

- $\tan \theta = \dfrac{\text{Opposite}}{\text{Adjacent}}$

These are all known as trigonometric ratios or 'trig ratios' for short.

◀ **Figure 3.8 A right-angled triangle**

## Worked example

The cross-section through a triangular, cantilevered canopy for a proposed warehouse is shown below. Using trigonometric ratios, work out:

**a** the height of the canopy strut BC
**b** the width of the cantilevered over-hang AC
**c** the angle that the rear stay makes with the warehouse roof at D
**d** the length of the rear stay BD.
**e** Undertake a suitable alternative check calculation for BD.

In the diagram, there are two right-angled triangles and in the left-hand side one, labelled ABC, we are given two pieces of information, so we should be able to work out the rest of the dimensions and angles for that

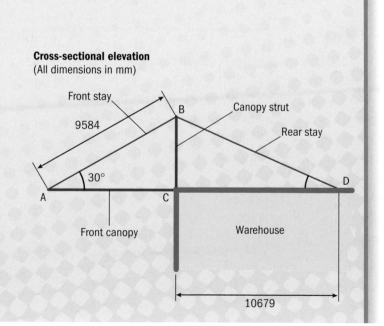

**Cross-sectional elevation**
(All dimensions in mm)

Front stay

9584

B

Canopy strut

Rear stay

30°

A

C

D

Front canopy

Warehouse

10679

triangle. Once this is done, we should be able to move on to triangle BCD using the height BC.

a  To find the height of the canopy strut BC, let's look closely at triangle ABC and identify the sides in relation to the angle, that is, find the hypotenuse, opposite and adjacent sides to the angle.

**Step 1:** It is always a good idea to label them up on a separate sketch collating all the information thus:

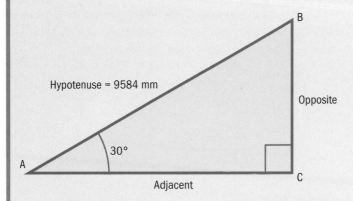

**Step 2:** Apply the trig ratio. If we want to find AC, the 'opposite' side to the angle, we need to use a ratio which has all the 'known' values and the 'opposite' specified. This can only be the sine ratio because:

$\sin \theta = \dfrac{\text{opposite}}{\text{hypotenuse}}$ and we know the values of the hypotenuse 9584 mm, and the value of the angle θ, 30°.

**Step 3:** Substitute in the known values:

$\sin 30° = \dfrac{\text{opposite}}{9584 \text{ mm}}$

**Step 4:** Rearrange the equation to make 'opposite' the subject of the formula:

opposite = 9584 mm × sin 30°
        = 4792 mm length of strut BC

The answer will be in the units of mm because the distance we put into the formula was in mm.

b  To find the width of the cantilevered over-hang AC, using trig ratios again, we can see that AC is the 'adjacent' side to the 30° angle. So we need to use the cosine ratio:

$\cos \theta = \dfrac{\text{adjacent}}{\text{hypotenuse}}$

$\cos 30° = \dfrac{\text{adjacent}}{9584 \text{ mm}}$

adjacent = 9584 mm × cos 30°
        = 8300 mm width of canopy AC

c  To find the angle that the rear stay makes with the warehouse roof at D, let's look at the other triangle that can be found as part of the canopy structure, the right triangle BCD.

**Step 5:** Draw out the triangle and jot down all the values that we know as well as the unknown angle that we are trying to find.

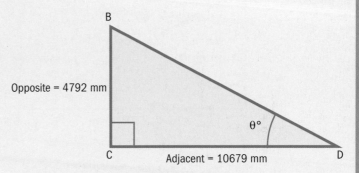

**Step 6:** Apply the trig ratio. We know the 'opposite' and 'adjacent' lengths and we want to find the angle θ°, so we need to use a trig ratio which has 'opposite', 'adjacent' and the angle θ° specified. This can only be the tangent ratio because:

$\tan \theta = \dfrac{\text{opposite}}{\text{adjacent}}$

**Step 7:** Substitute in the known values and work out the ratio.

$\tan \theta = \dfrac{4792 \text{ mm}}{10679 \text{ mm}} = 0.44873$

### Remember!

Always quote the trig ratios to 5 d.p. to ensure that you maintain good accuracy in your final angular value.

**Step 8:** The final step is to convert the tangent ratio calculated into an angle value that we can recognise. To do this, we need to identify the 'inverse trigonometric ratios' on our scientific calculators. Find the button marked with the symbol $\boxed{\text{tan}^{-1}}$ (inverse tangent ratio). Therefore:

$\tan^{-1}(0.44873) = 24.1672$ decimal degrees
$= 24° \, 10'$

**d** There are two ways to find the length of the rear stay: trigonometric ratios or Pythagoras' rule. Let's use the first one.

**Step 9:** Collate all the information in a sketch.

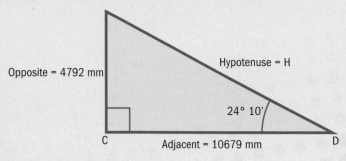

**Step 10:** Apply the trig ratio. We can use either the sine ratio or the cosine ratio to find the hypotenuse H. Let's do it using the sine ratio, where:

$$\sin \theta = \frac{\text{opposite}}{\text{hypotenuse}}$$

**Step 11:** Substitute in the known values and re-arrange to get the unknown on the LHS on the top.

$$\sin 24° \, 10' = \frac{4792 \text{ mm}}{H}$$

$$\therefore H = \frac{4792 \text{ mm}}{\sin 24° \, 10'}$$

**Step 12:** Use a calculator to work out the answer.

$$H = 11{,}705 \text{ mm}$$

Finally, to undertake a suitable alternative check calculation for BD, we can either apply the cosine ratio or use Pythagoras' rule. Using the cosine ratio:

$$\cos \theta = \frac{\text{adjacent}}{\text{hypotenuse}}$$

$$\cos 24° \, 10' = \frac{10679}{H}$$

$$H = \frac{10679}{\cos 24° \, 10'}$$

$$H = 11{,}705 \text{ mm}$$

This checks with the answer in (d). You might like to try Pythagoras' rule using the 'opposite' and 'adjacent' sides to see if you get the answer right a third time!

## Non right-angle trigonometry

So far, we have dealt with situations where we could always identify or reasonably assume a right-angled triangle was present. However, this is not always the case, so we need to explore what other trigonometric techniques are available for solving problems where there are no right-angled triangles present.

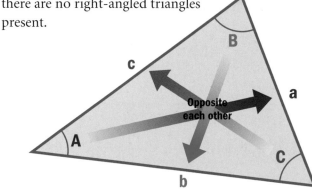

▲ **Figure 3.9 A non right-angled triangle**

## Remember!

Don't confuse the sine and cosine rules that we use in non right-angle trigonometry with the sine and cosine ratios used for right-angled triangles!

The two techniques that we can use for non right-angle trigonometry are called:

- the sine rule
- the cosine rule.

Let's start by setting out the notation for a non right-angled triangle. There is no hypotenuse or right angle, so we use the following convention when labelling sides and angles: all angles are given capital letters, e.g. A, B or C, and the sides that are *opposite* these angles are given lower-case letters, e.g. a, b and c (see Figure 3.9).

## The sine rule

The sine rule represents ratios of opposite sides, divided by sines of opposite angles, such that these ratios for a given triangle are all equal.

The formula looks like this:

$$\frac{a}{\sin A} = \frac{b}{\sin B} = \frac{c}{\sin C}$$

With its three fractions, it might not look like a normal equation, but you can take any part of the expression to make it work. For example:

$$\frac{a}{\sin A} = \frac{b}{\sin B} \quad \text{or} \quad \frac{b}{\sin B} = \frac{c}{\sin C}$$

or even $\dfrac{a}{\sin A} = \dfrac{c}{\sin C}$

Provided you know at least three values from the triangle, you will be able to find the fourth value. In fact, you can solve for all the lengths and angles in a triangle using the sine rule provided you are given either:

- one side and any two angles, or
- two sides and one angle (but not the angle between the two sides).

## Worked example:

A reinforced concrete bridge pier supports a sloping bridge deck, as shown below. The top of the pier has been splayed out to increase the bearing area. Calculate the length of bearing b shown with the information given.

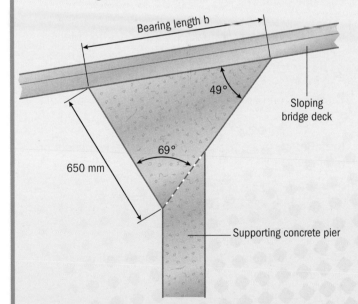

Bearing length b

49°

Sloping bridge deck

69°

650 mm

Supporting concrete pier

We can solve this problem by using the sine rule.

**Step 1:** Draw a diagram and label up the sides and angles according to the notation given earlier. Collate the information. Let the bearing length be b.

**Step 2:** Apply the sine rule:

$$\frac{a}{\sin A} = \frac{b}{\sin B}$$

**Step 3:** Substitute the values into the formula:

$$\frac{650 \text{ mm}}{\sin 49°} = \frac{b}{\sin 69°}$$

**Step 4:** Rearrange and carry out the calculations:

$$b = \frac{650 \text{ mm}}{\sin 49°} \times \sin 69°$$

$$b = \frac{650 \text{ mm}}{\sin 49°} \times \sin 69°$$

$$b = 804 \text{ mm}$$

# Worked example

A land survey was carried out where a greenfield was split up into two triangles, Triangle 1 and Triangle 2 based on one base line AC – all the distances and angles were recorded as shown below.

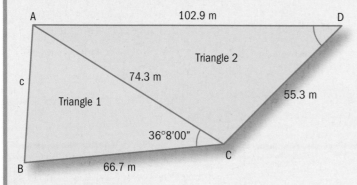

Using the cosine rule, find:

**a**   the length of side c.
**b**   the size of the internal angle at D.

**Step 1:** Starting with Triangle 1, draw a diagram to collate all the known information and add the correct notation.

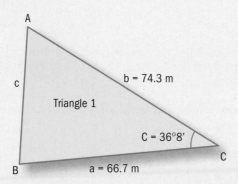

**Step 2:** Apply the cosine rule. We know sides a and b and the included angle at C, and we want to find the side length c. Studying the cosine rule, we see that we need:

$$c^2 = a^2 + b^2 - 2ab \cos C$$

**Step 3:** Substitute in the values and work out the length of side c.

$$c^2 = 66.7^2 + 74.3^2 - 2 \times 66.7 \times 74.3 \times \cos 36°8'$$
$$c^2 = 1964.29$$

$$c = \sqrt{1964.29}$$
$$c = 44.32 \text{ m}$$

**Step 4:** Moving on to Triangle 2, draw a diagram to collate all the known information and add the correct notation.

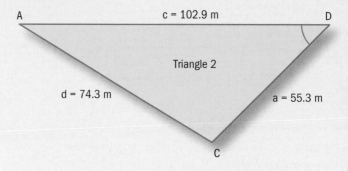

**Step 5:** Apply the cosine rule. We know all the sides but none of the angles. The angle we want, D, is adjacent to two known lengths. This is the starting point. We can now construct a cosine rule for Triangle 2 by looking at the pattern:

$$a^2 = b^2 + c^2 - 2bc \cos A$$

Therefore, we have:

$$d^2 = a^2 + c^2 - 2ac \cos D$$

**Step 6:** Rearrange to make the angle D the subject of the formula:

$$d^2 = a^2 + c^2 - 2a \cos D°$$
$$d^2 - a^2 - c^2 = -2a \cos D°$$
$$\cos D = \frac{d^2 - a^2 - c^2}{-2a}$$

**Step 7:** Substitute in the known values and calculate the required angle:

$$\cos D = \frac{74.3^2 - 55.3^2 - 102.9^2}{-2 \times 55.3 \times 102.9}$$

$$\cos D = 0.71401$$
$$D = \cos^{-1}(0.71401)$$
$$D = 44° \, 26' \, 13''$$

## ■ The cosine rule

In a triangle with internal angles A, B and C, and opposite sides a, b and c, as shown previously, the cosine rule states:

$a^2 = b^2 + c^2 - 2bc \cos A$,   or

$b^2 = a^2 + c^2 - 2ac \cos B$,   or

$c^2 = a^2 + b^2 - 2ab \cos C$.

You can see the similarity between this formula and the Pythagoras' rule that we have used before, except that there is an 'extra part' (e.g. $-2bc \cos A$). This is there to make allowance that we are not dealing with a right-angled triangle. In fact, if we substitute cosine 90° into this 'extra part', all we would get is zero as cosine of 90° = 0, and the equation reverts back to $a^2 = b^2 + c^2$ which is Pythagoras' rule.

## Theory into practice

Study all three cosine rule equations and you will see a clear pattern to them that is easy to remember.

The cosine rule can be used in non right-angled triangles to solve for all lengths and angles, provided the triangle has either:

● three given sides, or
● two sides and the included angle between those sides.

### Area of a triangle using angles

The general area of any triangle is determined by half the base multiplied by the perpendicular height:

Area = ½ × base × perpendicular height

With the aid of trigonometry, we can develop this into a very useful formula which ties in with angular measurement techniques used in surveying.

In Figure 3.10, where:

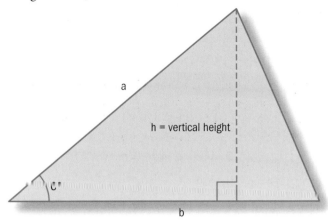

▲ Figure 3.10 Sine area rule

a = side a of the triangle
b = side b of the triangle
C = the given angle of the triangle between sides a and b.

The height (h) can be expressed using the angle and the sine ratio so that:

$h = a \times \sin C$

If we substitute that into '½ × base × perpendicular height', we arrive at:

Area = ½ ab sin C

## Worked example

An isosceles triangle has two sides, both 2500 mm long with an included angle of 38°.

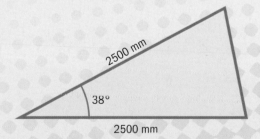

Calculate the area of the triangle in m² to 3 d.p.

Area = ½ ab sin C
    = ½ × 2.5 m × 2.5 m × sin 38°
    = 1.924 m²

# Knowledge check:
## trigonometric techniques

1 For the following non right-angled triangles, sketch and label them using the standard notation and find all the side lengths and angles.

Use the sine rule for **a** and **b**, and the cosine rule for **c** and **d**:

  **a**  A = 37°, B = 73°, b = 4.30 m
  **b**  A = 71°, B = 36°, a = 23.7 mm
  **c**  y = 11 cm, z = 15 cm, X = 55°
  **d**  $x$ = 62.8 mm, y = 41.2 mm, Z = 62°

2 A lean-to conservatory has a base which is 7.5 m long by 4 m wide. The glazed roof makes an angle of 36° to the horizontal, across the 4 m width. Calculate:

  **a**  the length of the sloping roof in m to 1 d.p.
  **b**  the area of glazed roof in m² to 1 d.p.

3 A vertical aerial mast RS is 21.8 m high and stands on ground that is inclined 13° to the horizontal. A steel cable connects the top of the aerial R to a point T on the ground 8 m downhill from S at the foot of the aerial mast. Using right-angle trig ratios, calculate the:

  **a**  length of the stay RT to the nearest 10 mm
  **b**  angle that the cable makes with the horizontal ground in degrees, minutes and seconds. (*Hint*: Take length TS to be the hypotenuse of a right-angled triangle for the first part of the calculation.)

4 The mast of a jib crane is 3 m tall and the stay is 4.8 m long. The angle between mast and the stay is 120°. Find the length of the jib.

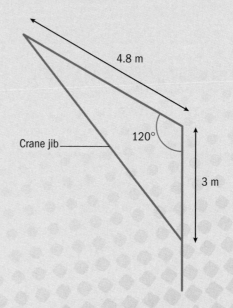

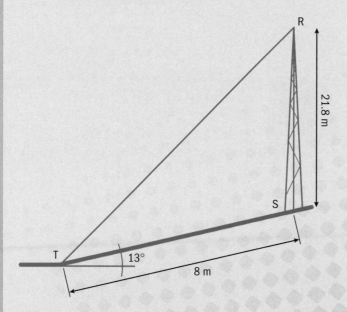

# Assessment practice

A symmetrical, timber roof truss is to be fabricated as shown below. All the dimensions shown relate to the centre lines of the timber members.

**Elevation on flat roof truss**

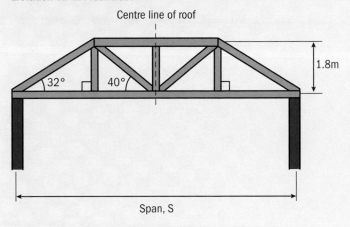

Therefore, you are required to calculate:

**a** the lengths of all the separate diagonal timber members, i.e. struts and rafters

**b** the span distance of the bottom member of the truss.  **P5**

A stainless steel luminaire or light fitting is to be designed for a new shopping centre. An elevation of the new fitting is shown below. The top of the fitting is a dome in the shape of a segment of a circle.

**Cross sectional elevation of luminaire**

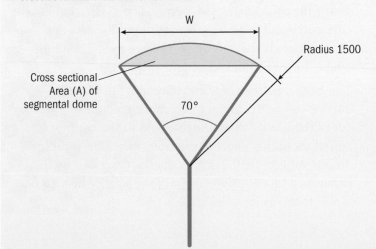

For costing purposes and fabrication processes, the building services engineer needs some information about the proposed fitting. Therefore, please provide calculations to find:

**a** the width (W) of the segmental dome

**b** the cross-sectional area (A) of the segmental dome.  **P6**

A church spire is being renovated. The timber structure is shown below. It is the shape of an eight-sided (octagonal) pyramid. In plan, the edges of the octagon are 3.2 m long and the vertical height of the spire is 8.4 m.

**View on octagonal church spire**

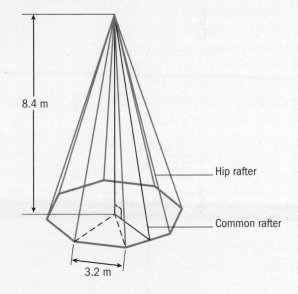

Calculate:

**a** the length of the hip rafter to be replaced

**b** the length of common rafter to be replaced

**c** the total area of the roof to be re-covered with copper sheet.  **M2**

(*Hint:* Consider the angles around the centre of the pyramid, at the base.)

# Graphical techniques

Graphs are most useful at showing how one measureable quality varies against another. For example, in Figure 3.11 the graph shows how the output of construction work varies over time between the UK and the East of England region. The horizontal axis is the time in years and the vertical axis is the percentage change of construction output. The steeper the line, the more quickly the percentage output rises.

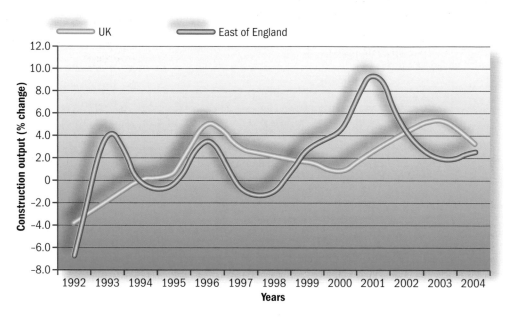

▲ Figure 3.11 Example of a graph

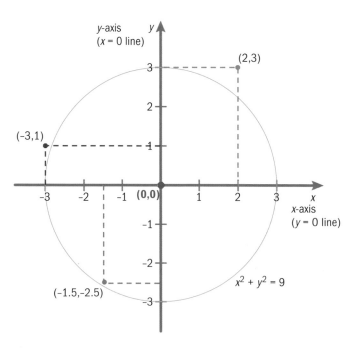

▲ Figure 3.12 Cartesian coordinate system

## Cartesian coordinates

All graphs are based on the Cartesian coordinate system. This system is used to fix a point by two numbers within a square grid. The numbers are called the *x-coordinate* and the *y-coordinate* of the point and written $(x,y)$. To define the coordinates, two perpendicular directed lines (the *x-axis* and the *y-axis*) are set up on the grid and equal scales are marked off on the two axes. The point where the axes cross is called the origin, O.

Using the Cartesian coordinate system lines (and curves) can be described by algebraic equations. These coordinates that fall on the lines will fit the algebraic equations of that line. For example, the circle of radius 3 units, and centre the origin, may be described by the equation $x^2 + y^2 = 9$; when $x = 0$, $y = 3$ and when $y = 0$, $x = 3$, as can be seen in Figure 3.12.

## Theory into practice

Figure 3.13 shows some examples of typical graphs. What do you think each of them might relate to?

The formula for a straight line is:

$$y = mx + c$$

where m is the slope or gradient of the line and c is the distance where the line cuts the y-axis, called the intercept.

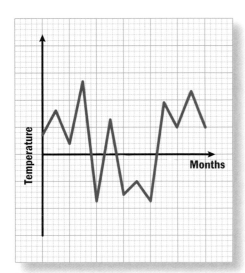

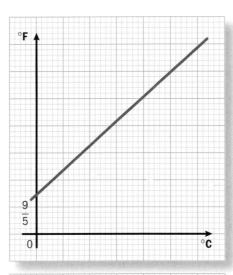

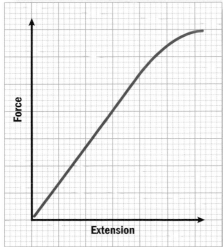

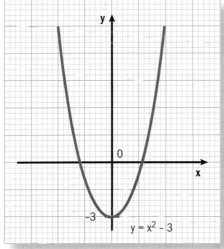

Figure 3.13 Types of graph

## Worked example

Let's look at the equation $y = 2x + 1$.

It has a positive gradient of 2 and cuts the y-axis at $y = 1$ because $m = 2$ and $x = 1$. This can be shown by plotting the graph, which means substituting values of $x$ into the formula and working out the corresponding value of y. These $x$- and y-values are coordinates which can then be plotted.

A good way to work out coordinates is to use a table. For example:

| x | 0 | 1 | 2 | 3 | 4 | 5 | |
|---|---|---|---|---|---|---|---|
| +2x | 0 | +2 | +4 | +6 | +8 | +10 | } ADD |
| +1 | +1 | +1 | +1 | +1 | +1 | +1 | |
| y | 1 | 3 | 5 | 7 | 9 | 11 | |

The graph can now be plotted:

We can clearly see that the line cuts the y-axis at $y = 1$, but the gradient is harder to see; but for every +1 unit we move to the right, the graph goes up +2 units. This is the gradient of the line and it equals +2. Thus:

$$\text{Gradient} = \frac{\text{Vertical distance}}{\text{Horizontal distance}} = \frac{+10}{+5} = 2$$

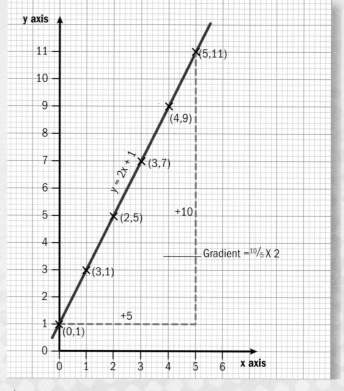

▲ **Figure 3.14 Straight line graph**

## Remember!

A line sloping up from left to right has positive gradient, while a line sloping up from right to left has negative gradient.

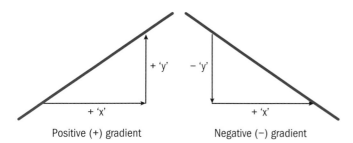

▲ **Figure 3.15 Gradients**

## ■ Practical use of graphs

In practical work involving construction materials and their properties, tests are often undertaken to understand and prove basic concepts. In some cases, we are trying to prove that there is a link between the variables

## Remember!

When choosing scales for graphs:

- Decide the range of $x$ values to be plotted.
- Show the scale of the axis clearly.
- It is not always necessary to show the origin (0,0).
- Fit all points on the graph.
- Show data as accurately as possible.
- The scales on the $x$- and $y$- axes can be different.

being measured. If there is a linear relationship, this can be shown by plotting a 'best-fit' straight line between the experimental coordinates and then working out the equation of the straight line that is produced.

## Worked example

An experiment to find the coefficient of friction between two types of metal cladding material produced the following results:

| Weight W (N) | 10 | 20 | 30 | 40 | 50 | 60 |
|---|---|---|---|---|---|---|
| Friction Force F (N) | 1.4 | 4.2 | 7.5 | 10.3 | 13.4 | 15.5 |

It is thought that both these are linked by a straight line equation F = m W + c. Show that this is the case and work out the equation of the experimental straight line.

**Step 1:** Plot the graph with F as the vertical axis and W as the horizontal axis.

**Step 2:** Draw the best fit line through the points.

**Step 3:** Work out the gradient by choosing two points on the line as far apart as possible, A and B. Construct a triangle as indicated and divide the vertical distance by the horizontal distance. Gradient is 0.28.

**Step 4:** Continue the line until it cuts the vertical 'y' axis and read off the value. This is the intercept c and in this example it scales off as –1.2.

**Step 5:** Collate all the data together and substitue into the standard form for an equation for a straight line.

F = m W + c
F = 0.28 W – 1.2

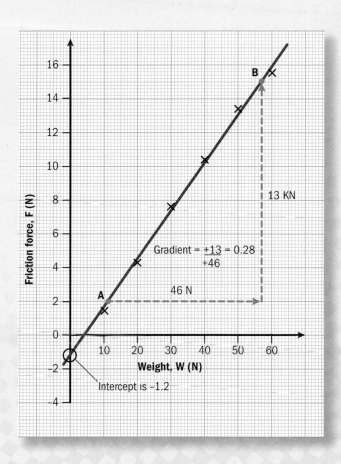

Unit 3 | Mathematics in construction and the built environment [129]

## Solving simultaneous equations using straight line graphs

We have already come across simultaneous equations in the first section of this chapter and have solved them using algebriac methods. This method using a straight line graph is often preferred by students as it is visual and uses graphical skills rather than numerical transposition.

## Worked example

Find the values of $x$ and y which solve the following simultaneous equations:

$x + y = 10$
$y - 2x = 1$

**Step 1:** Re-arrange the equations into the form

$y = mx + c$.
$y = 10 - x$
$y = 1 + 2x$

**Step 2:** Plot the graphs by choosing suitable values for $x$. This may take some time by 'trial and error' to get both lines to cross (see opposite).

**Step 3:** Find where the two lines cross, then read off the $x$- and $y$- coordinates of this point. This gives the solution of $x = 3$ and $y = 7$.

**Step 4:** As a check, substitute the figures back into the original equation to see if both equations balance, for example:

$x + y = 10$
$3 + 7 = 10$

Correct! And . . .

$y - 2x = 1$
$7 - 2 (3) = 1$

Also, correct!

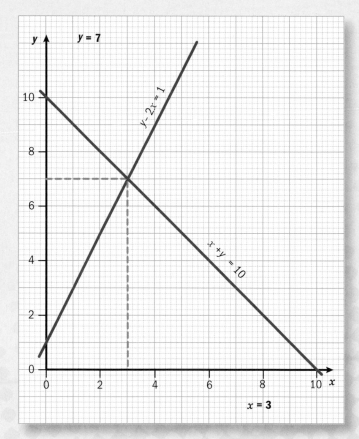

## Solving quadratic and cubic equations using graphs

In a similar way, more complex quadratic and cubic equations can be solved graphically.

### ■ Quadratic equations

## Worked example

Find the solution to the equation $x^2 - x - 2 = 0$.

**Step 1:** Set the equation to $y$ as the subject:
$y = x^2 - x - 2$

**Step 2:** Work out the y-coordinates for a range of selected $x$-coordinates by substituting them into the equation.

| $x$ | -3 | -2 | -1 | 0 | 1 | 2 | 3 | 4 | |
|------|----|----|----|----|----|----|----|----|----|
| $+x^2$ | 9 | 4 | 1 | 0 | 1 | 4 | 9 | 16 | |
| $-x$ | 3 | 2 | 1 | 0 | -1 | -2 | -3 | -4 | ADD |
| $-2$ | -2 | -2 | -2 | -2 | -2 | -2 | -2 | -2 | |
| $y$ | 10 | 4 | 0 | -2 | -2 | 0 | 4 | 10 | |

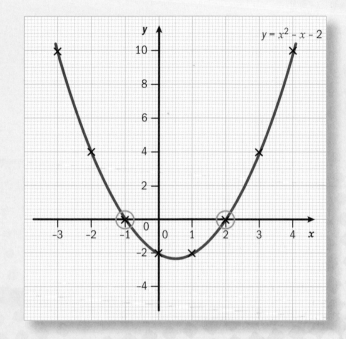

**Step 3:** Plot the graph and see where the line y = 0 cuts the curve $y = x^2 - x - 2$ to find the solutions to the equation.

The solutions are $x = -1$ and 2 when $y = 0$

**Step 4:** Check your answers by substituting back into the original equation.

When $x = -1$
$x^2 - x - 2$
$= (-1)^2 - (-1) - 2$
$= 1 + 1 - 2 = 0$

When $x = 2$
$x^2 - x - 2$
$= (2)^2 - (2) - 2$
$= 4 - 2 - 2 = 0$

Therefore, both values of $x$ are correct.

## Solving simultaneous linear and quadratic solutions

This graphical method can be used for more complicated problems, such as trying to find what values of x and y satisfy simultaneous linear and quadratic equations, like the one solved previously by algebraic methods on page 00.

The graphical method, like the previous simultaneous straight line worked example, involves plotting the two lines on the same graph and identifying where they cross, which will give you the solution.

## Worked example

Find, by plotting a graph, the solution to the two following simultaneous equations:

$y = 3x + 1$
$y = x^2 + 2x - 1$

**Step 1:** Plot a graph of the quadratic $y = x^2 + 2x - 1$

| x | -4 | -3 | -2 | -1 | 0 | 1 | 2 | 3 |
|---|---|---|---|---|---|---|---|---|
| $x^2$ | 16 | 9 | 4 | 1 | 0 | 1 | 4 | 9 |
| +2x | -8 | -6 | -4 | -1 | 0 | 2 | 4 | 6 |
| -1 | -1 | -1 | -1 | -1 | -1 | -1 | -1 | -1 |
| y | 7 | 2 | -1 | -2 | 1 | 2 | 7 | 14 |

Also on the same graph plot the graph $y = 3x + 1$ to the same scale.

| x | -4 | -3 | -2 | -1 | 0 | 1 | 2 | 3 |
|---|---|---|---|---|---|---|---|---|
| +3x | -12 | -9 | -6 | -3 | 0 | 3 | 6 | 9 |
| +1 | +1 | +1 | +1 | +1 | +1 | +1 | +1 | +1 |
| y | -13 | -8 | 5 | -2 | 1 | 4 | 7 | 10 |

**Step 2:** Identify where the two lines cross and read off the solutions for x and y at each of these points.

The graphical solution of this is shown opposite.

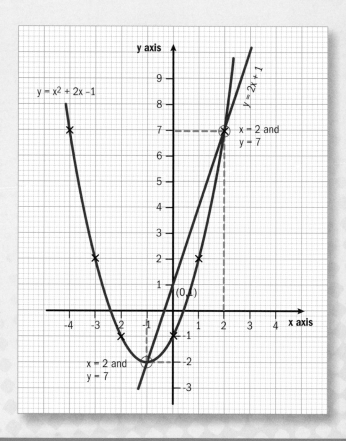

## Knowledge check:
### graphical techniques

**1** Study the following graphs and determine the straight line equation of each line.

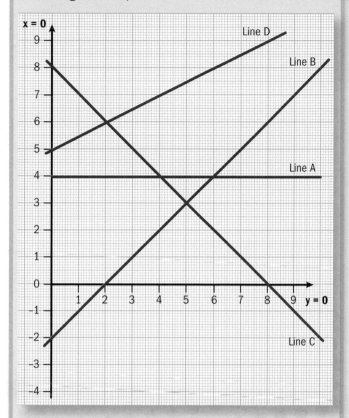

**2** Solve the following equations using the graphical method:

**a** Simultaneous equations $4x - 3y = 1$ and $x + 3y = 19$
Plot values of $x$ from 0 to 6 in increments of 1

**b** Quadratic equation $2x^2 + x - 3 = 0$
Plot values of $x$ from −2 to + 2 in increments of 0.5

# Statistical techniques

Statistics involve the collection, preparation, analysis, presentation and interpretation of data. The construction industry gathers and analyses data to enable it to make decisions on future plans, strategies and investments. The data may be collected from primary sources such as questionnaires or face-to-face interviews, or they may be taken from secondary sources such as published books or reports.

The National House-Building Council (NHBC), for example, collects information on new house prices, the size and structure of the house-building industry, house building by house type, and building times for new homes. Government departments with an interest in the built environment such as the Department for Communities and Local Government (DCLG) produce a wealth of housing statistics, for example monthly house prices, and annual land-use change and housing densities.

## Presentation of statistical information

Statistical information may be displayed in tabular or visual form. Diagrams are used to show the general pattern of the data including the maximum or minimum values and the spread of data across the different categories. The most commonly used diagrams are pictograms, pie charts, bar charts and, as we have seen previously, line graphs.

### ■ Pictograms

These use simple pictures to show the information, and hence make the presentation of results more visually engaging compared with other diagrams. Generally, pictograms are for straightforward 'whole or half number' statistics – see Figure 3.16, for example.

| House building company | No. of house sales 2004–05 |
|---|---|
| Brookway Homes | 🏠🏠 |
| Bestend Properties Ltd | 🏠🏠🏠🏡 |
| Countryfield Developers | 🏠🏠 |
| EFT Design & Build | 🏠🏡 |
| Surefire Property Investments | 🏠🏠🏡 |
| Key | |
| 1000 New Start Homes 🏠  500 New Start Homes 🏡 | |

▲ **Figure 3.16 Example of a pictogram**

Figure 3.17 Example of a multi-rim pie chart ▶

## ■ Pie charts

A pie chart is a circle divided into a number of sectors, each sector representing one category of the data. In order that the sizes of the sectors are in accordance with the values they represent, angles at the centre of a pie chart are determined as a fraction of a whole circle. Several variations of a pie chart can be used such as a simple pie chart, exploded pie chart, multi-rim pie chart, etc. Figure 3.17 shows a multi-rim pie chart which allows us easily to compare construction output by main industry subsector in the East of England region against the UK total in 2004.

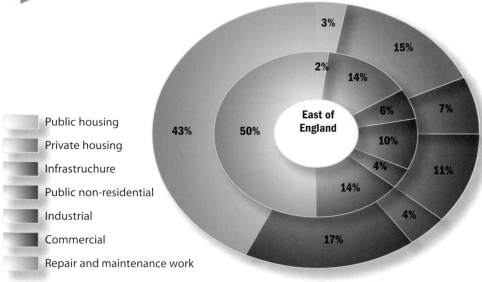

Public housing
Private housing
Infrastruchure
Public non-residential
Industrial
Commercial
Repair and maintenance work

## ■ Bar charts

Bar charts consist of data represented in the form of vertical or horizontal bars of equal width and are very common in construction. Their heights or lengths vary depending on the quantity they represent. A bar chart may consist of:

- single category bar charts
- multiple category bar charts
- sequential bar charts, such as Gantt charts that show progress against time.

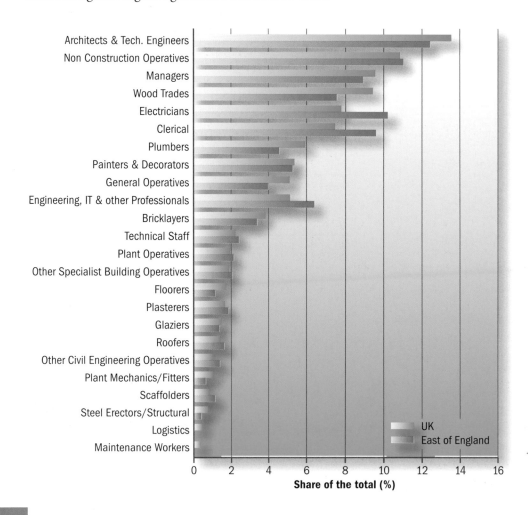

Figure 3.18 Example of a bar chart to show construction employment by occupation

**Discrete data** – only whole number values are possible for the data items and where intermediate values do not exist. For example, the point scores in a test or the number of people who do a particular job.

**Continuous data** – all values are possible for the data items, such as the time taken to perform a given construction task that is used in work study analysis.

**Frequency** – the total number of times a data value occurs. In Table 3.7 the 'No. of choices made' is the frequency.

**Mean** – the total of the numerical values is divided by the frequency.

**Mode** – this is the most popular from a given set of options or values. For example, when fitting out the kitchens of their new properties the house developer may offer the customer a range of four different styles of kitchen. In Table 3.7 the mode or modal average is 'American Shaker' because it is the most popular customer choice.

| Kitchen style | No. of choices made |
|---|---|
| Country Cottage | 1 |
| Urban Class | 3 |
| American Shaker | 8 |
| Regal Classic | 2 |

**Table 3.7**

**Median** – this is the middle value when all the data are arranged in ascending order. It is often quoted as the data value corresponding to 50% of the 'cumulative frequency' (see below). The spread of values about the median can be similarly expressed through the following terms:

– Lower quartile – the data value corresponding to 25% of the cumulative frequency.

– Upper quartile – the data value corresponding to 75% of the cumulative frequency.

– Inter-quartile range – the difference between the upper quartile value and the lower quartile value.

## ■ Cumulative frequency

A cumulative frequency distribution enables you to estimate the median average and the spread of values about the median. For example, Table 3.8 shows the test results of 30 applicants for a senior construction management post.

| Test score mark | Frequency | Cumulative frequency |
|---|---|---|
| 0–10 | 1 | 1 |
| 11–20 | 4 | 5 |
| 21–30 | 12 | 17 |
| 31–40 | 8 | 25 |
| 41–50 | 5 | 30 |
| | 30 TOTAL | |

**Table 3.8 Data summarised in a frequency table**

This table can be plotted as a cumulative frequency curve and in Figure 3.19 we can see that:

● the median score was 29, i.e. 50% or 15 applicants scored 29 or higher.

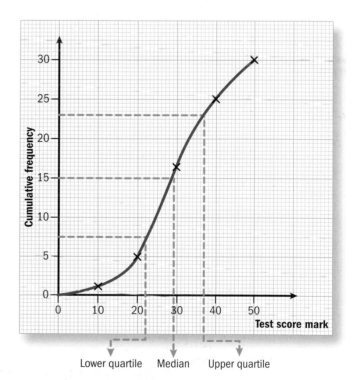

**Figure 3.19 Cumulative frequency curve**

- the lower quartile was 22.
- the upper quartile was 38.

Therefore, the spread of results about the median was 38 – 22 = 16 marks, i.e. 50% of applicants were within + or – 8 marks from the median value.

## ■ Mean

To find the arithmetic mean the total of the values is divided by the total frequency. For example, if a company is currently running five building contracts for a total sum of £3.5 million, then the mean value of contract is £3.5 million divided by 5 giving £0.7 million.

This method is fine for a small amount of data, but where the amount of data is large and has to be grouped together into more manageable 'classes', then a more complex method is required.

### Standard deviation

Working out the mean of a set of values is useful. However, it is also important to know how all the values distribute themselves about this mean. The simplest way is to calculate the 'range' of the values, where the range is the difference between the lowest and highest value in the set. However, this does not give an indication of where all the other values lie. Therefore, another method called the 'standard deviation' is often used to provide information on how tightly or loosely the values are clustered around the mean.

Let's look at an example. One hundred concrete cubes are crushed as part of a materials test. In an ideal world, the designed strength of the concrete would match exactly the value that was obtained in a test, and that would be the 'average' mean value. However, because of errors in the manufacturing process, there will be lower values than the designed strength and there also may be higher ones. If the debris of the 100 crushed cubes was piled up in a line from the lowest to the highest value, the shape of the heap of crushed concrete might look something like the blue line in Figure 3.20. What you are seeing is the physical spread of results for the whole set of cubes, and they form a 'bell-shaped' curve which is known as a 'normal' distribution of results.

If the test was repeated on another set of 100 cubes, but this time the mix was very closely supervised and

## Worked example

Fifty concrete blocks were tested for compressive strength (N/mm²) during a large concrete pour for a road bridge and abutments. The following results were obtained:

| 20 | 27 | 21 | 26 | 22 | 25 | 24 | 23 | 32 | 27 |
| 28 | 27 | 29 | 28 | 27 | 20 | 29 | 28 | 27 | 26 |
| 30 | 29 | 28 | 27 | 26 | 25 | 30 | 29 | 28 | 27 |
| 24 | 23 | 35 | 28 | 34 | 29 | 33 | 30 | 32 | 31 |
| 25 | 32 | 27 | 31 | 22 | 29 | 33 | 30 | 28 | 29 |

Calculate the mean strength based on the test results.

The amount of data is large, so to make it more manageable we separate it into six classes and 'tally up' the results that fall into these classes. We also need to determine for the 'class' group its mid point. The data is set out as follows:

| Class interval | Class midpoint (m) | Frequency (f) | m × f | |
|---|---|---|---|---|
| 19–21 | 20 | 3 | 20 × 3 = | 60 |
| 22–24 | 23 | 6 | 23 × 6 = | 138 |
| 25–27 | 26 | 14 | 26 × 14 = | 364 |
| 28–30 | 29 | 18 | 29 × 18 = | 522 |
| 31–33 | 32 | 7 | 32 × 7 = | 224 |
| 34–36 | 35 | 2 | 35 × 2 = | 70 |
| | | $\Sigma f = 50$ | $\Sigma(m \times f) = 1378$ | |

Mean strength =

$$= \frac{total\ (frequency \times class\ midpoint)}{total\ frequency} = \frac{\Sigma(m \times f)}{\Sigma(f)}$$

$$= \frac{1378\ \text{N/mm}^2}{50} = 27.6\ \text{N/mm}^2$$

∴ mean strength is 27.6 N/mm²

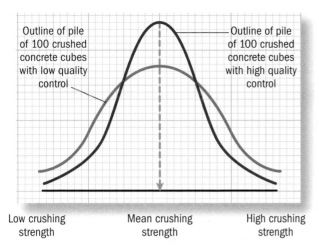

Outline of pile of 100 crushed concrete cubes with low quality control

Outline of pile of 100 crushed concrete cubes with high quality control

Low crushing strength

Mean crushing strength

High crushing strength

 **Figure 3.20 Normal distribution curve**

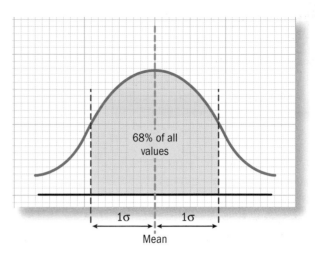

68% of all values

1σ     1σ

Mean

**Figure 3.21 Area under normal curve**

monitored, we would expect more of the concrete to be closer to the mean 'designed' value – and the outline of that pile of crushed cubes is shown by the red line in the diagram. Both these lines represent a 'normal' distribution graph, where the results fall symmetrically about the 'mean' average value and the area under the graph represents all the samples tested.

The measure of how the values cluster around the mean is called the 'standard deviation'. In 'normal' distribution, one standard deviation is the measured distance from either side of the mean such that 68% of all the values tested lie between these two measured distances. This can be seen more clearly from the normal distribution diagram in Figure 3.21.

## Remember!

Standard deviation is usually given the symbol, σ ('sigma'), and tells you how much your data values vary from the mean. It uses the same units as the original data and it is calculated by using all the data values in the set.

## ■ How to work out standard deviation

Standard deviation is worked out from the following formula but it is best to work it out in tabular form. Here is the simplified formula:

$$\text{Standard Deviation} = \sqrt{\frac{\Sigma f(x - x_m)^2}{\Sigma f}}$$

## Worked example

| Class strength interval [$N/mm^2$] | Class strength mid-point [$N/mm^2$] ($x$) | Frequency ($f$) | Deviation from mean ($x - x_m$) | Deviation squared ($x - x_m)^2$ | Total deviation squared $f(x - x_m)^2$ |
|---|---|---|---|---|---|
| 19–21 | 20 | 3 | –7.6 | 57.76 | 173.28 |
| 22–24 | 23 | 6 | –4.6 | 21.16 | 126.96 |
| 25–27 | 26 | 14 | –1.6 | 2.56 | 35.84 |
| 28–30 | 29 | 18 | 1.4 | 1.96 | 35.28 |
| 31–33 | 32 | 7 | 4.4 | 19.36 | 135.52 |
| 34–36 | 35 | 2 | 7.4 | 54.76 | 109.52 |
| | | $\Sigma 50$ | | | $\Sigma 616.40$ |

Let's continue with the previous worked example, where 50 concrete blocks were tested for compressive strength ($N/mm^2$) during a large concrete pour for a road bridge and abutments. We can now work out the standard deviation and see how the results are clustered around the mean value, which we worked out to be 27.6 $N/mm^2$.

**Step 1:** Tabulate the deviation from the mean ($x - x_m$), which is simply the difference between the mean value and the mid-point class value (as we are dealing with grouped data, we have to use the mid-point value), e.g. 20 – 27.6 = –7.6.

**Step 2:** Tabulate the deviation from the mean squared value ($x - x_m)^2$. This ensures that all values become positive, e.g. (–7.6)$^2$ = 57.76.

**Step 3:** Multiply the frequency by the 'deviation from the mean squared' to give the total for the class, e.g. 3 × 57.76 = 173 .28.

**Step 4:** Repeat for all other classes, then total up the final column to give a value of 616.40.

**Step 5:** Calculate the standard deviation where:

Standard deviation (SD)

$$= \sqrt{\frac{\Sigma f(x - x_m)^2}{\Sigma f}} = \sqrt{\frac{616.40}{50}} = 3.5 \text{ N/mm}^2$$

Therefore, we can conclude that the mean strength of these 50 concrete cubes is 27.6 $N/mm^2$ and that 65% of the whole sample fall within + or –3.5 $N/mm^2$ of this mean value. This gives a clear indication about the range of results and allows factual comparisons between other sets of results. In this case, the quality of the concrete can be monitored throughout the whole project.

## Knowledge check:

1  In each of the following examples select the most appropriate method of presenting statistical data from the methods studies:

   a  The causes of reported accidents on construction sites in the past year in order to compare the main categories.

   b  The labour, plant and materials used on six of a company's London construction sites to compare main areas of expenditure.

   c  The experimental results of tests on an insulation material to compare the thickness of the material with the temperature difference across the internal and external faces.

2  The following data was recorded on tests of a new metal alloy to be used in a system of internal metal studwork.

| Tensile strength N/mm² | Frequency |
| --- | --- |
| 101–105 | 5 |
| 106–110 | 9 |
| 111–115 | 19 |
| 116–120 | 25 |
| 121–125 | 18 |
| 126–130 | 4 |
|  | 80 |

Using this data calculate

a  the median strength to 1 d.p.
b  interquartile range
c  the mean stength to 2 d.p.
d  the standard deviation
e  Describe and compare the results in **b** and **d**.

## Assessment practice

Describe and compare with examples taken from current publications and reports the various different ways in which data in construction is presented. **P7**

Bestend Properties plc is carrying out a quality audit on two of its finished housing projects, 'The Lawns' and 'Meridan Waterfront'. The company produced a questionnaire for all new purchasers and asked them to rate their satisfaction with the quality of the build. The scores of the survey, out of a total of 100, are reproduced below for each of the developments, whereby the higher the score, the more satisfied are the residents.

By calculating the mean and standard deviation from the results to both surveys compare and contrast the quality of the build as perceived by the residents. **M3**

**Satisfaction questionnaire responses from residents**

| Satisfaction score | Response from 'The 'Lawns' | Response from 'Meridian Waterfront' |
| --- | --- | --- |
| 1–20 | 6 | 4 |
| 21–40 | 10 | 13 |
| 41–60 | 22 | 22 |
| 61–80 | 8 | 11 |
| 81–100 | 2 | 1 |

# Grading tips

**P1** Show clearly all your workings step by step one line at a time. All formulae used should be balanced with the LHS equalling the RHS.

**P2** Where calculations are done, clearly show in writing how you used your calculator and state any mental checks that you did.

**P3** To help you find the co-ordinates of the straight lines, construct a table to work out the values of y for a range of suitable x values. Draw a well labelled graph that fits on to an A4 sheet of graph paper showing clearly where the two lines cross.

**P4** The solutions should be set out methodically and clearly using the correct mathematical conventions. Units should be clearly stated to match the physical properties being calculated at each stage.

**P5**
**P6** You should provide solutions that clearly show how you have approached the problem and collated the data. This is best done by drawing a clear, labelled diagram. The solutions should be set out stage by stage and line by line with the correct units clearly stated throughout.

**P7** You need to choose a range of examples and describe the similarities and differences between them. Comment on whether you feel that the data was presented in the most appropriate form, and if possible carry out some checks on the figures supplied.

**M1** You will need to develop the quadratic equation for the area through a process of 'trial and error' and then solve it using your preferred method of solution. Remember to show all your workings.

**M2** You should extract data from this problem in a methodical way using a number of relevant sketches that clearly show how you broke down the problem into more manageable parts.

**M3** Working independently, and using knowledge of averages and standard deviation techniques, comment on the results received from the survey about the home buyers' satisfaction with their purchases. Justify your comments with evidence from your statistical calculations.

**D1** You will need to demonstrate your analytical understanding of the other solution methods of solving a quadratic equation and will need to draw suitable conclusions from the results obtained and comment on any variations.

**D2** You need to demonstrate an analysis of the accuracy and rounding of data and its effect on the calculated outcome, and make suitable conclusions that relate to this situation.

# Preparation for assessment

1  In a catalogue of plumbing supplies, the cost of elbow joints (e) and straight joints (s) is linked by the following two equations:

75e + 120s = £180

300e − 260s = £165

Solve this pair of simultaneous equations to work out the individual cost of each type of joint using an algebraic method, and then check your answers using a graphical method.   **P1 P2 P3**

2  a  A diagram of a hipped roof for a new block of flats is shown below. Calculate the length of the following roof members to 2 d.p. with the aid of Pythagoras' rule:

   • Common rafter

   • Hip rafter

   • Ridge board

   b  Calculate the angular pitch of the following roof members using right-angled trigonometry ratios. Give your answer in degrees and minutes.

   • Common rafter

   • Hip rafter

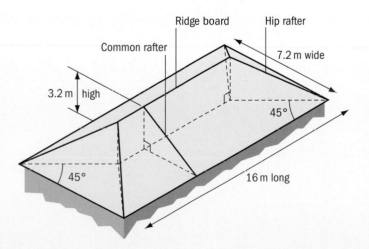

Ridge board    Hip rafter

Common rafter

7.2 m wide

3.2 m  high

45°

45°    16 m long

c  Calculate the volume of the internal roof space in cubic metres to 3 d.p. (Hint: assume the two hipped ends are oblique pyramids.)   **P4 P5 P6**

3  Using a selection of professional and trade journals available in your college library in a given week, carry out suitable research about the number and type of job vacancies for trainees in the following disciplines:

   • Architecture

   • Surveying

   • Civil engineering

   • Construction management

   • Building Services

From your research determine the following:

   a  The modal trainee position by discipline.

   b  The mean starting salary in each of the above disciplines.

   c  Produce a suitable visual representation of your findings for **a** by means of a pie chart, and for **b**, produce a suitably annotated bar chart.   **P7**

4  Write down a quadratic equation in the form:

$ax^2 + bx + c = 0$

where a, b and c are whole positive or negative numbers. Then solve it by one of the methods previously studied in this chapter. To check if you have achieved the right answer, solve the equation by using at least one different solution method.   **M1 D1**

5  An old inclined sewer pipe has silted up and is to be renewed. It runs south at a bearing of 180° for a horizontal distance of 140.5 m and rises at a steady gradient to a vertical height of 3.45 m. The sewer then turns and heads off at a bearing of 120° for a further horizontal distance of 74.8 m and rises another 1.75 m. This entire sewer is to be replaced by a new straight section of pipe.

a   Draw an appropriate sketch of the old sewer showing clearly all the dimensions given.

b   Find the length of the old sewer and hence the volume of silted-up material that it contains.

c   Calculate the length of the new straight replacement sewer pipe in metres and show this clearly on your diagram.

d   What approximations and limitation are linked to the solutions you produced in **b** and **c**?   **M2** **D2**

6   Explain clearly in writing what 'standard deviation' is and how it can be used to monitor the quality of manufactured materials such as the strength of manufactured cement.   **M3**

## Grading criteria: Unit 3

| To achieve a pass grade the evidence must show that the learner is able to: | To achieve a merit grade the evidence must show that, in addition to the pass criteria, the learner is able to: | To achieve a distinction grade the evidence must show that, in addition to the pass and merit criteria, the learner is able to: |
|---|---|---|
| **P1** use the main functions of a scientific calculator to perform calculations and apply manual checks to results **Assessment practice pages 94, 95, 141** | **M1** select and apply a variety of algebraic methods to solve linear, quadratic and simultaneous linear and quadratic equations **Assessment practice pages 95, 141** | **D1** independently undertake checks on calculations using relevant alternative mathematical methods and make appropriate judgements on the outcomes **Assessment practice pages 95, 141** |
| **P2** use standard mathematical manipulation techniques to simplify expressions and solve a variety of linear formulae **Assessment practice pages 94, 95, 141** | **M2** extract data, select and apply appropriate algebraic methods to find lengths, angles, areas and volumes for one 2D and one 3D complex construction industry related problems **Assessment practice pages 95, 125, 141–2** | **D2** independently demonstrate an understanding of the limitations of certain solutions in terms of accuracy, approximations and rounding errors **Assessment practice pages 95, 125, 141–2** |
| **P3** use graphical methods to solve linear and quadratic equations **Assessment practice page 141** | | |
| **P4** produce clear and accurate answers to a variety of problems associated with simple perimeters, areas and volumes **Assessment practice pages 119, 141** | **M3** use standard deviation techniques to compare the quality of manufactured products used in the construction industry **Assessment practice pages 139, 142** | |
| **P5** produce clear and accurate answers to a variety of simple 2D trigonometric problems **Assessment practice pages 125, 141** | | |
| **P6** produce clear and accurate answers to a variety of simple geometric problems **Assessment practice pages 125, 141** | | |
| **P7** describe and illustrate the use of statistics in the construction industry **Assessment practice pages 139, 141** | | |

# Science and materials in construction and the built environment

## Introduction

Science and materials technology is becoming increasingly important as the world's environment changes. It is now vital that we look after the planet, its resources and the pollution that we release into the environment. To achieve this, there have been developments, for example, in the increased thermal properties of housing, and commercial buildings, material recycling, sustainability and green technology.

Science now plays a part in technological developments that can save energy, make us become more efficient and extend the life of the resources we still have. Materials are developing to keep pace with these changes. The manufacturing processes involved in materials now has to encompass recycling for the future life of the material, the embedded energy contained within them and the effect on carbon emissions released to the atmosphere.

We need to feel comfortable in our homes and places of work and recreation. Many factors have to be taken into account when designing structures, including heating, lighting and ventilation. This chapter looks at materials used for construction and their engineering properties, which involves analysing the forces that are contained within them and predicting their value to enable a design to be safely constructed.

The life of a material is often of importance and the performance criteria for materials will be explored along with the manufacturing processes associated with some common construction materials. Finally, material properties together with their modes of failure and how this can be prevented will be analysed for a series of deterioration modes involving the elements of the weather and their exposure to these.

An understanding of science and materials can greatly educate us in the selection, use and properties of a material for incorporation into a design that is both aesthetic and efficient.

Do you think you would be comfortable living in a dark, damp house for six months of the year during winter?

How would you select modern materials to provide an efficient sustainable house of the future?

This unit is internally assessed by your tutor. A variety of activities is included in this unit to help you understand all aspects of science and materials used in construction.

After completing this unit you should be able to achieve the following outcomes:

1. Know the basic factors that affect human comfort and an acceptable range of values for each factor
2. Understand how forces act on simple structures
3. Know the performance criteria applicable to a range of vocationally relevant construction materials and the techniques used to produce such materials
4. Understand the properties of construction materials, how such materials deteriorate and the techniques used to prevent their deterioration

## Thermal and air quality

The human comfort within an internal environment has several variables that are inevitably linked together. Air quality is affected by how hot it is outside and inside your environment. Similarly, the amount of moisture that is present within the air will have an effect on humidity, which is linked to the amount of ventilation entering the environment.

Humans like to feel warm; our bodies maintain a core temperature on average of 37°C depending upon your metabolic rate. If the surrounding temperature drops below this, you feel cold; if it increases, then your body loses heat by sweating which evaporates and reduces your temperature. We live in a climate that has seasons which vary in average daily temperature over the course of a year, so there is no constant to design against. Houses now contain central heating to balance out these effects when the outside temperature is lower. Similarly, we have developed artificial cooling by air conditioning to cool the environment during periods of high temperatures.

The Earth is covered with a layer of gases that we refer to as the atmosphere. Air is made up of: nitrogen (N) (78 per cent), oxygen (O) (20 per cent), argon (A) (less than 1 per cent) and carbon dioxide ($CO_2$) (less than 0.5 per cent). The other ingredient is water vapour ($H_2O$), which is present within the air in varying amounts.

### Nature of heat

To understand the design of buildings in relation to human comfort, we need to look at some specific elements of heat.

### ■ The measurement of heat
#### Celsius temperature scale

Practical temperature measurements are usually made in degrees Celsius (°C). The lower point 0°C is fixed at the melting point of ice at a standard atmospheric pressure of 101.32 kN/m².

The upper point 100°C is fixed at the temperature of steam above boiling point at the standard atmospheric pressure. Normal design internal temperatures are taken as 21 degrees inside and –1 degrees outside on average but will vary from continent to continent with the conditions required.

#### Thermodynamic temperature scale

This is the basic scale of temperature and is measured in degrees Kelvin (K). The unit of thermodynamic temperature is the fraction of the thermodynamic temperature at the **triple point of water**:

$$0°C = 273.16 \text{ K}$$
$$100°C = 317.16 \text{ K}$$

### Remember!

Air quality is affected by any pollution that is released into the atmosphere. Smoke and exhaust fumes cause smog over some of the world's largest cities, which has a significant on breathable air quality.

### Key Term

**Triple point of water** The temperature and pressure at which the three known phases of a substance can exist. The triple point of water is the equilibrium point 273.16 K at 610 N/m² between the three phases of: pure ice; air free water; water vapour. It is one of the fixed points of international standard measurements of temperature.

The unit of Celsius temperature, the degree Celsius, is by definition equal in magnitude to the degree Kelvin. A difference of temperature may be expressed in Kelvins or degrees Celsius. The interval of 1°C is equal to the interval of 1°K. In practice, 0°C is taken as 273 K.

## ■ Quantity of heat

Heat is one of a number of forms of energy whose units are measured in joules (J) which is a measure of the work done. The rates of expenditure of energy or doing work, or losses of heat, are measured in watts (W). A watt is equal to 1 joule per second:

1 joule/second = 1 watt (1 J/s = 1 W)

## Remember!

Using one bar of an electric fire is equal to 1000 watts of electrical energy use to heat the element.

## Heat transfer

Heat energy is able to transfer from one mass to another in the following ways:

- Conduction – the passage of heat from molecule to molecule across a body, e.g. hot water in pipes.
- Convection – the bodily movement of a fluid, gas or liquid. Air expands on heating, thereby becoming less dense, and is forced upwards by cooler, more dense air taking its place underneath, e.g. radiator heat rises up and is replaced by colder air below.
- Radiation – the rays of heat travelling across a space, with or without matter being present, e.g. the heat from an infrared lamp or the sun's rays.

## Thermal comfort in terms of activity

The more active you are in the environment, the more heat you will give off. The rate at which this heat is generated (metabolic rate) will depend on several factors, including:

- your surface area
- age
- gender
- level of activity.

Generally, the older you become, the less heat you give off, and the heat output from females is approximately 85 per cent of the male equivalent.

Table 4.1 illustrates some heat outputs expressed in watts for various activities to illustrate what activity does to your heat output.

**Table 4.1 Typical heat output of an adult male**

| Activity | Example | Heat output |
|---|---|---|
| Immobile | Sleeping | 70 W |
| Seated | Watching TV | 115 W |
| Light work | Office | 140 W |
| Medium work | Factory, dancing | 265 W |
| Heavy work | Lifting | 440 W |

Source: Adapted from the CIBSE Guide (Chartered Institution of Building Services Engineers)

## Clothing

The amount of clothing that we wear generally depends on the season and affects our thermal comfort. In summer, we wear fewer clothes – the heating is switched off in our homes and the windows are often open for ventilation. In winter, we tend to wear some additional clothing to feel warmer indoors, particularly in older properties where there may be open chimneys, fireplaces and sash windows which do not seal effectively. The function of warm clothing is to trap a layer of warm air against your skin which heats up and makes you feel warmer, increasing your comfort.

The Chartered Institution of Building Services Engineers has categorised clothing in an attempt to produce an acceptable parameter to design from. This measures clothing in terms of a scale called a clo value. One clo represents 0.155 m² K/W of insulation to the body and typical values range from 1 to 4 clo. Table 4.2 illustrates how the amount of clothing you are wearing will affect the temperature of the room that has to be maintained.

Table 4.2 Clothing values

| Clo value | Clothing | Typical comfort temperature when sitting |
|-----------|----------|------------------------------------------|
| 0 clo | Swimwear | 29°C |
| 0.5 clo | Light clothing | 25°C |
| 1 clo | Suit, jumper | 22°C |
| 2 clo | Coat, gloves, hat | 14°C |

Source: Adapted from the CIBSE Guide (Chartered Institution of Building Services Engineers)

## Room temperatures

In order to understand how we maintain a steady temperature and comfortable thermal indoor environment, we first need to look at some basic scientific principles of materials. These are the resistance of a material to restrict heat, or the thermal conductivity of the material in passing the heat along.

## ■ Heat losses from buildings

In order to maintain a room at a comfortable temperature for humans, it must be provided with as much heat as is lost through ventilation and conduction through the fabric so that a balance is maintained. This optimum temperature will depend upon the use of the room and the ventilation will vary with the number of people present, the structural losses will depend upon the material used, the type of construction, the orientation of the building to the sun and the degree of exposure to rain and wind

## ■ Thermal conductivity (k)

This is the amount of heat loss in one second through 1 m² of material, whose thickness is 1 metre; with a one-degree temperature difference between the faces. The units are W/mK (watts per metre Kelvin).

▲ This thermal image shows heat loss from a house. The areas shaded red are where most heat is escaping

**Table 4.3 K value of materials**

| Material | K value (W/mK) |
|---|---|
| Asphalt roofing (1700 kg/m³) | 0.50 |
| Bitumen felt layers (1700 kg/m³) | 0.50 |
| Brickwork, exposed (1700 kg/m³) | 0.84 |
| Brickwork, internal (1700 kg/m³) | 0.84 |
| Concrete, dense (2100 kg/m³) | 1.40 |
| Concrete, lightweight (1200 kg/m³) | 0.38 |
| Concrete block, medium weight (1400 kg/m³) | 0.51 |
| Concrete block, lightweight (600 kg/m³) | 0.19 |
| Fibre insulating board | 0.050 |
| Glass | 1.022 |
| Glass wool, mat or fibre | 0.04 |
| Mineral wool | 0.039 |
| Plaster, dense | 0.50 |
| Plaster, lightweight | 0.16 |
| Plasterboard | 0.16 |
| Polyurethane (foamed) board | 0.025 |
| Rendering, external | 0.50 |
| Screed (1200 kg/m³) | 0.41 |
| Stone, sandstone | 1.30 |
| Timber, softwood | 0.13 |
| Timber, hardwood | 0.15 |

Source: Adapted from the CIBSE Guide (Chartered Institution of Building Services Engineers)

## ■ Thermal resistivity (r)

Thermal resistivity is the reciprocal of thermal conductivity, that is:

$$r = \frac{1}{K}$$

Resistivity is sometimes more convenient to use than conductivity for thermal conductivity of materials. The thermal conductivity (r) can often be obtained from a manufacturer's data sheet on the material.

## Air movement

Current building regulations dictate that air tests have to be undertaken upon newly constructed domestic and commercial buildings. These test their airtightness, which is linked to the heat loss through ventilation of the property. Draught seals have to be fitted to all openings to restrict thermal losses and assist the overall global picture.

Air movement locally within a room can cause certain problems. If the warm air entering a room is not mixed, then the room becomes hot nearer the ceiling and colder at floor level initially. This can cause discomfort to the occupants of the room. Secondly, a draughty room also causes discomfort when cold air passes over the surface of your skin – it raises the coating of hairs on your skin as the skin tries to trap warm air against its surface. The skin's hair follicles are also raised and you will shiver as a reaction to the sudden cold environment.

During the summer months in the UK, windows are opened for ventilation, which causes the rapid movement of air as you try to cool down the internal environment by causing movement across the surface of your skin.

## Remember!

Many older properties have open fireplaces that act as natural ventilation and cause air movement within the building.

## Humidity and ventilation

## ■ Relative humidity

Rather than quoting the actual humidity of the air in grams per cubic metre (g/m³) or in terms of pressure, it is more usual to quote the relative humidity, or percentage saturation, which is the criterion that affects human beings and other things to a greater extent than the actual humidity. Relative humidity is the percentage saturation and is defined as:

$$\frac{\text{Actual amount of water vapour present in air}}{\substack{\text{Maximum amount of vapour that can be held} \\ \text{at the temperature}}} \times 100\%$$

Humans are used to a relative humidity of between 40 and 60 per cent. More than this and we describe the air as being 'close', 'humid', etc. The temperature also feels a degree or two warmer if the air is humid, because we cannot perspire readily into an atmosphere with a high relative humidity. High humidity causes clothing to deteriorate and encourages the growth of moulds.

## ■ Heat loss due to ventilation

The natural ventilation of buildings, for example by open windows, results in the complete volume of air in a room being changed a certain number of times in one hour. Typical air change values are given in Table 4.4.

**Table 4.4 Air ventilation rates**

| Type of room | Air changes in 1 hour |
|---|---|
| Halls and passages | 1.0 |
| Bedrooms and living rooms | 1.5 |
| WCs and/or bathrooms | 2.0 |

The fresh air entering the room will need to be heated to the internal temperature of the room/building, so as not to cause a nuisance. This is calculated from the formula:

Volume of room × Air change rate × Volumetric specific heat for air × Temperature difference

This will give the number of joules required per hour which then has to be changed into watts in order to find the rate of heat loss. This is achieved by dividing the number of joules by the number of seconds in one hour, that is, 3600 seconds (60 × 60).

The volumetric specific heat capacity of air is approximately 1300 J/m³K and is considered a constant in this formula.

The rate of heat loss due to ventilation is calculated from:

$$\frac{\substack{\text{Volume of room/building} \times \text{Air changes per} \\ \text{hour} \times 1300 \text{ Joules} \times \text{Temperature difference}}}{3600 \text{ s}} = \text{Watts}$$

In heat loss calculations for buildings in most parts of the UK, the external air temperature during winter is assumed to be on average –1°C.

The design room temperatures in a building will depend on the purpose of the room, for example bedrooms and passages can be much cooler than sitting rooms. It is convenient when carrying out heat loss calculations to assume an average internal temperature of 19°C – this will give a temperature difference of 20°C between the inside and the outside.

## Condensation

Condensation is formed when hot, humid air meets a cold surface and condenses onto this surface forming droplets of water vapour. This needs to be avoided within the internal environment of a dwelling as it:

- can cause timber rot
- encourages mould growth on walls and windowsills
- produces cold spots
- produces high humidity
- causes corrosion to steelwork
- can wet insulation, reducing its effectiveness.

If condensation occurs in a cavity wall within the solid construction of a brick, it is named interstitial condensation.

## Acceptable parameters

### Remember!

*Standard units:*
Celsius: degrees
Thermal conductivity (k): Watts/metre Kelvin (W/m K)
Thermal resistivity (r): Kelvin/Watt
U-value = W/m² K

**U-values** is a complicated topic and you will need to refer to the Building Regulations Part L Conservation of Fuel and Power for guidance on the acceptable U-values that are required in today's modern sustainable designs.

## Key Term

**U-value** A measure of the rate of heat loss through a structure in that comparisons can be made between structures and values set by Building Regulations.

Ventilation is also clearly linked to the Part L of the Building Regulations that restricts the airtightness of modern structures. Forced ventilation has to be provided in the form of fans to bathrooms and cooking areas to reduce the amount of condensation produced.

### Calculating thermal resistances, surface resistances, U-values and heat loss

### ■ U-values

Part L of the revised Building Regulations provides a detailed guide to the application of U-values to new and existing structures, which is a complicated process and is outside the scope of this unit. We shall look at how an elemental U-value is calculated using the definitions explained above.

In order to calculate the U-value of a construction element, for example a wall, we need to establish the thermal resistances of the materials it is constructed with and add to this the internal and outside resistances. The U-value is then calculated using the following formula:

Thermal transmittance: the U-value is the amount of heat lost, in one second, through one square metre of a structure, when there is a one degree temperature difference between the air inside and the air outside. The units are: W/m² K.

The U-value for a structure is calculated from:

$$\text{U-value} = \frac{1}{R_T}$$

where $R_T$ is the total of all the resistances.

We shall now look at how to calculate these resistances for the materials using their 'k' values and their 'r' value.

### Thermal resistance (R)

The thermal resistance of a slab of building material can be calculated in two ways. In both instances, it is

essential that the thickness of the material is known and that the thickness is stated in metres.

## Worked example

Calculate the thermal resistance for 100 mm thickness of brickwork.

Assume the area of brickwork is 1 m².

Assume the temperature difference between the two sides of the wall is 1°C, thus 1 K.

## Remember!

Don't forget to specify the units for the thickness in metres. For example, if a wall is 100 mm wide, then this is 0.100m in this formula.

*Method 1: Using conductivity of material*

$$R = \frac{t}{k}$$

where  R = Thermal resistance for that thickness of material

t = Thickness of the material in metres

k = Thermal conductivity of the material

$$R = \frac{0.100 \text{ m}}{0.84} = 0.119 \text{ m}^2 \text{ K/W}$$

*Method 2: Using resistivity of the material*

$$R = t \times r$$

where  R = Thermal resistance for that thickness of material

t = Thickness of the material in metres

r = Thermal resistivity for that material

$$R = t \times r$$

$$R = 0.100 \times 1.19 = 0.119 \text{ m}^2\text{K/W}$$

### Surface resistances

The total resistance, R, to the passage of heat across a wall is built up from the resistance of the material r and at least two surface resistances which have to be taken into account in any U-value calculation. They are:

1   The inside surface resistance $r_{si}$
2   The outside surface resistance $r_{so}$

If there is a cavity present, the resistance of the cavity will also have to be included $r_{cav}$

Surface and cavity resistances are shown in Table 4.5.

**Table 4.5 Surface and cavity resistances**

| Typical internal surface resistance | 0.13 m²K/W |
|---|---|
| Typical external surface resistance | 0.05 m²K/W |
| Typical cavity resistance 5 mm – 19 mm cavity | 0.11 m²K/W |
| Typical cavity resistance 20 mm + cavity | 0.13 m²K/W |

The total resistance to the passage of heat is therefore calculated from:

$$R_T = r_{si} + \frac{t}{k} + r_{so}$$

where $R_T$ = Total resistance to the passage of heat
   $r_{si}$ = Internal surface resistance from the table
   $t$ = Thickness of the material in metres
   $k$ = Thermal conductivity of the material (W/mK)
   $r_{so}$ = External surface resistance from the table

**Remember!**

If you already have the material resistances from the manufacturer for its material thickness, then you can replace t/k with this R figure provided.

**Worked examples**

1   Calculate the U-value for a 102.5 mm thick brickwork wall.

102.5 mm thick brickwork $rsi + \frac{T}{K} + rso$

$$0.13 + \frac{0.1025}{0.84} + 0.05 = 0.30 \text{ (RT)}$$

$$\frac{1}{0.30} = 3.33 \text{ W/m}^2 \text{ K}$$

2   Calculate the U-value for the following cavity wall construction:

15 mm dense plaster finish to inside walls
100 mm concrete blockwork medium weight
85 mm wide cavity
102 mm wide facing brickwork

$$0.13 + \frac{0.015}{0.50} + \frac{0.100}{0.51} + \frac{0.085}{0.13} + \frac{0.1025}{0.84} + 0.05$$

$$= 0.13 + 0.03 + 0.196 + 0.654 + 0.122 + 0.05$$

$$= 1.182$$

U-value $= \dfrac{1}{1.182}$

$$= 0.846$$

**Remember!**

You will need to use the table of k values – see Table 4.3 on page 149.

## ■ Heat loss due to ventilation

### Theory into practice

Calculate the rate of heat loss due to ventilation for the building shown below. The number of air changes in one hour is 1.35. The bungalow measures 10 m × 12 m in plan and has a ceiling height of 2.4 m.

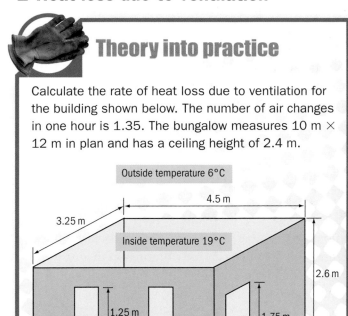

Outside temperature 6°C

4.5 m

3.25 m

Inside temperature 19°C

2.6 m

1.25 m

1.75 m

0.6 m

0.6 m

0.85 m

# Sound

### Nature of sound

Sound is an aural sensation caused by pressure variations in the air, which are always produced by some form of vibration, for example the movement of air as a wind.

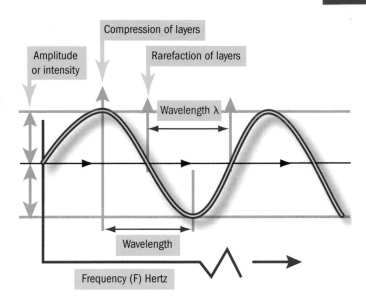

▲ Figure 4.1 Sound waves in still air

Compression of layers

Amplitude or intensity

Rarefaction of layers

Wavelength λ

Wavelength

Frequency (F) Hertz

Sound is a form of energy, which is transmitted through the air as a pressure wave (see Figure 4.1); these fluctuations may take place slowly, such as with atmospheric pressure change, or very rapidly as in ultrasonic frequencies.

Sound waves are like a ripple on a flat body of water. They generate out from the source and slowly dissipate until the flat surface resumes again. This ripple produces a series of compressions (compactions) and rarefactions where the air pushes from molecule to molecule transferring the energy pulse, as shown in Figure 4.2.

### Sound levels

Sound is commonly measured in decibels (dB), which are equal to 0.1 bel (B), which is a measurement that was

◀ Figure 4.2 Still air and the effect of sound waves in air

Molecules of air in still conditions (molecules are equally spaced)

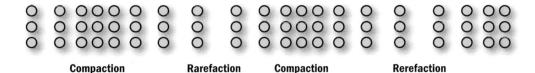

**Compaction**     **Rarefaction**     **Compaction**     **Rerefaction**

Molecules of air being displaced by a sound wave passing through them
- **Compaction** molecules of air pushed closer together
- **Rarefaction** molecules of air pushed further apart

too large to use with modern instruments. The Control of Noise at Work Regulations 2005 contains a set of decibel levels where hearing protection must and should be worn. These are:

- lower exposure action values:
  - daily or weekly exposure of 80 dB
  - peak sound pressure of 135 dB
- upper exposure action values:
  - daily or weekly exposure of 85 dB;
  - peak sound pressure of 137 dB (HSE, 'Noise at Work: Guidance for Employers on the Control of Noise at Work Regulations 2005').

Some typical noise levels:

- a quiet office – 40–50 dB
- power drill – 90–100 dB
- road drill – 100–110 dB ('Noise at Work: Guidance for Employers on the Control of Noise at Work Regulations 2005').

## Nature of hearing

The ear is divided into two parts: the outer and the inner ear. The outer ear contains the cartilage that forms the external ears and a tube that directs sound into the inner ear. The eardrum is at the bottom of this tube which vibrates when sound reaches it. Connected to the eardrum is a series of bones called the ossicles. A mechanism passes the sound as vibration via these bones into the inner ear. Here a liquid vibrates which contains tiny hairs which move with the sound vibration. When they move this is transmitted to the brain in the form of an electrical signal which is interpreted. Having two ears gives humans the ability to detect from where sound is coming in stereo.

## Measurement of noise

In selecting a scale to measure the intensity of sound it is necessary that the method chosen reflects the way in which the human ear responds to sound. Two important aspects need to be considered.

- The minimum sound that the ear can actually respond to, which is expressed as a value of 10 to the

power of $-12$ watts/m² @ 1000 Hz. The audible range for those with good hearing is 20 –20,000 Hz.

- The Weber/Fechner law suggests that the response of the ear to sound intensity is logarithmic, the bel (B) is the unit used to measure the energy of sound, the start point of the bel scale is 10–2 W/m².

A one bel increase in energy gives an intensity of $10 \times 10$ and so on.

## Noise control and sound insulation

### ■ Methods of sound insulation

For airborne sound, the best insulation is mass – thick, dense walls are not easily set vibrating. In theory, if the mass of a wall is doubled, it should give a sound reduction of 6 decibels; in practice, the actual reduction is about 5 decibels.

Sound deadening quilts can be used within the construction (e.g. fibreglass quilt in cavity walling) and soft finishes can be added to the finishes. Airborne sound can be prevented from travelling to other parts of the building by completeness of construction and air passages around windows and doors should be sealed. Lightweight partitions give little resistance to sound transmissions unless built in multiple layers. Glass is a very poor sound insulator – it has little mass and is thin.

### ■ Insulation for impact sound

A soft covering can be effective when used on the top of floors; the soft covering absorbs the sound before it gets onto the structure. In order to prevent the noise of machinery travelling through a structure, we use discontinuity within the construction in the form of anti-vibration pads.

## Noise transfer

### ■ Airborne sound

This starts off as a sound produced in air, for example a voice, musical instrument, loud speaker. It starts at the source and then travels through the air to the ear of the hearer. Airborne sound may travel in four ways:

- through any openings in the structure, e.g. small holes formed by removal of services
- by direct transfer through the structure
- by a structure vibrating like a drum skin and transferring the noise
- by direct transfer along the structure, e.g. air conditioning duct – this is called flanking transmission.

## Structure-borne sound

This originates by impact on the structure or on pipes within the structure. It may be footsteps on the floor above; the sound travels through the structure to be recreated in other parts of the building.

### Remember!

*Standard units:*
decibels (dB)
Hertz frequency (Hz)

## Velocity of sound

The wavelength multiplied by the frequency is equal to the distance travelled by the sound in one second (s). Thus:

Velocity = Frequency × Wavelength

$$V = f\lambda$$

where V = velocity

F = frequency (Hertz)

$\lambda$ = wavelength (metres)

### Theory into practice

Calculate the wavelength of sound in air at:

**a** 20 Hz

**b** 50 Hz.

The velocity of sound in air is 340 m/s.

The speed of sound in air is more or less constant, varying between 330 m/s and 340 m/s. In more dense materials sound travels faster, not because of greater density but because of the greater elasticity.

## Reverberation time

Often, especially in concert halls, we need to establish how long it takes for a sound to die away as we may need to increase the amount of absorption on the walls, floors and ceiling of the structure. The following formula tries to establish the time it takes for a sound to die by 60 db and is expressed as follows:

$$t = \frac{0.16\,V}{A}$$

where t = reverberation time in seconds

V = volume of room

A = the existing area of absorption in m$^2$

Basic calculation

Calculate the reverberation time for a hall which has a volume of 1500m$^3$ and the rear wall of 150m$^2$ is covered with sound absorbing curtains

$$t = \frac{0.16 \times 1500}{150}$$

t = 1.6 seconds

# Illumination

### Nature of vision

Vision is a sensation caused in the brain when light reaches the eye. The eye initially treats light in an optical manner, producing a physical image which is then interpreted by the brain in a manner that is psychological as well as physical, as many optical illusion games show you.

The eye contains a convex lens which produces an upside down image on the retina, which is at the back of the eye, of the object you are focusing on. When relaxed the lens is focused on distant objects. To bring it closer the eye muscles contract increasing the curvature of the lens. The amount of light entering the lens is controlled by the iris, a coloured ring of tissue, which expands and contracts with the amount of light present. This ring varies in colour between individuals.

The light energy falling on the retina causes chemical changes in the receptors which send electrical signals to the brain via the optic nerve. A large proportion of the brain is dedicated to processing this information. The initial information interpreted by the brain includes the brightness and colour of the image. The stereoscopic effect of the two eyes gives further information about the size and position of objects and enables us to judge distances.

## Simple colour rendering

### ■ Visible and non-visible light

Our eyes have the ability to detect colour. They contain three colour receptors: red, blue and green. These are mixed to create the colours that the brain interprets. When you split the white light from the sun into its primary colours using a glass spectrum you get the following seven colours: violet, indigo, blue, green, yellow, orange and red.

Ultraviolet (UV) light has wavelengths just less than those of violet light. It is emitted by the sun and other objects at high temperature. UV radiation keeps the body healthy but overexposure can damage skin and eyes. The Earth's atmosphere protects the planet from overexposure to UV radiation.

Infrared radiation has wavelengths slightly above those of red light. It can be felt as heat from the sun and other heated bodies.

## Need for daylight

Our body clock needs to see daylight in order to set our patterns of sleeping and awaking. People on night shifts have to reverse this trend with their work patterns. Daylight makes you feel good; a large bright sun feels both warm and appealing. Natural daylight does influence certain chemicals within our brains that resist depression and anxiety. People can suffer from a syndrome known as seasonal affective disorder (SAD). This occurs during the winter months when the sun is low in the sky and the levels of light are often obscured by clouds. Light boxes which mimic the sun's natural wavelengths and frequencies are used to produce artificial light to stimulate the brain's chemical balance.

Of course, the obvious need for daylight is to see! We can see in the dark, but our eyes are more attuned to daylight and not night vision. The eye is a remarkable tool that can detect a single torch beam over a mile away.

## Measurement of lighting

The lux (lx) is the unit of illuminance. It is used to measure the intensity of light and is used in modern light measurement meters. Table 4.6 illustrates some lighting levels in Lux.

Table 4.6

| Light source | Lux |
|---|---|
| Moonlight | Less than 1 |
| Brightly lit drawing office | 500 |
| Sunlight | 32,000–100,000 |

More commonly we buy our light bulbs in watts, which is electrical energy.

Standard unit:
Lux [lx]

## Acceptable parameters for natural and artificial light

Highly intense light can cause discomfort in the form of glare. The eye can detect a wide range of light levels, but vision is affected by the range of brightness visible at any one time. Glare is the discomfort or impairment of vision caused by an excessive range of brightness in the visual field. Glare can be caused by lamps, windows and painted surfaces being too bright compared with the general background.

- Disability glare is due to glare that lessens the ability to see detail. It does not necessarily cause visual discomfort.
- Discomfort glare is glare that causes visual discomfort without necessarily lessening the ability to see detail.

## ■ Daylight factors

The average British day taken from summer to winter is normally measured at 5000 Lux. To make sure that we can see reasonably well all year round using daylight within our homes, we need to check that a proportion of this 5000 Lux is entering our homes through windows and openings. A figure of 1–2 per cent is reasonable.

The CIE (*Commission Internationale d'Éclairage*) has produced the following formula in order to take into account the internal surfaces of the room that reflect light.

$$\text{Daylight factor at any point in room} = \frac{\text{Internal illuminance at that point}}{\text{External illuminance from unobstructed sky}} \times 100\%$$

### Worked example

Calculate the illumination in Lux at a desk in a room where there is a requirement for a 6 per cent daylight factor as this is a drawing office. The external bright sky has been measured at 7500 Lux.

$$DF = \frac{\text{Int. illuminance}}{\text{Ext. illuminance}} \times 100\%$$

$$\text{Int. illuminance} = \frac{7500 \text{ Lux} \times 6\%}{100}$$

$$= 450 \text{ Lux}$$

## Assessment practice

The interior designer of a housing development that you are working on has asked for some basic information before they can complete the design layout for the new house type coming onto the market. Provide the following:

**a** An identification of three factors that will affect human comfort in the new homes.

**b** How these can be measured.

**c** What would be typical acceptable values for each of the three factors? **P1**

Produce clear and accurate answers to a variety of calculations relating to human comfort in the internal environment.

**1** Calculate the U-value for the following construction:

15 mm plasterboard and skim
100 mm lightweight block

100 mm cavity filled with mineral wool
100 mm brickwork

**2** Calculate the illumination in Lux at a desk in a room where there is a requirement for a 4% daylight factor as this is a drawing office and the external bright sky has been measured at 5000 Lux.

**3** Calculate the reverberation time for a village hall which has a volume of 750 m³ and the rear wall of 80 m² is covered with sound-absorbing tiles. **M1**

Look closely at the factors that affect your human comfort (not just the three which we have explained above). Undertake an analysis of these and discuss how they interact both in quality and quantity, e.g. increase the amount of heat in a room and what effect does this have on quality and what other factors are concerned, e.g. humidity? **D1**

# Structural members

## Struts and ties

This part of a structure has a compressive force acting upon it. Newton's laws state that there must be an equal and opposite reaction and so the strut pushes against the compressive force. Figure 4.3 illustrates the strut working in position on a canopy roof. The weight of the roof is pushing down the strut which has to resist this and pass it on to the wall.

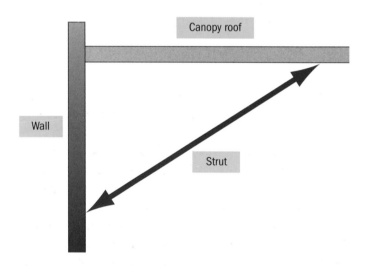

▲ **Figure 4.3 A strut**

Ties carry tensile forces and are stretched under this force by a pulling action. Figure 4.4 illustrates a TV mast which has wire ties to anchor it against the pulling force of the wind from each direction

## Beams and columns

Beams span between supporting walls. In spanning this distance, they have two forces exerting upon them – tension and compression – which are dealt with later in this chapter. A beam tends to sag when supported at its ends (see Figure 4.5). Beams tend to be deeper in cross-section than columns, and can be lightened by turning them into girders, which increases the depth and takes

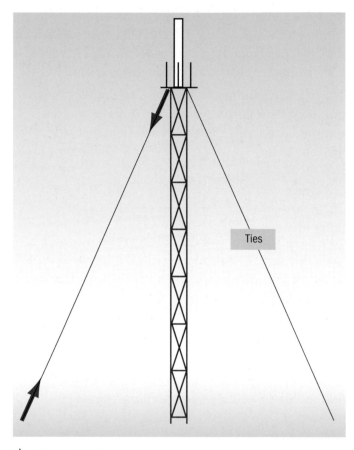

▲ **Figure 4.4 Ties**

out some voids within the webs. These are often known as vierendeel beams.

These are vertical beams in essence as they have the same 'I' section but tend to be squarer in cross-section than beams. They mainly carry a vertical load downwards to

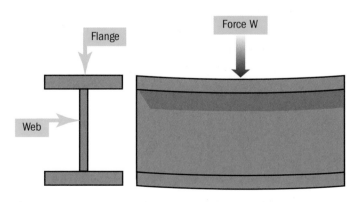

▲ **Figure 4.5 A beam**

the supporting foundation. Columns support beams are connected to them either by bolted or welded connections. Columns have to be considered structurally for slenderness; too long and thin and they may distort and bend under loading conditions. The beams hold the column into position at each storey. Columns can also form the vertical part of the portal frame as we shall explore under frames.

## Walls and frames

Walls can be classified as load bearing or non load bearing infill panels.

Load bearing walls take part of the building loads, which are shared with the frame, and are deemed structural elements as they carry a force safely down to the foundations. These types of wall tend to be solid in construction and use denser materials in their construction, and are often manufactured from solid brickwork or reinforced concrete

Non load bearing walls, as the name suggests, do not contain any structural strength, only the ability to hold themselves vertical. They are normally lightweight infill panels that are decorative, often constructed out of timber or lightweight blockwork.

A frame is a structure formed from many of the elements that we have discussed above. These elements can be arranged into many framed structures as follows by connecting them together.

- An arrangement of columns and beams that form grid skeleton structures.
- An arrangement of struts and ties and beams that form truss frame structures.
- An arrangement of columns and beams that form portal frame structures.

Frames can be complex structures to design and analyse structurally. It is often best to leave this to a structural engineer. Software programs make the process easier but require interpretation of the results.

# Loadings

## Dead loads

These are loads that have no live application. The majority of dead loads are those that remain static or stationary.

They do not change during the normal operation of the building. The dead weight of the structure is a dead load, or the self-weight of a beam; it is neither added to nor taken away during the life of the building.

## Imposed loads

These are the live loadings which are sometimes called dynamic loads as they are added to and taken away with the use of the building. People are a good example of this. If you fill a theatre, you increase the live loading on the floors. Live loads are difficult to consider in structural design as factors of safety have to be considered with their level of force. Water storage tanks again vary with the weight of water within them; similarly, full filing cabinets exert a point load on the floor structure.

## Wind loads

These are loads exerted from the wind and can be classified as a live load. Similarly, snow and rain need to be considered under this category as they too exert a live load on a structure. Wind loads vary with the location and exposure of the structure within the UK. The western side of the UK tends to receive prevailing wind loads. The leeside of a hill will also have less wind loading than the prevailing side. With structural design, buildings have to be anchored against the uplift created by the force of the wind and made stiff enough to resist distortion from wind pressure against one face.

# Forces

Force may be defined as: 'That measurable and determinable influence tending to cause motion of a body' (*OED*).

Sir Isaac Newton defined force as: 'The product of the mass of the body and the change of rate of velocity caused by the application of the force.' As Newton discovered, all objects on the earth are held down with the force of gravity. At sea level, this gravitational acceleration can be measured at 9.81 metres per second ($m/s^2$). So all objects are weighted down with this force which has a measurable size of 9.81 times its weight. Therefore, the units of force can be expressed as:

Weight of an object in kilograms $\times$ 9.81 m/s²
= 1 Newton (N)

1000 N = 1 kg/N

## Coplanar forces

These types of forces exert their force in one plane, that is, they act in an invisible layer as indicated in Figure 4.6, where the forces upwards act in the same plane as the force downwards. They can be concurrent or non concurrent.

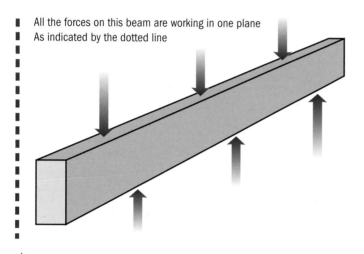

- All the forces on this beam are working in one plane
- As indicated by the dotted line

▲ Figure 4.6 Coplanar forces

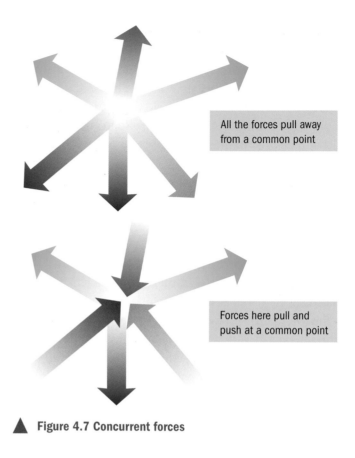

All the forces pull away from a common point

Forces here pull and push at a common point

▲ Figure 4.7 Concurrent forces

## Concurrent and non-concurrent

Concurrent is a collection of two or more forces that join at a common point of intersection. They can either pull away from a common point or point towards it, as the Figure 4.7 illustrates. Each arrow represents a force.

Non-concurrent is simply a mixture of forces that are in no format or do not intersect at a common point, as shown in Figure 4.8. They consist of a number of forces or vectors whose magnitude would involve great effort to try to calculate in structural design.

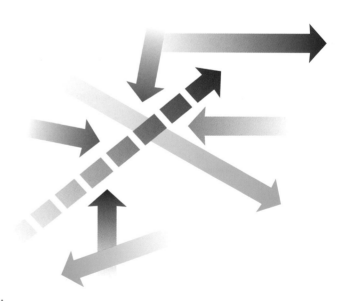

▲ Figure 4.8 Nonconcurrent forces

# Load configurations

## Point loads

These are a load that acts at a particular point. Figure 4.9 illustrates a simple beam upon which point loads act on the top of the beam; for example, these could be items of heavy machinery, water tanks or aerial masts on a roof. Equal to these point loads are the end reactions on the beam that must push upwards with equal force to place the beam into **equilibrium**.

## Key Term

**Equilibrium** This is where all the forces are balanced. For example, forces up equals forces down and forces clockwise equals forces anticlockwise. A structure will then not move or fall down.

## Uniformly distributed

These are forces that are considered in design terms to be evenly placed along a structure such as a beam. They can be considered as the live loads of a building such as people, furniture and the self-weight of the structure. It is far easier to design on this basis as people and furniture move around a building. Figure 4.10 illustrates how this force is represented.

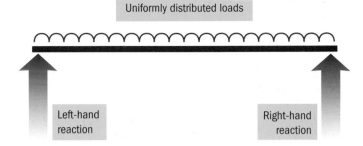

▲ **Figure 4.10 A simple beam with a uniformly distributed load upon it**

# Stresses

## Compression, tension, bending and shear

Compression is formed when a vertical force, for example, pushes down on a cube. The fibres within the cube have to push back with an equal force to resist being crushed and deforming under the load – see Figure 4.11. Compression and tension are often found within the same structure, such as a beam.

The fibres within the material in Figure 4.12 are being torn apart under the tension force shown by the arrows and have to resist this to avoid being torn apart

A force that causes bending is known as a bending moment. In order for a structure to be in equilibrium, anti-clockwise moments must equal clockwise moments.

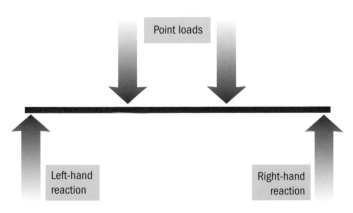

▲ **Figure 4.9 A simple beam with two point loads upon it**

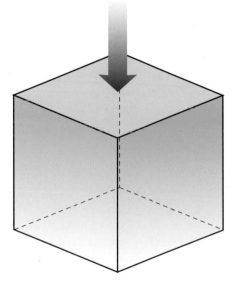

▲ **Figure 4.11 Compression**

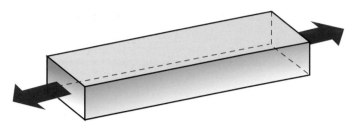

▲ **Figure 4.12 Tension force**

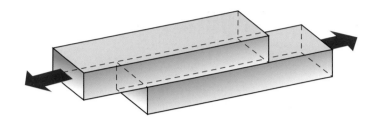

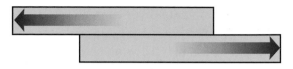

▲ **Figure 4.14 Shear force**

Figure 4.13 illustrates this. If you tied a piece of string, the length of which would be L, to the force and point A and then applied the force, it would rotate clockwise about point A. To counter this, the wall has to restrain the end of the beam with a downward reaction force at A equal to force F in an anti-clockwise direction.

Bending moment = Force × Distance acting

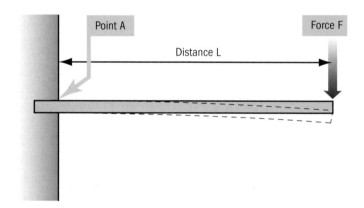

▲ **Figure 4.13 Bending moment**

With shear force, the two forces are pulling apart the two pieces which are held together by welding or bolted connection. The bolts or welds are being put under shear stress and will break across their width, shearing off at that point between the two pieces of structure – see Figure 4.14.

# Calculations

## Stress

When a member is subjected to a force of any type, the fibres of the material transmit the load from section to section throughout the length of the structural member. Such a system of internal transmission of these forces is termed stress.

The intensity of stress is defined by the following formula:

$$\text{Stress} = \frac{\text{Force}}{\text{Area}}$$

The units used to describe stress are: N/m²; kN/m²; N/mm²; kN/ mm²

where N = Newtons; kN = kiloNewtons.

### Worked examples

1   A steel tie with a cross-section measuring 25 mm by 25 mm is subjected to an axial pull of 100 kN. Calculate the normal tensile stress.

$$\text{Stress} = \frac{\text{Force}}{\text{Area}}$$

$$\frac{100 \text{ kN}}{25 \text{ mm} \times 25 \text{ mm}} = 0.16 \text{ kN/mm}^2$$

2   A concrete cube, of sides 200 mm is tested in compression; the failing load was 650 kN. Calculate the normal compressive stress at failure.

$$\text{Stress} = \frac{\text{Force}}{\text{Area}}$$

$$\frac{650 \text{ kN}}{200 \text{ mm} \times 200 \text{ mm}} = 0.02 \text{ kN/mm}^2$$

## Strain

When an item of a structure is loaded by a force and is placed under some measure of stress, some changes in its properties are bound to take place. This change may be dimensional in its length or section or shape. An object placed under such changes is said to be in a state of 'strain'.

As the bar is pulled an increase in its length occurs as the dotted area indicates

▲ **Figure 4.15 Tensile strain**

The effect of load (force provided by loading the member) is therefore to develop in the fibres of the member both stress and strain simultaneously.

The conventional way of expressing strain is to relate the changes in a particular dimension to the original value for that dimension. There are three types of different strain:

- Tensile strain – the material is being stretched, as Figure 4.15 illustrates. A force is pulling from both ends of the bar which is stretching the bar by an amount indicated by the dotted lines.
- Compressive strain – this is where the object has a force which is compressing or crushing the member and a reduction in length occurs as indicated by Figure 4.16, where the force applied from the top has compressed the cube to the dotted line.
- Shear strain – as you can see from Figure 4.17, the force from the left has pushed the anchored cube to the right causing shearing strain as it distorts out of shape.

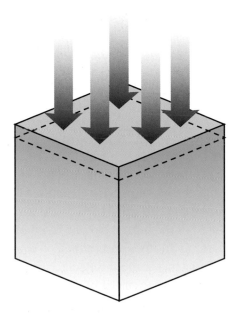

▲ **Figure 4.16 Compressive strain**

Strain is calculated using the following formula:

$$\text{Strain} = \frac{\text{Extension or reduction in length}}{\text{Original length}}$$

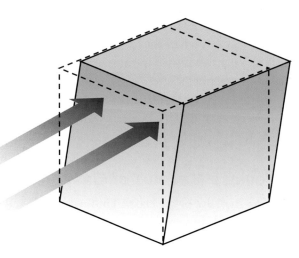

▲ **Figure 4.17 Shear strain**

## Worked examples

1. A steel bar 1.25 m long was subjected to a tensile force of 150 kN and extended by 1.5 mm. Calculate the strain which took place.

$$\text{Strain} = \frac{1.5 \text{ mm}}{1250 \text{ mm}} = 0.0012$$

### Remember!

Always use the same units above and below the formula and note strain has no units!

2. A 100 mm cube of timber was test loaded so that the compressive strain was 0.0014. Calculate the reduction in length that took place.

$$0.0014 = \frac{\text{Reduction in length in mm}}{100 \text{ mm}}$$

Therefore, reduction in length $= 0.0014 \times 100$
$= 0.14 \text{ mm}$

## ■ Elasticity

If you take a rubber band and stretch it under load and then release this load, the rubber band returns to the original properties it started with. Similarly, in the above diagrams when the loading condition is released, all the structures return to their original dimensional shape and characteristics. Most of this recovery is complete for most materials, as long as the load does not exceed each material's elastic limit, which varies between materials.

## ■ Young's Modulus of Elasticity

This is a measure of the elastic limit we mentioned above. Most materials return to their original dimensions. However, if their elastic limit is exceeded, then the material permanently deforms when the stress is removed.

This measurement of stress is termed the elastic limit. Many materials used in construction are elastic and it is useful to study the relationship between stress and strain. Young's Modulus of Elasticity starts to measure the relationship between stress and strain and is expressed as the formula below. This is known as the Modulus of Elasticity or Young's Modulus. It is denoted by the symbol 'E'.

$$\text{Modulus of Elasticity (E)} = \frac{\text{Direct stress}}{\text{Direct strain}}$$

*Standard units:*

Strain has no units quantity, thus the units used to express Young's Modulus are the units of stress, e.g. N/mm², kN/mm².

Strain is a dimensionless quantity, having no units, thus the units used to express Young's Modulus are the units of stress, e.g. N/mm², kN/mm².

These are used to build into a structural design an element of margin for over engineering. This over engineering is used to extend life expectancies,

## Worked examples

1  In a tensile test on a 9 mm diameter steel bar, a load of 20 kN caused an extension of 0.072 mm on a 50 mm length of bar. Assuming that the limit of elasticity had not been reached, calculate the value of Young's Modulus.

$$\text{Stress} = \frac{\text{Force}}{\text{Area}} = \frac{20 \text{ kN}}{\pi r^2} = 0.314 \text{ kN/mm}^2$$

$$\text{Strain} = \frac{0.072 \text{ mm}}{50.00 \text{ mm}} = 0.00144$$

$$\text{Young's Modulus (E)} = \frac{\text{Direct stress}}{\text{Direct strain}}$$
$$= \frac{0.314}{0.00144}$$
$$= 218.05 \text{ Kn/mm}^2$$

2  Calculate Young's Modulus in compression for a timber beam 150 mm × 150 mm in cross-section, which reduced in length by 0.015 mm on a timber test for a 1250 mm test sample, when a load of 35.8 kN was applied.

$$\text{Stress} = \frac{\text{Force}}{\text{Area}}$$
$$= \frac{35.8 \text{ kN}}{150 \times 150}$$
$$= 0.00159 \text{ kN/mm}^2$$

$$\text{Strain} = \frac{0.015 \text{ mm}}{1250 \text{ mm}} = 0.000012$$

$$\text{Young's Modulus (E)} = \frac{\text{Direct stress}}{\text{Direct strain}}$$
$$= \frac{0.00159}{0.000012}$$
$$= 132.5 \text{ kN/mm}^2$$

for example in aircraft design, and to allow future adaptation and change of use of a structure. A factor of safety (FoS) is the equivalent of a 'What if?' margin that can be used in the future. No one batch of materials will be the same as another and so the FoS compensates for these inconsistencies, including deterioration of the material over the lifespan of the building.

The FoS is simply a number that can vary depending on the material and the circumstances in which it is used, by which we divide the ultimate (failing) stress of the material to give the permissible working stress.

## Worked examples

1.  The tensile strength of a bar is 395 N/mm². If the maximum permissible stress is 145 N/mm², calculate the factor of safety

    $$\text{Factor of safety} = \frac{395 \text{ N/mm}^2}{145 \text{ N/mm}^2} = 2.72$$

2.  A concrete beam is required to have a permissible stress of 14 N/mm², with a factor of safety of 3. Calculate the ultimate compressive stress of the concrete.

    $$\text{Factor of safety } 3 = \frac{\text{Ultimate compressive stress}}{14 \text{ N/mm}^2}$$

    Ultimate compressive stress = 3 × 14 = 42N/mm²

## Worked examples

Calculate the left and right reactions.

If we start at the left-hand reaction:

Anti-clockwise moments = Clockwise moments

RR × 11 m = 100 kN × 8 m + 50 kN × 4 m

RR × 11 m = 1000 kN/m

$$RR = \frac{1000 \text{ kN/m}}{11 \text{ m}}$$

RR = 90.91 kN

Similarly, if we start at the right-hand reaction:

Anti-clockwise moments = Clockwise moments

100 kN × 3 m + 50 kN × 7 m = RL × 11 m

650 kN/m = RL × 11 m

$$RL = \frac{650 \text{ kN/m}}{11 \text{ m}}$$

RR = 59.09 kN

Check RR+RL = sum of loads

59.09 + 90.91 = 150 (50+100)

correct

## Simple beam reactions for point loads

Figure 4.18 illustrates a simply supported beam with reactions at each end left and right and two point loadings of 50 and 100 kN. We shall calculate the value of the end reactions. Before undertaking this calculation, we need to recap some of the basic laws associated with this type of structure:

* The sum of the forces down equals the sum of the forces up.
* Anti-clockwise moments equal clockwise moments

## Simple beam reactions for uniformly distributed loads

Figure 4.19 is a simple uniformly distributed load; the total load is calculated on the beam and is deemed to be acting at the centre of the beam.

If we start at the left-hand reaction

Anti-clockwise moments = Clockwise moments

RR × 8 m = (10 kN/m × 8 m) × 4 m

RR × 8 m = 80 kN × 4

$$RR = \frac{320}{8} - 40 \text{ kN}$$

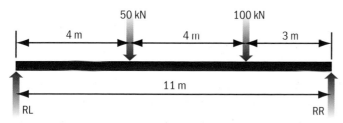

RL = Reaction Left
RR = Reaction Right

▲ **Figure 4.18 A supported beam**

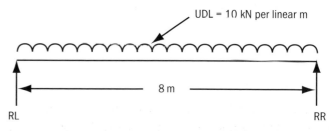

▲ **Figure 4.19 A uniformly distributed load**

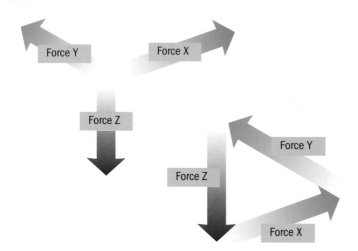

▲ **Figure 4.20 Triangle of forces**

If we divide the total weight by two, then this should equal the end reactions, which it does. Therefore RR = RL.

# Graphical methods

## Triangle of forces

This is a useful rule that can be used when a force can be represented by three sides of a triangle. For example, in Figure 4.20 the weight is being pulled down by gravity but is held by the two ties holding it in position. As long as the three forces are balanced or in equilibrium, then they can be represented by a triangle. Any unknowns can be identified by scaling the sides of the diagram.

## Parallelogram of forces for simple frames

When two forces act from a known point they can be represented graphically into a parallelogram by drawing in the resultant diagonal. This diagonal represents the combined force of the original two forces. Figure 4.21 illustrates the stages of drawing this out.

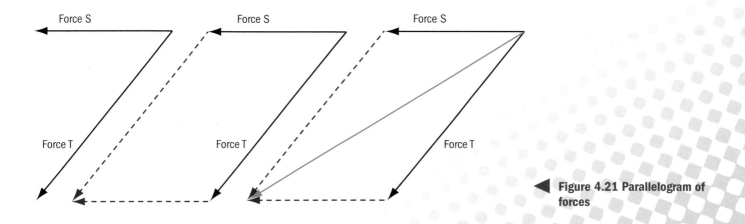

◀ **Figure 4.21 Parallelogram of forces**

# Assessment practice

The company you work for has recruited a structural engineer and you have been asked to work as this person's assistant. They have decided to test your knowledge of structures and have asked you to answer the following descriptions with a definition (what it means) and where it would appear in a structure under load.

**a** Shear

**b** Tension

**c** Compression

**d** Stress

**e** Strain

Predict the simple structural behaviour from the following:

**a** A steel portal frame is overloaded at the bolted joint with the column.

**b** A concrete lintel only has an end bearing of 50 mm each end above a window.

**c** The amount of stress that a concrete foundation can take is 30 N/mm². You know that a future loading will be 50 N/mm². What will happen to the concrete?

Produce clear and accurate answers to the following problems involving simple structures under load:

**a** A tie rod 25 mm diameter is subjected to a pulling force of 200 kN.

**b** A concrete foundation 600 mm × 600 mm × 600 mm supports a force of 50 kN spread evenly over its surface. What is the stress in the concrete?

**c** A steel bar 1.50 m long was subjected to a tensile force of 125 kN and extended by 1.25 mm. Calculate the strain that took place.

**d** Predict the value of the end reactions for a UDL beam 10 m long with a UDL of 50 kN per metre.

# Criteria for specification

## Fitness for purpose

Materials are normally specified by a quality standard, either a British Standard, a European standard or any other recognised body. This measures a known '**fit for purpose**' against an agreed standard that is recognised worldwide, so that the same product can be purchased globally to the same specification.

## Key Term

**Fit for purpose** A material must be able to be used in the context of the design. For example, glass in windows is required to let light through; any other material would not be appropriate.

Obviously, there are occasions when a substandard material is fitted to a structure; this may be a temporary repair or an inclusion without the owner's knowledge. Substandard materials obviously have no guarantees.

## Visual appearance

In design, the visual appearance of materials means a lot to the designer or architect. Visual appearance can also be linked to the texture of the materials used. Light plays an important part in appearance with reflectance and shadows that can alter a building appearance during the day or time of year. Aesthetics is important to humans – we like things that are good to look at, and the more attractive they are, the more willing we are to purchase them, for example a house. Brickwork is a good example, where appearance can be altered by the use of coloured mortar in the joints which makes walls much more attractive to the eye. Greener, less dense materials are now rapidly developing for the market which is moving away from the heavy construction materials that we have used for thousands of years.

## Costs

Budgetary control of projects is always a consideration in material specification and selection. If a project is over budget, then material specifications are changed to lesser quality ones in order to reduce costs.

There are two ways of looking at material costs:

- Do you spend efficiently now and incur higher maintenance costs in the future?
- Do you spend more on quality against the returns on low maintenance costs in the future?

Quality also has a relationship with cost; you get what you pay for. Higher quality materials cost more, but if they can be afforded at the initial stage, this will save money in the long-term life of the project.

## Resistance to degradation

Wear and tear on materials is linked to cost, quality and often density of the material. For example, high traffic areas, such as school corridors, require dense materials to the walls. Degradation can occur as a result of:

- vandalism
- wind – excessive gusts
- the action of rain
- frost – due to freezing of water
- sunlight – harmful UV rays
- age of the material
- air pollution – acid rain.

Design plays an important part, especially with regard to water run off on a building, for example ensuring that weathering drips are placed in the right place to avoid staining on external brickwork. Material selection must take into account the location of the material and the usage of the environment surrounding it.

## Ease of installation or use

A material that is complicated and requires skilled trades people to install it will obviously prove expensive in its use. For example, glass curtain walling requires specialist design and installation. The key to the extensive use of a material is its ease of installing, the reduction in wastage as a result of installation and the use of semi-skilled labour to install it. Materials tend to follow trades, for example bricklayers lay bricks, joiners deal with timber products, etc. Coupled with the ease of installation must be the ease of maintenance in the future. How easy will it be to replace a material that requires remedial works through damage needs to be considered at the selection stage of the design. A material may be cheaper but incur massive financial costs when it has to be replaced at the end of its life or during accidental damage replacement.

## Environmental implications

Green issues are now a major issue in the selection of construction materials, especially in housing construction. The amount of **embedded energy** that is contained within the material must be carefully considered along with the amount of carbon that has been released during manufacture.

## Key Term

**Embedded energy** This is the amount of energy that has been used to produce the material and is often expressed in terms of how much carbon has been released into the atmosphere during its manufacture and transport.

Environmentally friendly products that are renewable or contain a percentage of recycled materials should be considered over materials that contain none in order to reduce the effect of global warming. Timber products are a prime example as the renewal of timber locks up

carbon, produces oxygen as a by-product and it can be regrown over and over again.

## Sustainability and recycling potential

A material must now encompass sustainable elements in that it should be produced with regard to the environment so that it does not use up valuable resources. Timber products are great examples of sustainable materials that have little impact on the environment, can be grown relatively quickly and their waste products can be recycled into other timber engineered products.

- Cedar boarding used as a cladding material to the external faces of houses is an attractive, sustainable and cost-effective method of providing an environmentally friendly product.
- Green planted roofs can be used as an alternative instead of using finite resources. Green roofs live and breathe and in urban areas provide a green environment to relax in.
- Older materials produced from demolition such as bricks and concrete can now be crushed and graded to provide hardcore fill to make up levels. Steel can be recycled back into the production process by melting down and reforming.

## COSHH considerations

The Control of Substances Hazardous to Health (COSHH) Regulations 2002 must be considered with regard to:

- chemicals used in the manufacture of materials
- the use of chemicals to treat materials
- the chemical additive part of a material.

Chemicals such as solvents are steadily being replaced by water-based products, for example water-based gloss paints. Solvents harm the environment both in production and use in modern products. Care should be taken to ensure that the manufacturer's data sheet is read and, if required, a chemical replaced with one that produces less harm to the environment.

There are a number of products that require careful control for inclusion within buildings. Asbestos is now banned due to the harm fibres cause when inhaled.

Some foam insulation products require trained operatives to install them.

## Compatibility

Some materials are incompatible with each other. For example, certain metals when they come into contact and are then combined with water react to give galvanic corrosion. The only way to prevent this reaction is to apply a surface finish to one of the metals. Removal of water is another control method that can be used to prevent the reaction, so the metals might be used internally rather than externally.

### Remember!

To find out if two metals are likely to react with each other, check the anodic index, which is a chart of metals. The closer together the metals are on the index, the less likely there is to be a reaction. Selecting metals far apart can cause reactions.

# Production and manufacture

## Limes

Lime is an additive that is added to mortars and plasters to make them more workable and easier to spread. Lime mortars were used for many years before the modern plasticisers were introduced. Lime washes were used to paint the outside of houses to give the walls a white appearance.

The raw material is excavated from a quarry by selecting suitable limestone rocks of the correct quality and transported to the processing factory, where it is crushed down into a finer material, by two crushing processes. The limestone and dolomite are then fired in a kiln where a chemical reaction turns it into quicklime at 900°C. The resulting material is then graded and processed into various types of lime and finally stored in silos for bulk delivery or bagged as a product.

## Cements

The constituent raw materials in cement are limestone or chalk mixed with clays and fine sands. These are excavated in mass from quarries using large excavators and hauled to a manufacturing plant. The location of the cement works will depend on whether the cement uses chalk or limestone as its raw material. Limestone is broken up by crushing or, if a chalk process, by a water wash mill. Both these separate processes are then combined with clay slurry and passed into a ball mill. The slurry is fed from large storage tanks into a kiln which is a long rotating tube. The cement materials are heated and make their way down the kiln as a reaction takes place and cement clinker is formed. The product is cooled and stored where it is ground into a fine powder – Portland cement – and stored in silos, where it is either bagged or bulk delivered.

## Aggregates

Aggregates can be two types: crushed or uncrushed. The basis of both is that they are excavated from the earth and processed. Crushed aggregates are excavated from rock which is crushed, graded and stockpiled before use. Gravel aggregates are excavated from water-deposited beds, and may require washing to remove any contaminants.

Aggregates are used as:
- large boulders for coastal defence systems
- the basis for concrete manufacture
- the basis for road tarmacadam
- a decorative landscape material
- a drainage trench filter material and pipe bedding
- fine aggregate sand for mortars
- hardcore fill to make up levels.

## Concrete

Concrete is made up of several constituents:
- Water – this must be free from any contamination.

- Fine aggregates – the sands and fine gravels that fill the small voids within concrete.
- Coarse aggregates – the larger 20 mm diameter aggregates.
- Cement – this provides the strength and binding agent.

## ■ Additives

The design of concrete is very complex, and you will need to refer to the 'Design of Normal Concrete Mixes' for a detailed explanation of this process. Briefly, the raw materials are mixed within batching plants from specialist suppliers. Various strengths of concrete are available and depend on the variations in the mix and the use of the concrete, for example roadways or foundations. The process of the hardening of the concrete is through the hydration of the cement, where the cement reacts with the required amount of water that has been added and hardens over a period of 28 days to reach its design strength. The categories for specifying concrete vary with use and you should refer to a supplier's website for information on this aspect.

Various additives can be combined with the concrete to make it do different things, for example self level, delay setting and increase waterproofing.

### Remember!

Concrete slump is a measure of the workability of concrete so it can easily be poured and moved. This is normally specified by the engineer.

### Gypsum plasters

These are manufactured from gypsum rock which contains calcium sulphate. When this rock is heated at low temperatures, it breaks down and can then be processed. Quantities of rock are excavated and taken to crushers that reduce gypsum to a fine powder. This is then heated and water driven off to produce various grades of plaster.

After a final grinding, the product is packaged into bags. When this material is mixed with water it sets hard.

Gypsum products can be used in several ways:
- as a plaster to cover walls
- combined into a plasterboard material
- used within gypsum floor screeds
- as plaster mouldings'

### Remember!

Workability is the key to using plasters as they will start to set from the moment water is added and mixed. A great deal of skill is required in their application.

### Timber

Timber can be classified into two categories: softwoods and hardwoods.

Hardwoods differ from softwoods in that they contain two types of cell: those that transfer sap and those that provide strength to the tree. Hardwoods such as oak, beech, ash and walnut take longer to grow. Softwoods include Douglas firs, many of which are grown in Scandinavia and Russia.

Timber gains its strength from the direction of the grain – splitting across the grain is much stronger than down the grain. Timber has been used in buildings for thousands of years. The production of timber stems from managed forests where selected mature trees are cut and processed within a saw mill. At this stage, the timber is wet containing high moisture contents. Air or kiln drying of the timber reduces its moisture content and greatly adds to its strength. Various timber products can then be produced from the dried timber when its moisture content drops below 20 per cent.

Because of the inconsistency of timber it has to be stress graded for different uses, such as:
- floor joists
- ceiling joists

- roof rafters
- hip rafters
- roof trusses manufacture.

**TRADA** literature illustrates the various timber grades and their use and the typical spans that timber can be used for.

## Key Term

**TRADA** The Timber Research and Development Association.

## Metals

There are many metals used in construction, for example:

- mild steel reinforcing bars
- stainless steel wall ties
- lead roof coverings and flashings
- mild steel lintels
- structural steel frames
- galvanised roof straps.

The main metal is mild steel, and we will look at its manufacture in detail. The UK steel industry uses two processes for the manufacture of steel: the arc furnace which is powered by electricity and the basic oxygen converter. The raw materials used to produce steel are molten iron, coke and fluxes.

The arc furnace process uses cold materials to start with. A vessel is charged with scrap steel which contains a lot of recycled materials. The vessel lid is closed and electric probes are dropped down inside. When the power is switched on an electric arc forms which produces heat. This melts the mixture; other metals are added as required to produce the correct quality steel. Oxygen is blown into the vessel to purify the steel. The secondary process forms the steel again into the final product.

This basic oxygen converter process uses molten iron which has been produced in a blast furnace. Molten iron is poured into a vessel along with some scrap steel and a lance blows pure oxygen through the mixture. This

drives off any impurities, which float on the surface as a slag that is then removed by scraping it from the top. The pure steel is then taken to be processed into its solid form on ingots, billets or continuously poured into its final product and rolled into shape during a secondary process. This whole process takes about 40 minutes.

## Paints

The production of paints is a complicated chemical process. Paints consist of many ingredients, such as:

- solvents – these are used to thin the paint but are now being replaced by water
- driers – to increase the speed at which paint dries
- pigments – added to produce a variety of colours in a powder form
- binders – the main ingredient that binds and holds together to produce the quality finish.

These are mixed in varying quantities to produce a variety of paints, including:

- gloss paints
- emulsions
- two-part epoxy paints
- lacquers
- varnishes
- stains.

Paints are normally stored in cans or drums until use and can be sprayed or painted by brush or roller onto surfaces.

## Bricks

For thousands of years, people have been manufacturing bricks, from the mud brick pyramids to the present day. In the UK, the basic raw materials are clays which vary in colour and are the principal ingredient of the brick. Clay is excavated using a shave cutter that works along a face of clay cutting it and then transporting it by conveyor belt to the process plant. Here the clay is processed so it can be moulded or extruded. Extruded bricks are cut by wires from a continuous length of extruded clay.

After processing, the bricks are dried in air and stacked ready for firing in a kiln. This firing process hardens the brick and gives it its unique colour. Various applications of sand can be added to the surface faces of the brick to produce a variety of colours. Wire-cut bricks and moulded bricks produce different textured faces. When the firing process is complete the bricks are stacked randomly to produce brick packs that are evenly distributed in colour, and finally shrink wrapped for transportation.

## Plastics

'Plastic: Any of various complex organic compounds produced by polymerisation, capable of being moulded, extruded, cast into various shapes and films, or drawn into filaments used as textile fibres' (*Webster's Dictionary*).

The manufacture of plastics is a chemical-based process. It starts with the conversion of crude oil into a variety of chemical products, for example petrol, oils and gases. Ethane and propane are derived from this process using a cracking tower and the resultant is ethylene and propylene. A catalyst is added and the resulting powder is a polymer-based substance. Various additives are then added and the mixture is melted and formed into pellets. These are then sold to other manufacturers for extrusion into many plastic products, such as upvc window frames, or high pressure injection moulding into any shape.

It can be said that plastics use a finite resource of oil, and their production is less than environmentally friendly, but they are an economical solution and can be recycled into other fibre products. Many of the commercial items we consume contain a high level of plastic.

## Liquids (especially water)

The production of water for use in construction is the same as for drinking water as the quality must be ensured before it is mixed with materials. Water is normally obtained from boreholes, rivers and reservoirs. It requires treatment to remove particles from it and has chlorine added to prevent microbiological decay. It is then pumped under pressure around the UK by a pipeline distribution system.

## Assessment practice

Describe the performance criteria that the following construction materials must meet to provide a minimum standard specification:

**a** A facing brick in an outer wall

**b** Cement mortar

**c** Concrete foundations

# Properties

Properties of materials vary between materials. Below we describe the common ones that can be applied to many of the current construction materials that we use on today's modern buildings. The only one not listed is dimensions of materials. We now use the metric system for the **modular coordination** of buildings such that materials fit into the dimensions specified by an architect or a designer

## Key Term

**Modular coordination** The grid lines on which the designer lays out a building. For example, a window opening must work in brick courses to avoid excessive cutting of the material.

## Strength

This is the amount of stress or tension or weight that a material can endure before it starts to deform and lose its dimensions or shape. Strength varies between materials:

- Concrete is great in compression but very weak in tension and will require reinforcing with steel bars to prevent its failure by cracking.
- Timber is strong when pressured across the grain as its fibres have to be torn across but is weak along its grain and can be split easily.
- Steelwork copes very well in tension and compression and shear, but loses strength within a fire and will eventually buckle and fail if it is not fire protected.
- Brickwork and blockwork are relatively strong on compression but can be pushed over laterally and rely on a strong bond between the material and the mortar that holds the bricks and blocks together.

- Glass requires much support to help it resist the action of the force from the wind. Secondary support is required when large panes are used; these also have to be toughened by a heating process to prevent them shattering.

## Elasticity

As we have seen, this is the amount of stress that a material can take before its elastic limit is reached and the material permanently distorts causing dimensional change. Plastics are very elastic by their nature. Concrete does flex, but it is not an inherent elastic material. Glass can bend in large panes and return to its original shape. Steelwork is very good at retaining its shape under load and has a high elastic limit.

## Porosity and water absorption

Porosity refers to the pores or air pockets that are present within a material and can be linked closely to the density of a material, which means the heavier a material per unit volume, the fewer pores there are within the material. Lightweight blocks have an **air entraining agent** within them that captures many tiny bubbles of air which act as an insulator within the block. Therefore, the lightweight block is a very porous material.

## Key Term

**Air entraining agent** This forms bubbles within the concrete which capture air that is used to insulate the concrete from extreme cold.

Porosity of a material is normally tested by weighing its mass and soaking it within a container over a set time period. Reweighing its mass will provide a measurement of how much water has been absorbed into the material. This can then be expressed as a percentage.

Obviously, high density materials may not be porous, for example steel work does not absorb any moisture and so can be said to be waterproof. It can be used to hold water or prevent its passage, an example being steel roof-sheeting panels.

## Thermal and moisture movement

Thermal movement of materials from one season to another must be taken into account when designing buildings with certain materials. Expansion and contraction joints must be provided for in brickwork and concrete where large areas of these materials are used. These joints allow for the expansion of the material during summer and its contraction during winter months. This is especially true in climates that experience a wide variety of temperatures. All materials expand with heat and contract with cold; some have high rates of expansion such as copper.

Moisture movement is especially obvious in timber-based products, which are **hydroscopic**. This can cause expansion and deformation when dried timber is placed into unheated houses and then the heating is switched on. The result is shrinkage and distortion of the finished product. Internal materials that absorb water and move prevent cracking, for example plastering shrinks as it dries out and cracks along junctions with other surfaces.

## Key Term

**Hydroscopic** The ability of timber to easily absorb moisture from the air.

## Thermal and electrical conductivity/resistivity

Thermal and electrical resistivity or the ability to restrict the passage of heat and electricity are closely linked. For example, copper is a very good conductor of electricity and is used in electrical wiring because it can be bent; similarly, it is low in thermal resistance and can easily

transmit heat and is used for hot water pipework distribution. Plastics are a non-conductor of electricity but also have low resistivity thermally and again can be used for hot water distribution. As such, they are used effectively to insulate the copper conductors in electrical cabling.

Any metal has the ability to conduct electricity; the only other element that can conduct this energy is water. Great care has to be taken with electrical wiring to ensure that metal materials are not made live to the touch where wires pass through them.

## Thermal transmittance (U-values)

As we saw earlier on in this chapter, U-values are a measure of how thermally efficient a construction is to the passage of heat. The lower the U-value, the more resistant is the material to let heat out through the fabric. The more air that is trapped within the construction, for example a wall cavity filled with insulation quilt, the more thermally efficient a structure becomes. Since a U-value is based on the resistance of a material and the temperature difference across the structure, it is a good measure of thermal efficiency.

## Durability

Durability may be a material's resistance to surface scratching or abrasion, or how hard wearing it is, or refer to the life cycle of a material in use. Denser materials will have much more hardwearing properties than lighter materials. Glass is very durable against the weather, is scratch resistant, but is prone to breakages if forced suddenly. Brickwork is very durable as long as the joints are maintained and a good quality facing brick is used. Concrete has a long life span but weathers poorly becoming dirty from the atmosphere.

## Workability

This property is best expressed using the product of concrete as an example. Concrete has to be workable in that, if it were not, then it would not be able to be poured from the cement mixer as it would be too stiff. Concrete has to be workable so it can be **compacted**.

Secondly, it would not level itself when placed into shuttering and would be useless. Concrete has to be able to flow and many factors affect its workability, including:

- the amount of water within its mix, i.e. the water/cement ratio
- the amount of cement within the mix
- the inclusion of any plasticisers
- the shape of the aggregate.

## Key Term

**Compacted** Concrete is vibrated by mechanical means or by hand to remove all the air bubbles which would weaken it when it has dried out.

## Density

This, as we have seen, is how heavy something is for the volume it occupies, and can be expressed as:

$$\text{Density} = \frac{\text{Mass}}{\text{Volume}}$$

### Remember!

The unit of density is kg/m³.

The standard against which other materials are judged is: 1 m × 1 m × 1 m of water, that is, 1 m³ weighs 1000 kg. So the density of water is represented as '1'.

## Specific heat capacity

The specific heat capacity of a substance is the number of joules of heat energy taken in or given off when the substance is heated or cooled by 1 Kelvin without a change of state, for example melting or expanding, such as water or ice. Thermal capacity is a measure of how much of a structure can store heat energy and can be expressed as:

Thermal capacity = Mass × Specific capacity

The quantity of heat required to produce a change in temperature of TD in a body of mass M with specific heat capacity (C) is given by:

Quantity of heat = MC TD

where M = mass (kg)

C = specific heat capacity

TD = temperature difference.

## Viscosity

Viscosity or thickness is the resistance of a liquid or substance to flow. Water has a very low viscosity and easily flows under the influence of gravity. Liquid plastics and silicones have a high viscosity and are able to be moulded before setting occurs, for example window frame sealants. Viscosity of construction materials is important in the vertical and horizontal plane with regard to gravity. Movement joint sealants then require different viscosities in their use and application. Viscosity is, of course, related to workability; the thicker a product becomes during its application, then the harder the product is to use and apply. Many construction products have a limited workability before final setting occurs.

# Deterioration and failure

The following are just some of the common types of failure of construction materials. Many materials have a certain life span and simply wear out and have to be replaced or maintained.

## Corrosion

This occurs mainly with ferrous metals that contain iron and results when iron, water and air come into contact. When these three are present rust forms on untreated metals turning it an orange colour which stains and runs down surfaces.

Corrosion on bolts has to be avoided as structural steelwork is mainly held together by bolted connections. For this reason, bolts are generally manufactured from stainless steel.

## Electrolytic action

As we have seen earlier, certain metals in the presence of water and other dissimilar metals react causing electrolytic action in which one metal corrodes. Care has to be taken when choosing metal roof coverings, for example lead, copper and zinc, and the type of fixings used to hold the materials down onto the roof structure, otherwise you might inadvertently cause long-term corrosion. Many steel-cable suspension bridges contain thousands of steel wires that must be regularly inspected for corrosion to avoid the possibility of a catastrophic failure.

## Fungal attack

This mainly attacks timber-based materials in the form of wet or dry rot. Dry rot is caused by fungal attack; wet rot is the natural decay of the timber through excessive high moisture content which could be caused by a roof leak. Both lead to structural failure of load bearing timber. Wet rot can travel across concrete and brick walls and is very destructive. The only remedy in both cases is to remove the infected timber and the fungus.

Damp, dark, unventilated conditions will encourage the growth of mould on surfaces that are cold spots and surfaces frequently wetted, for example the base of old single-glazed window frames.

## Insect attack

This mainly covers wood-boring beetles, for example death watch beetle or house longhorn beetle. They bore into timber and eat away at the sub-structure causing severe structural damage as the timber loses its strength internally and eventually crumbles to powder. In 2004, termites were accidentally released into Devon, which is a warmer area. These are tenacious timber eaters and can easily wreck a timber building.

## Frost attack

Frost is part of the action of the reduction of temperature below freezing and the freezing of water vapour onto a surface causing ice crystals to build up. We have all had

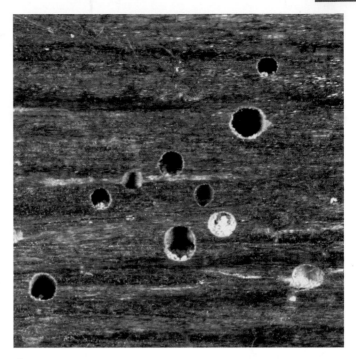

▲ **Woodworm – holes left by wood-boring beetles**

to clear a car windscreen at one time or another. Frost can attack external brickwork at low levels where it often stays wet, especially below the damp-proof course. Older, more porous brickwork absorbs water into the surface that then freezes when the temperature drops. The freezing of water causes expansion as ice crystals form. This expansion leads to the face of the brickwork shelling off and spalling the brick.

## Chemical and sulphate attacks

Acid rain on sandstone structures is the chemical attack of the stone by a weak acid solution that gradually wears away the surface of the stone removing any carved features. Fumes from traffic in city centres gradually build up a layer on buildings that contains high emissions from the burning of fuel which can cause discoloration and damage to certain building materials.

Sulphate attack is also a chemical attack, primarily on areas where sulphates can react with the cement contained as the strength agent in concrete. It is also found in coal-fire chimneys where sulphates from the combustion of coal leech through the mortar joints of the exposed chimney and weaken the brickwork structure. Sulphate attack can occur on concrete foundations where water collects sulphates from the soil or hardcore fill and attacks and weakens the foundations of the building.

## Efflorescence

This is caused by the effect of water moving through a material, for example brick and concrete. As the water migrates through the material, it dissolves soluble salts contained within the material. As the water leaves the outside of the material, it evaporates depositing a salt crystal. Over time, these gradually build up causing a white area of salt which is obvious to the eye on the outside of the material. This type of cosmetic damage generally appears on new buildings and will eventually clear once all the salt is washed out and treated.

## Ultraviolet (UV) attack

Ultraviolet contained in the sun's rays affects the colours of materials, eventually bleaching out the original colour and making it fade with time. Timber is especially affected and turns from its dried state into a grey, grainless, aged state if not treated.

▲ Efflorescence on brickwork

## Stress fatigue

Continual stress on structures and the release of this stress will eventually lead to the permanent deformation of a structural member, with cracking and weakening around the crack. This is very rare in building structures but with ever-taller skyscrapers planned, the stress effects from metal fatigue must now be considered from the force of the wind. Roof sheeting fixings are a weak point that must be designed by manufacturers to resist upload forces from negative air pressures on leeward sides of buildings. Maintenance of the building envelope is essential as, if one fixing breaks and is not repaired, then the wind can take hold and peel away complete roof and wall panels.

## Role of water in failure mechanisms

Water does have a role in failure as we have seen in its expansion or freezing which causes damage to brickwork. Excessive rain can overflow guttering systems and enter a building causing internal damage. Water also acts under capillary action and can seep through the smallest of cracks. Design of buildings must take into account the force of gravity on water with regard to staining from the dirt contained within our inner-city environments which washes down the faces of buildings.

# Preventative techniques

Table 4.7 takes the above types of deterioration and establishes current preventative techniques to control them. (You should undertake some further research on these in order to satisfy the requirements of the distinction criteria.)

**Table 4.7 Techniques to prevent deterioration of construction materials**

| Deterioration | Damage | Prevention |
|---|---|---|
| Corrosion | Rust | The use of stainless steel<br>Sacrificial anodes<br>Full painting programme |
| Electrolytic action | Metal breakdown and loss | Use metals which are similar and will not react<br>Isolation |
| Fungal attack | Wet and dry rot | Treated timber<br>Ventilation<br>Removal and replacement of infected timber<br>Prevent moisture entering timber |
| Insect attack | Structure of timber eaten away | Woodworm chemical treatment<br>Timber treatment using pressure impregnated chemicals |
| Frost attack | Shelling of outer surface of brickwork | Use class B or A engineering bricks below damp-proof course<br>Good design<br>High specification facing brickwork<br>Mortar joint maintenance |
| Chemical attack | Breakdown of limestones | Replacement of stone with harder material<br>Treatment of surface of stone |
| Sulphate attack | Breakdown of chemical bonds of cement | Use of sulphate-resistant cement<br>Repointing using sulphate-resistant cement mortar |
| Efflorescence | Formation of salt crystals | Wash down and remove salt<br>Surface treatment with chemicals<br>Quality specification on bricks<br>Known source of sands |
| Ultraviolet (UV) attack | Colour fading | UV fixed colours resistant to UV light |
| Stress fatigue | Metal fracture and failure | Over design on fixings<br>Factors of safety<br>High strength stainless steel fixings |
| Role of water in failure mechanisms | Water staining<br>Frost attack<br>Efflorescence<br>Dirt build-up | Good design<br>Use of weather drips<br>Overhangs to direct water<br>Regular maintenance of guttering overflows and downpipes |

- One side of the factory to be clad in glass curtain walling **M3**

Analyse and discuss, in both qualitative and quantitative terms, the factors that affect human comfort that you identified in the P1 criteria. **D1**

Evaluate the following range of preventative and remedial techniques applicable to the failure of materials.

a The application of creosote to sub-floor timber floor joists

b The introduction of steel reinforcement to the bottom of concrete lintels

c The application of painting systems to exposed structural steelwork

d The use of UV fixed colours **D2**

## Grading tips

You will need to provide some calculations on a range of items that add to human comfort; heat, light and sound could be considered. **M1**

The calculation of end reactions, stresses in materials, strain and Young's Modulus all could be considered. **M2**

This requires some form of calculation to reinforce the specification decision that is required to be made; density, absorption and strength could all be considered. **M3**

It is easier to answer this difficult task by relating the two elements above and link them into other factors that affect human comfort. **D1**

This needs to be appropriate to the vocational pathway you are following. Your pathway will provide the materials selected for an analysis and the preventative technique needs to be looked at over a range of materials. **D2**

## Knowledge check

1 What are the three methods by which heat can be transferred?

2 What does a U-value measure?

3 Why are air changes in a building essential?

4 What effect does condensation have on a building?

5 Name one way of reducing airborne sound?

6 Why do humans require daylight?

7 What is the unit of measurement for light?

8 Where do tension and compression exist in a concrete lintel?

9 What is a shear force?

10 What happens when a material's elastic capacity is exceeded?

11 Why are factors of safety important?

12 Name four ways in which a building material can be degraded.

13 Why is sustainability important?

14 How can we accommodate the thermal movement of brickwork panels?

## Grading criteria: Unit 4

| To achieve a pass grade the evidence must show that the learner is able to: | To achieve a merit grade the evidence must show that, in addition to the pass criteria, the learner is able to: | To achieve a distinction grade the evidence must show that, in addition to the pass and merit criteria, the learner is able to: |
|---|---|---|
| **P1** identify and describe each of the basic factors that influence human comfort in the internal environment; describe how each factor is measured, and state acceptable values for each factor **Assessment practice pages 157, 181** | **M1** produce clear and accurate answers to three different calculations relating to human comfort in the internal environment **Assessment practice pages 157, 181** | **D1** analyse and discuss, in both qualitative and quantitative terms, the basic factors that affect human comfort **Assessment practice pages 157, 182** |
| **P2** define and interpret important concepts relating to simple structures under load **Assessment practice pages 167, 181** <br><br> **P3** predict simple structural behaviour from given data **Assessment practice pages 167, 181** | **M2** produce clear and accurate answers to two different problems involving simple structures under load **Assessment practice pages 167, 181** | |
| **P4** describe the main performance criteria relating to the specification of a range of vocationally relevant construction materials including, as appropriate, basic details of the production and/or manufacturing processes **Assessment practice pages 173, 181** <br><br> **P5** identify and describe the most important features and properties of a range of construction-related materials and the mechanisms by which these materials can fail in use **Assessment practice pages 180, 181** | **M3** make and support valid decisions relating to the specification of materials for a tutor-specified application, using given design data and using calculations where appropriate **Assessment practice pages 180, 181–2** | **D2** evaluate a range of preventative and remedial techniques applicable to the failure of materials appropriate to the learner's vocational pathway **Assessment practice pages 180, 181–2** |

# Construction technology and design in construction and civil engineering

## Introduction

Construction Technology and Design involves planning and working with materials to construct buildings. In today's world buildings are becoming more complex, so an understanding of construction details along with an ability to communicate your ideas effectively is essential if a project is to be satisfactorily designed, planned and translated into reality.

Construction Technology and Design is a core unit. It is intended to encourage you to develop your understanding of designing construction projects and other factors that affect this process through structured plans and by recognising the contribution of other members of your design team. There are many opportunities for you to develop your understanding of the work while working with others and within a team.

Learning to use technical language and terminology that correctly represent the items and the structures that you will design is essential if you are to make good progress in this unit. You will use this ability to specify requirements and express ideas effectively. Building projects pass through various stages from design to construction, including the implications for changes and variations while construction works are in progress. You will learn to accommodate changes and integrate them into revised plans so that the overall project can continue and the other members of your team can be kept informed of changes and the revisions that have an impact on their work too.

### How you will be assessed

This unit is internally assessed by your tutor. A variety of activities is included in this unit to help you understand all aspects of construction technology and design.

After completing this unit you should be able to achieve the following outcomes:

1  Know the factors that influence the design process and the need to work with others to create a suitable design solution

# Thinking points

Building homes is a process that involves several different trades and disciplines. For large buildings and projects, several hundred people may have been involved with the construction and the development. There are several large structures and building projects that are known all over the country, for example the new Wembley stadium complex, the New Media City planned for Manchester as the BBC moves its headquarters north, new motorways and many more.

As you work through this chapter, you will see the complexities of creating one small project and working in a small team – imagine how the difficulties are increased when working on larger projects and with much bigger teams who are often based several miles apart. Planning and organising of work takes a great deal of skill, organisation and the ability to communicate your ideas concisely and precisely.

One model of how to plan construction work is the Royal Institute of British Architects (RIBA) Architect's Plan of Work. This works particularly well with small projects and developments when all the details can be worked out in advance. However, if you are working on a design and build contract where the contractor's expertise is used to provide solutions to the design as work proceeds and problems develop, the RIBA Plan of Work can sometimes seem inflexible. This can mean delay in the construction work and the building being delivered late.

1  How long does it take to build a stadium like this and what organisational skills would you need to have to supervise the project?

2  What are the main features of this type of building and how do you get everyone to work to the same set of drawings?

3  What impact would a design change at an early stage have on the work taking place on the construction site?

4  How can these changes be accommodated and what needs to be done to communicate changes to the whole team?

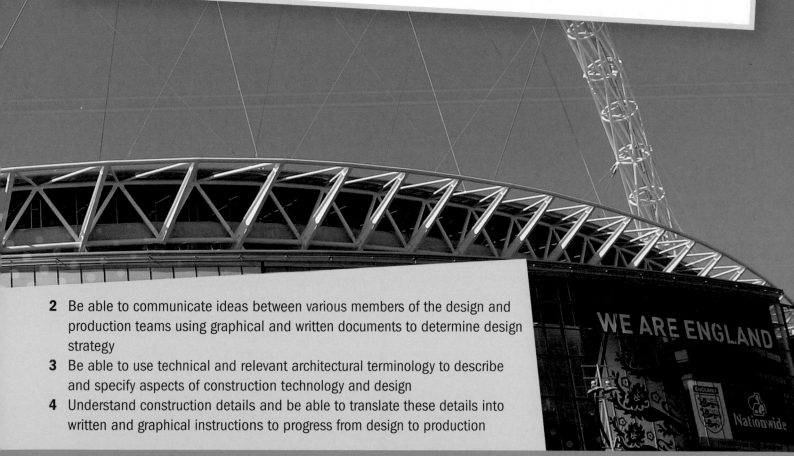

2  Be able to communicate ideas between various members of the design and production teams using graphical and written documents to determine design strategy

3  Be able to use technical and relevant architectural terminology to describe and specify aspects of construction technology and design

4  Understand construction details and be able to translate these details into written and graphical instructions to progress from design to production

## Stages of design process

Most buildings are complex structures. They represent many things such as landmarks, a type of statement by architects and designers who want to leave a legacy of their work for the communities that use them. Buildings allow us to function in many ways. Schools, hospitals, airports, railway stations and many other buildings provide shelter and through their use of materials, style of building and their appearance represent our cultural values. Even a simple dwelling or house has many components and is designed to meet everyday activities and provide safe shelter. Buildings are incredibly expensive to construct and over their lifetime need to be modified to enable them to be adapted to change of use. They also need considerable amounts of maintenance if they are to be preserved and their upkeep allows them to be used effectively.

### Need for and benefits of a structured framework for design

A lot of work goes into deciding whether a building project can be built. This is known as assessing the **feasibility**. When a client asks an architect to design a building, an appraisal of the criteria for success is completed to determine whether the building can go ahead. When the feasibility is completed, much more work goes into designing the building before any construction work takes place; this is known as the pre-construction phase. When all the pre-construction work is complete, the drawings and specifications can be passed so that the actual construction and site work can begin.

### Key Term

**Feasibility** Deciding whether the building is either practicable or will proceed.

Planning for a coordinated and structured approach to building is necessary so that all the key players – architects, architectural technologists, landscape architects, structural engineers, services engineers and facilities managers – are aware of the developments of the design as it proceeds. Imagine a big building project, such as the building of a motorway bridge across a river. The initial design may begin so that the architects can start to frame up the structural form that the bridge will take. As work proceeds on the exploration of the ground conditions, the data and information will need to be updated which, in turn, will allow the architect to amend the plans. Naturally, if these changes and amendments are to be accommodated, all the key players will have to understand the framework and how these changes affect all the other players in the process of building a sophisticated structure.

### ■ The RIBA Plan of Work

For most complex works in construction the RIBA Plan of Work is chosen as this has been established for some

### Remember!

The RIBA plan is usually accepted as the most suitable plan, although many other types of plan are acceptable for smaller building projects or for instances where the RIBA plan may be too inflexible when conditions change frequently. For this unit, and for the work that we are going to do here, we will consider the RIBA plan to be the most suitable method of working, but you should be aware that in other circumstances other plans may be chosen. Essentially, it is not important if you use the RIBA plan or another plan; the main thing is that construction work will need to be well planned, coordinated, adopt a structured approach and, most importantly, that all the people who are contributing to the plan know what is expected of them in their respective job roles.

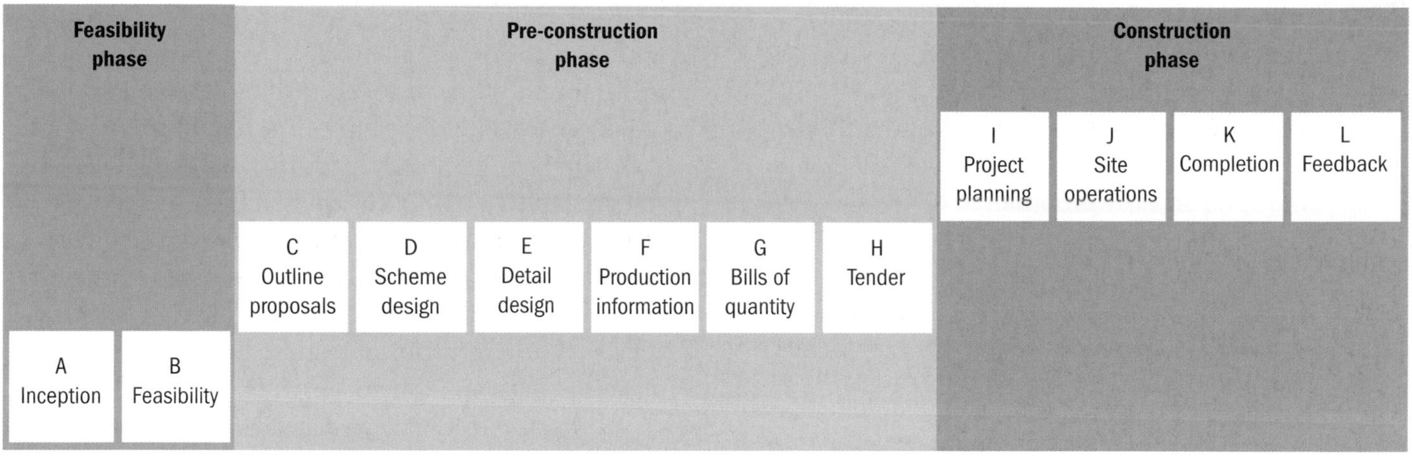

Figure 5.1 The three phases of the RIBA Plan of Work

time (see Figure 5.1). Some people also accept that this framework has the advantage of being easily understood and the key personnel all understand their roles within it.

## Characteristics of individual stages and factors affecting them

### ■ Inception and feasibility

At this stage of the plan, the architect will work closely with the client to determine and prepare the requirements of the building project. Architects will provide clients with an appraisal and recommendation so that they can determine the form in which the project is to proceed, ensuring that it is feasible both in technical and financial terms.

## Key Term

**Inception** An event that is a beginning, a first part or stage of subsequent events.

### ■ Outline proposals and scheme design

At this stage, the architect will usually have determined through **sketch plans** the layout, design and construction in order to obtain approval of the client on the outline proposals and accompanying report. To complete the brief and decide on particular proposals,

including planning arrangements and appearance, constructional method, outline specification and cost, the architect will then draft plans and drawings for submission to the local authority to obtain all approvals such as **building control** and planning consent.

## Key Term

**Sketch plans** An architect or designer develops a sketch plan according to the needs and wants discussed with a client at the consultation stage. This is the time when the designer is creating, refining and rejecting ideas as appropriate.

**Building control** The local authority department responsible for checking the proposal against various legislative controls and regulations to ensure that the building project complies.

### ■ Detail design

At this stage, the architect will have to obtain final decisions on all matters related to design, specification, construction and cost. By creating working drawings and finalising the full design of every part and component of the building, the architect draws together the construction team. Meetings of the team will take place to discuss and decide materials, finishings, services, contributions by specialist firms and a range of other matters relating to the finalising of the building. It is important that any changes or modifications to the scheme are noted and accommodated so that everyone can be updated and work from the latest drawings. Changes can be accommodated at this stage, although they may result in increased costs due to the scheme being planned on an early proposal.

## ■ Production information

This part of the plan includes the preparation of product information used in the building, the drafting of **bills of quantities**, **tender documents** and project planning materials such as the programme of works showing duration of activities and the time taken to create the building itself. This is a very important stage in the process and particular care must be taken to ensure accuracy of the work involved in drawings and specifications so that the contractors undertaking the building work have all the necessary information to hand to complete the work to the appropriate standard. Drawings required at this stage include a **location plan** of where the work is found, a layout drawing of the construction site itself and a general arrangement drawing that shows the layout of the work to be done. From these drawings, a series of schedules and specifications will be drafted to provide any necessary additional information.

## Key Terms

**Bills of quantities** Documents that quantify the amount of materials and components in a building. Preparing a bill of quantities involves measuring and estimating the quantities of items and materials needed.

**Tender documents** A document or series of documents that offer to do the work at a price – contractors tender for work by providing an estimate of how much they will charge for the works to be completed.

**Location plan** Used to guide and identify where the work takes place. It is a kind of map so that the contractor knows where the site is located.

### Bills of quantities

Specifications are dealt with in more detail later on, but their link with the bills of quantities is important.

Bills of quantities are prepared by a quantity surveyor who reads the drawings and determines the quantities and amounts of materials needed to complete the construction work. Any part of the building that is not yet finalised or has missing information can be allocated a **provisional** or **prime cost** so that there an amount for the work to take place is allocated even when the actual cost or amount to do this work may be finalised some time later. If the architect has not yet appointed a construction contractor or team to complete the works onsite, discussions at this stage will begin to determine an appropriate company or contractor to appoint who is capable of undertaking the work.

## Key Terms

**Provisional cost** When the actual cost of something is not yet known, so an allowance or a provisional sum is allowed.

**Prime cost** When a cost is already known and an allowance has been made to meet this cost.

## ■ Tender information and process

The idea of tendering is to allow the client an opportunity to present a batch of work or a construction contract to contractors who learn about the complexity, the stages of construction, the limits and the constraints anticipated within the work so that a realistic and accurate price can be calculated by the contractors. The contractors then identify the price of the works and the client chooses the contractor best suited and able to do the work. Frequently, the cheapest tender or quote is selected as this can represent best value for the client.

### Remember!

Sufficient time must be allowed in the planning of the work for the **tendering process** to take place. Typically, this would be around four weeks although this can be smaller for more simple jobs and small contracts.

## Key Term

**Tendering process** Where an architect may ask several known or well-established contractors who are interested and are capable of completing this work to provide an estimate of how much it will cost.

For some work selective tendering may take place, where an architect and quantity surveyor invite contractors that are either known to them or have an established reputation for completing work similar to the one they are working on, to tender. Again, the cheapest quote is most commonly selected in this process.

Contractors may be approached so that they tender an interest in the work. Sometimes a pre-tender meeting may be held with contractors and the complexity and the details of the work can be communicated to the contractors so that the contractors, the architect and the client can satisfy themselves that they are all capable of completing the work within the appointed timescale and budget. A letter of invitation to tender can then be issued together with all relevant drawings, specifications and bills – the contractors can then visit the site of the works and the contractor will determine and cost the project. Tenders are returned to the architect at an agreed date and time. Initial comparison of the tenders received from different contractors takes place by the architect and sometimes this includes the client or their representative. This analysis of the tenders usually results in the lowest priced tender winning the contract and being appointed as the contractor.

### ■ Project planning

This is where the work to produce the building starts on the building itself. Contract documents are prepared and signed. At a project planning meeting, the architect will usually clarify any points undecided at this stage and agree any further contractual points. Contractors draft a **programme of works** that illustrates the milestones and the total duration of the work. Key milestones include taking possession of the site, dates of project progress meetings and other key dates that are achieved during the lifetime of the contract.

## Key Term

**Programme of works** A bar chart showing the duration and the resources needed to complete the job. It shows how long the contract will take and how long the contractor intends to spend on each task.

The contractor is expected to sign the contract documents at this stage, which include:

- a copy of the contract
- a full set of construction drawings
- bills of quantities
- specifications
- a register of drawings
- **site diary** and associated report forms.

## Key Term

**Site diary** A record of relevant information about the progress of the construction works completed by the contractor.

### ■ Operations onsite

The site is officially handed over to the contractor who can begin construction-related operations. The site is now the responsibility of the contractor who has to comply with all legislative requirements and legal constraints. The contractor should be informed of any rights of way, preservation orders, protection requirements and any other environmental issues that need to be considered in terms of the work and the activities on site in the months ahead.

### Remember!

Once operations begin, the site becomes the official responsibility of the contractor.

**Interim certificates** are issued at regular intervals during the contract period based on a quantity surveyor's assessment of the work completed so far. These certificates form the basis of the calculation necessary to prepare and authorise stage payments from the client to the contractor.

## Key Term

**Interim certificates** Issued by the architect to say that some of the work has been completed. Contractors can then be paid for the work that they have done so far.

The contractor has a duty to ensure the appropriate site supervision of all those involved in activities onsite. A clerk of works will check on behalf of the client and the architect that the contractor is complying and building the project to the appropriate standards of materials and workmanship. Samples are taken of various materials, sometimes by a specific request from the architect and other times by established practice in some cases, such as the sampling of concrete which is regularly tested by way of a **slump test** to ensure workability when it arrives on site, and its strength assessed by testing to destruction samples at regular intervals after the concrete has been placed. Brickwork panels are sometimes erected to enable the architect and the client to see what the brickwork will eventually look like. Tiles, blocks, panels, etc. may also be subject to a request that the contractor builds a **mock-up** or sample panel for viewing by the architect and the client so that the quality and the desired finish of the work can be ascertained and ensured.

## Key Terms

**Slump test** A test of the concrete's workability. It shows that the concrete is of the right quality and can be poured with the correct results. Contractors can send back the concrete to the manufacturer if it is not of the right consistency and quality.

**Mock-up** Sometimes created by contractors and subcontractors as a sample of what the work will look like when it is finished.

The contractor's duties at this stage of the plan are to work diligently on the construction works adhering to all relevant health, safety and welfare legislation. The contractor is also expected to maintain a site diary to record relevant information about the progress of the construction works. Typically, a site diary will include information on:

- weather conditions
- visitors on site for the period
- any deliveries of materials to site
- progress of work to date
- personnel onsite including subcontractors
- any comments and notes taken about the work undertaken
- discrepancies and any inconsistencies in contract documents.

## ■ Completion

As the building starts to take shape, the contractor may be required to hand over part of the building to the client. The actual date of handover is planned and any outstanding issues relating to the construction works can be determined and a solution found. The period of notice required varies from site to site, but usually adequate notice is required in order to prepare the area and any other supporting documentation. The client should be in a position to accept the building for its proper use so the architect will usually insist on inspecting the area and determining for themselves that the work is to the appropriate standard of materials and workmanship, that all services and equipment are functioning appropriately and effectively and that the 'as-built' record drawings are a true record of the actual building. The building manual which in the case of a simple domestic dwelling or house will be simple could extend to a complex and detailed manual of several volumes for an industrial or more intricate commercial building.

A certificate of practical completion can be issued by the architect to the contractor which then enables the contractor to claim monies due for the construction work and address any defects and snags that have arisen so far. At this stage, the contractor has effectively completed the construction stage and has no responsibilities for the insurance of the building or its works. When all defects or amendments or outstanding issues are addressed, the architect will issue a final certificate and the account will be adjusted for **variations**, subsequent instructions and fluctuations in labour and materials prices and/or costs.

## Key Term

**Variation** Something different or changed within the main contract.

## ■ Feedback

The final part of the RIBA plan is to analyse and evaluate the progress of what was expected with what was actually delivered. Architects will need to determine what has happened in order to achieve better performance in the future. Typically, an analysis and evaluation could include the following:

- What does the client think of the completed building?
- Does the building function effectively?
- What parts of the design were particularly successful or problematic?
- Could this design process have been undertaken differently and have provided a better service to the contractor or the client?
- What relationship and communication existed between the design team and the construction team? How could these be improved in the future?
- Did the contractor meet all performance targets in a timely and effective manner?
- Did the design process run smoothly? If not, why?
- Was the job profitable and was the contract fulfilled?

### Stages of design

Using the RIBA plan requires two processes: an integrated design approach and an integrated team process to complete the construction project, whatever the building is.

Integrated design asks all the members of the team such as the technical planning, design and construction team

to look at the project objectives, building materials, systems, assemblies from many different perspectives which relies on the expertise of specialists who work in their respective specialties. Building design in practice also requires an integrated team process in which the design team and all affected stakeholders work together throughout the project phases and to evaluate the design for cost, quality of life, future flexibility, efficiency; overall environmental impact; productivity, creativity; and how the occupants will be enlivened. The process draws from the knowledge pool of all the stakeholders across the life cycle of the project, from defining the need for a building, through planning, design, construction, building occupancy and operations. The end result is a high-performance building.

Building design rarely means thinking of one specific need. Often a range of considerations will need to be included in order to make the building suit many requirements of society. Frequently, there are legislative controls that insist that buildings conform to regulations such as the Disabled and Disabilities Act which ensures that buildings are accessible by wheelchair users or people with specific disabilities. Designing a suitable building means making sure that the finished product is:

- accessible – that all heights, clearances, entrances, exits and services are integrated to address the specific needs of disabled people
- aesthetically pleasing – that the physical appearance and image of building elements and spaces are pleasing to the eye and act in harmony with the buildings and environment in which the building is located
- cost-effective – that building elements are selected and utilised on the basis of life cycle costs as well as basic cost estimating and budget control
- functional/operational – that the building delivers the functional dimensions that it was designed to do, including spatial needs and requirements, system performance as well as durability and efficient maintenance of building elements
- productive – relating to occupants' well-being (physical and psychological comfort), including building elements such as air distribution, lighting, workspaces, systems, and technology

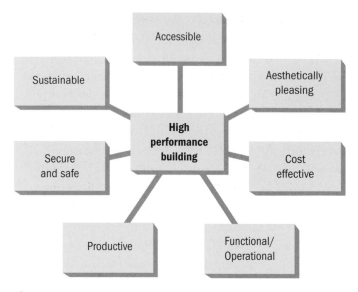

▲ **Figure 5.2 Criteria for a successful design**

- secure/safe – provides a safe and secure environment for occupants and assets from hazards and inclement weather patterns
- sustainable – utilises and maximises environmental performance of building elements and strategies over the life cycle of the building.

## Implications of financial, legal and environmental constraints for design team

Designers must consider a range of factors that will have an impact on the process that takes the client from the initial idea of a project through the various pitfalls and constraints until the final building is built and handed over. Naturally, many of these constraints will revolve around the availability of funding and finance where ideas will be conceived, but the cost implications may mean that the client has to accept a different proposal.

Notwithstanding the limits of available finance, any design must satisfy the requirements of planning legislation and how this design fits in harmony with the environment. More than ever before, sustainability and ecological factors will need to be considered, certainly by the designer who should advise and guide clients to the integration of a project into the built and natural environment. Building regulations are principally about workmanship and quality. Building projects will need to comply with these regulations if they are to consume

a maximum amount of energy, provide adequate light, acoustics and a suitable place to live and work.

## Construction (Design and Management) Regulations

The Construction (Design and Management) (CDM) Regulations 1994 are aimed at improving the overall management and coordination of health, safety and welfare throughout construction projects to reduce the large numbers of serious and fatal accidents and cases of ill health which occur every year in the construction industry. They have introduced new documentation and place responsibilities on key team members, especially those involved with the design of construction works. Not all construction projects are affected by these regulations.

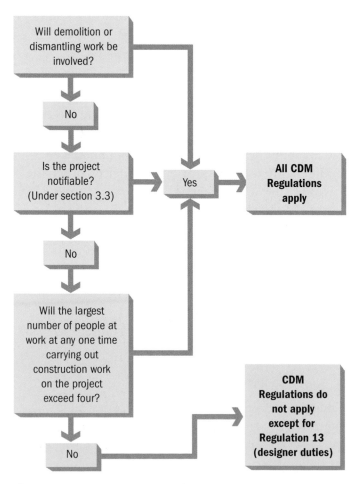

▲ **Figure 5.3 Do the CDM Regulations apply to the construction project?**

## ■ Duties of the client

The client's key duties, as far as is reasonably practicable, are to:

- select and appoint a competent planning supervisor and principal (main) contractor
- be satisfied that the planning supervisor and principal contractor will allocate adequate resources for health and safety
- be satisfied that designers and contractors are also competent, and will allocate adequate resources when arranging for them to work on the project
- provide the planning supervisor with information relevant to health and safety on the project
- ensure construction work does not start until the principal contractor has prepared a satisfactory health and safety plan
- ensure the health and safety file is available for inspection, after the project is completed.

## Remember!

The concept of what is 'reasonably practicable' means that a company should take all reasonable steps to protect workers against risks balanced against the cost and time of doing so. (See also Unit 1 Health, Safety and Welfare in Construction and the Built Environment, page 2.)

## ■ Duties of the planning supervisor

The planning supervisor has to coordinate the health and safety aspects of project design and the planning to ensure as much as they can that designers comply with their duties – in particular, the avoidance and reduction of risks involved in the construction of the project. Designers must cooperate with each other for purposes of health and safety and in order that a health and safety plan is prepared before arrangements are made for any principal contractor to be appointed.

Planning supervisors also give advice, if requested, to the client on the competence and allocation of resources by designers and all contractors. This advice can also apply to contractors appointing designers in other forms of contracting arrangements and for projects that do not use the RIBA Plan of Work. Planning supervisors are usually qualified professionals with several years' experience in developing construction projects and hence can advise the client on the health and safety plan before the construction phase starts. If the CDM Regulations apply, the planning supervisor will also notify the Health & Safety Executive and ensure that the health and safety file is delivered to the client at the end of the project.

## ■ Duties of the designer

The designer's key duties are to be as proactive as possible in alerting clients to their duties and consider during the development of designs the hazards and risks which may arise to those constructing and maintaining the structure. Within the context of design, the building project should be designed to avoid risks to health and safety so far as is reasonably practicable and at least to reduce risks at source if avoidance is not absolutely possible.

Designers must also consider measures to protect all workers if neither avoidance nor reduction to a safe level is possible, and thus ensure that the design includes adequate information on health and safety so that they can pass this information on to the planning supervisor in order that it can be included in the health and safety plan. Above all else, it is the designers' responsibility to cooperate with the planning supervisor, and any other designers involved in the project to achieve the safe and efficient completion of the project.

## ■ Duties of contractors

Contractors also have obligations under the CDM Regulations. The principal contractor's key duties are to develop and implement the health and safety plan and ensure that only competent and adequately resourced contractors carry out any work where it is subcontracted. It is also the contractor's responsibility to ensure the coordination and cooperation of all other subcontractors, including the findings of their risk assessments and details of how they intend to carry out high-risk operations during the construction process. The main contractor also has a duty to pass on this information to the planning supervisor for inclusion in the health and safety file.

## Case study

You work for a small architectural designer's practice that has been approached to handle and manage a house building project with a speculative developer. The small housing project consists of the demolition of a single-storey warehouse that used to house chemicals and household detergents. The site will be prepared to accept six new semi-detached houses. There is a preservation order on two mature oak trees adjacent to the site. Work is expected to last only 90 days. The houses that you are designing are standard layout, three-bedroom, semi-detached that will include an en-suite to the master bedroom, a family bathroom, a kitchen, separate dining room and a living room. An integral garage will be included which will need separation and require fire resistant materials where the garage makes contact with the house itself.

As the designer, decide how you will begin to plan and organise the work ahead. Consider these questions:

1   Do the CDM Regulations apply?

2   Are you familiar with relevant health and safety legislation, including CDM Regulations?

3   What do you need to do regarding construction practice relevant to the CDM Regulations?

4   Are there any special or specific measures that you need to apply regarding the approved codes of practice for asbestos, lead, substances hazardous to health, etc?

5   Are you conversant with British standards relevant to construction safety, e.g. scaffolding, steel erection, demolition, etc?

6   Are you satisfied that you have sufficient health and safety training and practical experience?

7   Are you familiar with the concept of risk assessment for the construction industry?

Contractors perform many duties onsite and so are in the best position to ensure that site activities are carried out safely. Contractors must ensure that subcontractors have information about risks onsite and that all workers and operatives working on the project have adequate training and a suitable induction to site procedures.

Contractors and site operatives must comply with any site rules which may have been set out in the health and safety plan and make sure only authorised people are allowed onto the site. In essence, the role of the contractor under the CDM Regulations is to monitor health and safety performance by those persons on the construction site.

# The design team

Architects and designers of buildings need to be clear about what a client needs from a building and then work closely with the construction team to ensure that these dreams are realised into a fully functioning building. Sometimes construction projects become so complex

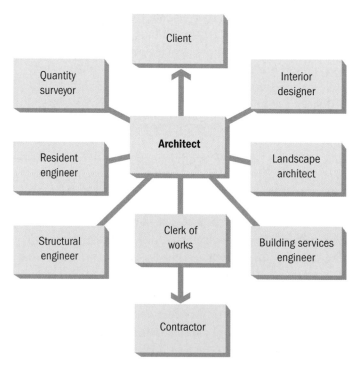

▲ Figure 5.4 The architect sits at the centre of the design team

that the whole team is very large, comprising people with specialist skills and experience who all contribute to the finished product. The exact requirements of each construction project vary with the type of building and availability of labour in the region.

A typical design team establishes a clear contractual relationship between all parties and allocates roles and responsibilities for specialist activities in the process of completing the project.

## Architects

Architects and designers usually need to have the following skills:

- An ability to identify and articulate a client's brief to meet both user and longer-term needs as well as society's concerns for sustainable development.
- An understanding of the client's perspective and an ability to communicate effectively with each member of the construction team.
- An understanding of relevant legislation and its potential effect on programme cost and quality of design.
- An understanding of health, safety and welfare legislation and its implications on design and construction.
- An ability to construct the team; to coordinate and integrate the work of the team members.
- An ability to communicate effectively with the client and an understanding of methods of reporting.

## Architectural technologist

Technologists usually work in partnership with architects to establish contract procedures and administration of work. They also draft out and develop drawings and construction-related details so that the project can be completed. Architectural technologists have a deep understanding of construction technology and can translate ideas into sound, accurate drawings that a contractor can follow. Quantity surveyors will need to read these drawings so that the bills of quantities and the specifications can be drawn up, hence the production

of precise and accurate details of construction technology is essential.

## Interior designer

Interior designers are sometimes used on contracts where the internal finish and décor is important or of a prestigious nature. Some high-profile house building projects or city-centre apartment conversions have been developed in conjunction with interior designers who can add considerable value to a project.

## Landscape architect

Landscaping, or the arranging of the external environment, like the interior design, can be enhanced by a specialist who can develop this theme to improve the completed project. Frequently, speculative housing projects will benefit from a landscape architect who will design open spaces, leisure areas, land drainage and improve the appearance of the development.

## Clerk of works

A client will want assurance that a contractor is producing a building that meets the specification in terms of both materials and workmanship. The clerk of works is employed directly by the client but also reports to the architect on progress of the construction works. The clerk of works will need to inspect the works as work proceeds and hence needs to be a frequent visitor to the site. On some larger sites, a clerk of works will have a resident office and spend their entire working time there. Clerks of works do not issue instructions and do not have authority to impose variations or changes to the design.

## Structural engineer

Structural engineers determine the design of load-bearing elements of the building and ensure that each component is designed to safely withstand and carry the loads that are imposed on the building. Structural engineers typically work for the client but are frequently engaged by the architect to inform and supervise the design and installation of structural elements as work proceeds.

## Resident engineer

Resident engineers are based on the construction site itself, close to the construction works and supervise and report back to the structural engineer and the architect on matters relating to the structure and the load-bearing components that have been detailed and designed by the structural engineer.

## Quantity surveyor

Quantity surveyors accurately determine the amount of materials needed for the project to be built. They prepare a bill of quantities establishing a record of all the materials needed and identifying all the information necessary to draft out a specification of the works. Having established this information, the quantity surveyor can then advise and guide the architect or the client on the cost of the job, check tenders and evaluate any costs as work proceeds.

## Building services engineer

Building services and the effective use of heat, light, acoustics and other electrical appliances have seen significant improvements in recent years. Building services engineers design and implement a range of items into the project that improve the resources and the quality of the building. Many of these items such as lifts, escalators, air conditioning and heating and ventilation systems need to be integrated into the contract drawings at an early stage to avoid conflicts of space or to ensure that the design can accommodate machinery, plant and equipment.

## Facilities manager

Facilities managers maintain the building once it is built. Their duties include the maintenance of the physical structure by undertaking construction works such as painting, decorating, easing doors, replacing carpet and floor finishes and so on. Their role also includes the essential duties to ensure that the building functions; examples of this are the cleaning of the building, the replacing of lamps and fittings, checking and repairing heating controls and other such essential items that are required to enable the building to be occupied.

## Interactions between team members

There are many interactions between the design and construction team members. Those listed below are a sample of the interactions that occur in a project's life cycle:

- Client/architect – discuss the design brief and different solutions producing an agreed design and specification.
- Architect/structural engineer – this interaction involves the structural feasibility of the agreed design with any amendments.
- Architect/quantity surveyor/client – discuss the client's budget and the costs of various schemes.
- Principal contractor/quantity surveyor /architect – discuss, amend or negotiate tenders and quotations for work.
- Main contractor/architect/quantity surveyor – agree the final account on completion of the work.

## Theory into practice

You have been asked to help set up a team to design and build a health centre. The team needs to recruit an architect, quantity surveyor and an engineer.

Draft a recruitment advertisement to appear in the local paper and a person specification for each of the above positions.

## Assessment practice

Outline what you think will influence how buildings are designed. What procedures are necessary to communicate your ideas to the team? **P1**

Describe how the RIBA Plan of Work operates and explain the merits of using the plan. **M1**

Analyse and evaluate the effectiveness of the RIBA Plan of Work in terms of teamwork and the introduction of changes to design once construction has started. **D1**

## Thinking point

Is the RIBA plan a useful, methodical way of working in construction or does it impose a structure that is too rigid to adapt to the changing way that contractors react to construction works?

# The brief

## The initial brief – sketch plans and designs

Architects draft out a sketch plan that starts to show the client what they can expect from the design. Sketch plans have to take account of a range of constraints and influences on the proposed building, for example town planning restrictions such as zoning of areas to accept residential, commercial or industrial buildings or projects; green belt or conservation areas that insist any development introduced or undertaken in the area is in sympathy with the existing environment and maintains the culture or influence of an area; environmental issues such as sustainability or ecological interests such as the development or protection of nature reserves or local wildlife.

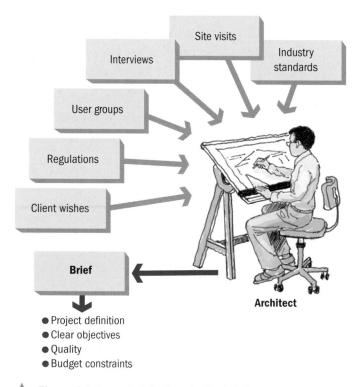

**Figure 5.5 From sketch plans to the brief**

## After consideration of client's requirements

Clients very often approach architects for advice and guidance – frequently, at this stage, clients are not aware of the multitude of influences and constraints that make a building either possible or improbable. A well-defined brief is rare and members of the design team have to liaise with each other to frame up and develop this brief within parameters that the client can agree to, which usually takes a number of meetings or consultations to develop.

## To aid design

At this stage, architects test their designs by creating cost models and working out the feasibility of the design within the client's budget and finance available. The brief moves from an initial idea to a cost model which is then modified to take account of financial constraints. This modified brief is then adopted as the new and revised brief. During this period, the adopted brief is subject to **cost analysis** and is confirmed as either acceptable or rejected before it moves on to a point where the team can work out the specification of the building project. Visualisations, frequently made from computer-generated models from plans, are created to provide an opportunity for the client to understand what the building will look like if it were to proceed.

## Key Term

**Cost analysis** The process of providing estimates of what a building project's costs and benefits are likely to be, comparing these estimates and making a judgement as to whether it is acceptable to proceed to the construction stage.

# The decision-making process

## Factors contributing to design decisions

The factors that contribute to making design decisions such as costs, sustainability, environment and buildability are considered by the architect when taking the initial brief from the first exploratory sketches to a worked-up model that can be presented to the client for approval. Clients will naturally want to get value for money and will have ideas on how they wish the completed building to look and perform. The architect and the design team will be able to consider how each of these influences affects the final outcome of the project. Some architectural practices take a methodical view of such criteria for success by scoring each factor and totalling up these scores to select the winning proposal. Others may wish to consider all options in descriptive terms including seeking out the opinions of neighbours or people in the area to develop the notion of how the building performs and how the building will be accepted into the local area by the people who will work or live around the project.

## Influence of decisions on the final project

### ■ Modifications and variations

Alterations to the original brief can be accommodated despite the nuisance and the extra time/money that these variations cost. An architect can issue a variation order to change the specification for a number of reasons:

- statutory requirements or lawful changes brought about by legislation
- omissions or additions that were overlooked in the initial briefing documents and consultation
- an error while compiling the bills of quantity that has not been picked up until construction work has started.

Contractually, the architect must issue the variation order in accordance with the contract – this variation must be exactly what the name implies, a variation, and as such represents something different or changed within the main contract. It cannot however be

something that radically changes the nature of the work, requires a different contract or asks that the contract undertake something completely unreasonable in the course of the contractor's main duties.

# Legal aspects

## Legal position of each member of a design team

### ■ Client

The client is effectively the employer of the architect and since they are investing their money and engaging the design team to create a building to serve their needs, they will have the final say on whether they accept the design. This legal position puts them at the head of any hierarchical chain and so long as they comply with any or all legislative constraints, then they ultimately decide whether to go ahead with the building project. Clients sometimes place responsibilities on the architect, the design team and the contractors to promote sustainable construction methods, utilise local labour availability and promote social agendas for change.

Clients can be individuals who wish to build a house, a speculative housing project to sell on for investment purposes or a commercial or industrial building to carry on their business. Local authorities, municipal governments or government agencies can also be clients, these typically require buildings of a much bigger nature such as roads, highways, airports, schools, hospitals and so on.

### Remember!

It is the client who will make the final decision whether to go ahead with the project.

### ■ Architect

The architect is in a unique legal position. In commercial terms, the architect answers to the person who is paying them to design the building project, namely the client. In addition to this, architects are required by law, and in order to practise, to hold qualifications that show that they understand design principles, build an adequately strong structure and comply with all aspects of legislation such as planning, building regulations, Construction Design and Management Regulations and the Disabled and Disabilities Act. They are also expected to promote sustainable construction methods by 'designing in' relevant innovatory techniques to enable building life to be prolonged and durable for future use. Architects have to have adequate public liability insurance to protect any third parties from any defects or problems associated with their work.

## ■ Architectural technologist

An architectural technologist typically works for or very closely with the architect. They usually create the working drawings and technical details that the contractor needs to be able to translate the architect's ideas into specifications and actual construction information. In order to do this, their understanding of technical guidelines, structural design, scientific principles and awareness of legal frameworks is very important. Architectural technologists have to carry compulsory insurance to ensure that they have adequate cover should there be any liability to third parties in the event of a problem with the design of a building project.

## ■ Landscape architect

Landscape architects have assumed greater status in the past 30 years or so. During this period, the work of a landscape architect has become more relevant to the overall design of a project. As these have become more complex, so too have the landscaping and the external environment become more complex and demanding. As a consequence, the specialist area of landscaping and external development has similar demands to that of the architectural technologist. Landscape architects have to comply with all aspects of legislative constraints and carry public liability insurance in case of defects or implications to third parties.

## ■ Structural engineer

Structural engineers occupy a specialist area in construction and have very specific legal requirements. Their status in the design team is very high since they will have to calculate the forces and loadings exerted upon a building, and determine what size and shape the

building elements will take to resolve these loads safely. Structural engineers have to be adequately qualified and belong to a relevant professional body to practise. They, too, have to carry adequate public liability insurance in case issues are raised with the standard of workmanship or adequacy of design with the building. In many cases, the structural engineer is employed by the architect, although they will work very closely with the architectural technologist and the principal contractor.

## ■ Services engineer

Engineers that are responsible for building services are specialists in areas such as heating, ventilation, acoustics, telecommunications and lift or escalator installation. Each of these areas may have its own engineers or designers who typically will be employed by the architect who will check to see that relevant services are integrated into the final building. Services engineers are expected to carry public liability insurance in case of issues being raised with the design and installation of their services.

## ■ Facilities manager

Facilities managers will require information about the building when it is complete, although it may well be desirable to have this information available as the design and construction work takes place. Facilities managers are responsible for the maintenance and servicing of the building once the project is complete. Facilities managers are usually employed by the building owner or quite possibly the building tenant and as such their legal position is different to the other members of the team.

### Rights of client

The client has a right to expect that the architect as their agent complies with relevant legislation and ethically acts in the best interest of the client at all times. The client can reasonably expect that their right to ethical and professional practice should enable the building project to be completed through the following items:

- The provision of an adequate brief to enable the architect to develop this idea from outline sketch to a series of completed technical drawings that meet the needs of the building.

- Reasonable changes to the brief during design stages, or during construction can be accommodated.
- Fees and charges are established and identified in advance to ensure that any disputes and concerns that the architect is over-charging can be settled.
- That the architect will progress the project at an appropriate and adequate pace that mitigates any delay or keeps delays to a minimum.
- That an architect communicates adequately with all interested parties and anyone who needs information to effect the work safely and speedily.
- That an architect discloses any conflict of interest which could affect the project, its outcomes or the personnel involved.
- That any defect, once discovered, is disclosed so that adequate and appropriate changes or modifications can be made.

Architects who are members of the Royal Institute of British Architects (RIBA) also subscribe to a code of practice. RIBA will deal with matters of unacceptable professional practice or aspects of professional incompetence and can fine, reprimand or strike off any architect who it feels has fallen short of the RIBA expectations and has not provided the client with an appropriate service. RIBA will also promote a mediator service in some cases, or appoint an adjudicator to resolve disputes, provide information about the availability of expert witnesses or arbitrators who could provide technical information or reports that could be used to agree a settlement or advocate compensation.

## Theory into practice

Find out more about RIBA by visiting its website, www.riba.org.

Despite the RIBA sanctions, a negotiated settlement for any disputes is preferable to any imposed penalty. Most architects will offer full and frank explanations to the client of any relevant information and enter into agreements on the legally binding nature of arbitration or adjudication.

## Damages

Damages is the legal term applied to any breach of a contract between parties when the terms of the contract have not been fulfilled. In construction there are many contracts between clients, contractors and subcontractors which contain clauses relevant to workmanship, responsibilities, the contract sum and any fees to be paid, and the duration or time allocated to enable the delivery of the services or product.

Contracts are used to determine the legal position and obligations of each party, although in some cases disputes arise and will need the services of the legal system to arrive at a decision as to who is responsible and what action can be taken. Once a court, an arbitrator or an adjudicator has arrived at a decision as to who is responsible for a breach of contract, there will have to be a calculation of what damages can be awarded. The most common form of award is in monetary terms. It is important to note that any award should reinstate the damaged party to a position where they would be had the contract been fulfilled. Construction contracts frequently contain a liquidated damages clause.

## Liquidated damages

Liquidated damages are a predetermined method of establishing what will be paid in the event of a party not fulfilling their part of a contract. Some clients build in a liquidated damages clause to encourage the contractor to deliver the building project on time with a fixed amount paid for each day or week that the building is not completed over the agreed date. The important thing to note about any liquidated damages clause is that it must not penalise either party and that the damages must be reasonable. Several legal cases have established that this must be a genuine estimate of any loss and any unreasonable penalty would be unenforceable.

## Negligence

Proving that somebody has not fulfilled their obligations under a contract may often lead to claims that there has been some form of negligence.

Architects can be proven to be negligent if they do not comply with the respective legislative constraints and fulfil their obligations to the initial brief, hence it is very important that they work closely with the client to establish the exact needs of the client through discussion and proposing outline plans and sketches.

In the preambles to a contract, a mechanism for calculating the amount of monies due for variations and other changes to the contract conditions will have been established such as pricing within the bills of quantity or a day work rate for completing work on a daily rate basis. Variation orders are issued by architects as an instruction for additional or modified work and as such are considered under the terms of the contract an architect's instruction.

## Theory into practice

Find out more about CIAT by visiting its website, www.biat.org.uk. Find sample letters and documents used by architects such as:

- letters of appointment
- town planning and application forms
- start of detail design stage of RIBA Plan of Works
- invitation to tender letter
- return letters to successful and unsuccessful tenderers
- requests for information forms (RFI)
- architect's instruction form (AI)
- interim certificate (IC)
- practical completion.

RIBA and the Chartered Institute of Architectural Technologists (CIAT) have standard documentation to guide and direct members to use appropriate documents for communicating with other members of the team.

## Health, safety and welfare

The duties of all the parties to the contract are set out in the Health and Safety at Work Act 1974, where everyone has a duty of care with regard to themselves and others. There is also a separate section within this Act applicable to manufacturers and designers whose products must be intrinsically safe in their design and use. This also applies to material suppliers who import goods into the UK. All employers have employees and the Health and Safety at Work Act lays down several rules that an employer must follow with regard to their employees' health and safety. (For more information on the Health and Safety at Work Act, see Chapter 1 Health, Safety and Welfare in Construction and the Built Environment, page 00.)

## Environment

There are many pieces of environmental legislation that can be applied to construction projects – from the careful tipping of waste materials to burning rubbish onsite, from pumping waste water offsite to the safe disposal of contaminated ground. These are all environmental legal considerations.

Green issues are more and more prevalent in today's society due to the impact of global warming and this is now steadily filtering through various regulations such as the building regulations (see also Chapter 2 Construction and the Environment).

## CDM

The CDM Regulations expressly state the roles and legal responsibilities of the client, planning supervisor, designer and principal contractor in the running of the pre- and post-contract situations. Architects and designers now have to assess their final designs for risks to the occupants and for maintaining the building. For example, windows can be made to tilt and turn so they can be cleaned from the inside of a building and not from height externally.

# Assessment practice

This assessment is based on the plan layout of the house below.

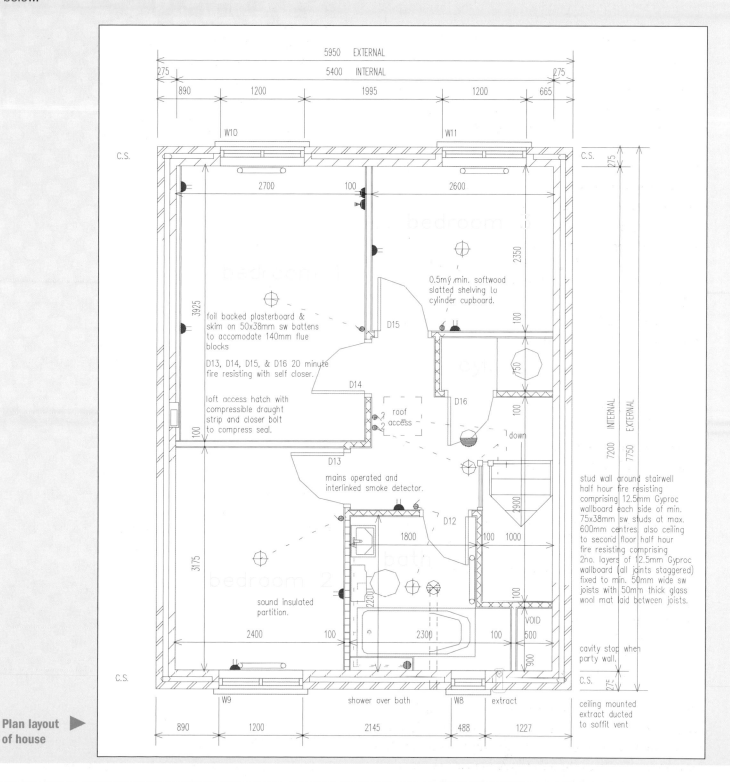

**Plan layout of house** ▶

## Assessment practice

You will need further information as to what quality and finish your client requires in order to complete the work.

Prepare a request for information (RFI) to the manufacturer of the staircase to ascertain the information necessary to build the staircase into the house. **P2**

Describe the method of construction and components that you will use to build the house and the arrangements necessary to incorporate them into the completed building. **P3**

Make a list of all the methods you can think of in which information is transferred to and from each member of the design team. **M2**

## Remember!

Remember there are many ways to build the house and your selection has to be realistic and workable. It may not be the only way to complete the work.

# Construction methods

## Characteristics

Each construction method has distinct characteristics; these are mainly focused on the type of material that is used to construct the finished buildings. The following materials will produce different characteristics for each building in which they are utilised:

- brickwork and blockwork
- structural steel – portal frame, skeleton frame, multi-storey
- precast concrete
- in situ concrete
- timber framed
- composite – a mixture of many materials
- various cladding materials – stone, clay, steel and glass.

As you can see from the list, each can be applied to different types of buildings from:

- commercial high specification offices
- factory business units
- industrial production
- government offices
- armed services facilities
- domestic housing.

So the function of the proposed building has a great effect on the characteristics of the materials used to build it.

## Applications and limitations of traditional and modern methods

### ■ Traditional

A traditional building historically has used brickwork, then a combination of brickwork and blockwork to form the external walls of the structure. The space between them formed a cavity which is now filled with insulation to increase the thermal efficiency of the overall construction. The traditional wall can only be applied to three- to four-storey buildings before the thickness at the base requires to be increased to take the greater loadings from above. External walls constructed in this way, therefore, have a limitation with height and need to be restrained at some point for stability. This can be achieved at the intermediate floor level and at the roof level through a physical connection with floor joists and with the roof ceiling joists. Gable ends are secured to the roof using straps.

### Remember!

Traditional building methods have a unique and historical relationship with much of our UK heritage; many old buildings are constructed from handmade bricks and are hundreds of years old. Modern technology has to be adapted when refurbishments are undertaken on such buildings.

Other types of traditional building incorporated a green oak frame which was used to carry the loads of the structure onto which local materials were placed to form walls and roof, thatch and stone with lime-washed rendering. Elements of this have been taken into modern construction with timber and rendered panels.

### ■ Modern

Modern buildings incorporate columns and beams made of concrete and steel. These have revolutionised the development of high-rise structures. Steel provides high strength to weight, and concrete provides high compressive strength but low tensile strength and has to be reinforced. Developments in concrete technology have enabled pre-casting components offsite which are then installed onsite. Roofs can now be made of steel sheeting which rests on cladding rails and enables much larger spans to be achieved without the use of additional columns.

The traditional timber oak frames have developed into the modern timber-framed construction. This replaces the inner skin of brickwork or blockwork. By applying the frame this way, great benefits can be achieved. The timber-framed building can be erected much faster, has greater insulation properties, can be used with any design shape and has excellent green characteristics with regard to environmental issues. Limitations on this process are, of course, fire. The internal surface of the timber frame has to be lined with plasterboard to increase fire protection. Secondly, a damp-proof membrane has to be installed to act as a moisture barrier to prevent internal condensation forming.

The development of the portal frame shape, which can be manufactured in concrete, timber or steel, has brought about a radical development of small to large single-storey industrial units. These can be erected speedily, and can incorporate a variety of external envelope types. The limitations of steel-framed buildings is that they require some form of fire protection to the steel as it loses 50 per cent of its strength when the temperature of a fire reaches over 500°C.

## Influence on design

Both traditional and modern construction methods have influences on design. Heritage and history associated with the traditional approach obviously have a great effect on the design requirements. This is further reinforced by the **listing** of buildings along with the formation of conservation areas in places of natural beauty.

## Key Term

**Listed building** A building of special architectural or historic interest in the UK. Alterations to these buildings must be carefully considered before they are made.

Structural steelwork has enabled larger spans and height to be reached. Inner cities now have skyscrapers along their skyline. With the advent of post-tensioned concrete, which is where steel reinforcement is put into tension on the concrete, larger spans that can bear more weight have been established.

Timber glue-lam beams, where a number of strips of timber are glued together in a mould and finished into beams, can now mimic the oak-framed buildings of the past. The Winter Garden building at Sheffield is a classic example.

Glass and glazing systems have a tremendous impact when coupled with the modern framed structures and can be used to great effect with systems that can now hang off a steel frame as a complete wall of glass.

## Multiple construction options

This is a modern technique that enables a series of multiples of one module to be constructed. The modules are constructed offsite and then are simply bolted together and finished onsite. This is sometimes referred to as volumetric construction. It has many advantages over traditional techniques, including:

- speed of construction
- savings on labour onsite
- savings on site preliminaries
- no limitations due to weather conditions
- high-quality factory finishes
- services integrated into the design.

Many modern hotels are built on this principle where the bathrooms are constructed as modules and simply craned into position.

## Variety of construction options

### ■ Primary and secondary requirements of a design

The primary requirements of a design are the structural frame of the proposed structure; the secondary requirements are the building envelope that hangs off the frame. As we have seen, there are several methods of producing a primary element. These can also be combined to form composite structures. For example, you can produce a design based on a steel-framed structure. The intermediate floors can be built using floor steel profiled decking, which is then used as a mould for a concrete floor which is poured into this. Hence the term composite construction.

The secondary elements, as we have seen, hang off the frame. These can take many forms such as:

- profiled steel cladding sheets
- profiled steel composite panels with insulation sandwich
- curtain walling in glass
- glazing spider systems
- traditional brick cladding
- cedar boarding.

The list can be extensive and technological advances mean that new materials are continually being developed.

# Terminology

Design and construction use a large number of technical words. Table 5.1 lists some of the main ones.

## Assessment practice

Design a two-storey, four-bedroom domestic dwelling of 180 m² with ensuite bathroom to master bedroom.

Produce a simple sketch design and sample floor plans of your proposed construction using standard conventions and symbols. **P4**

Create a sample specification for a section of your proposal such as the ground floor or the walls to provide suitable instructions to the construction team. **P5**

Interpret and evaluate construction details using recognised technical terminology by developing the specification into a full window and door schedule for the property. **M3**

**Table 5.1 Construction technology**

| Terminology | Definition |
| --- | --- |
| *Construction and design* | |
| Portal frame | the portal shape formed by the use of two columns and two beams that meet at an apex and form a portal shape |
| In situ | often given to concrete works which are cast in situ, i.e. in place supported by formwork |
| Superstructure | the visible works above ground |
| Substructure | the foundation and works below ground level that cannot be seen |
| Building envelope | the coverings of the building |
| *Architectural* | |
| Grid centres | the dimensional setting out of a building using a grid format of either squares or rectangles |
| Working drawings | the final set of detailed drawings that enable the principal contractor to construct the building |
| Plan of work | see the detailed section explanation on page 00 |
| Column | a vertical support |
| Lintel | horizontal support member over openings |
| *Legislation* | |
| Enforcement | the process of enforcing the legislation, e.g. the HSE |
| Prosecution | the court system of punishment |
| Acts or regulations | the law and subsequent regulations produced by the EU and the UK |
| *Health, safety and welfare and environmental factors* | |
| EPA | Environmental Protection Act |
| Wastage | the product left after processing a material |
| Risk | the level of harm associated with a hazard |
| Environmentally friendly | a chemical or process that does not harm the environment |

## Sketch designs

These are a series of sketches, often three-dimensional, that illustrate the designer's interpretation of the client's brief. Several interpretations of the brief may be drawn. The client can then decide which parts or design they like and this can be taken forward into a final sketch design which is then approved and moved on to the next process. Often the local authority is involved if outline planning permission is required along with any other agency that has an input.

**Remember!**

The information produced and illustrated by the designer must be accurate, clear and easy to understand by the contractor or the builder undertaking the work onsite. Errors and omissions can be costly to put right after the event or can lead to indecision or delays in the work taking place. They also lead to confusion and a loss of confidence in the team members' ability to complete the job effectively.

## Drawings

### Construction drawings

Drawings are the main medium by which designers convey their meaning to builders. The ability to work from drawings is a well-developed skill practised over time with each team member seeking out the information that they require from the illustration. For instance, a building control officer will be interested in the materials and that the completed job will comply with the existing regulations, whereas the builder will be most concerned with how they will be able to complete the job and the logistical problems

**Remember!**

Drawings are the main way that we communicate our ideas – your drawings need to show all relevant information clearly!

of arranging all the components in a reasonable and workable sequence.

ISO drawing sizes are standardised – see Unit 8 Graphical Detailing, page 314 for the dimensions of the most commonly used sizes.

Before creating drawings and beginning work on a project, it is customary practice to establish what is required from the work such as:

- title of each drawing and date that it will be needed
- contents of each drawing
- what scales are to be used for each drawing
- what size sheets are to be used
- referencing system to be adopted
- tolerances and style of the content.

Construction drawings are important documents and a register of their issue will need to be kept so that everyone concerned can be assured that they are using the correct version of the drawing and any amendments have been correctly assimilated by the team.

### Location drawings

Location drawings show where the work will take place (see Figure 5.6). They also give an overall impression of

**Remember!**

Location drawings are the first drawings most people see – a good impression of the quality is required!

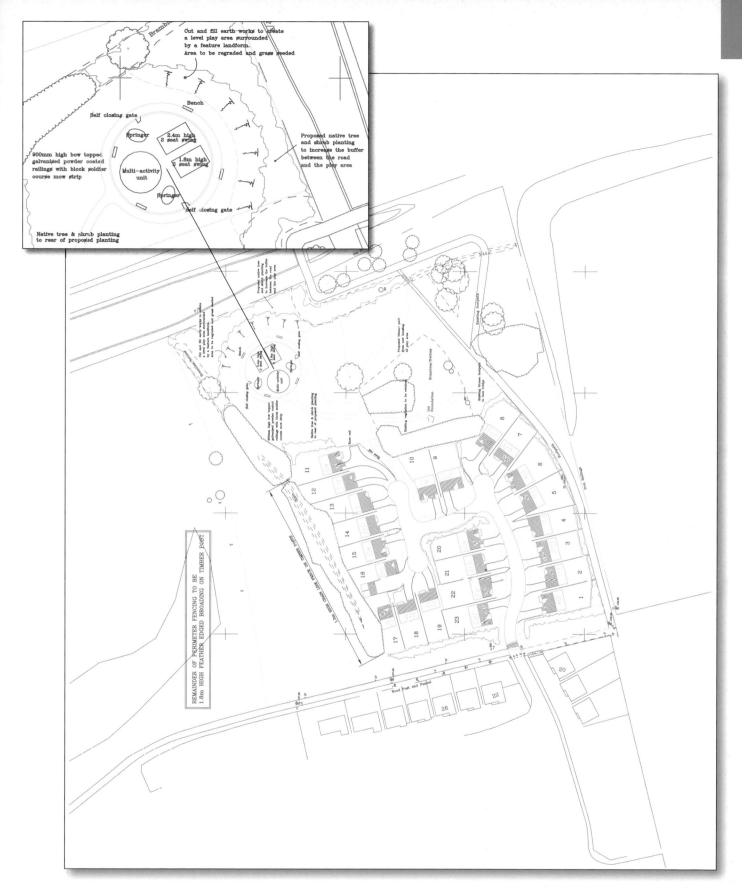

Figure 5.6 A location drawing

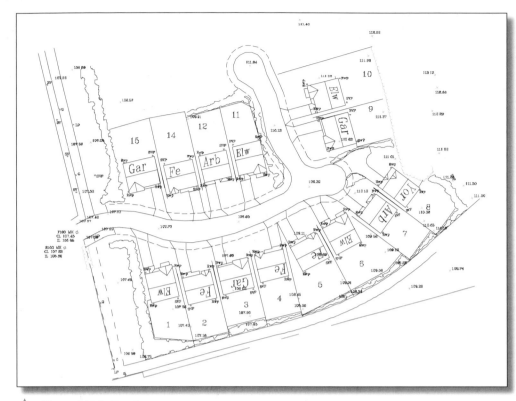

▲ Figure 5.7 A site plan

the whole building or project to set out the building. Location drawings also include references to site plans, floor plans, sections and elevations.

## Site plan

Site plans locate the buildings, roads, landscaping and datum used for the development (see Figure 5.7). Frequently, they are drawn at a scale of 1:200 or 1:500 and show the overall layout of the site.

## Floor plans

Rooms, layout, doors, windows are usually shown on layout plans and illustrated by various scales – 1:100 is the most common although several instances may be found where 1:50 or 1:200 is used (see Figure 5.8).

## Section drawing

A section drawing gives a vertical view of the building and shows technical details that could not be seen on a plan or floor layout (see Figure 5.9). The most appropriate scale used for vertical sections varies, but frequently 1:50 is used and for sections or drawing of individual components a scale of 1:10 or full size could be adopted.

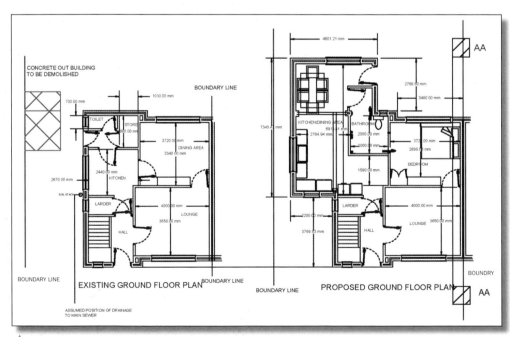

▲ Figure 5.8 A floor plan

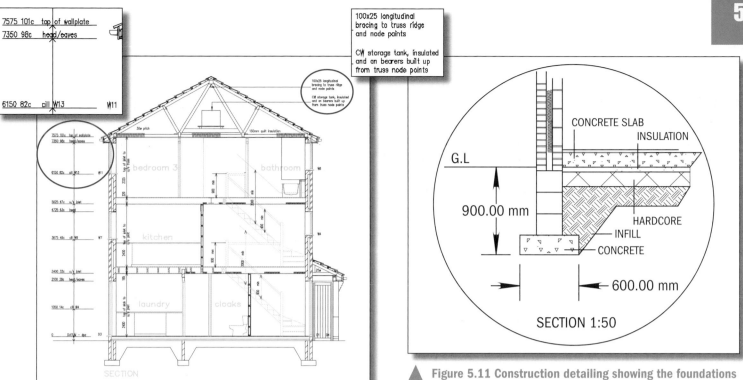

**Figure 5.9 A section drawing**

**Figure 5.11 Construction detailing showing the foundations**

## Construction detailing

Construction detailing means providing clear details about each component. On a scaled drawing at 1:500, many of the intricate features of the components and their interface will not be seen, hence a more detailed section will need to be provided. In Figure 5.10, the

foundations can be seen on the main cross-section, but the details and the actual components cannot be easily extracted. A section to show this part of the works is necessary. This process is known as construction detailing and can be seen in Figures 5.11 and 5.12.

The section of the foundation is circled and the contents need to be shown on a separate drawing to a scale that shows the actual components more accurately. The

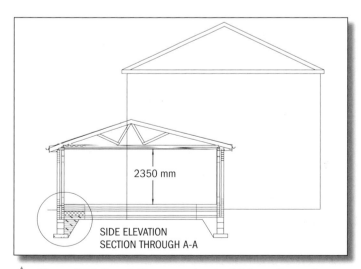

**Figure 5.10 Foundations are clearly visible on the main cross-section**

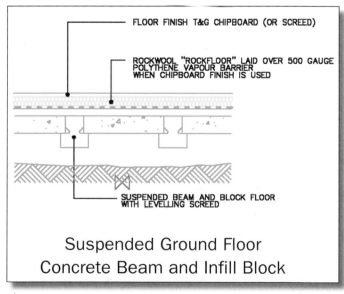

**Figure 5.12 Pot and beam floor construction detailing**

section is thus drawn to a more appropriate scale with dimensions shown to help the contractor to carry out the works more accurately.

## WINDOW SCHEDULE

| Window Number | Boulton + Paul Reference | Size W x H mm | Birtley Lintel Ref x length mm | Catnic Lintel Ref x length mm |
|---|---|---|---|---|
| W1 | HN10C | 488 x 1050 | see D1 | |
| W2 | N10C | 488 x 1050 | see D3 | |
| *W3 | HN12C | 488 x 1200 | | |
| *W4 | HN12C | 488 x 1200 | CB70 x 1500 | |
| *W5 | C312CC | 1440 x 1050 | CB70 x 2100 | |
| W6 | 212C | 1200 x 1200 | CB70 x 1500 | |
| W7 | 210C | 1200 x 1050 | CB70 x 1500 | |
| *W8 | HN10C | 488 x 1050 | CBEV50 x 750 | |
| *W9 | C213CC | 1200 x 1350 | CB70 x 1500 | |
| *W10 | 212CC | 1200 x 1200 | CBEV50 x 1500 | |
| *W11 | 212CC | 1200 x 1200 | CBEV50 x 1500 | |

 Figure 5.13 A window schedule

**Processes and procedures required to obtain planning consent**

Local authorities have a wide range of powers to control construction development in their area. There are numerous Acts of Parliament and legislative controls that need to be considered for larger developments, although the main ones to consider for most residential or small developments are:

- Town and Country Planning Act 1990
- Town and Country Planning (General Development Procedure) Order 1995
- Town and Country Planning General Development Order 1988
- Town and Country Planning (Fees for Applications Amendments) Regulations 1997
- The Planning (Listed Buildings and Conservation Areas) Act 1990

Local authorities will develop plans for the area in a number of ways. They have a requirement to develop the area but also to protect the area from developments that would have an adverse effect on the natural and built environment while considering the need to allocate land and areas for development by entrepreneurs or to satisfy local needs.

## Theory into practice

Visit the website of your local authority – you can find this by visiting www.direct.gov.uk and clicking on a link to your local council. Check out the planning department and the services that it offers.

As well as the power to control the class of buildings, local authorities 'zone' areas of land for industrial, residential, conservation and natural beauty. Hence, in these areas the appearance of any building will also be controlled so that new buildings will be in harmony or natural accord with the existing surroundings. Most of these conditions have been considered for new developments or buildings. Several other conditions exist for change of use and adaptation of buildings.

There are some exemptions:

- small developments such as extensions to semi-detached and detached houses of not more than 70 cubic metres or 15 per cent, whichever is the greater; up to 115 cubic metres in industrial buildings or up to 25 per cent of the total volume or 1000 square metres of floor space
- agricultural buildings or buildings on agricultural land
- temporary construction site accommodation
- erection of garden walls, fences and gates
- certain developments undertaken by the local authority.

### ■ Planning permission

To obtain **planning permission**, an application must be made to the planning department at the local authority offices. Early discussion between architect and the department is nearly always beneficial to rule out or take into account any objections or obvious conditions

## Key Term

**Planning permission** Formal consent from the local authority allowing you to build. You must not build without planning permission (except in the case of the exemptions listed above).

that will apply to any application that may follow. These discussions often advise and guide the architect as to whether a full application is likely to pass through the planning committee and approval to proceed be granted.

In order to gain outline planning permission, your application will need to be supported by the following items:

- four copies of the application forms available from the local authority
- one copy of a certificate confirming the ownership of the land on which the development will take place
- one copy of the site plan or a block plan indicating the position of the development.

At this stage, the planning committee may grant outline planning permission for the development to proceed to full planning permission. In this case, the information as stated above is required, but in addition four copies of every floor plan and four copies of every elevation will be required. These drawings should show any relevant features of the site, the location of any existing and proposed building and the external finishes such as the colours and textures of brickwork, type of curtain walling and so on.

Planning permission is granted or refused and the applicant informed by letter after the planning committee has reached a decision. The planning committee sits every month throughout the year. Sometimes the committee will state that permission will be granted subject to a condition or improvement to the application. By all accounts, this condition will need to be reasonable, fair and relevant to the development concerned; an example of this is that the committee may insist that the development include sufficient car parking space for all occupants of the building.

The planning authority must provide a decision on all applications within eight weeks of the application being

made unless there is an agreement to extend this for some reason. Outline planning permission will remain current for three years and if full permission is granted, construction work must begin on the site within five years.

Appeals can be brought should an applicant be dissatisfied with a decision. These decisions can be heard in the first instance by the local authority and then by the Secretary of State and, finally, if the applicant is still dissatisfied, by a court of law.

### ■ Building Regulations applications

The Building Regulations apply in England and Wales and exist to promote quality workmanship and to ensure the health and safety of those people that use the building. Building Regulations apply to domestic dwellings and commercial buildings but have differing levels of compliance so that buildings are built fit for purpose – for instance, applying Building Regulations for houses means ensuring one level of heat retention that would be inappropriate for shops and retail outlets where large glass areas allow for shop displays, hence the maximum amount of heat loss will be quite different for each building.

### Remember!

Building Regulations apply to most new buildings and many alterations of existing buildings, whether domestic, commercial or industrial.

Building Regulations promote:

- standards for most aspects of a building's construction, including its structure, fire safety, sound insulation, drainage, ventilation and electrical safety (electrical safety was added in January 2005)
- energy efficiency in buildings
- the needs of all people, including those with disabilities, in accessing and moving around buildings.

# Specifications

Drawings and illustrations convey to the reader an image of what the finished product ought to look like when completed. In addition to the contract drawings, a specification provides essential information to the contractor about the materials, the finish and the workmanship required of each element of the building, hence the **specification** is a very important part of the documentation necessary to complete the works. The specification is therefore complementary to the drawings.

## Key Term

**Specification** A written document that expresses information from the drawing in technical terms. It helps the reader to understand what the drawings represent.

Quantity surveyors typically and usually write the specification and so it is essential that they have a command of both construction technology and linguistic skills to express themselves in writing. Building legislation and current standards, codes of practice and requirements for the quality of the finished product are all criteria that will need to be considered if designers and specification writers are to work closely together to ensure that the harmony between drawings and specifications is maintained.

The specification is used for the following purposes:

- By the design team as their proposals are being drafted and developed. Notes, comments and initial thoughts on the suitability and durability of materials in the construction can be maintained so as to determine whether the building project can proceed in the present form. This then has an impact on the standards adopted by the design team and the methods of quality control expected of the work completed onsite. Used in this way, the specification is a design tool to be applied to the construction project as work proceeds.
- By the quantity surveyor to explain and amplify the bills of quantity into detailed descriptions of all the components in the building project. Measured

items should be accounted for methodically and systematically and the reader should be left in no doubt as to what is required and what the completed product should look like. The specification will be read by contractors who wish to tender for the project, which will enable an estimation of the time and resources needed to complete the works.

- By the construction team onsite as a reference to what the designer instructed them to build. The contractor will use the specification as a guide to the tests and quality control mechanisms that ensure the building is fit for purpose.

Well-crafted and explicit specifications make clear the extent of the works, show information that cannot easily or readily be shown on a drawing and include references to current standards and practice. Specifications also provide a useful explanation of the materials to be used and the standards of the quality expected within them. Included in the description is often any caveat (warning) or restriction on the use or installation or conditions during which the work can be carried out, such as time factors, responsibilities, curing times, application periods, which could not be effectively described or shown on a drawing.

## Remember!

The specification forms a very important part of the contract documents and includes a considerable amount of information.

Correctly written specifications should be:

- complementary and must agree with the drawings and the other contract documents. Cross referencing is essential if they are to be read in conjunction with existing drawings
- logically developed and straightforward to use. They should follow a reasonable and easy-to-understand format that allows the reader to see each component in turn and in an appropriate sequence
- full and descriptive which allows the reader to clearly ascertain the details of the components that they describe

- specific and precise, free from ambiguity and should not lead to any chance of misinterpretation
- concise, brief and to the point avoiding any superfluous language or unnecessary descriptions.

The specification relates information about the construction details, but it does not lay down how the construction work should take place. This is usually a matter for the contractor, except where there are health, safety and welfare issues, and in this case the specification may well remind the contractor of the requirements for the safe and successful installation of a particular component in line with current legislation. Hence, specification writing is about describing the end results rather than the means of achieving this end result.

Specifications should be set out consistently and in a standard way, work from general principles and then move into specific elements of each component. A typical sequence of this operation is to consider the subject, then move to a description of the circumstances and finally to consider the size of the element. Descriptions taking this format usually relate specific instructions and commands better than wordy, rambling explanations.

The nature of the construction industry and the use of technology means that there will inevitably be a degree of jargon and/or technical expressions that specification writers assume the reader is capable of either understanding without explanation or is able to seek their meaning from suitable sources. Specification writers ought to be aware of local variations and vernacular expressions that could lead to confusion. They should also avoid writing specifications in legal terminology.

### Remember!

Specifications should use only words in common usage and that are universally accepted so that contractors are readily able to understand them.

Standard specification clauses exist in databanks and databases which can be very useful. The advent of computers, word processors and spreadsheets has aided this development and precious time and energy can be saved by using readily available software that allows the use of standard specifications.

## Performance specification

Specifications can also be used to provide information to a manufacturer or supplier of components, for example subcontractors who supply doors, window frames, staircases, air conditioning, telecommunication equipment and so on. The specification states what is needed in terms of performance rather than how a need is to be met. Examples of performance specifications state such things as the fire resistance, the acoustic performance, the dimensional tolerance and the durability of the component rather than a full description of the way the component is used in the building. Bricks, for example, can be specified as type, size, colour and texture and then several manufacturers can be approached to see if they have a product that fits the performance of what the architect is looking for so that the architect can choose the one that provides best value on behalf of the client.

## Sample specification

Specifications help and guide the builder. They provide information that cannot readily be seen on the drawing. Let's start with the foundations of this house. The specification shows reference to the ground conditions, the local authority building control officers and the dimensions of the trenchblock that the designer has specified for use in the footing.

Refer to the cross-section of the house in Figure 5.10.

### Sample specification:
#### Foundations

Assumed ground class IV (firm sandy/firm clay) to be checked on site and confirmed by Building Control. Depth of foundations to Local Authority approval. Concrete strip footings minimum 200 mm thick projecting 150 mm to each side of load-bearing walls 275 mm thick. 'Trenchblock' to be used below ground level.

Now, let's consider the walls. You have to explain what the components are, the dimensions, thickness and the nature of how they go together. This is where your knowledge of construction technology is important. You will need to include references about the insulation filling necessary to comply with the building regulations and how the steel ties that bind both leaves of the external walls together will be built into the structure. Important items such as the damp proof course and the filling made to cavities at low level along with the closings at junctions such as windows and doors will need to be explained if you expect the contractor to complete the work to the appropriate standard.

## Sample specification: Floor

Powerfloat finish to 100 mm thick concrete slab on a 1200 gauge polythene sheet. Damp proof membrane on 50 mm sand blinding on 150 mm clean and dry well compacted hardcore base. Damp proof membrane to lap damp proof course at edges and external walls.

## Sample specification: External walls

275 mm cavity walls, 100 mm facing bricks, 75 mm cavity with blown fibre insulation. 100 mm medium density concrete block inner leaf, dry lined with 9.5 mm plasterboard on dabs, seated around all junctions with floors, walls and ceilings.

200 mm long stainless steel butterfly wall ties at maximum 450 mm vertical centres and 750 horizontal centres. Cavities filled with weak mix concrete up to ground floor level. Horizontal damp proof course 150 mm above ground level and to vertical cavity closures. Cavities closed at eaves, verge and all openings with insulating blockwork/dpc to reduce the risk of cold bridging. Flexible closers to be used vertically at all junctions with party walls.

The floor is not immediately obvious from the drawing and even when the floor is shown on a plan, there is vital information required to allow the building to construct the components missing from the illustration in conventional drawings. Hence the specification would then include a description of the main things that the designer has included.

So, from the specification we can gather that the ground floor is made of concrete and has damp proofing resistance built into the construction. Let's now consider the upper floors which are of a different type of construction and will need a specification of their own. The underside of the upper floor which also forms the ceiling of the room below is also specified here with the ceiling finished with a 12.5 mm plasterboard and finally skimmed with gypsum plaster.

## Sample specification: Upper floors

19 mm tongue and groove flooring grade moisture resistant type 2/3 chipboard on softwood joist. Double joists under partitions with 38 mm thick minimum solid strutting at mid span for joists spanning 2500–4500 mm. 2 no rows equally spaced for spans over 4500 mm. 30 × 5 mm galvanised mild steel straps at 2 m centres with 100 × 50 mm sw noggins fixed to external walls. Galvanised mild steel joist hangers at party walls. 12.5 mm plasterboard and skim to soffits.

The roof specification is very important and includes information on the pitch of the roof, the tiles and the roof covering along with details that the builder will need to be able to construct it according to the standard of workmanship that the designer wishes to incorporate. Reference to bracing, mild steel straps and additional timbers included for strength is identified along with the finish to the underside of the ceiling in the upper rooms.

## Sample specification: Roof

Concrete interlocking roof tiles on 38 × 25 mm preservative treated softwood battens on sarking felt. Gangnail trussed rafters to BS5268 Part 3 1985 laid at 600 mm centres with 100 × 25 mm sw diagonal bracing to BS5268 Part 3 30 × 5 mm galvanised mild steel straps at maximum 2 m centres with 75 × 50 mm sw noggins fixed to 3 no trusses and external wall at ceiling & roof level.

150 mm fibreglass quilt insulation laid between ceiling members. Ceiling finish 12.7 mm plasterboard and plaster skim. Eaves ventilation equivalent to a continuous 10 mm slot with proprietary insulation restrain. 25 mm eaves vent to sloping soffits with ridgevent.

## Assessment practice

Consider what happens when design changes are made during the construction phase. Evaluate what will happen when the design team has to make changes to the design. **D2**

# Preparation for assessment

## ■ Brief

You have been approached by a client who wishes to build two detached houses on plots of adjacent land shown in the location plan below. The client wishes to build two dwellings in order to sell one of them and move into one of them themselves. The houses will need to be no more than 100 m² floor area each and have three bedrooms, one bathroom and one ensuite to the master bedroom, one kitchen/dining area and a lounge. The buildings will consist of a ground floor and a single upper floor made of timber joists and floorboards. The local authority has granted outline planning permission for these houses and is likely to pass appropriate plans if they are submitted to the planning committee.

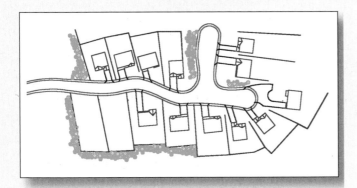

▲ **Location plan**

Complete the following tasks:

Identify the people that you will need to employ on this project. Draw a diagram to show the working roles and responsibilities. **P1**

List the factors that influence how the design takes shape. Describe the impact and the importance of these factors to the finished house. **P1**

Your client has asked you to advise them on whether the RIBA Plan of Work is suitable for this project. Examine the advantages and the disadvantages of the RIBA plan and explain whether the RIBA plan would work effectively on this project. **M1**

Prepare the following series of drawings to show the building and the extent of the project:

- Elevations
- Ground floor plan
- First floor plan
- Cross section drawing
- Structural detailing of window frames and door frames **P3 P4**

Write a specification to accompany the drawings explaining the standard of workmanship, quality and components identified on the drawings in P3/P4. **P5 M3**

Write a letter to invite suitable contractors to tender for the works. **P2**

Following a design change you will need to make a variation to the original specification. You have now decided to use pot and beam floors on the ground floor. Produce a Variation Order for the contractor. **P2**

For the Variation Order you have created in P2 above, rewrite the specification. **P5**

Write a letter to the contractor to explain the impact that the variation will have on the project duration and the integration of the work. **P2**

Write a letter to the client to illustrate and compare methods of making changes to the design. Appraise the effectiveness of how these changes will be communicated to the contractor. **M2 D2**

The RIBA Plan of Work may seem rigid in its application to small projects like this. Evaluate the RIBA plan of work in terms of effective teamwork and the introduction of the changes to design once construction has started. **D1**

## Grading tips

You will need to have an awareness of the RIBA Plan of Work – this question will allow you to analyse the effectiveness of the RIBA plan. **M1**

You will have to show how you have interpreted and analysed the technical content of the drawings and worked them into a technical specification. **M3**

You will achieve a merit if you can show that you have compared the methods of making changes. To achieve a distinction, you will need to extend this and appraise the effectiveness of how these changes are communicated. **M2** **D2**

This task takes you further than analysing (merit) and asks that you begin to evaluate the plan of work and its use with teams. **D1**

## Knowledge check

1 What are the stages in the RIBA Plan of Work?

2 Explain the advantages of using the RIBA plan.

3 List the disadvantages of using the RIBA plan.

4 List four members of the design team and identify their main functions.

5 How does an architect differ from an architectural technologist?

6 Explain the architect's responsibilities to the client.

7 Define the term 'specification'.

8 What are the characteristics of a well-written specification?

9 What are the duties of a quantity surveyor?

10 To whom does the clerk of works report and what is the function of the role on construction sites?

11 How does an invitation to tender differ from a selective tender?

12 What documentation is necessary to support a planning application?

13 What is the difference between building regulations and planning consent?

14 What scale is most suited to a location drawing?

15 List six components shown on a floor plan layout drawing.

| Grading criteria: Unit 5 | | |
|---|---|---|
| **To achieve a pass grade the evidence must show that the learner is able to:** | **To achieve a merit grade the evidence must show that, in addition to the pass criteria, the learner is able to:** | **To achieve a distinction grade the evidence must show that, in addition to the pass and merit criteria, the learner is able to:** |
| **P1** identify and describe factors that influence the design process in terms of procedures, communication and the need to work with others and the roles of four different team members **Assessment practice pages 197, 218** | **M1** explain for a complex project the operation and effectiveness of the RIBA *Architect's Plan of Work*, including examples of where it is modified/not followed **Assessment practice pages 197, 218** | **D1** analyse and evaluate the effectiveness of the RIBA *Architect's Plan of Work* in terms of teamwork and the introduction of changes to design once construction has started **Assessment practice pages 197, 218** |
| **P2** construct and write suitable instructions or requests for information to members of the design team **Assessment practice pages 203–4, 218** | **M2** compare and explain the methods recommended for communicating design changes to members of the design team **Assessment practice pages 204, 218** | |
| **P3** describe construction methods and components and the arrangements necessary to incorporate them into the completed building **Assessment practice pages 204, 218** | | |
| **P4** produce sketch designs, plans, drawings and/or sketches of construction details using standard conventions and symbols **Assessment practice pages 207, 218** | **M3** interpret and evaluate tutor-provided construction details, using recognised technical terminology **Assessment practice pages 207, 218** | **D2** appraise the implications of a tutor-provided set of instructions produced by a design team, that represent modifications to the original contract. **Assessment practice pages 207, 218** |
| **P5** create sample specifications for construction details to provide suitable instructions to the construction team **Assessment practice pages 207, 218** | | |

# Building technology in construction

## Introduction

Today's construction industry requires technicians who understand modern construction methods, have an appreciation of traditional materials and a knowledge of plant and equipment that will be required to put these components together.

Buildings have evolved over time from simple shelters to the complex and sophisticated structures that we see around us today. Combinations of traditional materials such as brick, mortar and timber form the basis of most buildings, but the increased use of modern materials such as structural glass, plastics and prefabricated components is found in abundance as buildings become more efficient, integrate greater building services systems and other features to make them a more appropriate place to live and work. The challenge for the constructors of future buildings is to combine sustainable building technology with the ability to deliver high-quality buildings for society. The need to plan and organise this work, including the use of skilled labour, is necessary if constructors are to meet this challenge.

### How you will be assessed

This unit is internally assessed by your tutor. A variety of activities is included in this unit to help you understand all aspects of building technology used in the construction industry.

After completing this unit you should be able to achieve the following outcomes:

1 Understand common forms of low-rise construction currently used for domestic and commercial buildings
2 Be able to describe, illustrate and evaluate the requirements and techniques used in the construction of substructures for low-rise domestic and commercial buildings
3 Be able to describe, illustrate and evaluate the techniques used in the construction of superstructures for low-rise domestic and commercial buildings
4 Understand the implications of environmental issues and legislative constraints on building construction and the infrastructure required to support typical construction processes

# Thinking points

Designing and building houses requires understanding of building technology and the ability to translate these details into the finished product. Imagine that you have acquired your site, and you intend to build a pair of semi-detached houses on the plot. What will you do first? How can you bring all the elements together at the right time?

As you work through this chapter, you will need to consider all the elements of houses in turn, from exploring the site, choosing the right foundations, laying the ground floor and then moving on to the upper floors. When these are complete, the roof will need to be installed and the building made weatherproof. Once complete, the shell will need to be fitted with a staircase and a suitable floor surface, some windows and the living area will need fitting out with a kitchen and a bathroom. You may also wish to fit built-in wardrobes. Doorways, with suitable locks, keys and latches, will secure the property so that you or your client is ready to move in and furnish the house turning it into a home.

1 How long will these operations take?

2 How many tradespeople will you need to complete these tasks?

3 Prepare a set of drawings to allow contractors to complete the work to your specification

4 How will you ensure that the foundations and excavations are carried out safely?

5 What type of building do you wish to create and what materials are necessary?

6 Make a list of all the elements in the substructure.

7 Make a list of all the elements in the superstructure.

8 What services and utilities will be needed in the house?

9 What plant and equipment will you need to build the house?

10 If you are selling the property, what good things can you say about the quality of materials that you have used?

## Building uses

Creating a safe enclosure was the first requirement of humankind in the development of housing. Since then, our requirements have included many more things to improve our standard of living and our built environment.

### Houses and flats

Houses are typically small structures of one or two storeys with simple components such as bricks, mortar, timber to make floors, roofs, windows and so on. Plastic resins and other synthetic materials have become available in recent years and have made houses significantly more efficient in **thermal performance** and noise exclusion. Improvements in the comfort features of houses, such as integrated kitchens, built-in bedroom furniture and building services, have meant that our houses have become increasingly sophisticated structures, which have to comply with legislation and regulations that place high standards of performance on both the quality of the finished product and also the workmanship of the assembly of these components.

### Key Term

**Thermal performance** The ability of a material to retain heat in the structure.

### Theory into practice

Working with a partner, list how many different types of buildings you can think of. Explain how these differ from each other.

Flats and apartments group together individual dwellings in a common structure, making the construction and assembly of these units more economic than if one unit only was occupying the land.

### Warehouses and light industrial units

Warehouses and light industrial units are commercial buildings and do not list comfort as their main criterion. More likely, they are **open-span buildings** with steel frames and clad with aluminium or functional materials that allow space to be enclosed both economically and safely.

### Key Term

**Open-span buildings** These are typically built using a skeleton frame, which allows an open-plan floor area that can be divided later into smaller spaces. This clear floor space is particularly well suited to offices where the final floor plan can be changed to suit any client who wishes to move into the building.

### Retail

Retail outlets such as shops and commercial buildings can be purpose built or adapted from existing buildings. Newly built premises often take the form of large open-span, **portal frame** buildings which provide a large floor space such as those used in supermarkets and low-rise department stores. Smaller shops and retail outlets modified from larger-type houses need special works to adapt them from a residential property into a building

### Key Term

**Portal frame** A structural frame that forms the building with lightweight cladding to provide weather resistance and to create an enclosure.

A portal frame ▶

that meets the requirements of employment and more frequent visitors that a retail outlet will have. The requirements for fire resistance, noise reduction and ventilation are stricter for commercial buildings than they are for domestic dwellings, and any modification will need to take account of these if the adaptation is to be successful.

## Theory into practice

Working with a partner, list all the things that you would need to change in order to convert a house into a small retail shop. What difference, if any, will it make to the types of commodity the shop sells?

### Offices

Offices also use large open-span buildings, with many employers choosing to create smaller working spaces based on the functional requirements of the work that will be undertaken there, for example secure areas for accounts or transactions requiring the storage or exchange of money, or the creation of small private units where individual discussion can take place and privacy is required for clients. Small office buildings can be built in much the same way as housing, although should the

requirement be for more than four storeys or for larger spans, then a more robust method of construction will be necessary, perhaps including the use of structural steel rather than bricks, mortar and timber.

# Forms of construction

### Traditional building

Traditionally, houses have used bricks and mortar to build **monolithic walls** which support the roof, floors and all other components. The established and traditional method of building houses is to take material to the site and to build the property to design plans **in situ**.

## Key Terms

**Monolithic walls** Single structural elements that form the basis of the building. Typically, walls and floors are monolithic because they support loads in one direction.

**In situ** Building each component on site.

## Prefabricated construction including timber frame

Timber-framed houses have been built in the UK for over 300 years, but they represent a modern method of working. Rather than building each component in situ as builders would do with more traditional methods, modern construction techniques have enabled timber panels to be crafted in workshops and then taken to site for assembly. This development, along with the use of modern materials and the increased use of insulation to comply with legislation on heat loss, has made homes more efficient. The reduction in on-site time has made timber-framed housing more attractive to builders who can offer better homes at lower prices.

The use of timber-framed panels has also changed the function of some of the elements of the structure. Some items that were at one time load bearing are now no longer used to support other parts of the structure.

## Load bearing and non-load bearing

Timber-framed buildings use timber panels, typically made from a 100 mm × 50 mm softwood carcass with plywood or other sheet materials nailed to it to give it strength. The timber panels are load bearing as they support the roof, while any **cladding**, such as brickwork, acts only as a decorative facing. Internally, the partitions simply divide the interior into useable space and provide privacy. They do not support the structure and are therefore non-load bearing. The partitions may need special fixings and fittings if they are to be used to support other items such as cabinets or other wall-mounted items.

## Key Term

**Cladding** The lightweight material that forms the enclosure of the building. Cladding is usually lightweight because it does not have to carry the structure.

## Single-storey buildings

In commercial premises used as retail outlets or small industrial buildings, the main structure is frequently made from a frame of structural steel. This frame provides the anchor points for rails or cross rails – known as purlins – that support aluminium sheeting which has been formed and shaped into a corrugated profile that adds to its strength. Again, this type of cladding uses significant amounts of insulation material to enable the building to comply with relevant heat loss legislation and it provides some stiffening of the frame to wind forces but is mainly considered to be non-load bearing. In most portal frame buildings, the first two metres of the walls are made from traditional masonry (brickwork/blockwork) walls, which provides additional security at low level.

## Low-rise buildings

Buildings that increase in height will need additional bracing and strengthening as they get taller. Commercial buildings of up to three storeys are typically made from structural steel in standard sections that provide an open-plan area which can be split further into smaller spaces by the occupier and tailored to their needs using demountable partitions and non-load bearing elements.

## Detached housing

Speculative housing in the UK involves house builders constructing houses and domestic units for sale to a buoyant market that at present shows no signs of slowing down. House building across the country cannot keep up with demand and as such many designs for detached houses have been simplified and standardised to National House-Building Council (NHBC) standards. The rising standards have led to an increased number of features being incorporated into most detached houses, including en-suite bathrooms, home offices, fire and intruder alarms.

### Terraced housing

In Victorian times, terraced housing provided volume housing at cheap prices and the ability to accommodate large numbers of people in a given area. This was at a time of significant migration from rural England to the industrial cities. Modern designs use a similar format of structural walls coupled with roofing systems that stretch across multiple properties with appropriate fire and privacy breaks to create individual dwellings.

### Roofs

#### ■ Pitched roofs

Roofs can take many forms ranging from flat, monopitch, gabled, hipped or accommodating multiple pitches and features. Traditionally, roofs have been built by carpenters on site using large sections of timber with the features being created as work proceeds. More recently, the use of trussed rafters has meant that the roof is crafted using a series of manufactured triangles of frames to create the roof in pieces that are then assembled in situ. The use of trussed rafters has resulted in improvements in the standard of workmanship and thermal performance, and the use of smaller, more economic sections of timber has made roofing more affordable.

#### ■ Flat roofs

Flat roofs are cheaper than pitched roofs. The cheapness of their construction has led to them being used for smaller contracts, especially small extensions to existing domestic dwellings. Flat roofs, incorrectly constructed, suffer from a great deal of condensation. For bigger projects, the use of large sheet materials or rolled

aluminium profiled sheeting with correctly positioned **vapour checks** has been much more successful.

## Key Term

**Vapour checks** Impermeable barriers or membranes used to prevent moisture passing through the structure.

## Theory into practice

Draw a traditional pitched roof with a hip section and a dormer window. Identify the components of the roof, using the correct terminology for each part.

### ■ Short-span and medium-span roofs

Short-span roofs can be made from timber, whereas longer-span requirements will need stronger members made from either steel or concrete. Short- and medium-span roofs are cheaper to construct.

# Implications of different forms of construction

Traditionally built buildings are labour intensive and require most of their construction to be built on site.

This makes the process expensive and difficult to monitor for quality control. Various tradespeople are required such as a ground working crew, a bricklaying gang, several joiners or carpenters, roof tilers/slaters, plasterers and then the services engineers, such as plumbers and electricians, to fit out the interior services. It also requires that materials are delivered to site which then have to be stored ready for use.

## Prefabrication

In recent times, there has been a shift towards prefabrication of single or multiple components which has increased the speed of erection on site for the completed units and has also resulted in improved performance based on the high quality of materials and workmanship. A high level of quality control can be maintained in workshop conditions and the completed components taken to site for assembly.

### Remember!

Prefabrication involves manufacturing and constructing components such as kitchen units, staircases and window frames in a factory. The components are then taken to the site where they are assembled. Using prefabricated components reduces the amount of time spent on site compared with the traditional method of constructing everything on site from scratch.

### Thinking points

In 2003, Forest Bank Prison was built near Manchester. The use of prefabricated cells allowed the prison to be built in reduced contract time since all the cells were designed to be constructed off site, prepared with all the necessary fittings and taken to site for assembly on a prepared base. Later, when all the cells were bolted together, services were connected and secure doors were fitted.

The success of prefabrication within the construction process depends on the following:

- *A well-designed construction site layout.* This typically relies on the construction site manager having a detailed knowledge of the operations and the layout of the construction site to ensure that each component is integrated at the appropriate time.
- *Correct sequencing of the construction works.* This relies on the designer and the construction site manager working together to ensure that the correct plant and components are delivered to the site in the right sequence.
- *Use of prefabricated components wherever possible.* Careful consideration of the structure and the design brief will enable the designer to identify all components of the project that are suitable for prefabrication. The construction site manager should be consulted as they are also likely to have detailed information on the practicalities of delivering large items to site and whether it will be feasible to assemble and install large items on site.
- *Use of plant at all stages of construction.* Wherever possible, skilled craftspersons should use machinery to help them assemble and install components correctly. The reduction or elimination of as much physical labour as possible is a key feature in improving the economic viability of prefabricated housing and building projects.

### Remember!

Using prefabricated components improves the quality of the finished product and also speeds up work on site.

## ■ Advantages and disadvantages of prefabrication

Kitchen cabinets, door frames, bedroom furniture and many other components are now frequently made off site and taken to the building project for installation and assembly rather than being built in situ. This

**A prefabricated house**

prefabrication of components has not been restricted to non-load bearing elements, and for offices or other steel frame buildings standard forms of structural steel sections can be cut, bent and shaped to specifications obtained from the design drawings and specifications, then taken to site and placed on prepared slabs and linkages to assemble the building in sequence from the ground upwards.

While there has been a significant improvement in the standard of workmanship and the speed at which buildings using prefabricated components can be built, there are some limitations to the use of prefabricated elements. Not all components are likely to be built off site and there will always be a need for some minor alterations as work proceeds. This is especially true of instances where the design has been agreed in advance. If the design needs to be changed, then it may be easier to make any alterations required on site while work is taking place. Only if the contractor can contact and communicate changes to the workshops and other subcontractors can these changes be made if the project relies on prefabricated elements.

Where the whole building is completely prefabricated, that is, taken to site fully assembled and lifted in position using a crane onto a prepared base, variations are possible, although care must be taken to ensure that the designers are consulted to check that the removal of or amendment to any component does not adversely affect the structural integrity of the building.

## Portal frames

A portal frame is a shape that looks like a **portal**. It has a low pitched roof member that is attached to a column at either end. Portal frames can be constructed from several different materials: timber, steel or reinforced concrete. Generally, modern portal frames are constructed from steelwork that enables a high strength-to-weight ratio, which gives a large economical span. Concrete portal frames are generally pre-cast within a factory environment that ensures consistent quality. They are then assembled on site, like the steel portal frame, using a mobile crane. Timber portals are constructed using **Glulam** construction and stainless steel fixings. With all three methods, cladding rails hold the portals together along with eaves beams. Portal frames have the following advantages:

- large spans can be achieved
- speedily erected
- factory-produced quality
- easily extended and adapted
- good height-to-strength ratio
- enable lighter foundations than traditional construction of brick and block
- aesthetic when timber used
- enable recycling when the building comes to the end of its life.

## Key Terms

**Portal** A large gateway or doorway.

**Glulam** A process of gluing timber strips together to form a solid beam within a mould.

Their disadvantages and limitations include the following:

- require some form of coating to prevent rust
- require fire protection coating
- expensive to bend
- external coatings have to be maintained.

## Concrete frames

Concrete forms of construction are generally divided into two forms:

- in situ
- pre-cast.

In situ concrete frames consisting of beams and columns require some form of formwork in which mixed concrete is poured and held until it has set and attained enough strength to have the formwork shuttering removed. Pre-cast concrete is similar to that previously described and may require some of the beam-to-column connections to be cast on site or bolted to form a rigid structure.

The advantages of concrete frames:

- in-built fire protection
- can be moulded into any shape
- high strength in compression
- do not require a secondary finish
- faster construction period using pre-cast
- variety of surface finishes can be achieved.

Their disadvantages or limitations:

- require support initially
- crainage required
- poor strength on tension
- require highly skilled workforce to assemble.

## Steel frames

Once again, these are a series of beams and columns and may be composite in design, which means they can contain concrete floors and steel supporting beams, that is, a mixture of the two technologies.

The choice and selection of the building type will rely largely on the functional requirements of the building and the use to which it is put. In order to determine the suitability of the ground and its capacity to support the building, a thorough and detailed site investigation is necessary so that the foundations and the fabric of the building can be selected.

# Subsoil investigation

## Site survey and subsoil investigation

The main objective of a site investigation is to examine the ground conditions so that the most appropriate type of foundation can be selected. A typical site investigation begins with a **desk study** and a **walk-over survey** to establish the geology of the site and continues with an examination of the **geotechnical properties** of the ground. We are going to look more closely at a variety of techniques for a direct investigation and the selection of appropriate methods for given locations.

## Remember!

It is very difficult to be precise when investigating the subsoil. It is only an indication of what you may find in excavations.

## Recording and interpretation of results

### ■ Purpose of the site investigation

## Remember!

Site investigation takes place to check whether the proposed structure can be built on the site.

Site investigation involves gathering all the information on ground conditions which might be relevant to the design and construction of a building on a particular site. On a site intended for low-rise development, the desk study is the first stage of investigation. This involves checking existing records such as geological maps of the site, utilities records, local historical archives, etc. The desk study, along with the walk-over survey, will (hopefully) give sufficient information about the ground and groundwater conditions, and the problems that they may pose for the construction and the finished building. The walk-over survey:

- checks the accuracy of desk study information
- obtains any additional information required to ensure that the building can be constructed safely and within budget.

## Key Terms

**Desk study** An investigation of information about a piece of ground undertaken by reviewing existing records.

**Walk-over survey** Visiting the site enables the surveyor to match the information from the desk study to what they see in the field. Experienced surveyors can get a feel for ground conditions by undertaking a walk-over survey.

**Geotechnical properties** How soil is likely to perform when imposing loads on it or what will happen when water is removed to allow work to take place.

## Theory into practice

Where can you find information about soil or site conditions? Use the Internet to see what information is available through utilities companies and the local authority.

There are many cases where a site investigation is specific and tailored to a particular site. Generally, all site investigations should provide the following information:

- classification of soils
- soil profile
- soil parameters.

### Classification of soils

Ground investigations classify the soils beneath the site into broad groups. Each group contains soils with similar engineering behaviour. The simplest classification used by geologists is:

- rock
- granular (sands and gravels)
- cohesive soils (clay)
- organic soils (peat)
- fill or made ground.

Broad soil classifications, coupled with simple tests to determine **soil parameters** or to detect the presence of chemicals harmful to construction materials, are normally sufficient for low-rise buildings.

## Key Term

**Soil parameters** How the soil will react to building work and imposing loads. The soil can be expected to carry a certain amount of weight depending on its parameters and its characteristics.

### The soil profile

Ground investigations identify the levels of the various soil or rock types on the site by recognising the boundaries between them. This builds up a picture of what the ground looks like under the surface of the earth – this is known as the soil profile. Boundaries between the various soil types are not always distinct – many layers of the earth (strata) change gradually from one to another with no clear point where just one condition exists, which means it is difficult to tell what conditions you will actually find when you dig into the earth.

### Soil parameters

Engineering design and calculation may require finding out the soil parameters. In many situations, soil parameters may not be required, for example where conditions are particularly good (such as rock), which in most cases will support buildings very well, or particularly bad (such as peat), which should be excavated away to deeper, better load bearing ground. The parameters of soil found in difficult ground (clays and the like) must be determined since these soils perform variably; hence the need to quantify the load imposed by a building and the ability of the clay to support this load.

## ■ Planning and carrying out the site investigation

Desk studies and the walk-over survey are both indirect investigations. They are normally cheaper than direct investigations which involve drilling into the ground, extracting samples and then laboratory testing of samples to determine their properties. These operations require planning if they are to be fully effective. The stages of a full investigation are as follows:

*Stage 1:* Carry out a detailed desk study and walk-over survey. Identify the probable ground and groundwater conditions. Locate areas on the site that are likely to cause problems such as areas of fill, old hedgerows and trees, mineshafts, low-lying ground, etc.

*Stage 2:* Make initial designs for the structure and the site. Work out the positioning of the proposed structure so as to avoid as many problems as possible. Design structural forms, for example lightweight construction of timber-framed houses as opposed to dense, heavyweight concrete design, with special regard to anticipated ground hazards such as peat or excessive water conditions. Make preliminary estimates of the type of foundations required; determine the position of critical slopes and retaining walls.

*Stage 3:* Plan the direct methods required for the site investigation. Identify the depths of investigations required at different locations around the site. **Boreholes** should always penetrate completely through **made ground** or in-filling. Identify suitable in situ and laboratory testing methods for the expected soil conditions. Decide on the number of exploratory holes and the sampling and testing frequency, making allowances for the presence of unforeseen ground or groundwater conditions.

## Key Terms

**Boreholes**  Holes sunk into the ground to extract soil samples at differing levels. The information is recorded as the holes are drilled so that the design engineer discovers at what depth each soil is found.

**Made ground**  Any ground that has been artificially made from material placed from previous works, for example layers of stone compacted and laid to form a level surface ready for construction work.

*Stage 4:* Keep records of the investigation. Record the basis of the planned site investigation and the expected ground conditions. The specialist contractor who carries out the work will then know if the ground conditions they encounter are unforeseen, in which case they may have to alter the scope of the field or testing work.

## ■ Ground investigation techniques

Many different methods of ground investigation are available for direct site investigations. It is important to select methods which:

- will work in the particular ground conditions expected at the site
- give the information required to resolve any construction problems that might be expected
- give information that will allow the structural design calculations to be resolved

- are sufficiently economical given the financial constraints of the construction process.

Let's look at some of the methods available for site investigation.

### Exploratory holes

There are a number of techniques involving the excavation of or drilling into the earth.

*Trial pits.* These are extremely valuable if the depth of the investigation is limited to approximately 5 metres or less. This is the depth that can be conveniently excavated in most soil types using a back-actor or 360-degree slew hydraulic excavator. Trial pits are particularly useful in the investigation of sites intended for low-rise construction because the foundation types for this type of structure are generally 0.4–0.5 metres wide and 1–3 metres deep, so the depth of the investigation is 3–5 metres. Routine trial pit records are normally kept as a 'log' with the soil profile recorded as the hole is dug. Trial pit excavations are relatively cheap and offer quick results, but care needs to be taken with exposed excavations, as some pits may need shoring with timber supports or hydraulic earth props. Open excavations are dangerous and should be clearly marked or cordoned off to prevent anyone falling into them.

## Theory into practice

List the equipment you would need to complete the work on excavations on site.

*Auger holes.* These are normally made by hand turning an auger drill into the ground. Some light power tools may also be used. Auger holes, unlike trial pits, do not allow the soil to be examined in situ. Typical auger holes are 75–150 mm in diameter. Samples of the soil are collected at the surface when the earth is displaced by the helical auger flight (which is a technical term for a large spiral drill), the information is recorded and the descriptions collated to allow an engineer to produce a cross-section drawing which represents the conditions below ground.

▲ **Ground investigation techniques**

*Window sampler.* This is a steel tube, usually about 1 metre long with a series of 'windows' cut in the wall of the tube through which to view or take specimens of the soil sampled. It is driven into the ground by a lightweight percussion hammer, then extracted using hydraulic jacks. Samplers come in a range of diameters allowing the largest diameter to be driven first, then a sample from the bottom of the hole taken with a sampler of smaller diameter. Next, a sampler with a smaller diameter than the first is driven: this process continues with the use of smaller diameter samplers until an adequate depth is investigated. The results are recorded as an ongoing process up to a depth of approximately 8 metres.

*Boreholes.* In the UK, 150 mm or 200 mm boreholes are normally made using light percussion equipment. This type of equipment is portable and is often towed behind a four-wheeled drive vehicle.

In clay soils, the borehole is made by dropping a hollow tube – a claycutter – into a hole so that the clay becomes lodged in its base. The claycutter and its contents are then lifted carefully to the surface.

In granular soils, a hollow tube with a flap valve is surged or pressed in the ground using water pressure creating a water/soil mixture. Soil drops out of this mixture and is collected. Material taken from the drilling tools is usually retained as small 'disturbed' samples which can affect the results of the soil analysis. In some cases, the strength of the soil will have changed because it has been remoulded into the sample from the water/soil mixture; it may also have removed small particles from the soil; it may have increased the water content of the soil sample. Ideally, undisturbed samples are better since they show what the soil is actually like. However, disturbed samples can be analysed in a laboratory, which is more costly but more accurate in determining the soil's load bearing capability.

In cohesive soils, samples are taken at intervals of 1.0–1.5 metres by driving a sample tube into the bottom of the hole. These undisturbed samples are often taken to a laboratory for analysis. On site, the supervisor records data which is relevant to the sampling such as weather conditions, ground conditions, etc.

The main advantage of light percussion drilling is its ability to make deeper holes in a wide range of ground conditions such as is necessary for civil engineering projects, medium-rise construction and low-rise construction built on poor bearing ground, although the drawbacks include the fact that it is considerably more expensive than shallow trial pits and auger holes.

### Depths, numbers and locations of exploratory holes

Borehole depth depends on the **stress distribution** under the foundation. Boreholes should penetrate all deposits unsuitable for foundation purposes such as unconsolidated fill or material that needs further compacting such as peat, organic silt and very soft, **compressible clay**. Depth requirements should be reconsidered when the results of the first borings are

## Key Terms

**Stress distribution** How the foundation distributes the load of the building. A very wide, flat foundation will support more load than a narrow strip foundation.

**Compressible clay** Clay that can be compressed or compacted to increase its strength or load bearing capacity.

available. It is often possible to reduce the depth of subsequent borings or to confine detailed and special exploration to particular strata.

The maximum number of boreholes will depend on the complexity of the local geology and the planned construction project – it may change as information becomes available from the early investigations. The location of boreholes depends on the nature of the site. Additional boreholes should be drilled at problem areas and at locations near the site of the proposed structure. Where practicable, they should be located along **grid lines** at regular intervals to enable **section drawings** to be produced.

## Key Terms

**Grid lines** An imaginary series of lines running north–south and east–west allows designers and engineers to plot exactly key positions on site.

**Section drawings** A profile of the ground using the information from the boreholes next to one another – that way engineers can predict what happens to the ground between each borehole.

### Remember!

The cost of the site investigation is around 0.5–1 per cent of the **capital cost** of the construction contract. It is considered good practice to invest adequately at this stage of the construction.

## Key Term

**Capital cost** The total cost of all the equipment and necessary expense required to complete the works.

## ■ Radon gas

Radon is a radioactive gas that occurs naturally and is found in most locations in the UK, although there are areas where it occurs more frequently and with higher concentrations such as Cornwall or South Wales. Radon gas has no taste, smell or colour. Radon gas comes from the decay of uranium that is found in small quantities in all soil and rocks. Concentration levels of radon gas can build up in enclosed spaces such as excavations during construction work. Environmental health officers are appointed by the local authority to determine safe levels of radon gas in existing properties; the Health & Safety Executive has the task of monitoring how contractors deal with radon gas during construction work. Contractors have a duty of care under the Health and Safety at Work Act to provide a safe and healthy place of work.

Building Regulations require that buildings and buildings extensions (workplaces and dwellings) constructed after 2000 in radon-affected areas have protective measures installed during construction. To prevent the build up of radon gas, barriers are built into the structure. This barrier must cover the total area of the foundation of the building.

### Remember!

Building Regulations are appropriate for England and Wales. Separate documents exist for Scotland and Northern Ireland. Find out what these documents are called.

## ■ Groundwater conditions

Groundwater is found below the ground in the spaces and cracks between soil, sand and rock. The general level of water in the ground is known as the water table – the level of the water table is of interest to builders since their operations will be affected by its presence in the works that they will undertake. Digging into the ground can cause groundwater to fill up any trenches and excavations. It will also affect the building, so construction companies have to plan how to remove or deal with the water during construction.

Groundwater conditions are significant because they can affect construction in a number of ways:

- A high **water table** can lead to extra costs – from de-watering techniques (using either a temporary or a permanent solution), increased support for trenches and excavations, ground stabilisation requirements, etc. – and make construction more difficult.

- The presence of chemicals in groundwater, such as acids and sulphates, can lead to damage if foundation concrete and other materials used in the substructure are not of an appropriate quality.
- A high groundwater table implies that **pore-water pressure** in the soil is high, which usually means that the soil is weaker. As well as influencing foundations, high pore-water pressures will adversely affect the stability of slopes and the pressures on **retaining structures**.

### Theory into practice

What are the implications for health, safety and welfare of personnel working on site in excavations where water is present? What can be done to minimise risks?

### Impact on foundation design

Foundation design is complex and the following factors need to be considered fully in order to select the correct foundation:

- *Loading* – the imposed load from the building including the deadweight of the structure and any live loads exerted from wind forces.
- *Water table* – the presence of water in the ground will need to be taken into account. The usual choice is to remove the water found in excavations either as a temporary solution or to install land drains and remove the water on a permanent basis.
- *Contamination* – water and nitrates in the ground combine and produce acid that erodes concrete over a period of time. Sulphate resistant concrete is specified for these purposes but care is required both in its handling and its placement to ensure that it reaches its compressive strength in good time.
- *Bearing capacity of the soil* – following a thorough site investigation, it should be accurately determined how much force the soil will support. The bearing capacity of the soil can be enhanced or improved with ground stabilisation techniques or further excavated to lower levels of earth that will support the load with better bearing capacity.
- *Cost* – the respective costs of these options should be explored by the design engineer who must take account of the excavations, the plant and equipment necessary balanced against the need to locate suitable bearing strata.

## Foundation design

Foundations spread the load of a building over an area of the ground to avoid any settlement and also support the building. The **safe loading** of the building will need to be determined by calculation and by assessing the capability of the soil to carry the load. Reference tables in the 'Building Regulations Document A 1/2 Minimum Width of Strip Foundations' allow designers to select foundations of known dimensions and performance matched to the soil characteristics.

## Key Term

**Safe loading** The solution calculated from the soil's ability to carry a load plus a factor of safety.

## Remember!

Foundations carry the weight of the building, transferring the load safely to the ground below. They spread the weight of the building, and hence the load, to an acceptable level of force exerted on the ground.

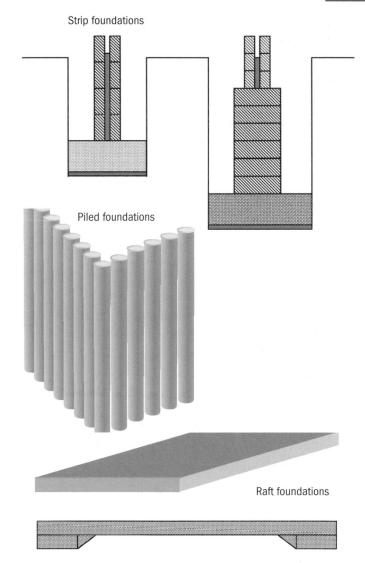

Figure 6.1 Strip, raft and short bored piled foundations

## Principles of design and factors affecting choice of foundations

The selection of a foundation for a particular project depends upon:

- the type of building structure
- soil conditions
- external or site constraints, e.g. the size and shape of the site layout
- type of foundations available (see Figure 6.1).

### ■ Type of building structure

Low-rise buildings, such as most houses or domestic dwellings, up to about four storeys with load bearing walls, generally allow line loads from walls to be distributed to the earth below via strip foundations.

## Theory into practice

Which types of foundation are most suited to a portal frame, low-rise flats and a simple detached house? Which of these foundations are suitable for more than one application?

Heavyweight buildings and those with a requirement for open plan spaces, such as offices, result in heavier loads that are usually delivered to the foundations in isolated points via columns from a structural framework.

### ■ Soil conditions

The two main characteristics that affect the choice of foundation are the maximum loads that can be carried without failure and excessive **settlement**. Normally, the settlement characteristics of a soil relate to spread foundations such as strip, raft and pad foundations whereas the actual strength of the soil is more important with piles.

## Poor soils

Poor soils such as peat, silts, soft alluvial soil and filled ground have very poor load bearing and settlement characteristics and are suitable for buildings that can readily accept large amounts of movement. In most cases, these types of soil prove unsuitable for bearing loads. Poor cohesive soils such as clays are very sensitive to changes in moisture content. In many cases, the excavation of these unsuitable soils and the siting of foundations on better load bearing ground at a lower level will prove to be the most satisfactory solution. There is also a range of techniques that can be employed to 'stabilise' the ground and improve the load bearing capacity.

## Cohesive and non-cohesive soils

Cohesive soils are weak compared with sands and gravel but have reasonable bearing capacities. However, they are prone to some long-term settlement and, with this in mind, foundations should be of an appropriate size. As with poor soils, cohesive soils are sensitive to changes in the moisture content and are prone to swelling and shrinkage when the water content of the soil is altered.

Non-cohesive soils such as sand and gravel are generally stronger and have a higher bearing capacity and low **compressibility** compared with cohesive soils. Settlement usually occurs instantaneously during the construction of the building. This type of soil may prove acceptable to any of the foundation types selected, for example strip foundations, piled foundations and raft foundations.

## Rock

This is generally the strongest material on which to put a foundation and its safe bearing capacity is not usually a major consideration. Some rocks such as chalk are the exception to the rule – this type of rock will behave more like weak soil especially when the moisture content is high.

## Contaminated soils

These soils may prove problematic for the work taking place on the foundation and the other substructure works. For these conditions, a more detailed investigation is normally made in order to determine the extent of the contamination and the concentration. The primary concern is to health, but some aggressive contaminants can cause damage to buried services and structures. The site investigation results are used to determine the extent and the severity of the contamination. Only after these are known should the overall strategy for the site be decided: heavily contaminated sites may be costly and impractical to clean up but may prove suitable for light industrial use. Typical examples of contaminated land are:

- landfill sites
- gasworks sites
- sewage farms and works
- scrap yards
- industrial areas.

The two most common approaches to the problems associated with contaminated ground are either removal or capping. Removal of the soil is costly and disposal to licensed tips awkward because of the nature of the material. However, this is a positive and permanent way of approaching the problem. Capping involves the sealing of the material by a layer of clean material of approximately one metre deep. This effectively places the contaminated soil in a zone that is not readily accessible.

## Theory into practice

Use the Internet to find out how you could dispose of contaminated ground or materials. What legislative controls are in place to ensure safety when disposing of contaminated materials?

Although consideration must be given to the effects of placing material in such proportions, capping is usually the most economical and common form of treatment.

## ■ Foundations on poor ground

Poor ground with insufficient strength can be considered in one of two ways:

- to excavate it away until ground of good bearing capacity is found
- to improve it so that it can accept the load of the building.

Ground improvement increases the density of the soil and enhances its bearing capacity. This allows the construction of lightly loaded spread foundations at high level. A specialist subcontractor with the necessary plant, equipment and expertise usually carries out this kind of work. These techniques normally employ large pieces of machinery that can have an effect on the site and its constraints. The nature of making adjustments to the ground conditions can make these techniques suitable for isolated or relatively exposed sites where there is little risk of damage to adjacent buildings.

### Vibro-compaction of poor soils

This technique has been employed for more than 30 years. A large vibrating poker is vibrated into the ground on a grid pattern of approximately 2–3-metre centres. Vibration rearranges the particles of the soil to make them more dense. Sand is then pumped in through the poker as it is extracted to fill the void. The treated soil is then suitable for light-use spread foundations such as strips and rafts. The foundation must be designed to accept local soft spots that have been missed by the treatment.

### Vibro-replacement of poor soils

This is similar in concept to vibro-compaction but more suitable for poor cohesive soils such as peat and silt. The technique requires that stone columns are formed through the poor soil on a grid pattern of 1–3-metre grids over the site. The columns are formed using a poker similar to the vibro-compaction treatment or a suitable piling rig to drill holes in the earth. The installation of stones compresses the ground, increasing its density and also acting as a weak column transferring the load to a lower level of the ground that can support the load more effectively.

### Dynamic compaction of poor granular soils

Over the past 20 years, dynamic compaction has been used for the compaction of poor soils on remote sites. The technique uses a large crane to drop weights of approximately 20 tonnes from a height of approximately 25 metres on a grid pattern across the site. Most sites need about three to five passes before a satisfactory density is achieved. There are problems with the use of this method, most notably the restriction on the site conditions: it can only be considered where the dropping of a 20-tonne weight will have little or no effect on neighbours, hence dynamic compaction may prove to be unsuitable for some sites with neighbours close by.

## ■ Piling

Piling is used in situations when the ground is unsuitable for heavy load and in particular where the loading of the building is transmitted by a framework in such a way that the total load is concentrated on a few points.

Piles are employed usually where, because of soil conditions, economic or constructional considerations, it is desirable to transmit the load of the building to strata beyond the depth of the practical reach of spread foundations. There may be a high water-table level where spread foundations could be employed but where piling may provide a cheaper answer than lowering the water table. Piled foundations may also provide a satisfactory solution where a site is restricted and spread foundations or their excavation may cause problems to adjacent buildings.

Piles can also act in tension to resist uplift, which might be caused by wind loads, or buoyancy conditions from a fluctuating water-table level. Piles are designed to take vertical loads but can accommodate some horizontal movement – where this horizontal movement is expected to be of a sizeable nature, raking piles are usually used.

Piles can be either replacement or displacement. Replacement piles remove the earth and place another material – typically concrete – in the hole created by the boring tool. Displacement piles are driven by a machine by dropping a hammer a 'set' number of blows.

The following are the main types of pile:

- Bearing piles – transmit the building load directly to solid strata.

- Friction piles – rely on shape and frictional resistance to the ground. They are used where safe bearing strata cannot be reached.
- Consolidated piles – used in a situation where the ground is weak or waterlogged, the aim being to strengthen the overall nature of the ground rather than to provide a specific point support.
- Sheet piles – used to contain earth and prevent movement that would result in a weakening of the natural foundation. They are more frequently used for temporary works but can be permanent.

The method of driving and sinking the piles depends on site conditions, space and height available, proximity of buildings, avoidance of vibration, number of piles required, etc (see Figure 6.2).

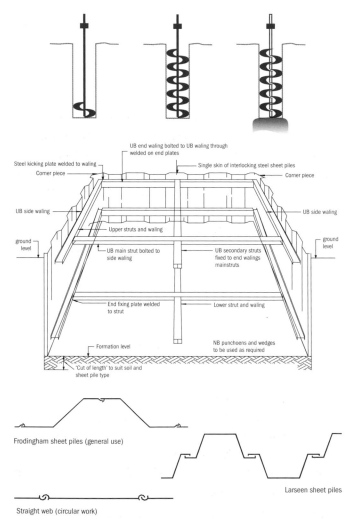

**Figure 6.2 Types of piles**

## ■ Materials used for piling

### Timber

Timber is a suitable material, but the length and sectional area are limited. Timber piles are frequently used adjacent to water forming piers, jetties and landing points. They are prone to rotting if alternately wet and dry conditions exist.

### Remember!

Timber piles are quite rare nowadays. They are used for small projects, usually on piers or jetties, adjacent to water courses.

### Steel

Piles from steel generally consist of two types: bearing and sheet. Sheet piles will be considered in more detail later. Load bearing piles are usually single or multiple, universal beam or column, which provides a good profile for the required friction in the ground. The use of multiple sections also creates stiffness and rigidity in the section used. Steel is a material that is flexible and versatile – it can be cut and welded fairly easily on site.

### Concrete

Concrete piles driven in one section are suitable for unrestricted sites where long piles do not pose handling problems. They require minimum site work in that, once driven, the pile is ready apart from stripping of the top to expose and integrate the reinforcement to the main structure.

These piles are generally cheaper than a cast in situ and control on quality is very good. Protection to the head of the pile may be necessary to allow the pile to be driven, but this is more for practical purposes than appearance since the top of the pile is cut away. Some disadvantages do exist – the pile could be deflected by obstructions too long to be driven.

Pre-cast piling such as this requires an extensive site investigation in order to determine the subsoil conditions to avoid problems such as those mentioned above.

Piles can also be driven using short lengths that are easier to manipulate on site and transport. They consist of concrete shells, which are driven by a steam hammer transmitted to a special concrete or steel shoe. When driven, there exists a watertight concrete tube in the ground and the main reinforcement is inserted into this – the whole is then concreted. The advantage of this method is that using prepared casings, the ground can be fairly unstable such as running sand, made up ground, gravels, etc. Pre-cast piles are hollow inside and are guided into the casings using a steel mandrel. A cage of reinforcement steel is prefabricated and lowered into the pile. The casings are then withdrawn by a hoist.

### In situ piles

Using a sealed tube and mandrel, the tube is sunk by a piling rig to the correct depth. The concrete and reinforcement is then introduced. The concrete assumes the ground profile, but care must be taken to ensure that the level of concrete is above the bottom of the sleeve since the earth pressure can cause 'necking' or 'waisting' at low levels. An alternative is to drive the pile with a steel cylinder weight complete with a semi-dry concrete mix in the bottom of the pile. When the pile reaches the required set, the plug is forced out, concrete and reinforcement is introduced to form the completed pile.

### In situ excavated piles

A single flight auger drill on the end of a Kelly bar is used to bore a hole into the earth. Extending the Kelly bar can increase the depth. The spoil is removed by retracting the drill to the surface. This method is generally slow and is restricted to depths of up to about 13 metres. Using a continuous fight auger, the earth is removed, which gives a belated indication of the subsoil conditions. The use of a lining in cohesionless soils may be necessary to prevent collapse of the pile into the vacant hole. Some piles may have an added advantage of being hollow through which the concrete is pumped under pressure as the drill is retracted. This creates two major positive features: first, the need for a lining is removed; second, the concrete is forced into the surrounding subsoil which provides a good frictional interface.

▲ **A piling rig with auger drill**

Piles can also be under-reamed to provide increased base for end bearing piles. However, under-reaming is a slow process requiring a stop in the drilling to change the tool for the actual under-reaming operation. In some clay soils it may prove more profitable to use a deeper, straight-sided shaft. Consideration should be given to arranging the piles into a pattern that might include clusters of piles grouped together with a pile cap.

**Structural requirements, effects of and precautions against subsoil shrinkage, ground heave and differential settlement**

### ■ Subsoil shrinkage

Foundations, whether they are piled, raft, strip or pads, should be sufficiently deep and robust to withstand the effects of being in the ground. Acid and sulphate resistant concrete should be used in all foundations to prevent acidic attack and corrosion through nitrates and other impurities found in the ground.

The effect of water in the ground should not be underestimated. If the level of water rises due to increased amounts of rainfall, any building of lightweight construction has the potential to 'float' or be lifted by the rising level of water. This movement, which is likely to represent differential forces on the building at various points, will lead to cracking and possible failure or rupture of the building components. The stability of the ground should be considered, bearing in mind that any temporary excess amount of water in the ground may well subside in times of dryness. A prolonged lack of water on the ground could lead to ground shrinkage and cracking. Foundations that are subject to ground conditions such as this may also crack, move and deform if they are not designed with sufficient density to resist these forces in the ground.

## ■ Ground heave

Ground heave due to the water level freezing in very cold conditions needs to be considered. Again, the effect of water freezing in the ground will result in an expansion of the ground conditions which could lead to differential movement in the building.

The effect of water freezing in the ground can also 'crush' elements of the building that are not sufficiently protected. As a consequence, compressible materials are placed in the excavations and foundations to enable the ground to take up this differential movement without affecting the structure.

## ■ Differential settlement

Buildings will exert differing levels of point loads on the earth at their foundations that sometimes leads to differential settlement. These loads will result in a twisting and buckling of some of the structural elements of a building as it settles more or less in each part of the building. Naturally, the foundations will have to be robust enough to deal with these movements and, in addition, the inclusion of flexible joints and opportunities for the building to accept these movements will need to be incorporated into the design.

# Excavations

## Excavations up to 5 metres depth

Most buildings up to three storeys high will have foundations of less than 5 metres deep. Excavations in excess of 5 metres deep are specialist operations with specific health and safety requirements for the contractor. There are significant dangers in excavating earth and working in the ground which will need to be considered in the foundation design and the method of constructing the foundations.

## ■ Earthwork support

In order to place the foundations at a suitable level, earth is excavated to load bearing strata. Building control officers from the local authority are usually involved in determining the suitability of the depth of foundations and can advise builders on local ground conditions that have frequently been exposed through site investigation and soil analysis.

Excavations in the ground can be very dangerous. Safety of those operatives working in trenches must be paramount when designing suitable foundations and therefore, wherever possible, the depth of a trench should be kept to a minimum. To protect other people in the area, trenches should be cordoned off and clearly marked with suitable warning signs.

## Thinking points

Earthwork support is essential if personnel are to work safely in excavations. In 2005, there were several casualties and deaths in construction resulting from earthwork collapse during excavations.

## Water elimination

Water exclusion may also be necessary using temporary pumping and removal to enable the work to proceed safely. As we have seen, fluctuations in the water table found in the ground can have a detrimental effect on the foundation and other building components, and rising, falling or continuous variation in the water level can have a disastrous effect on the ongoing construction works.

## Temporary supports and health and safety issues

As earth is excavated, the ground becomes more unstable. Therefore, it is necessary to support all surrounding ground to prevent any sudden or unplanned collapse of the surrounding ground. Timber shores or planks were used until very recently to support the ground while the excavated material was carted away and the foundation concrete poured. Modern methods of supporting the ground include sheet piling or purpose-made 'boxes' of steel braced with hydraulic or mechanical jacks that enable operatives to work safely while there is any danger of the earth crumbling or capsizing into the trench.

## Excavation and earth moving plant

Hand excavation in all but very small and shallow excavations has now been replaced by the use of mechanical excavators. Before an excavation takes place, the area should be examined both visually and from any available drawings to see if there are any signs of underground services. Additionally, the use of cable avoidance tools (CAT) scanners that send ultra-sonic rays through the ground can detect underground services prior to the excavation. In any event, mechanical diggers and plant should not operate within 500 mm of any services, which means that most excavations near to services should be finished off by hand excavation when they become close to services.

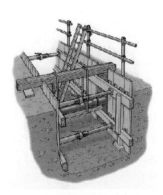 

▲ An earthwork support prevents the trench from collapsing

# Foundation construction and design

Domestic foundations are commonly formed from either 600 mm wide concrete strip or 450 mm wide concrete trench fill foundations excavated to 1 metre below final external ground level. However, there are several alternative foundation methods such as in situ rafts or a number of types of piled foundations, such as pre-cast concrete, shell, continuous flight auger, all of which support the load bearing walls and ground floors of a building. For the first time, the Building Regulations 'Approved Document A – Structure: 2004 edition' requires minimum depths for strip foundations; these are 750 mm in clay and 450 mm in others. In practice, foundations are usually 1 metre or so deep.

The main requirement of the Building Regulations for foundations is set out via 'Approved Document A' regarding loading and ground movement in relation to domestic buildings no higher than a specified height that takes into account the topography, altitude and the basic wind speed at a given site. In practice, this height is usually no more than three storeys. The main requirement is that foundations are designed and constructed so that all the loads that are applied to a building, such as from wind, snow and occupiers, as well as the self weight of the building's construction, for example roof, intermediate floors, walls and ground floors, if suspended, are safely transmitted to the ground without impairing the building's safety.

Prior to construction, the ground substratum should be checked to ensure it has adequate bearing strength to support the foundations and is free of possible conditions that may affect its integrity. These may include swelling, shrinkage, slippage or subsidence that could be caused by geological conditions or other factors such as mining, landfill or moisture take-up from tree roots. If some of these conditions exist, it may be possible to overcome them by the use of specialist foundation techniques of rafts or piling with suspended floors, as necessary, in conjunction with ground stabilisation such as grouting of old mine workings or vibration compaction of filled or made-up ground where, due to economic, speed and safety factors, deep conventional foundations would not be viable.

## Construction techniques used for strip, pad, raft and pile foundations

Foundations should be constructed in sufficient depth of ground and with appropriate materials to ensure that they adequately support the building. 'Approved Document A – Structure' of the Building Regulations contains guidance about the design and construction of plain in situ strip foundations for domestic construction up to three storeys in height.

The design is based upon a number of assumptions:

- The concrete mix is ST2, GEN 1 or a ratio of 50 kg Portland cement, 200 kg fine aggregate and 400 kg coarse aggregate.
- The concrete mix in soils that contain aggressive elements/chemicals such as sulphates should be designed accordingly.
- The ground and level that the foundations are formed at has no major strength variation, e.g. rock and clay, that may cause uneven settlement problems.

The total load applied to strip foundations does not exceed 70 kilo-Newtons (kN) per metre length and the width of the foundation is based upon Table 10 in 'Approved Document A'.

The Building Regulations require that, where the proposed foundation design or conditions do not fall into the above guidance, they are designed upon proper structural principles with necessary calculations to prove the adequacy and the stability of the design.

The Approved Document guidance regarding the design and construction of strip foundations requires the following points to be adopted:

1. That walls are positioned centrally on foundations.
2. That the foundation concrete has a minimum thickness equal to the foundation projection on either side of the wall or a minimum of 150 mm.
3. At the ends of walls or around projections such as chimney breast/piers that there is a foundation under them and that the projection is maintained.
4. That foundation bottoms are level and that changes in foundation levels are accommodated by steps not exceeding the foundation concrete thickness.

5. At foundation steps that the concrete is continuous and overlaps the lower section by twice the height of the step.

For the first time, the 2004 Building Regulations provide minimum foundation depths. These are 0.45 metre for all strip foundations (to prevent risk of frost) and 0.75 metre in clay soils. The Regulations acknowledge that these depths may need to be increased to suit local circumstances. Prior to this, 'Approved Document A' did not give a specific minimum depth but required it to be at a depth where the ground is not subject to movement. This has been (and still is) generally interpreted by most local authority building control surveyors as 1 metre below finished external ground level in average soil conditions. However, foundations may need to be deeper below the zone of influence from trees, as well as provided with other precautionary measures such as clay board to avoid damage by ground movement. Conversely, it would be pointless to excavate a foundation trench to 1 metre depth if solid rock is encountered, as this would not be subject to heave or subsidence.

## Environmental issues

### ■ Foundations and drains

The Building Regulations 'Approved Document H – Drainage and waste disposal: 2002 edition' requires that precautions are taken for drains passing under buildings or within their zone of influence (see below). This is because damage to the drains could cause them to leak or block and cause local settlement of the building's substructure.

1. Where foundations are excavated alongside existing drains, etc. they should be excavated to a level below the influence of existing or proposed drain level.
2. Conversely, if drains are excavated below a foundation zone of influence or within a metre, the drainage trench should be filled with concrete up to the foundation's level of influence.
3. Where drains pass through the building's substructure and foundations, an allowance should be made for the settlement of the building or drains. This is usually achieved in two ways, either by building the pipe solidly into the wall with flexible

joints and rocker pipes either side, or lintelling over the pipe leaving at least 50 mm gap around the pipe and filling the gap with a flexible inert material such as mineral wool or sheeting covering the opening over with rigid flexible material. Also, the pipe should be bedded and surrounded with a minimum thickness of 100 mm granular material such as pea gravel.

Where building near public sewers, foundations should be constructed and positioned not to influence or damage the sewer. They should be at least 3 metres away from the sewer if the pipe is 225 mm, or the pipe is 3 or more metres deep. The purpose of this is to provide working space around the sewer. Smaller adopted sewers may be built over with the agreement of the water authority, but this should not exceed a 6-metre length or cover any access points.

## ■ Rafts and pad foundations

### Key Terms

**Raft foundation** A slab that supports the building over a large area.

**Pad foundation** A mini raft similar in function to a raft but not connected to other pads that support structural members.

In the 1940s and 1950s, **raft foundations** were quite common, particularly beneath the thousands of prefabricated, pre-cast concrete or steel buildings erected during the years following the Second World War. Most of these houses were built on good quality farmland where the soil was generally of modest to high bearing capacity. Rafts (or foundation slabs as they were sometimes called) were often used because they were relatively cheap, easy to construct and did not require extensive excavation (trenches were often dug by hand).

In modern construction rafts tend to be used:

- where the soil has low load bearing capacity and varying compressibility – this might include loose sand, soft clays, fill and alluvial soils (soils comprising particles suspended in water and deposited over a flood plain or river bed)

- where pad or strip foundations would cover more than 50 per cent of the ground area below the building
- where differential movements are expected
- where subsidence due to mining is a possibility.

Flat slab rafts offer a number of advantages over strip foundations:

- No trenching is required.
- They are simple and quick to build.
- There is less interference with subsoil water movement.
- There are no risks to people working in trenches. Detailing needs careful thought, for example they may be subject to frost attack around the edges, the edges themselves are exposed, and there is the risk of cold bridging around the perimeter. They are generally suitable for good soils of consistent bearing capacity.

Flat slab rafts (that is, no perimeter or internal beams) have been recommended in some mining areas. These rafts will flex if ground movement is considerable, so the superstructure needs to be designed accordingly.

In the UK, rafts have to be designed on a one-by-one basis, in other words there are no 'deemed to satisfy' provisions in the Building Regulations as there are with strip foundations. In practice, engineers are advised to consider local practice with regard to raft design. Shallow rigid rafts for one-, two- and three-storey housing can be cheaper than piles. On poor ground, the raft must be stiff enough to prevent excessive differential settlement. This usually requires perimeter and internal ground beams to help stiffness and minimise distortion of the superstructure. Some overall settlement of the house will inevitably occur, but differential settlement should be kept within acceptable limits.

On filled sites, depending on the fill depth, rafts can be a cost-effective alternative to piling. They can also be used on sloping sites as an alternative to stepped strip foundations. A well-compacted (in shallow layers), graded granular fill can form a suitable base. Designing the fill and the raft is obviously specialist work and many speculative house builders would probably prefer 'tried and tested' stepped strip foundations.

## Assessment practice

List three methods of investigating the earth prior to starting construction work on a commercial building. Describe the process of subsoil investigation and explain the significance of this information to the building contractor.  **P1**

Describe how foundations spread the load of a building over the ground. Produce a sequence of operations to create a strip foundation of 900 mm deep. What equipment would you need and how would this differ from short-bored piles as a foundation for a commercial building?  **P2**

You have been asked to plan the substructure of a single detached house which is to be built on an area known to suffer from mining subsidence. What type of foundation – raft, strip or piled – do you think is best suited for this and what materials will you need to produce the foundation?  **M1**

Try to think of all the factors involved in the use of materials used in foundations and substructures. Make a table of alternative materials that could be used and evaluate their performance in use and their environmental impact.  **D1**

# Superstructure design and construction

## Principles of design, factors affecting choice and construction techniques

The superstructure, or the building shell, is the part of the building that sits on top of the substructure and forms the outer envelope of the building. The superstructure includes all the walls, the roof, the floors and the doors and windows which will enable the building to become a weather-tight structure.

## ■ Walls

Walls are traditionally made from bricks, although nowadays house builders more frequently use timber-framed buildings.

The UK, like most EU member states, now has its own National Annex, published as part of BS EN 771-1:2003 to provide informative guidance to specifiers/users. Each **National Annex** is not a formal part of the Standard and will certainly vary from one EU member state to another. For example, BS EN 771-1 distinguishes between high density (HD) and low density (LD) clay masonry units. The UK National Annex provides guidance on the fact that all clay bricks currently produced and traded within the UK are of HD classification. This annex provides specification guidance on other aspects of HD type clay brick such as:

- dimensions and tolerance
- configuration and format

## Key Term

**National Annex** A document that supplements the British Standards specifications that ensures materials meet quality requirements. These documents apply to all members of the European Union (EU).

- density
- compressive strength
- freeze/thaw resistance
- active soluble salts content
- durability designations
- water absorption
- reaction to fire
- bond strength
- clay engineering and DPC bricks.

Concrete blocks have been in common use since the 1930s. Early blocks were often made from local aggregates, most of which are no longer available. The aggregates were often industrial waste products such as breeze and clinker. Blocks can be used in either leaf (or both leaves) of a cavity wall. The nature of the blocks will depend, to some extent, on the nature of the insulation. Insulation is typically in the form of cavity boards and a thermal drylining. Blocks are also used for internal load bearing walls and partitions.

## Theory into practice

Using the Internet to source bricks and blocks, investigate how many colours, shapes, sizes and finishes are available from a range of manufacturers.

Blocks used to form internal leaves of external walls are frequently made from aerated concrete. They form the internal leaf of a cavity wall and will be finished by plasterboard fixed with plaster dabs. Most blocks can also be plastered. Aerated blocks can be used for lightweight partitions and load bearing internal walls. They have been available for about 40 years and have replaced earlier lightweight blocks made from a variety of lightweight aggregates.

For commercial buildings, where larger open span areas are required, portal frames are common (see Figure 6.3).

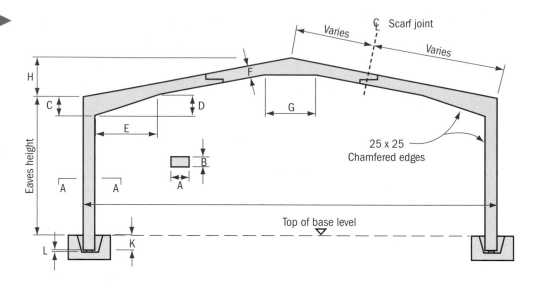

Figure 6.3 A portal frame ▶

This allows the use of brick and profiled aluminium sheeting for the cladding and enclosure of the structural elements.

For domestic dwellings, brickwork walls are usually constructed with a cavity to ensure that they comply with Building Regulations and offer an adequate resistance to the passage of heat energy and therefore are energy efficient. Successive legislation has adopted more stringent measures to make new buildings as efficient as possible with additional insulation and a range of different materials used to promote sustainable building projects. Cavities also reduce or eliminate any excessive amount of moisture or damp from entering the property from the outside.

Since building in a cavity means that the external walls are usually comprised of two separate but connected 'skins' of brick or blockwork construction, the inner leaf of the wall can be built using materials that are usually high in energy efficiency. In some cases, the inner leaf acts as an anchor for plasterboards or other materials that finish off the wall and provide a smooth finish ready for decoration.

Within the construction, a barrier to the entry of moisture usually takes the form of a damp-proof course, a thin layer of pitch polymer plastic that prevents any moisture from getting to an area that is required to be moisture free. It is very important that these barriers are built in at the correct position and in no way bridged or broken so that moisture cannot pass to the superstructure from the ground. In normal conditions, the damp-proof course is set no more than 150 mm above ground level (see Figure 6.4).

## ■ Timber-framed housing construction

Timber frame is a method of constructing houses and low-rise buildings using structural timber, typically prefabricated in a factory and assembled on site. These panels are taken to site and assembled in sequence according to manufacturers' instructions. The prefabrication of panels in workshop conditions improves quality control and timber-framed houses are renowned for their energy efficiency.

Flooring grade chipboard
Rockwood "FLEXI" between joists
Polypropylene netting to support insulation
Perimeter edge insulation between joist and wall
Ventilated air space
Concrete subfloor
Hardcore
Subsoil

▲ Figure 6.4 Damp-proof course

## Theory into practice

Compare the advantages of building in traditional materials with materials used in timber-framed housing.

Most timber-framed houses in the UK use platform framing methods whereby each storey is assembled, and each subsequent floor forms the platform for the next storey (see Figure 6.5). External walls are usually constructed from 100 mm × 50 mm softwood studs nailed together to form a frame. Wind bracing using 18 mm plywood or other sheet materials is fixed to one side; the void between the inside plasterboard finish is filled with glass fibre insulation. A suitable cladding is then applied, either brickwork or in some cases a lightweight cladding system to provide an external finish and keep out the weather. Due to the likelihood of condensation forming inside the walls, a moisture barrier or vapour check is essential. This barrier usually takes the form of polythene sheet or foil backing to the plasterboard.

## Remember!

The most common form of cladding in the UK is brickwork – one reason why timber-framed houses can be difficult to spot.

Modern timber-frame houses can provide very high levels of thermal insulation. The wall insulation is contained within the panels. If the panels are 90 mm thick, typical **U-value** is 0.35W/m2K; 140 mm panels

## Key Term

**U-value** The overall coefficient of heat transmission which indicates the heat flow through materials – the higher the figure, the greater the heat loss. (See also Unit 4.)

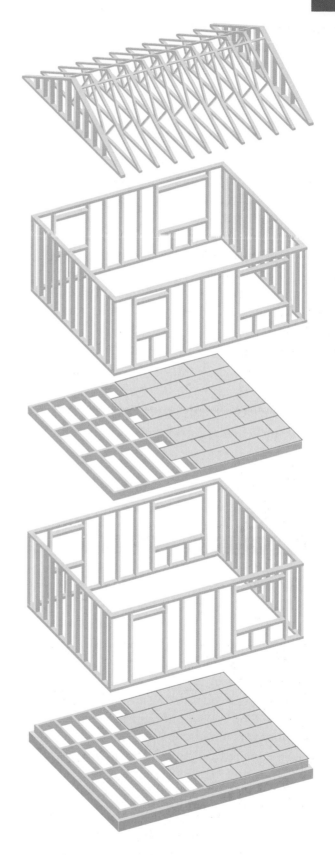

▲ Figure 6.5 A timber-framed house

will provide a level of about 0.25W/m2K. The internal lining usually comprises a layer of plasterboard with some form of vapour check behind. The purpose of the vapour check is to prevent moist air migrating through the panel and condensing on the cold side of the insulation.

Most timber-frame systems are factory made. The panels are made on large jigs, usually by hand, although in some plants automation is replacing the need for operatives. A waterproof breather paper covers the outer face of the panels partly to protect them during transport and site erection, and partly to prevent water crossing the cavity and wetting the panel once the building is complete. It is the timber-frame structure which carries all the building loads; the brick facing is merely a cladding.

## ■ Floors

The upper floors of timber-framed houses are supported by the wall panels. No load is carried by the brick outer leaf. The load bearing wall panels usually comprise the external panels, load bearing partitions and the party wall panels. The floor itself is no different from a timber floor in a brick/block house. It comprises a series of joists supporting some form of boarding. Boarding is normally in the form of chipboard, strand board or ply. In some cases, the timber floor is prefabricated (assembled into panels) in the factory, in others the timbers are pre-cut to length but not assembled.

The floor gives its name to the most common form of timber-frame system – the platform frame. The joists sit on top of the head binder. The construction varies depending on whether the joists are parallel or at right angles to the panels. In the former, two header joists sit on the lower-storey panels. The inner header joist is slightly offset to provide a fixing for the plasterboard ceiling. Where the joists are at right angles to the panels, a header joist is required to provide additional support for the upper panels and to provide a fire barrier to prevent smoke and fire (in the cavity) entering the floor void.

Most timber-suspended ground floors have now given way to concrete slabs that form the base of typical housing and domestic properties in the UK. Ground-floor slab construction is regulated to ensure that the

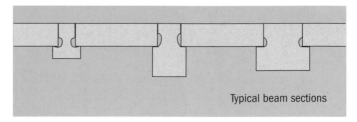

Typical beam sections

▲ **Figure 6.6 Beam and block floor systems**

maximum heat loss permissible through this structure does not exceed the amounts shown in the Building Regulations. To ensure that the floor complies with this requirement, insulation is built into the slab.

Suspended floors consisting of concrete beams with blocks to infill the separating space have become very popular, and again insulation is required to ensure compliance. Typical beam sections and their size and interval are determined by the span and the space that they can carry safe working loads.

Beam and block floor systems combine pre-cast concrete beams and infill blocks to produce high performance yet economic ground and intermediate floors in housing and other building types. Both lightweight and dense aggregate concrete blocks complying with British Standards can be used for beam and block floor construction with the following advantages:

- Simplicity – exactly the same blocks may be used for both walls and floors.
- Cost saving – long spans are readily achieved without intermediate support.
- Performance – requirements for thermal, acoustic and fire resistance are easily achieved.
- Reliability – eliminates effects of ground heave or shrinkage.
- Versatility – beam and block systems may be used for ground and intermediate floors.
- Working platforms – once installed, the floor may be used as a working platform.

## ■ Roofs

Roofs need to be weatherproof and provide shelter from the elements. They also need to have the qualities of strength, durability, fire resistance, heat retention and a pleasing appearance. Most roofs on domestic dwellings are of pitched construction, although a significant number of flat roofs exist for smaller properties and extensions to existing homes. For industrial or commercial buildings that require a large uninterrupted span, the roofing system forms a major part of the structure such as in the case of a portal frame building.

## Insulation and ventilation of roofs

The roof construction has to limit the loss of heat from a building and in domestic construction this is usually achieved by incorporating a suitable thickness of insulation into the roof construction. However, if the roof construction is a cold construction where the insulation is either or both between or under the rafters/ceiling joist, the construction must be ventilated to prevent condensation in the roof and the possibility of moisture damage or rot.

Alternatively, a vapour permeable felt fixed in accordance with both the felt and tile manufacturers' recommendations is an acceptable alternative to ventilation in a cold roof construction. If, however, a warm roof construction where a continuous layer of insulation is provided above the rafters is used with a suitable felt and cladding/covering, ventilation does not have to be provided within the roof construction as condensation and associated damage should occur on the outside face of the felt and not damage the roof

Whichever type of roof construction method is used, the Building Regulations specify a maximum U-value that the construction has to achieve to reduce the heat loss from the roof, which is the part of a building where most heat is lost. There are various ways to meet Building Regulations U-values. The elemental method takes each element of the building and then finds the overall heat loss for these elements added together. The permitted U-values using the elemental method to prove compliance are as follows and vary depending upon the type of roof and insulation position:

- Pitched roof with insulation between rafters: 0.2 W/m2K
- Pitched roof with integral insulation: 0.25 W/m2K (e.g. insulation over rafters as warm roof)
- Pitched roof with insulation between joists: 0.16 W/m2K (e.g. insulation between ceiling joists)
- Flat roof: 0.25 W/m2K

- Insulated sloping ceilings for loft conversions: 0.30 W/m2K
- Metal framed roof lights: 2.2 W/m2K
- Other framed roof lights: 2.0 W/m2K.

However, if the target U-value is used to show compliance with the Building Regulations, a higher (poorer) general U-value of 0.35 W/m2K is permitted for roofs. It is usually easier to increase the level of insulation in roofs using these methods to allow lower levels of insulation to be used elsewhere in the building.

The Building Regulations, through 'Approved Document C – Site preparation and resistance to contaminants and moisture: 2004 edition' and BS 5250:2002 'Code of practice for control of condensation in buildings', require that cold roofs are ventilated to limit condensation build-up and associated long-term problems of rot, dampness and mould growth which can both damage the fabric of the building and the occupants' health. The amount of ventilation required depends upon the design/form of the roof and is expressed in the form of equivalents of continuous gaps which means that the amount of air passing through a gap needs to be quantified and assessed as adequate for an enclosed space. These gaps might take the form of spaces between eaves or soffit casings in the structure. However, ventilation can be provided by other means such as ventilation tiles or air bricks provided they are equally and adequately positioned within the roof construction.

Pitched roofs may consist of rafters and purlins alone, with the purlins supported on posts, masonry walls or primary trusses. They may also consist of an arrangement in which the lower ends of each pair of rafters are tied or trussed together.

The most common form of roof construction, particularly in today's housing, is trussed rafters which have a tie between the lower ends of each pair of rafters and some form of cross bracing between (see Figure 6.7). They are normally designed and made by a specialist manufacturer using computer-controlled design and fabrication. The members are usually 38 mm or 35 mm wide and are all in line with each other because the joints are made with punched metal plates. Proprietary trussed rafters are used extensively in domestic construction because they are quick and easy to erect.

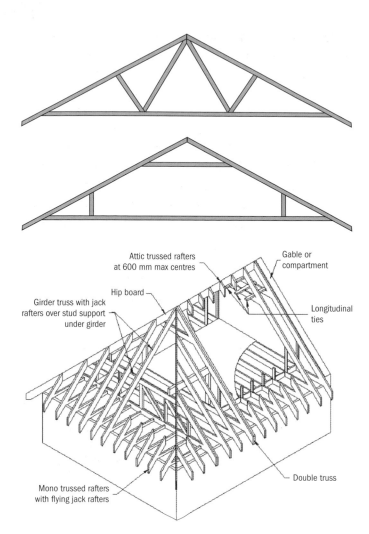

Attic trussed rafters
at 600 mm max centres

Gable or
compartment

Hip board

Girder truss with jack
rafters over stud support
under girder

Longitudinal
ties

Mono trussed rafters
with flying jack rafters

Double truss

▲ **Figure 6.7 Trussed rafters**

Trussed rafter roofs are designed in accordance with BS 5268-3:2006 'Structural use of timber: Code of practice for trussed rafter roofs'. Many manufacturers have their own software to calculate appropriate truss designs in accordance with this Standard. They will need to know:

● height and location of building (to determine wind conditions)

● profile, span, spacing and pitch of trussed rafters

● overhang at eaves and verges

● method and position of support

● nature of roof coverings and ceiling materials

● size and position of water tanks and loft hatches.

Under Building Regulations, pre-treatment of roofing timbers is required in certain parts of the country (in the south east, for example, to protect against House

Longhorn Beetle). This usually requires some form of pressure impregnation. The chemicals are designed to guard against rot as well as insect attack. Some developers treat the timbers as a matter of course, although there are increasing environmental concerns regarding some of the material used.

Prefabricated trussed rafters can also be designed to accommodate rooms in the roof – called attic trusses. Prefabricated roof panels are increasingly being used as an alternative to roof trusses, particularly in association with timber-frame buildings. They can provide unobstructed roof spaces for occupation. The panels are similar to timber-frame wall panels and enable a weatherproof structure to be achieved rapidly on site.

Trussed rafters are sometimes purpose designed by an architect or engineer for an individual project and constructed by a carpenter on site or in a workshop. The members in these are usually lapped at joints and fixed with nails, bolts or timber-connectors. More traditional forms of roof include the use of primary trusses and site constructed, or 'cut' roofs using an arrangement of rafters and purlins. Primary trusses are designed to support purlins which in turn support rafters. They are of heavier construction than trussed rafters and are spaced at intervals which are normally a multiple of the rafter spacing, for example 1800 mm or 2400 mm. Purlin-supported rafters need no tie members. The rafters are notched or 'birdsmouthed' over the purlins or otherwise fixed to avoid displacement and to keep all loads vertical. The purlins are fixed to posts, walls or primary trusses and all or any of these supports are designed and built to remain in a state of equilibrium. The main reason to use purlin-supported rafter structures is usually either to allow the roof space to be used or for it to be seen.

## Remember!

Trussed rafter roofs are made from smaller sections than traditional roofs. The truss derives its strength from the way each member is tied together. It is not usually possible to cut out any members or make alterations.

## Position of insulation

There is a choice of insulation position in pitched roofs:

- at rafter level, either between the rafters or above and between the rafters
- at ceiling level.

Insulation between the rafters can be designed in two ways:

- 'breathing' roof with vapour permeable underlay as tiling underlay
- ventilated design (see Figures 6.8 and 6.9).

With breathing roof design, insulation fully fills the rafter space without an airspace between the insulation and tiling underlay, which must be vapour permeable. If a thin layer of insulation is installed, it is recommended that an insulation/plasterboard laminate is used as the internal lining to prevent thermal bridging. This is not necessary where rafters are at least 140 mm deep and fully filled with insulation.

A combined airtight/vapour control layer should be placed on the warm side of the insulation. This not only makes the ceiling convection tight but also restricts the amount of water vapour passing through the ceiling. Where cables and piped services are to be installed, the plasterboard lining may be battened out to provide a suitable duct. The services should be routed on the inside of the vapour control layer to avoid any puncturing.

With the ventilated design, there is 50 mm ventilated airspace between the top of the insulation and the tiling underlay. Should the rafter depth be insufficient to accommodate both the required thickness of insulation and the 50 mm ventilated airspace, an insulated dry lining is recommended. This has the added benefit of minimising thermal bridging. Ventilation openings should be provided at each and every roof void at both low and high level. At the eaves, ventilation openings should be equivalent to a 25 mm continuous gap. At the ridge, the ventilation opening should be the equivalent of a 5 mm continuous gap each side of the ridge.

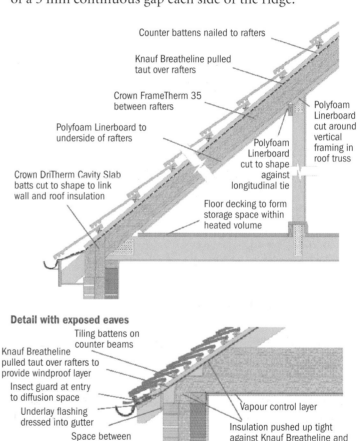

Counter battens nailed to rafters

Knauf Breatheline pulled taut over rafters

Crown FrameTherm 35 between rafters

Polyfoam Linerboard to underside of rafters

Crown DriTherm Cavity Slab batts cut to shape to link wall and roof insulation

Polyfoam Linerboard cut to shape against longitudinal tie

Polyfoam Linerboard cut around vertical framing in roof truss

Floor decking to form storage space within heated volume

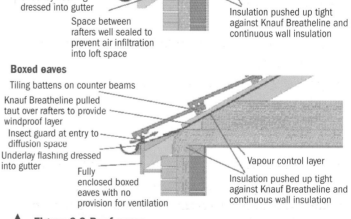

**Detail with exposed eaves**

Tiling battens on counter beams

Knauf Breatheline pulled taut over rafters to provide windproof layer

Insect guard at entry to diffusion space

Underlay flashing dressed into gutter

Space between rafters well sealed to prevent air infiltration into loft space

Vapour control layer

Insulation pushed up tight against Knauf Breatheline and continuous wall insulation

**Boxed eaves**

Tiling battens on counter beams

Knauf Breatheline pulled taut over rafters to provide windproof layer

Insect guard at entry to diffusion space

Underlay flashing dressed into gutter

Fully enclosed boxed eaves with no provision for ventilation

Vapour control layer

Insulation pushed up tight against Knauf Breatheline and continuous wall insulation

▲ **Figure 6.9 Roof eaves**

Gaps between tiles and slates allow vapour to escape

Vapour permeable underlay pulled taut over rafters to provide windproof layers

Ventilation space created by counter battens

Continuous diffusion of moisture through vapour permeable underlay

▲ **Figure 6.8 Section through roof members showing tiles and vapour barrier**

## ■ Stairs

Stairs are used to gain access to and egress (exit) from the upper floors of a building. They are traditionally manufactured from timber and must conform to the Building Regulations, which set a standard for the height of a step and the width of a step so that your body gets used to walking up and down stairs which are similar and safe all the time. Modern methods of construction have enabled prefabricated concrete stairs to be manufactured and lowered into place. These require finishing with a floor finish.

## ■ Windows

Windows were traditionally manufactured from timber. This material has to be treated by applying a painting system to the timber frames. Once this barrier is broken, then the timber can degrade and swell with moisture. With the introduction of the modern upvc technology, warmer and draught-sealed, high quality windows have substantially replaced the manufacture of timber windows. However, timber-engineered, high performance windows are making inroads into the current upvc market as an environmentally friendly product.

## ■ Doors

Doors are essential for maintaining the security of a home or commercial premises. There are many different types available, including:

- traditional timber-panelled, external doors
- plywood, flush internal doors
- part-glazed doors
- roller-shutter doors
- upvc French and patio doors
- fire doors which are fire rated.

These are just a few of the wide variety of applications that a door can provide.

# Finishes

## Factors affecting the choice of finishes

Many factors affect the choice of finishes for a domestic or commercial building design, including the following:

- Cost – the budget for a project has to be maintained and often finishes of a lower quality are seen as a cost saving.
- Use – a school corridor will require harder wearing finishes than a library corridor.
- Cleanliness – finishes used in a hospital operating theatre must be capable of being sterilised.
- Aesthetics – the attractiveness of a finish to the eye is often an essential item.
- Fashion – finishes may be chosen because they are the current fashion, e.g. block paving of a driveway.
- Fire resistance – often finishes have to resist the spread of fire and flame.
- Sound resistance – the denser a material, the more effective it is at sound reduction.
- Health and safety – such as non-slip finishes.
- Function – a shower's finishes have to be waterproof.
- Colour – you would not use red finishes in a prison cell, for example, as it promotes anger.

## Types of finishes

## ■ Early plastering

Plastering is an ancient craft. Originally, the materials and techniques used were dependent on the geology of the locality, the materials to hand and the technology available to the local artisan.

In earliest times, buildings or structures were plastered to render (hence rendering) them windproof and weathertight. Simple mud daubs on basic interwoven wattle structures are among the earliest means of walling, even in localities with a ready supply of building stones or fellable timber. Early stone walls, often laid dry for lack of mortar, were rendered both flat and weathertight with basic plaster. Even timber buildings, such as log cabins in the past and in many parts of the world still today, were weatherproofed with layers of plasters as crude as clay reinforced with straw.

As early societies developed and the first cities came into being, people recognised the decorative potential of plaster work as well as its hygienic, fire and weatherproofing qualities. A flat, hard surface was easy to clean, did not harbour dirt, was comfortable to the touch and pleasing to the eye. It could be painted and decorated and also provide the substrate for three-dimensional decorative relief. It slowed the spread of fire, especially in timber buildings, and helped deaden sound as the needs for privacy and comfort became increasingly important.

## ■ Gypsum plasters

Gypsum is the basis of plaster as we know it today. It is a naturally occurring mineral – hydrated calcium sulphate – and is sometimes known as alabaster when found in its soft, translucent form. When burnt at relatively low temperatures (less than 200°C), some or all the water of hydration is driven off and a highly reactive powder remains. This powder, in its hemihydrate form, is known as plaster of Paris and reacts vigorously with water to set hard and quickly. With few exceptions, the plasters of today are based on gypsum.

## ■ Lime plasters

Limestone was much more commonly available and the vast majority of ancient plasters and mortars were based on lime and its various byproducts. Limestone is the mineral calcium carbonate when found in its purest form. Chalk is one of the purest forms of naturally occurring limestone and is nearly 100 per cent pure calcium carbonate. Many impurities exist in most limestones, mainly of a clay-like nature, and these impurities can be very important in the properties that they give to the finished plaster.

## ■ Cement plasters

Plasters based on cement rather than lime have been common for more than 100 years. They were mostly used for external renders, often gauged with lime to produce a more workable mix. Cement-based renders need to be used with care; strong mixes (with a high proportion of cement) are likely to shrink and may part from the background.

## ■ Plasterboard

Plasterboard has been available since the 1920s, although its early use was mainly confined to ceilings where it proved a cost-effective and quick alternative to traditional lath and plaster. Nowadays, it is available in a wide range of grades and sizes and is used for a variety of purposes, including ceiling linings, wall linings and proprietary partition systems. It can also be used to improve thermal insulation, sound insulation, fire protection and to provide vapour control layers. Early plasterboards were always intended to receive one or two coats of plaster, but in modern construction most plasterboard is self finished. Manufacturers produce their own specific products, many with trade names.

Plasterboard comprises a core of gypsum plaster (with added aggregates) with thick paper linings bonded either side. Their lightweight and low thermal capacity means that they will warm up quickly and will help reduce the risk of surface condensation. Plasterboard linings are not suitable for areas of high humidity or areas which are permanently damp.

## ■ Wallboard and vapour control wallboard

Wallboard, despite its name, is used for a variety of applications, including drylining walls, lining ceilings and on stud partitions. Typical thicknesses include 9.5 mm, 12.5 mm 15 mm and 19 mm. Wallboard is available in a range of sizes, for example 1800 mm × 900 mm, 2400 mm × 900 mm, 2400 mm × 1200 mm, 3000 mm × 1200mm, and can have tapered or square edges (on the long sides). The tapered edges are designed for direct decoration or skimming, and the square edges for skimming or textured (Artex) finishing.

Vapour control wallboard is the same as wallboard except that the inner face is covered with a thin vapour control membrane. Vapour control wallboard is used where there is a risk of condensation.

## ■ Thermal boards and moisture resistant boards

A thermal board is a wallboard with insulation bonded to the inner face. The insulation can be of various types, including polystyrene and phenolic foam. Thermal boards often contain an integral vapour control layer to minimise the risk of condensation.

Moisture resistant boards are usually 2100 mm × 1200 mm with a thickness of 9.5 mm or 12.5 mm. They can be used for external soffits or as a base for wall tiling around showers, etc.

## ■ Drylining

When plasterboard is used as a wall finish in place of wet plaster, it is referred to as drylining. In modern construction there are two main approaches: bonding the boards to adhesive dabs, or securing the boards to metal channels which themselves have been bonded to the background. British Gypsum and Lafarge, currently the two major manufacturers, offer both systems. They differ in detail but are broadly the same in terms of principle.

### Theory into practice

If dry lining is quicker and cheaper than more traditional methods of plaster finishes, find out how many contractors can do this work. Use the Internet to list specialist contractors in your area.

The use of adhesive dab is the simpler of the two systems. It comprises a series of adhesive dabs applied by trowel to the wall and typically 50 mm to 75 mm wide and 250 mm long. Three 'columns' of dabs are normally required per board (9.5 mm board 1200 mm wide usually requires four), with horizontal dabs between the columns at ceiling level, and a continuous band of adhesive at skirting level. When the dabs are in position the board (cut 15 mm short of wall to ceiling height) can be pressed and tapped into position, tight against

the ceiling. It is temporarily supported at floor level by off-cuts of board. An insulated reveal board is available where there are risks of **cold bridging**.

### Key Term

**Cold bridging** This occurs when the insulation layer within a wall or roof is interrupted by another material or is reduced in thickness. The thinner area of insulation leads to greater heat loss through that part of the wall or roof and provides a reduced internal surface temperature. When the warm, moist air inside the property comes into contact with the cooler surface, it is chilled and less able to carry moisture. This results in surface condensation or pattern staining of décor.

The procedure for thermal laminate board (a plasterboard with an inner layer of insulation) is similar, although two plug fixings are required, 15 mm in from the board edge and at mid height. These are required to ensure that the plasterboard is not distorted in the event of a fire.

In the second system, the boards are fixed to a series of metal channels bonded on dabs to the background. The channels are fixed at 600 mm centres (vertically) with top and bottom channels running horizontally. The boards themselves are fixed to the channels with special screws, typically at 300 mm centres. The boards must be well fitted to ensure there is no flow of air behind the boards. Failure to do this will reduce their thermal performance. Additional sealant can be provided around the edges of junctions, that is, around window reveals, external angles, etc. In long runs of drylining, Building Regulations require the provision of vertical cavity barriers to limit the spread of fire. This can be formed using a continuous vertical line of dabs running down the centre of a board.

## Case study

Modern requirements increasingly call for new build units of high quality and technical input, both traditionally and on a design and build basis. Ideally, you will have built up several years' experience and accomplished many successful projects, having constructed hundreds of new build units over many years to tender for appropriate contracts and seek out further work.

You will need up-to-date knowledge of Building Regulations, Scheme Development Standards, National House Building Council (NHBC) standards, etc. Imagine you have secured the contract to build a development of 44 new units. Think about the possibilities of creating a good place to live and a lasting legacy of your work that you can be proud of for many years to come.

---

## 3-bedroom, semi-detached

A large three-bedroomed semi-detached house which offers spacious family accommodation. The 'Beverley-Hills' incorporates a dining kitchen, WC and generously proportioned lounge with open-plan staircase to the ground floor. The first floor houses three bedrooms which includes an ensuite to the master bedroom.

### Dimensions

| Room | mm |
| --- | --- |
| Kitchen/Dining room | 4451 × 2752 |
| Lounge | 4451 × 4833 |
| Bedroom 1 | 4290 × 2423 |
| Bedroom 2 | 2912 × 2183 |
| Bedroom 3 | 2525 × 1812 |
| Ensuite | 2285 × 1675 |

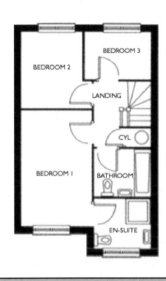

---

1. What kind of investigation is necessary to find out about the land that the building will sit on? How will you know that the foundation is strong enough to support the house and the loads imposed on it?

2. Having decided what type and size of foundation, how will you communicate your thoughts and decisions to the builders. Can you draw to a suitable scale all the components in the substructure so that the builder can clearly see how the building goes together?

3. What type of superstructure will you use and how will you explain to potential buyers that this type of house is safe, warm and uses good materials, particularly if they are of sustainable construction and do not cause problems for the environment?

4. What drawings and specifications are required to explain how the superstructure goes together?

5. What plant and equipment will you need to build the elements of the houses that need special equipment and tackle, e.g. the fixing of the roofs? How will you gain access to high-level work and how will you ensure that any operative working there will be safe in their work?

# Assessment practice

Produce a section drawing of the most suitable foundations for each of the following:

**a** a single detached house made of timber-frame construction

**b** a portal frame building made from structural steel sections and clad with lightweight aluminium sheeting. **P3**

Describe how the design of a commercial building superstructure differs from a domestic building superstructure. Explain what methods are used to create these two forms of building. **P4**

Make a list of all the materials you can think of that are used in the superstructure of a detached house and a portal frame building. Explain the main characteristics of each material and why you consider them suitable for use. **M2**

Consider one element of the superstructure of a house such as an external wall. List all the components that make up this element and identify how these materials are used. Evaluate the use of these materials and explain how their use impacts on the environment. **D2**

# 6.4 Implications of environmental issues and legislative constraints on building construction and the infrastructure required to support typical construction processes

# Environmental issues

## Environmental impact resulting from materials and methods used in construction

Sustainability is about balancing society with the environment. The construction industry uses natural products such as timber, clay, iron and other minerals. It creates our physical environment and contributes to the economy and the gross domestic product – nearly 2 million people work in the industry every day. The construction industry has to consider how its activities contribute to global warming and how we replace those materials taken from our planet.

### Remember!

Sustainable construction is not an option – all buildings will need to comply with legislation in the future.

There are three main threats to environmental sustainability:

- Global warming (climate change by emissions of gases).
- Resource depletion such as extracting minerals from the ground and how quickly we use up those resources.
- Pollution in the atmosphere due to how construction activities take place.

The most immediate of these threats is global warming, which can lead to climate change and a long-term rise in sea levels which could bring about flooding and damage to buildings in low-lying areas.

## Extraction and manufacture

The extraction and use of fossil fuels is the primary source of carbon dioxide ($CO_2$). It also causes the majority of eco-toxic pollution, and is the prime resource depletion issue in the UK as the economy is largely dependent on fossil fuels. Action to cut fossil fuel use not only helps prevent climate change, but also reduces resource depletion and pollution. Reducing $CO_2$ emissions is therefore by far the most significant issue in buildings. Designers and constructors of buildings have a duty to produce homes, offices and buildings that are energy efficient, reduce heat loss through the walls, roof and other parts of the structure by the inclusion of increased dimensions of insulating material, and to build in the provision to run energy saving appliances that display the 'Energy Saving' logo and are approved by the Energy Saving Trust, such as washers, dryers, dishwashers, boilers, etc. which operate at lower temperatures. Lighting and illumination can also be included in energy efficient lighting schemes that use low-energy light bulbs in preference to standard bulbs. Contractors during the construction process need to be aware of the tolerances of waste materials and that by operating efficiently they can contribute to overall savings and reduce costs that high levels of waste bring.

## Construction methods

### ■ Heavyweight traditional construction

Heavyweight or dense construction is preferred by many since this form of construction tends to store heat in the thick walls and materials. However, in summer heavyweight buildings tend to be cooler based on the idea that it takes a long time for any heat to penetrate or dissipate from heavyweight construction, hence it takes longer to heat up or for the building to dissipate its heat.

This effect is known as thermal mass. It tends to take longer and hence more energy to heat these buildings to a satisfactory level, but they will stay warmer for longer periods due to their dense constructional form.

## ■ Lightweight construction

Timber-framed housing provides a lightweight constructional form, quickly erected with excellent thermal performance. The increased use of prefabricated designs has also improved quality control and led to higher standards. In some cases, these efficiencies have been passed through the supply chain with this form of construction being the preferred option for those that need low-cost homes and social housing projects.

Construction activities and how homes and offices are used also impacts on sustainability issues. Designers have a responsibility to consider how water is used, how we generate and deal with waste products and the use of materials that add to pollution in the environment. Higher standards and awareness of sustainability issues will bring about improved performance in energy use, lower costs and generally increase the quality of life.

The Code for Sustainable Homes has been issued by the Department for Communities and Local Government, which should promote changes in the way that designers tackle sustainability issues in new developments. The UK government states that this will become a national standard to be used by designers and constructors of buildings to develop better homes and buildings as well as making clients and homeowners aware of sustainability issues around the home.

## Theory into practice

Use the Internet to find out whether major contractors operating in your area have a 'Sustainable Construction' policy. How do they differ from one another?

Developing an awareness of sustainable issues and relating these issues to construction should lead to a reduction in $CO_2$ emissions, better management of water disposal and an emphasis on recycling materials that would otherwise have been lost. Homeowners can be assured that changes made to the design and construction of a new building comply and promote sustainability and hence be aware of the improved standard and performance of the building. It is highly likely that contractors who comply with new codes of practice will use this fact in their advertising and promotional literature to demonstrate this improved performance and show the benefits of lower energy consumption and water efficiency.

### Recycling and waste implications

In order to conserve the Earth's finite resources, we have to be aware of the long-term implications of manufacturing materials. Materials need to contain an element of recycling in their manufacture and within their eventual demolition when the life of the building is exceeded. Concrete can be crushed and the reinforcing bars recycled into steel making, while the crushed concrete becomes hardcore fill for levelling sites. This can also be done with brickwork, but bricks can also be cleaned and reused for new house construction with any damaged ones recycled as hardcore. Steelwork from buildings and any metals can be reshaped into new products during steel making processes.

### Embedded energy

This is the amount of energy that has been used in the manufacture of a material. It is therefore far better to specify and select materials that have a low embedded energy, which should also include the transport costs of getting the material to its final point of use. Cement-based products such as pre-cast concrete and building blocks contain high levels of embedded energy from the manufacture of the cement.

### $CO_2$ emissions

This is the greenhouse gas that is associated with the current trend in global warming. Releasing $CO_2$ into the atmosphere increases the average temperature of the world which has consequences for weather patterns and the rise in sea levels. Using timber-based products will help $CO_2$ emissions in that when the tree is growing it absorbs $CO_2$ and gives off oxygen as a waste product through photosynthesis. During the processing of timber very little $CO_2$ is released into the air making this a very sustainable product; its waste can also be reused and turned into engineered timber.

## Noise

This is a form of pollution that can cause environmental disturbance to residents living near construction sites that produce a high level of noise. Where cutting and processing of materials is carried out onsite, noise suppression systems should be used where available.

## Case study

A new home being built today will have to meet any level of the Code for Sustainable Homes. For Level 1 this means that the home will have to be 10 per cent more energy efficient than one built to the 2006 Building Regulations standards. This could be achieved by:

- improving the thermal efficiency of the walls, windows and roof, e.g. by using more insulation or better glass
- reducing air permeability, that is, by improving the control of the fresh air into a home, and the stale air out of a home (a certain amount of air ventilation is needed in a home for health reasons)
- installing a high efficiency condensing boiler
- carefully designing the fabric of the home to reduce thermal bridging (thermal bridging allows heat to escape easily between the inner walls and the outer walls of a home)

The home will have to be designed to use no more than about 120 litres of water per person per day. This could be achieved by fitting a number of items such as:

- 6/4 dual flush WC
- flow reducing/aerating taps throughout
- 6–9 litres per minute shower (note that an average electric shower is about 6–7 litres per minute)
- 18 litres maximum volume dishwasher
- 60 litres maximum volume washing machine.

Other minimum requirements are required for:

- surface water management – this may mean the provision of soakaways and areas of porous paving
- materials – this means a minimum number of materials meeting at least a 'D' grade in the

Building Research Establishment's 'Green Guide' (the scale goes from A+ to E)
- waste management – this means having a site waste management plan in place during the home's construction, and adequate space for waste storage during its use.

But to get to Level 1 you need a further 33.3 points. So the builder/developer must do other things to obtain the other points such as:

- providing accessible drying space (so that tumble dryers need not be used)
- providing more energy efficient lighting (taking into account the needs of disabled people with visual impairments)
- providing cycle storage
- providing a room that can be easily set up as a home office
- reducing the amount of water than runs off the site into the storm drains
- using environmentally friendly materials
- providing recycling capacity either inside or outside the home.

1   Identify which of these elements are included in the current Building Regulations.

2   Use the internet to obtain the price of a selection of items such as a condensing boiler, a dual flush WC, aerating taps and fittings for the bathroom and kitchen.

3   What other items can be built into the design to encourage recycling of waste products?

## Pollution

Pollution and wastage must be controlled as these can damage the environment. Chemicals especially should be limited in use during the construction process. Care should be taken in what wastage is taken to landfill and all waste should be sorted into recycling skips. For example, some plasterboard manufacturers supply waste skips for recycling offcuts of their products.

# Legislative constraints

## Building Regulations

The Building Regulations apply in England and Wales and exist principally to ensure the health and safety of people in and around buildings. They also provide for access to and around buildings and energy conservation.

A detailed explanation of the Building Regulations, the Building Control system and how they might affect individual building projects is provided on the Planning Portal found at www.planningportal.gov.uk. The regulations apply to most new buildings and many alterations of existing buildings, whether domestic, commercial or industrial.

Building Regulations promote the following:

- Standards for most aspects of a building's construction, including its structure, fire safety, sound insulation, drainage, ventilation and electrical safety. Electrical safety was added in January 2005 to reduce the number of deaths, injuries and fires caused by faulty electrical installations.
- Energy efficiency in buildings. The changes to the regulations on energy conservation came into effect on 6 April 2006 and will save a million tonnes of

carbon per year by 2010 and help to combat climate change.
- The needs of all people, including those with disabilities, in accessing and moving around buildings. They set standards for buildings to be accessible and hazard-free wherever possible

## Health and Safety at Work Act 1974

The Health and Safety at Work Act provides the legal framework to promote, stimulate and encourage high standards of health and safety in places of work. It protects employees and the public from work activities. Everyone has a duty to comply with the Act, including employers, employees, trainees, the self-employed, manufacturers, suppliers, designers, importers of work equipment.

The Act places a general duty to 'ensure so far as is reasonably practicable the health, safety and welfare at work of all their employees'. Employers must comply with the Act. They must:

- provide and maintain safety equipment and safe systems of work
- ensure materials used are properly stored, handled, used and transported
- provide information, training, instruction and supervision, and ensure staff are aware of instructions provided by manufacturers and suppliers of equipment
- provide a safe place of employment
- provide a safe working environment
- provide a written safety policy/risk assessment
- look after the health and safety of others, e.g. members of the public or visitors to the site
- talk to safety representatives.

An employer is forbidden to charge an employee for any measures which they are required to provide in the interests of health and safety, for example personal protective equipment used during the construction process.

Employees have specific responsibilities too. They must:

- take care of their own health and safety and that of other people
- cooperate with their employer

- not interfere with anything provided in the interest of health and safety.

It is the responsibility of the Health & Safety Executive (HSE) to carry out inspections of construction sites. The powers of an inspector include:

- rights of entry at reasonable times, etc. without appointments
- the right to investigate and examine
- the right to dismantle equipment and take substances/equipment
- the right to see documents and take copies
- the right to assistance (from colleagues or the police)
- the right to ask questions under caution
- the right to seize articles/substances in cases of imminent danger.

The HSE can visit any site and report on whether there is an infringement of the Health and Safety at Work Act. It does this by producing **legal notices** that are issued to **improve**, to **prohibit** something from continuing or to bring about a prosecution. Both employers and employees may face prosecution.

## Key Terms

**Legal notices** Written document requiring a person to do/stop doing something.

**Improvement** Identifying what is wrong and how to put it right within a set time.

**Prohibition** Banning the use of equipment/unsafe practices immediately.

### The Construction (Health, Safety and Welfare) Regulations 1996

These regulations cover most aspects of site safety and welfare, including the following:

- Safe places of work – excavations, tunnels, work at ground level and at height, access to and from work area.
- Preventing falls – physical precautions or equipment to check a fall and prevent falls through fragile

materials; scaffolding and supervision by a competent person; safe use of ladders.
- Preventing falling objects – and/or provide covered walkways.
- Work on structures – prevent collapse of structures; plan demolition and dismantling and supervise such work by a competent person; take precautions with explosives.
- Excavations – prevent collapse and risk from underground cables and services.
- Preventing drowning – rescue equipment must be immediately available.
- Traffic routes, vehicles, gates and doors – make these safe and provide safe access and egress onto and from construction sites.
- Prevention and control of emergencies – procedures for evacuating sites, fire-fighting equipment, emergency exits.
- Welfare facilities – provide sanitary and washing facilities; provide rest facilities; provide facilities to store and change clothing.
- Site-wide issues – including fresh air, protection from bad weather, lighting, cleanliness on sites, marking of the perimeter of the site and maintenance of equipment in safe and sound condition.
- Training, inspections and reports – all work should be carried out by people with the training, technical knowledge and experience to do so safely, or should be supervised by those with such qualifications. Before work at height, on excavations, cofferdams or caissons begins, they must be inspected by a competent person, and a written report made.

### Town and country planning legislation

Towns and development need to be planned appropriately. Planning is necessary to ensure that the buildings and environment that we create is fit for purpose and does not interfere with other properties around a given site. Local authorities are responsible, through their planning committees to decide whether a new building or an alteration to an existing building is suitable. These alterations could be an extension to a house or the complete adaptation of a large building into an office building.

Planning permission is not always required. Internal alterations or work which does not change the appearance of the outside of a property does not require planning permission. In other instances, such as extending or altering the physical shape and size of a building, planning permission will be needed.

Some properties have special terms and conditions when they were built. Examples of this are the requirement for or restriction on the erection of fences around the front gardens which will require permission to make any changes to the original terms and conditions. It is not required, generally speaking, for changes to the inside of buildings, or for small alterations to the outside such as the installation of telephone connections and burglar alarm boxes.

Dividing a home into flats, or creating a separate home within an existing building will also need planning permission as would the alteration of a domestic building into a workshop or office building.

# Plant

## Construction plant

There is a huge range of construction plant available today to assist in the construction of modern domestic and commercial buildings. Here we shall have a look at the major pieces of plant that you would expect to see when visiting a complex, active construction site.

## ■ Scaffolding

This consists of scaffold metal tubing and timber scaffold boards (see Figure 6.10). All is tested to achieve a British Standard under current UK health and safety legislation. For health and safety reasons, scaffolding must be erected by a qualified and competent person and cannot be adapted, moved or dismantled by any unqualified individual. Scaffolding is a complex structural system of many components such as:

- standards – the vertical tubes
- boards – the element you walk on
- ledgers – a horizontal tube
- putlogs and transoms – a tube that is built into the construction as work proceeds or acts independently

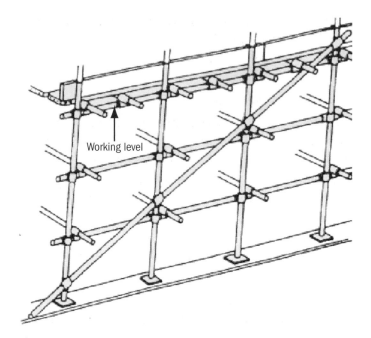

▲ **Figure 6.10 Typical scaffolding system**

- guard rails – two rails that prevent falling
- toe boards – a vertical board to prevent objects falling off the scaffolding
- bracing – diagonal bracing that secures the structure against collapse.

You should refer to the HSE's publications on scaffolding for detailed requirements. Scaffolding must be inspected by a competent person and the Construction (Health, Safety and Welfare) Regulations should be referred to for the frequency of inspections and the records to be kept.

## ■ Trench support systems

These are used to support the sides of excavations and can take many forms including:

- steel sheet piling which is driven in and propped
- hydraulic props between timber shores
- steel hydraulic trench boxes.

## ■ Forklift trucks

On construction sites, these are rough-terrain forklift trucks that have large off-road tyres in order to cope with site conditions. Modern forklifts have telescopic booms that can be used to reach onto scaffolding platforms to deposit materials. An access platform with a roll-over guard rail system has to be provided at these points. This type of plant is ideal for the unloading and distribution of materials in any 360-degree location, both vertically and horizontally.

## ■ Dumper trucks

These are available in a variety of weight and volume capacities. They are steered hydraulically and can have tipper facilities incorporated into the front and rear hoppers. They are ideal rough-terrain vehicles and can manoeuvre over any rough ground. These machines are used for moving loose, bulky materials, for example drainage bedding.

## ■ Cement mixers and silos

These range from a full batching plant that can produce concrete down to a small bag mixer. Cement silos and mortar producing plants should be used on larger construction sites where economies of scale can be obtained by purchasing raw materials in bulk.

## ■ Excavators

There are two types of excavator:
● 360-degree excavators
● Backhoe excavators which can only move 180 degrees.

The most common excavator is the JCB 3CX which is very versatile and can have many attachments incorporated onto its hydraulics. Excavators have two movable forms: wheeled and tracked. They are used mainly in demolition and earth excavation and removal but can also be used to lift materials if certified to do so.

## ■ Cranes

Crainage varies widely from small 15-tonne lifting cranes to large tower cranes. Their use is limited by the reach that is required and the amount that has to be lifted by the crane. A specialist hirer would provide all the necessary documentation and they must be used with a certified **banksperson**.

## Key Term

**Banksperson** A competent person who supervises the lifting operations of the crane.

### Small plant and tools

There are many small plant and tools that are regularly used on construction sites, including:
● cartridge guns – these fire a nail fixing
● 110v drills – for creating holes of various diameters
● generators – small petrol generators to produce independent power
● petrol-driven saws – used to cut materials using a rotating disc.

# Materials

### Supply of building materials for both traditional and modern projects

Many materials are supplied in construction and these are sourced either:
● direct in bulk from the manufacturer
● from a distributor such as a builder's merchant where smaller lots can be purchased.

When purchasing materials always select the 'crane off load option'. This is an attachment that goes on the delivery wagon which is, in effect, a crane. This enables easy off loading of large heavy materials onto the correct location. Where possible, materials should always be on pallets to prevent damage and wrapped from the weather.

### Prefabricated components and system building

For more on these topics, see pages 228–29.

## Assessment practice

You have been appointed to a design team that specialises in small design and build contracts. There are two projects available for you to work on which will require you to create detailed drawings of the superstructure. Produce a series of drawings that show how each of the elements of the building will fit together:

**a** A pair of semi-detached, three-bedroom homes with integral garage made using timber-framed construction with brick cladding to the exterior face. The upper floor is to have a family bathroom and an ensuite to the master bedroom.

**b** A small office/retail outlet made of traditional brick/block construction comprising two floors. The lower floor is to be used as a retail outlet and the upper floor is intended for use as office space. **P5**

For the pair of semi-detached houses in P5, consider the plant and equipment needed to complete the installation of the roof. Make a list of all the resources required to undertake this work. Justify why you will need to use this type of equipment. **M3**

# Preparation for assessment

## ■ Brief

As a small property developer, you have won the contract to build 14 units, comprising seven pairs of semi-detached properties and a small single-storey community centre on the parcel of land shown in the drawing below The client will need to assure themselves that you have considered all available options and will produce a high-quality plan that the builders will be able to follow accurately. This will mean producing clear and concise drawings, along with being able to justify and explain the details contained in the drawings. Environmental issucs will also need to be considered along with an evaluation of the performance of the materials you have selected for the construction of the buildings.

▲ **Location plan**

Explain the procedure involved in your subsoil investigation and how you will use this information in order to design the substructure. **P1**

Explain the principles of suitable foundation design and describe the methods used to construct different types of foundation that you could use for this building. **P2**

Produce a series of detail drawings showing the construction of your foundation for the houses and how they differ from the community centre. **P3**

Explain the principles that you have adopted in the selection of the superstructure design. Describe the methods used to construct all elements of this superstructure. **P4**

Produce a series of detail drawings showing the techniques used to construct all elements of the superstructure for the houses and how this differs for the community centre. **P5**

Explain and justify the selection of your materials and techniques used in the construction of the substructure for the houses and how these differ from the materials used in the community centre. **M1**

Explain and justify the selection of your materials and techniques used in the construction of the superstructure for the houses and how they differ from the community centre. **M2**

Identify and justify the plant and equipment requirements, including safety equipment, for the construction of the roof of one of the houses. **M3**

Evaluate the performance in use, and environmental implications of, alternative materials and techniques used in the construction of:

a   the substructures to the houses

b   the substructure to the community centre

c   the external walls of the houses. **D1** **D2**

# Grading tips

You will need to justify your selections.

You will need to identify plant and equipment requirements for at least one complex component of a building such as a roof. Then you will need to justify this selection in terms of cost, equipment, suitability and availability of the equipment to complete the construction of the element that you choose. **M3**

You will need to evaluate your selections if you are to achieve a distinction grade. **D1** **D2**

# Knowledge check

1 Identify and compare three different types of method used for soil investigations.

2 List six factors of ground conditions that would affect the type and size of foundation design.

3 Explain the principles involved in correct foundation design.

4 Sketch and annotate four different types of foundation suitable for low-rise domestic buildings.

5 Describe with the aid of appropriate well-annotated sketches and drawings, the process associated with the construction of a timber-framed house. The process should include:

  **a** site clearance

  **b** site set up and organisation

  **c** material storage

  **d** plant positioning

  **e** access and safety onsite

  **f** excavation and plant needed

  **g** water elimination

  **h** temporary support.

6 Draw a cross-section through a concrete pot and beam floor showing the structural components and the position of the insulation.

7 Compare the properties of steel and timber. Relate the properties to their performance when used as structural members.

8 Draw a vertical section through a timber-framed house showing all the key components and how the house is constructed.

9 Illustrate how the following elements can be integrated into the structure of a timber-framed house:

  **a** Upper floors

  **b** Window frames

  **c** Door frames

  **d** Stairs

10 Draw to a suitable scale a section through a portal frame building showing the structural frame and a suitable form of cladding.

11 Identify and describe three internal and three external finishes.

12 List four common forms for cladding used for timber-frame domestic housing. Identify the merits and disadvantages of each form.

13 List the plant and equipment necessary to fix a pitched timber roof on a low-rise domestic dwelling

14 Evaluate the impact of raw materials used in the building of the substructure of a domestic dwelling. Explain how building contractors can contribute to the development of sustainable construction.

15 Analyse and evaluate the performance of lightweight construction. Explain how this differs from heavyweight construction and what the implications are for global warming by selecting suitable materials for the construction of buildings.

## Grading criteria: Unit 6

| To achieve a pass grade the evidence must show that the learner is able to: | To achieve a merit grade the evidence must show that, in addition to the pass criteria, the learner is able to: | To achieve a distinction grade the evidence must show that, in addition to the pass and merit criteria, the learner is able to: |
|---|---|---|
| **P1** explain the procedures involved in subsoil investigation and how the information obtained is used in the design of substructures **Assessment practice pages 246, 267** | **M1** explain and justify the selection of suitable materials and techniques for use in the construction of substructures for low-rise domestic and commercial buildings, for two different tutor-specified scenarios **Assessment practice pages 246, 267** | **D1** evaluate the performance in use, and environmental implications of, alternative materials and techniques used in the construction of substructures to low-rise domestic and commercial buildings **Assessment practice pages 246, 267** |
| **P2** explain the principles of foundation design and describe the methods used to construct different types of foundation **Assessment practice pages 246, 267** | | |
| **P3** produce detailed drawings showing foundation construction for a low-rise domestic building and for a low-rise commercial building **Assessment practice pages 258, 267** | **M2** explain and justify the selection of materials and techniques used in the construction of superstructures for low-rise domestic and commercial buildings **Assessment practice pages 258, 267** | **D2** evaluate the performance in use, and environmental implications of, alternative materials and techniques used in the construction of a tutor-specified element of a superstructure, e.g. the external wall **Assessment practice pages 258, 267** |
| **P4** explain the principles of superstructure design and describe the methods used to construct all elements of a superstructure **Assessment practice pages 258, 267** | | |
| **P5** produce detailed drawings showing the techniques used to construct all elements of superstructure for low-rise domestic and commercial buildings **Assessment practice pages 266, 267** | **M3** identify and justify the plant and equipment requirements, including safety equipment, for the construction of a complex tutor-specified element of superstructure, e.g. a roof **Assessment practice pages 266, 267** | |

# Planning, organisation and control of resources in construction and the built environment

## Introduction

The success of any construction company depends largely on how well its construction projects are planned, organised and controlled. Success on a construction project is often measured in terms of the level of profit made – did the project meet expectations, or did it fall short of the profit margin applied at the tender stage when the work was won?

Planning and organisation are essential throughout the life of the project – from the initial ·design and briefing stage all the way through to completion of the construction phase. The resources required to complete the project – labour, materials, plant and machinery – also need to be carefully controlled.

This unit will help you to understand the management functions and techniques of the planning process, and the importance of information technology in monitoring the project. It looks at the roles of individuals and how they interact to achieve the client's goals, which are generally to produce the project within budget, to complete it within an agreed timescale and to an acceptable quality.

### How you will be assessed

This unit is internally assessed by your tutor. A variety of activities is included in this unit to help you understand all aspects of working efficiently in the construction industry.

After completing this unit you should be able to achieve the following outcomes:
1   Understand the roles and responsibilities of, and interaction between, the parties involved in the construction process
2   Be able to identify the resources required to complete a construction project and to explain their efficient management

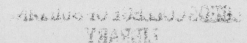

# Thinking points

Planning is essential on a construction site, both in the pre- and post-contract phases of the project. The size of the project will determine how much time will be needed to plan, organise and control the resources that will be required to complete *on time and within budget*. Both of these are important to the client – get them right and a single project quickly develops into repeat business for a construction company.

Leave a project unplanned and short of supervision to organise and control resources, and very quickly things will start to go wrong. A project that falls seriously behind the agreed programme may mean the contractor has to pay damages to the client for failing to hand over the structure on time. Any overrun on a budget may have to be absorbed by the contractor at their own expense, which could seriously affect the level of profit they make.

As you work through this unit, you will learn how the members of the design and construction team plan the construction process, how they interact and communicate with each other, in order to achieve a successful project for the client.

You have been asked to visit a construction greenfield site that will commence operations next week. Your task is to plan the construction site before operations begin. You will need to think carefully how you will accomplish this.

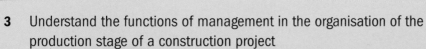

3   Understand the functions of management in the organisation of the production stage of a construction project
4   Be able to produce and interpret simple bar charts, networks and schedules used by construction teams

# Roles and responsibilities

## Management at director or site level

### ■ Managing director

The managing director of a construction company is responsible for overall planning. They look at the full picture of the company's current workload, its future workload for contracts already won and possible workload for contracts being tendered for. This global view enables strategic planning on the levels of supervision required for each contract, and may involve trained personnel to supervise the company's workload.

The managing director will also be involved in the financial planning of the business, including cash flow forecasts, financing of the workload, risk assessments on complex construction projects, bad debts and the type of work the company would like to undertake. These responsibilities differ from the planning decisions that are taken at construction site level (see below).

### Remember!

The managing director is often the owner of the company or may be answerable to shareholders. The majority of the decisions made at this level will be strategic or financial.

### ■ Site manager

The site manager (or supervisor) is concerned with the day-to-day planning, organisation and control of the construction site, including the organisation of resources. (There are several methods that can be employed to accomplish these tasks and they are explored later in the chapter.) The site manager has to ensure that the construction project is delivered on time, to budget and to the required quality.

One of the site manager's main responsibilities is to make the best use of resources. This involves maximising production and ensuring the use of the right labour skills to fulfil a task. Materials must be used efficiently and not wasted. Plant must be utilised to offset the establishment and running costs against the value of labour saved. Subcontractors must be organised and controlled to work effectively and safely within a team.

The site manager is also responsible for all the operations on site, although they may delegate some of these to general forepersons who may control sections or specific trade areas on the construction site such as bricklaying, carpentry and finishes (see below). The site manager is often from a trade background with wide experience of different construction situations, knowledge and training.

## Technical roles

### ■ Planner

The planner is usually based at the company's head office, although on complex, expensive projects, they may be employed full time in an office on site. The construction planner is generally responsible for:

- supervising contract programmes (main, monthly, weekly, daily)
- monitoring and reviewing progress
- materials delivery scheduling
- labour scheduling
- reporting procedures
- plant scheduling
- overseeing pre-contract tender programmes.

The planner is a managing resource, with an overview of the company's whole operation, and they will report on the progress of the company's construction workload either to the managing director or contract team director or manager. They are expected to plan how to make the most efficient use of resources, including responsibility for:

- working out how many operatives will be required on each project – to enable accurate labour forecasting
- supplying the buying or purchasing department with materials schedules of what is required, when and how much – to enable **economies of scale** in the purchasing of materials
- the movement of equipment from site to site – to ensure maximum utilisation of the contractor's own equipment or that hired by the company.

## Key Term

**Economies of scale** This is where a company can obtain better discounts on materials by combining orders from several sites and buying in bulk.

## ■ Quantity surveyor

The quantity surveyor is primarily responsible for the financial planning of the construction company's operations. They deal with all financial aspects such as payments for supplies, invoicing of clients, claims for **variations** and final accounts. The quantity surveyor will deal with the cash flow of the business. This is the amount of money flowing into the company from clients and the amount flowing out in payments – money flowing in should be greater than money flowing out. The quantity surveyor will plan the periods when the company will receive payment for the work undertaken on behalf of their clients. These are called valuation dates and are normally at 30-day intervals in accordance with the contract between the company and its client.

## Key Term

**Variations** Items that occur as part of the project that were not in the client's original budget and are therefore additional to the contract, for example obstructions encountered within the ground during excavation work.

## ■ Buyer

The buyer is responsible for the purchasing of materials and plant resources and ensuring their timely delivery. There is often insufficient space on site to store all the materials required throughout the life of the project, stored materials can become damaged, and suppliers have to be paid for them. The buyer will analyse the main contract programme to obtain a set of delivery dates for the materials. Ideally, resources need to arrive on site just before they are needed. Often the buyer will place a bulk order with a supplier, who will then deliver specific quantities to the site when requested by the site manager.

## ■ Estimator

The estimator undertakes tendering operations for the company. Tendering is the process by which the company obtains work. A potential client will ask a number of companies interested in carrying out their project to submit 'sealed bids' outlining the estimated cost of the work. It is the responsibility of the estimator to work out these costs, and they may also be expected to submit health and safety plans and construction programmes as part of the tender. During this process, the estimator will have a great deal of interaction with specialist subcontractors, who will be required for installations that cannot be undertaken by the company.

### Supervisory roles

## ■ Site supervisor

The site supervisor (or manager) is responsible for the day-to-day running of the construction site. They deal with the site workers, subcontractors, material and plant movements and resourcing, and are expected to maintain the construction programme. On larger, complex construction sites, there may be several site supervisors for different sections of the project, all reporting to a site manager. The site supervisor is also responsible for the health, safety and welfare of all the workers on their site.

▲ Bricklayers have a responsibility to produce work that is of the correct quality

## ■ General foreperson

The general foreperson reports to the site manager or supervisor and is often trade specific, for example carpentry. There may be a general foreperson for brickwork, joinery and finishes. Their role is to assist the site supervisor with labour control, materials control and some of the trade-specific plant.

## ■ Craft operative

Craft operatives are the joiners, bricklayers, steel fixers, etc. who have a craft background or trade. They are responsible for undertaking their trade duties in producing work that is of the correct quality. They collectively contribute to maintaining the construction programme, and have a duty under health and safety legislation to work safely.

## ■ General operative

General operatives undertake semi-skilled works, such as the excavation of drainage trenches, working with concrete, keeping the site clean and the movement of resources.

## Theory into practice

The following is a list of roles that particular members of the construction team would undertake. For each one decide whose role and responsibility it is.

a) The long-term business plan of the company.

b) The delivery date for a full load of bricks.

c) The checking of engine-oil level on the site rough terrain forklift.

d) The issuing of the monthly construction programme.

e) The fixing of timber stairs.

f) The pouring of concrete foundations.

g) The completion of the tender document.

h) The monthly valuation.

## Remember!

More than one person could undertake these activities. There is often an overlap between roles and responsibilities in small- to medium-sized companies.

# Team working and interaction of roles

### Head office and site organisational charts

The head office and the construction site are set up quite differently from each other, as shown in Figures 7.1 and 7.2. At site level, the administration is organised specifically for the individual site, its size and its complexity. The head office, on the other hand, is organised to administer all the company's construction sites. The organisation charts shown here are just one example – you will find that one company's layouts may be very different from another, for example construction companies may have more than one office and act regionally with several offices, so the structure will be far more complex.

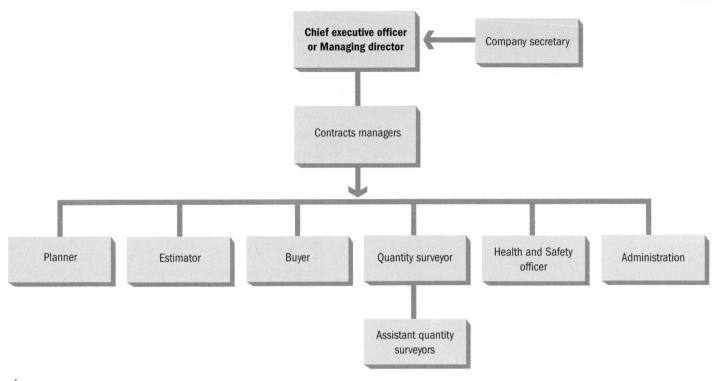

▲ Figure 7.1 Head office organisational chart

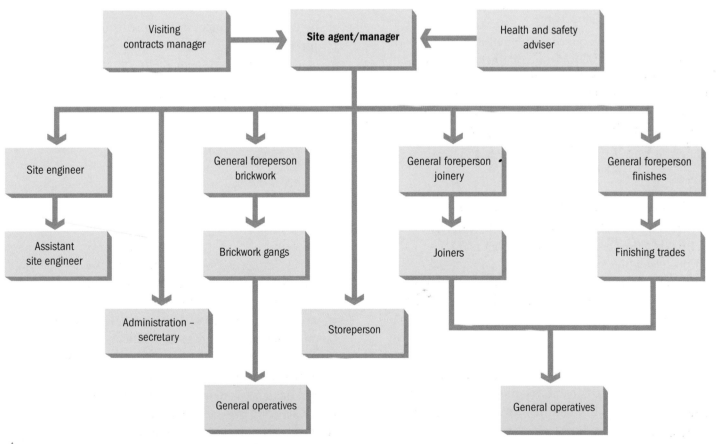

▲ Figure 7.2 Construction site organisational chart

Working within teams is essential. The team approach may be split between the client's team and the construction team. The client's team will initially be concerned with planning the design phase and may include the following personnel:

- architect or designer
- quantity surveyor
- planning supervisor
- structural engineer
- services engineer.

The construction company's team may be specialised depending on the type of work that they are involved in and may include subdivided into several teams involved in:

- maintenance work
- interior shop fitting
- sports complexes
- shopping developments
- housing
- commercial developments.

We have previously looked at the members of the construction team, namely the planner, buyer, estimator, site manager and operatives.

## Remember!

No one person can produce a construction project. It involves assembling the best team you have at the time, completing the contract and then dissolving the team.

Interaction between teams and within teams may involve several different types of communication. For example, many construction companies use 'virtual' construction sites where all design and construction information is held. Each member of the team can access this by logging into the system to communicate and transfer information.

Traditionally, interaction may take place between:

- the design team and the construction team via the architect or designer and the principal contractor's **contracts manager**
- the contracts managers and their site managers/ agents or supervisors
- the site managers and the general forepersons
- the general forepersons and the crafts operatives and general operatives.

## Key Term

**Contracts manager** Their role is to manage several contracts, each having a site supervisor who is answerable to them. The contracts manager moves resources around these different contracts as and when required, and deals with the designer and construction team on each.

Communication can take place in several ways:

- between the architect or designer through **architect's instructions**
- via verbal instructions between the architect and designer and the **principal contractor**
- through site meetings where all primary parties are invited to meet on site to discuss the construction programme and progress, including health and safety and the budget
- through the issue of drawings, illustrating changes to designs
- by email with attachments.

## Key Term

**Architect's instructions** Written instructions issued on behalf of the client which instruct the contractor to undertake a particular item within the contract.

**Principal contractor** Often referred to as the main contractor. A named person under the Construction (Design and Management) Regulations, who undertakes most of the construction work on site.

## ■ How communication is undertaken

### Between architect and principal contractor

The main communication from the architect or designer to the principal contractor is to ensure that once the design is started, it is finished on time, to budget and to the agreed quality. The architect is the client's representative (often referred to as the employer's representative) on the construction site.

The architect will issue 'architect's instructions', which may be either verbal or written. Communication also takes place through drawn information from the architect which is issued under a drawing register. This tells those receiving it which are the latest drawing revisions issued, so they can remove the old ones from the current files.

Architects also conduct many of the site progress meetings where all parties to the construction phase can meet face to face to discuss progress, problems and any other issues. Minutes of the meetings are recorded.

### Between contracts manager and site manager

This communication via phone, email and fax will take place daily with the contracts manager ensuring that the site manager has all the resources they need.

### Between site manager and general forepersons

This again will be daily, principally with an initial meeting first thing to establish the tasks for the day, the resources required and the deadlines to be met. Copies of any instructions received from the architect will be passed on at this point.

### Between general forepersons and craft and general operatives

Communication between these groups will be mainly verbal. The **ganger** in charge of the bricklaying gang will take direct instructions from the general foreperson. This will involve delivering materials to the section they are working on, and utilising any lifting equipment.

### Levels of responsibility and accountability

- Ultimate responsibility on the principal contractor's side rests with the company's managing director.
- The architect or designer appointed as the client's representative takes responsibility for the design phase and subsequent running of the construction phase.
- The head office function of estimator is responsible for the pricing of the client's work, while the planner is accountable for the smooth running of the main contract programme for the project.
- The site manager is responsible for delivering the project on time, the quantity surveyor to deliver on budget, and the general forepersons to deliver quality from the trades.

The company you are currently employed with is keen to develop links with a European partner through the local business enterprise initiative of twinning construction companies across Europe. Part of this process involves a technical exchange of personnel for a six-month period. An employee from the European company has been asked to shadow you to find out how a UK construction company plans, organises and controls its construction sites.

Explain to the European employee the roles and inter-relationships of those members of the construction team involved in the resource management, planning and production (the construction phase of the project) so they can obtain a good overview of how your company operates. **P2**

The managing director of the company you work for is not sure how the team's structures are organised on the company's construction sites. Produce an organisational chart to show a team working on a typical construction site, such that this can be used as a model for future site set ups. **M1**

# Phases of construction

These can be compared to the life cycle of the construction project, which is conceived as an idea, developed into a design, built, used and maintained and finally, when no longer of use, demolished. Figure 7.3 illustrates the life cycle of a construction project.

**Design**

This is the phase that requires the most planning and control. If you spend a lot of resources and time at this stage, the following stages will run much more smoothly.

Planning at this stage involves looking at the overall scheme, the feasibility of the scheme (that is, will it

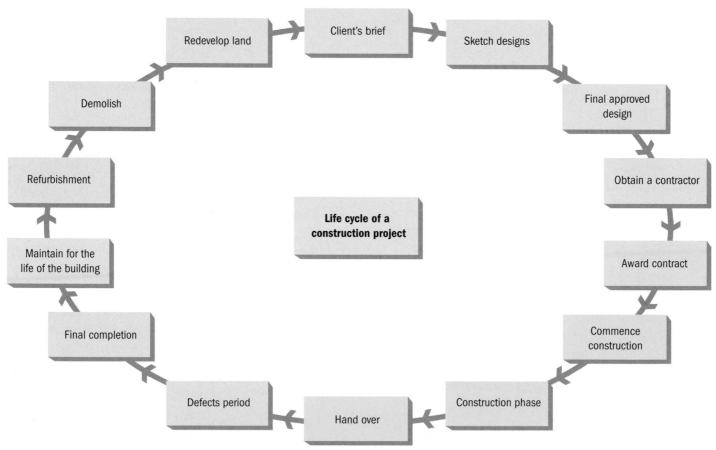

▲ Figure 7.3 The different phases of the life cycle of a project

▲ You will often see a rig taking soil samples in a green field

## Key Terms

**Brief** The client's idea of what they want, which the designer has then to turn into a reality in accordance with current regulations and legislation.

**Procurement** The process by which you select a construction company to undertake the work for you at an agreed contract price and time period.

completion when the building project is formally handed over to the client. The contractor has to put right any defects within a certain period – the defects period – usually six months. The liability of the contractor is then completed with the issuing of a **final certificate** and the payment of all monies.

## Key Term

**Final certificate** This is a certificate written by the designer that releases the contractual obligations of the main contractor with the final payment of monies withheld as retention.

work?), the budget for the scheme and the time frame in which to deliver the completed project. The design phase often starts with a site investigation that looks at the ground conditions and the site in general to see if it is suitable for the intended project.

The architect or designer runs this phase of the construction process. They will receive a **brief** from the client which sets out an idea of what they want to construct. The brief is then turned into a sketch design and, eventually, a final design. This process can take many months to complete. Permissions also have to be obtained from the local planning authority for planning consent to build.

### Production

The production planning phase begins with the **procurement** of a contractor, the company that will physically construct the design. Then the construction phase involves combining the materials using labour resources, assisted by specialist subcontractors and any plant and machinery. This phase continues until

In construction terms, production for a typical project may involve the following sequence:

1  Site set up
2  Excavation works
3  Construction of the foundations
4  Erection of the structural frame elements
5  Construction of the walls
6  Ground floor slab
7  Construction of the roof
8  Installation of openings – windows and doors
9  Joinery installation
10  First-floor installation
11  Installation of electrical services
12  Installation of mechanical services, including plumbing
13  Internal finishes – plastering, painting and flooring
14  External work – car parks, roads and landscaping
15  Drainage and connections
16  Clean and handover

This list is not exhaustive and will, of course, vary with the type of project that is being constructed.

## Maintenance

This phase of the lifecycle involves the day-to-day care required to keep and maintain the operational function and the purpose of the building for which it was designed. It will include:

- drainage – flushing and cleaning of the above and below ground drainage systems, including emptying of gullies
- cleaning of guttering to prevent blockages
- replacement of lighting elements
- renewal of roof coverings
- servicing of gas boiler
- redecoration of areas of high traffic
- oiling of door and window fittings
- servicing of air-conditioning units
- repainting of external joinery
- floor finish repairs to worn-out surfaces.

These are just a few of the maintenance items that have to be attended to in order to extend the life of the building. Maintenance is either:

- reactive – when the call comes in, fix it
- preventative – a regular programme of spending on repairs, or
- cyclical – where annual or biannual items are completed, e.g. painting programmes.

The quality and level of maintenance depends very much on the amount of finance that is set aside to look after and service a building.

## Alteration

Alterations tend to involve smaller items such as removing and repositioning doorways and windows. There is some planning involved to relocate the occupants while the alterations are carried out. Window replacements are a good example, where an old metal window is removed and replaced with a upvc window – this can often be accomplished within a day.

Extensions are major alteration works undertaken to domestic and commercial properties, as a need for more space develops and major alteration or rebuilding is uneconomical. An extension can be built leaving the break-through to the main building until last so lessening the disruption

## Refurbishment

Refurbishment involves potentially the whole building. An existing building can be given a new lease of life with a major refurbishment. Key elements can be updated in line with current legislation and technology. Often, at this time encapsulated asbestos can be removed, old heating systems refurbished and electrical wiring replaced with modern wiring including circuit breakers. Existing carpets, windows, doors and wall coverings are removed and replaced with new, bringing the building up to modern standards of construction.

Refurbishment of **listed buildings** has to be carefully planned as like for like must be replaced. This can often mean having paint specially manufactured to match.

## Remember!

In the long term, it is often better to spend more at the construction stage on low-cost maintenance materials than to have to plan how to access them in the future, for example upvc fascias and soffits.

## Key Term

**Listed buildings** Buildings of special architectural or historic interest in the UK. Alterations to these buildings must be carefully considered before they are made.

▲ **Demolition using machinery**

## Demolition

This is the process of removing the existing structure from the site that is to be redeveloped. Often these are structures near the end of their useful life, which cannot be adapted or refurbished due to cost constraints. Demolition may be instantaneous using explosives or by a slow, methodical approach using machinery to carefully cut and remove the building. Asbestos is a hazard that has to be planned for. It must be removed before any demolition process can take place and disposed of in a licensed tip. Recent examples of demolition are the removal of many local authority flats that lacked sufficient insulation and were damp and cold to live in.

There is a vast amount of planning for the destruction of a building using explosives. The building has to be structurally weakened in preparation for drilling and charging holes with explosives. The police and fire and highway authorities have to be contacted regarding road closures and notices to evacuate residents on the day of demolition.

Similarly, demolition involving the use of machinery has to be planned because of the noise, dust and volume of road traffic. The modern approach to demolition is to recycle parts of the structure. Metals can be reprocessed and brickwork and concrete can be crushed to produce a hardcore for reuse in filling materials.

## Assessment practice

You have been asked to undertake a survey of a local brownfield site that previously had some industrial process working on it. Part of this investigation involves looking at the previous history of the site. Identify and describe the various stages of the construction process undertaken on this site including the recent removal of the existing building. (Hint: use the headings from this section 'Phases of reconstruction'.) **P1**

# Construction process

## Planning in terms of feasibility studies

The Royal Institute of British Architects (RIBA) publishes the RIBA Plan of Work. This contains a detailed step-by-step planning process that can be used to control and organise the whole construction process from the client's idea to the **development of the brief** and the final design followed by the construction process. (For more information on the RIBA Plan of Work, see Unit 5 Construction technology and design in construction and civil engineering, page 186.)

## Theory into practice

Find out more about RIBA by visiting its website, www.riba.org.

## Key Term

**Development of the brief** The development of the client's idea for a design of a building or a concept, which is then extracted and evolved by the designer so it can be taken forward to the feasibility stage.

The feasibility stage is undertaken to see if the client's idea is viable. In other words, will it work? Typical questions that need answering before the project can enter the detailed design stage are:

- Is the proposed site large enough?
- Will the total cost be within the level of financial resources available?
- Are there any local authority planning constraints on the site, e.g. height of any proposed building?
- Is the ground-bearing capacity sufficient to support the weight of the building?
- What constraints are there on the proposed site?
- Will the design achieve value for the client's money?
- Is the design safe under the Construction (Design and Management) (CDM) Regulations 1994?

This list will then expand into more comprehensive questions upon detailed investigation of the proposed site. Money is well spent at this stage to avoid expensive mistakes during the construction phase. A detailed site investigation report will reveal any feasibility problems that a proposed site may have. Often the most expensive and unknown part of a construction project is the redesign of the foundations when the ground is excavated and problems are discovered.

The planning of the design team will need to be undertaken at this stage, for example what consultants will be needed to help with the initial feasibility studies, what roles and responsibilities and duties need to be established.

It is important to keep the client well informed at this initial stage and to seek their approvals before major financial commitments are made. Often a feasibility study may result in the project failing to enter the design stage because the project constraints are too great and the project would be too expensive to complete. In this case, another less expensive solution must be negotiated with the client or the project stops.

## The design process

Following the completion of the client's brief and the feasibility stage, the design process begins in earnest. The initial budget for the project needs to be established early on once the brief has been developed. Each design is costed by the quantity surveyor, until a final scheme is selected and the project budget finalised. Costings are important to ensure that the final construction will be within budget. A full project brief must cover all aspects of the construction proposal, all consultants must be engaged and the design team put together to start the next stage.

The design process may involve several different design schemes, with the client choosing the one that matches most closely their original idea, or they may pick parts of each design to arrive at a final solution. The final budget will then need to be agreed to ensure that the chosen design does not exceed this sum. This will need the client's written approval before the next stage of detailed designing begins.

▲ **Design sketch**

## Procurement

This is the method by which a suitable construction company is selected to undertake the work. There are several ways to undertake procurement, each requiring careful planning. The following are the most common:

- Design and build contractors – where the contractor undertakes not only the construction of the project but the design phase as well.
- Negotiated contracts – where the contract sum is negotiated between the client and the contractor; there is only one contractor pricing the work.
- Competitive **tender** – where the client normally obtains estimates from six contractors; generally the lowest wins the contract.
- Partnering – where the contractor works towards reducing the client's budget and any savings are split equally between both parties.

## Key Term

**Tender** To make a formal offer or estimate for a job.

The method chosen may depend on several factors: the client's budget, the type of work, the client's historical relationship with a contractor and the location of the work.

So what requires planning in the procurement stage?

- The criteria on which contractors may join the competitive tender list.
- How long contractors will be given to price the work.
- The contents of the tender documentation, e.g. what is to be sent out in the package to price.
- The length of time required to check the estimates, correct any errors and award the contract.

Once a contractor has decided to tender for a contract, they will also have to undertake a considerable amount of planning in order to produce an estimate. First, a site visit will look at potential site constraints that might have an effect on the price. The tender documents will be sent out for estimates for materials and to obtain prices from subcontractors. **Method statements** may need to be prepared by the estimator. The contract documents often call for a tender programme to be submitted with the estimate, which outlines the duration of work activities on site. The preliminaries or variable items such as site supervision, long-term plant hire and site accommodation will also need to be planned. The final planning will be the tender adjudication. This is a process whereby all who would be potentially involved in the project if it was won can assess the amount of risk. The estimator, buyer and contracts manager will sit down with the managing director and assess what percentage profit they will place on the tender and any amounts for risky elements.

## Key Term

**Method statements** Documents which identify the methods used to price the work items, that is the plant and labour required for each activity.

### Production

Production planning is essential for the smooth delivery of the completed construction project. The process will start once the contractor receives confirmation that their tender has been successful and they have been awarded the contract. Now, they will need to act quickly as, once they have received notice that they have been awarded the contract, the construction company normally has to start on site within two to three weeks. There is a considerable amount of work to do, all of which will require efficient planning, organising and controlling.

So what needs planning during this short period?

The designer will supply two sets of construction phase drawings and specifications, and will set a date for the pre-contract meeting, when all the interested parties meet to establish lines of communication, information required, the start date and a health and safety plan. The purchasing department in a large company (this may be one person's responsibility in a small company) will look through the estimate to establish which materials have a long delivery period, as these will need ordering first to avoid any delays in the building process.

A contract programme will be produced. This involves subdividing the tender and drawings into activities with their own time-duration requirements and setting up links with other activities so that a **critical path** is established.

At this point, the contracts manager and site manager, who will be responsible for running the project, will need to be selected. The labour resource will also need to be notified of their start date on site – the company will have to coordinate its labour requirements with the other projects it is currently working on.

## Key Term

**Critical path** The link between construction activities crucial for the contract to complete on time. Any hold up in these will delay the final handover date to the client. There is no flexibility of time within these activities.

A scale drawing of the construction site set up showing temporary facilities will be produced for the site manager to work from (see page 292 for more information on temporary facilities). Traffic routes, material storage areas, skip locations and the location of concrete mixing must be agreed. Lighting, power, heating and water will need to be provided for the temporary accommodation facilities, for example site cabins, box containers, toilets, meeting rooms, mess rooms and drying rooms.

The contract administration process will require initial planning as to how it will operate. This involves the contract documentation, instructions, materials requisition, ordering, placing subcontracts and administering the contract when it has been awarded. The construction phase health and safety plan will need to be completed before any work can begin on site. Site documentation will need organising – including setting up site diaries, confirmation pads and drawing registers. A drawing register shows all the drawings for the project in numbered order with the latest revisions issued. A confirmation pad can be used to confirm verbal instructions given on site. Vital to all this is communication: a site telephone will need to be ordered, along with email facilities and a fax machine, if the duration on site will be for a lengthy period.

On site, temporary services such as power and water supplies will need to be set up. The easiest way to do this is to establish on site the permanent services – gas and electricity – that will be required for the completed project and also obtain a temporary metered supply for the contractor to use.

## Maintenance and repair

Planning for maintenance and repair can often mean waiting for a 'shut-down' in a process so that a contractor can enter a building and work safely. This happens on many factory sites where the main activity cannot be stopped as this will mean a loss of production. For example, many oil refineries operate with specific periods where areas of production can be taken off line. These are often as short as two-week slots during which time all maintenance and repairs must be undertaken, so a great deal of pre-planning has to be done before work commences on site.

This is just one aspect of the commercial side of maintenance and repair; the other is where there are no chemical processes to shut down and the work can then be planned on an interval basis. This means that certain items of building maintenance can be undertaken on an yearly basis, such as:

- cleaning out and flushing through guttering
- gas checks to boilers and servicing
- electrical testing of the earth circuit
- painting external joinery
- drainage inspection
- oiling window hinges
- changing light bulbs.

The resources the client will need to put in place are the finances to fund this annual maintenance.

## Refurbishment

Planning for refurbishment work requires some time. A company may be aware that a major refurbishment of all or part of its premises is required, but this may delay this until a convenient time is available to undertake the task.

Refurbishment may be undertaken in phases, which will avoid disruption to the whole site, although some electrical cabling work may need to take place outside the designated refurbishment area. Handling a refurbishment in phases makes it a lot easier for the client. They will need to relocate fewer staff into temporary accommodation while the refurbishment takes place. Smaller phases also mean shorter durations to complete them. If the client decides on a whole project refurbishment, then the contractor must plan to undertake the project in the shortest time scale possible. If a client has multiple sites, they may be able to move production to another site while the work is undertaken, otherwise the disruption may be extensive.

## Case study

You have been asked to look at one of your company's construction sites where some problems have arisen. The contract started off well and, for a while, was both on target and on budget, but now costs have risen sharply and the project is falling behind on programme and may incur penalties. Read through the following case study and in small groups suggest how the situation could be improved.

Joel Moss is a newly qualified site manager who is working under Fred Smith, an experienced site manager. Both are responsible for running this large construction project. Joel deputises for Fred whenever he leaves the site.

The site was initially set up well, with perimeter fencing and a separate compound with box containers and site accommodation. Waste skips were provided and a rough terrain fork truck to transport materials around the site.

Fred is frequently disappearing off site for long periods. Wastage is increasing on site, valuable materials are having to be replaced and site labour costs are rising. There may be several reasons for this.

Discuss and list what may be going wrong on this site with the control of resources. Look closely at what is not stated in the case study.

# Resources

## Management

Management resources should be identified as preliminary costs that must be included in the estimate for a construction project. Supervision is essential in order to control the other resources of labour, plant, materials and subcontractors, ensuring that all run smoothly and efficiently. A good site manager is essential to any construction project. Multi-million pound contracts may require many levels of management, at the top of which is the project manager with overall responsibility for the project.

Managers are highly qualified personnel who are usually members of the professional society for construction managers, the Chartered Institute of Building (CIOB). Holders of a CIOB qualification 'are recognised throughout the industry as knowledgeable and competent in their field' (www.ciob.org.uk) and require training and experience before they can be accredited. The Construction Skills Certification Scheme (CSCS) also offers construction qualifications for managers through card schemes which cover health and safety issues.

### Theory into practice

Undertake an Internet search to find out more about:

- the CIOB
- the CSCS card scheme.

Look at both these institutions' websites to see what they undertake or what services they provide.

### Direct and subcontract labour including supervision

Direct labour costs relate to employees who are directly employed by the company. Subcontract labour refers to self-employed people or agency workers who are not directly employed by the company and who are therefore not entitled to the terms and conditions that directly employed people benefit from such as sickness pay and holiday entitlements with pay.

To obtain the correct quality of labour, a construction company can either:

- advertise for trades people, stating the level of qualifications and experience that the employment contract requires, or
- recruit at apprenticeship level and train the employee to the required level and standard – this has the advantage that the employee will understand how the company works.

Labour must be utilised efficiently which means the other resources of materials and plant must be coordinated to avoid delays in starting work on site. Multi-skilling of labour is now a modern approach where specific trade barriers are lifted and other skills are taught to employees. This allows companies to get maximum efficiency from their workforce.

### Remember!

The CSCS card schemes cover more than 220 occupations including supervisory and management roles. The card proves that the holder is competent in their work and has health and safety awareness (www.cscs.uk.com). This certification is widely used on construction sites – workers who do not carry a card are barred from working on site.

7.2

## Plant and machinery

These play a major part in any modern-day construction process. The following is a typical list of plant that may be used on site:

- excavators – 360-degree
- dumper trucks
- rollers
- vibrating plate compactors
- fork-lift trucks
- generators
- compressors and breakers
- drills
- cranes.

Some of this plant, especially the small tools, may be purchased outright as it may not be cost effective to hire them on a weekly basis. Contractor's plant must be utilised efficiently, preferably close to 100 per cent of the time, as plant standing idle costs the contractor money. The larger items of plant from the above list will be hired, typically for a day's minimum hire; the contractor also has to pay for travel to and from the site. The contracts manager must utilise plant sometimes across several sites to obtain maximum efficiency, and planning decisions will often involve considering whether the cost of hiring plant will be offset by savings in labour costs. Sometimes decisions have to be made on the grounds of health and safety under what is **reasonably practical**.

## Key Term

**Reasonably practical** A measure put in place to prevent injuries to workers that is both reasonable (sensible and sound) for that particular situation and practical (realistic) in safety terms.

Planning decisions in the selection of plant will be based on some of the following criteria:

- The weight of what has to be lifted.
- The height that a material needs to be placed at.
- The distances that materials will need moving.
- The experience of the trained operatives.
- The size of the construction site.
- The length of time on site.

## Materials

These are the physical resources that are used to construct the finished project. They arrive on site in a variety of forms, each with different properties and performance. Some are combined with water to be ready for use, such as plaster. Where possible, heavy materials should be delivered by crane offload. This is where the delivery vehicle has a crane attached to it in order to lift the materials off and place them on the ground using hydraulics. Much larger materials such as structural steelwork and roof trusses will require a stand-alone crane.

## Safety tip

Care must be taken in the manual handling of heavy materials, with no specific weight over 25 kg to be lifted individually by hand.

Construction sites can be very awkward to travel around due to uncompleted roads and external paved areas. To overcome this rough terrain, forklifts are used to place materials exactly where they are required.

Materials need to be stored correctly on site as some may react to moisture when stored outside. Cement in bags, for example, will not stay fresh for long when stored exposed to the weather. A site may require a shed to store cement and racking for scaffolding, while bricks should be delivered shrink-wrapped and on pallets so they do not get damaged.

Material security is another issue. Some materials can be very expensive, such as floorboards, while others are relatively cheap, for example sand and gravel. The higher the cost of the materials, the more thought will need to be given to their storage. Construction sites must be fenced in to prevent the theft of materials from the site. CCTV and security guards can often be deployed as a deterrent to theft. Storage compounds are an ideal solution, having separate fenced areas for materials to be stacked inside, ready for use.

Unit 7 | Planning, organisation and control of resources in construction and the built environment   [287]

On congested sites, materials may need to be delivered just before they are needed. The planner needs to schedule the materials against the contract programme to ensure that delivery dates are met by the suppliers.

## Remember!

It is essential to take care of materials as any damage costs will be at the contractor's expense and not the client's. Wastage equals loss of profits.

## Safety tip

A clean and tidy site is a safe site!

## Subcontractors

It is impossible for a construction company to undertake all the work. The reasons for this are twofold:

- It is expensive for a company to employ operatives who are specialised in a specific trade if it cannot keep them working all the time.
- The level of training required for highly skilled operatives, together with the associated costs, may be prohibitive.

Therefore, subcontractors are the ideal solution. They are specialised in their role, highly trained and very effective in undertaking large areas of work activity within the contract programme. Subcontractors typically undertake the following work:

- mechanical installation
- electrical installation
- fire alarm installations
- lift installations
- installation of CCTV systems
- flooring
- painting and decorating
- plastering.

# Factors in the planning process

## Labour factors

### ■ Availability and cost

The availability of labour for the construction process depends on many factors. Geography can play an important part. The further the construction project is from large cities and towns, the less local labour there is likely to be. The second issue is that the construction business relies on a strong economy to drive new enterprises in developing new factories and commercial units. When the economy is booming all available labour will be working earning high wages, so additional labour resources will not be available. Similarly, larger cities attract more work, which ultimately means higher wages to pay workers because they can pick and choose which projects to work on.

### ■ Skill levels

There is an increasing shortage of qualified and skilled trades people in many sectors. This can often be as a result of government funding in one area and not in another, or technological economic booms that draw all the available apprentices into that career path and out of construction. There are different skill levels within the construction industry, from labourers to skilled operatives, and each will have a specific trade, for example joinery, plastering or bricklaying. Since there are clearly defined lines between each trade, there is no overlap of roles in the working environment – bricklayers cannot hang doors, for example.

The skill level of general operatives can vary as they cross over several trade areas. General operatives tend to work with the substructure items of drainage, foundations, concrete works, assisting bricklayers, cleaning and waste removal. This list is not limited to these functions; often additional payments are made to general operatives who could be classified as semi-skilled, for example some will be able to **power float concrete**. Similarly, many will be able to drive different pieces of construction equipment, for example dumpers, forklifts and rollers.

## Key Term

**Power float concrete** A process whereby the surface of the concrete is machined smooth using mechanical equipment.

### ■ Motivation

The motivation of employees is essential in order to achieve the contract deadline completion date. Employees can be motivated in several ways. Money always is a driver of productivity, and bonus schemes work well as long as both company and worker receive something out of it. Complicated bonus schemes that nobody understands demotivate employees very quickly. Incentives such as company cars and vans again act as a reward for effort by employees. Team working is another motivational tool where rewards can be offered for the most competitive team. Many companies operate staff discount schemes and other benefits in the form of vouchers that employees can use to obtain services outside work, for example private health benefit schemes for the whole family.

A clean, warm environment where employees can work is the basis for the first step in motivating the workforce. Keeping people dry, or giving them a warm room to dry their clothes is essential, similarly with a place to eat, and with facilities for a warm drink and cooking.

### ■ Productivity

Productivity has to be maintained on a construction site in order to achieve the construction programme's final completion date. Behind-schedule activities

should be brought back into line. This is achieved by the redistribution of labour resources from one activity to another. Labour resources are often organised into 'gangs'. For example, a bricklaying gang may contain three people, two of whom are bricklayers with the third person being a labourer assisting them.

Progress is monitored by evaluating the level of production achieved on site against **contract programme** activity; output from the gangs can then be driven to meet any shortfall if an item is behind programme. Failure to accomplish any monitoring can result in the construction programme falling so far behind schedule that the handover of the completed project is late. If the contractor fails to hand over on time, the company may have to pay **damages** to the client for every day that the programme is late.

## Key Terms

**Contract programme** Often a simple bar chart, showing activities against time. The chart offers an effective visual representation of the construction project on which the percentage of actual work completed can be plotted against work that was scheduled to be completed.

**Damages** Financial penalties for every week or part week that the programme has overrun. They are charged for every day that the programme runs late.

### Plant factors

### ■ Output rates and efficiency

A piece of construction plant needs to run at 100 per cent efficiency because hired or purchased plant standing idle costs the contractor revenue and is a waste of a financial resource that could have been better placed elsewhere. However, plant on site rarely runs at 100 per cent efficiency for the following reasons:

- Drivers have to take rest breaks, e.g. to use the toilet.
- The machine may need to have one tool removed and another type fitted, e.g. the excavator bucket can be changed for different sizes.

- The machine's tyre may puncture – this can take up to two hours to fix.
- The machine may require servicing.
- Equipment may break down, e.g. damaged hydraulic hose.
- A newly trained operator will be slower than an experienced one.
- The machine may be old and worn and slower than a newer model.
- Plant size may not be correct for the type of work being undertaken, e.g. using a small excavator where a much larger one would be quicker.

These are just some items that will slow down the rate of efficiency on a construction site. For this reason, output rates will vary daily. The planner will therefore work out an average output rate which reflects the actual output achieved on site.

## Material factors

### ■ Availability

The availability of materials has become a problem in recent years, as suppliers no longer carry sufficient stock levels due to the financial implications of this strategy – materials standing in a supplier's yard tie up financial resources. Many specialised materials, for example special bricks, have to be made to order and can take many months to be delivered. Therefore, account has to be taken of this in planning this process, from the specification of the materials by the architect to the delivery periods that may have to be dealt with. This may mean the client purchasing a material and placing a provision in a tender document for the contractor to include a sum of money for this material. When it arrives the contractor is paid for handling, storage and delivery to the place where it is to be incorporated into the structure.

Some materials may be in short supply, and this can be caused by several factors:

- Strikes or disputes at the production plant.
- Lack of transport.
- Location of supplier, e.g. Germany where the material has to pass through UK Customs.
- Breakdowns in a production line.
- High demand in one country that draws supplies from another.

### ■ Delivery periods

This is the period from the receipt of the contractor's order to the supplier to the time that the material is available for delivery to site. Delivery periods can vary widely. If a material is not stored as stock in a builder's merchant's yard, then it will be delivered directly from the manufacturer to the yard when next available. If the delivery is a full load, then it may be delivered directly to site.

If a contractor is late placing orders for materials, this may affect the delivery period. Certain manufacturers only roll so many types of certain materials, for example roof cladding, then they change the rollers for another product. The contractor may therefore have to wait for the next scheduled production run for delivery of the material.

### ■ Site handling

When materials arrive on site, they are often temporarily stored before being moved to the correct location. Materials can be delivered loose, such as gravels and sands, or bagged or packaged, for example plaster. Greater discounts can be obtained by purchasing in bulk, for example a cement silo. The various modes of delivery include:

- by tanker
- by tipper
- by silo
- by pallets, shrink-wrapped, and with **crane offload**
- on a flat bed wagon with drop sides for forklift offload
- in a van
- by chute, e.g. a concrete wagon.

The method of delivery will depend on the type of material and how it is finally handled on site. Bricks are best delivered by crane offload on pallets or banded with forklift holes and covered in plastic wrapping. This

## Key Term

**Crane offload** This is a crane that is bolted onto the wagon delivering the load. It is operated by hydraulics and lifts solid material off the wagon safely onto the construction site.

• Incorrect ordering of quantity – human error.
• Poor workmanship on site by semi-skilled workers.
• Theft, requiring material to be replaced.
• Incorrect lengths ordered.
• Wrongly specified material for the job.
• Not checking quantities delivered and then finding they are short.
• Damaged materials as a result of transporting them around the site.
• Water damage due to poor storage.

▲ A telescopic handler

keeps them clean and enables them to be picked up and moved. Concrete is a material that can be moved by pumping it along a hose to the point where it is required – this can be done from some distance away.

Sands and gravels are best delivered in bulk and tipped onto a clean surface so they can be either shovelled up in a machine bucket or loaded into a dumper.

When a tender is prepared, the estimator will make certain allowances for wastage within the cost of the contract. These will be small amounts of 2.5–5 per cent which will vary with the amount of cutting needed to include the material into the finished product. Waste can be minimised by recycling and selling what is left over, for example skips on site for metal, timber and cardboard will soon pay for themselves.

## Remember!

With most materials, there are packaging disposal and wastage issues, as the materials need to be unwrapped and cut to size.

## ■ Waste

Some of the materials utilised on site will be wasted in the course of the construction phase of the programme. For example, timber is normally delivered in lengths to the nearest 300 mm – lengths in between will require cutting on site. Wastage can occur due to several factors:

## Assessment practice

The contracts manager has just been to a site meeting for the new city library building that your company is currently half way through constructing. The contracts manager has been asked to find out for the next meeting why the contract is behind programme. You have been asked to prepare a report for submission to the client.

Discuss in your report the factors that could contribute to the poor planning and organisation on the site and, for each of the factors you have highlighted, the possible effects. Typical factors would be labour, motivation, efficiency, etc.

# Context

## Finance

Finance is a resource on construction projects. The client has to establish the finance required to see their design through into a finished structure, and the contractor has to finance the construction works on site. To assist this process, regular payments are made called 'valuations'. Each month the work is measured on site to establish how much has been completed and the architect will then issue a certificate to certify this as a payment from the client to the contractor. (The certificate is similar to an invoice and states what the client must pay to the contractor.) From these payments, a deduction is taken for retention. This retention ensures that the contractor will complete in accordance with the contract conditions. The retention is normally 5 per cent, which is not paid to the contractor until the practical completion of the contract, that is, when the project is handed over to the client.

## Site layout and organisation

Site layout and organisation, done correctly, will greatly add to the efficiency and safety of the construction site. Detailed planning at the pre-commencement stage, the stage just before work starts on site, will benefit from using a site layout plan to assist the organisation and control of the construction phase works.

Site layout involves organising the temporary facilities that are required to construct the site. These include:

- site accommodation
- waste removal
- temporary services
- traffic routes
- car parking
- security
- fencing
- storage of materials
- transport
- positions of cranes
- scaffolding.

**Remember!**

The site layout will be governed by the size of the site and the **footprint** of the building that is going to be placed upon it, so no two site layouts will be the same.

## Key Term

**Footprint** The shape the outline of the building leaves on the ground when viewed in plan from above.

## Temporary facilities and works

Temporary facilities are the items on site that will not be combined into the final construction project that is handed to the client. They cover the site cabins required to house, feed and keep dry the labour workforce constructing the project. Temporary supports required during construction can be steel piles to support excavations, temporary props, scaffolding, cranes and forklifts. Compound areas will need to be constructed to keep materials stored inside protected, and the site will need temporary fencing around it to prevent harm to others outside. Temporary supplies of power and water will be required to construct the project, along with lighting for some of the winter months.

## Health, safety and welfare issues

For more on these issues, see Unit 1 Health, Safety and Welfare.

# Management functions

## Production of long- and short-term programmes

The contract programme is the only visual reference that can be used to control the progress of the project. The most common form is a bar chart (see page 30)7. The programme is best displayed on site within the supervisor's site accommodation. Here daily discussions about each activity will take place. Programmes are produced by taking the contract drawings and the specification and the time allowances from the estimator and dividing the contract up into specific activities. These are then represented as a 'bar' on the chart. The length of the bar represents the duration of the activity on the site. A short-term programme can be a weekly or a monthly programme and may take a particular activity and break it down into some detail for issuing to operatives on site to control progress.

## Scheduling of material requirements

Materials require some form of organisation and often need scheduling, to enable materials to be ordered from a supplier. Often tenders consist of a set of drawings and a specification; there are no **bills of quantities**. The estimator therefore has to schedule the materials that are present in the drawings. For example, there may be a variety of window types and a different number for each, which will need adding up so they can be ordered.

### Key Term

**Bill of quantities** The document that contains all the contract in measured quantities, for example so many square metres of brickwork. It is used to prepare an estimate for the project as the contractor places rates into it to produce a sum for the tender.

Schedules are typically prepared for:
- ironmongery
- doors
- reinforcement
- windows.

Figure 7.4 is an example of a reinforcing schedule that the structural engineer would produce. It shows the diameter of the reinforcing bars and their length. From this, the total weight of reinforcement can be calculated. Scheduling has to take place before materials can be requisitioned (see below) and subsequently ordered.

Simple Analytical Engineers
Contract: New College Library                    Bar Schedule No: 003/147/SAT03

| Member | Bar Mark | Type & Size | No of members | No in each | Total | Length of each bar – mm | Shape Code | A | B | C | D | E |
|---|---|---|---|---|---|---|---|---|---|---|---|---|
| Beam on centre line | 1 | T20 | 4 | 3 | 12 | 1517 | 20 | 385 | | | | |
| | 2 | R10 | 5 | 25 | 125 | 2168 | 405 | 196 | | | | |
| | 3 | T32 | 3 | 5 | 15 | 1916 | st | | | | | |
| | 4 | R16 | 8 | 7 | 56 | 547 | st | | | | | |
| | 5 | R25 | 6 | 51 | 306 | 256 | 405 | 205 | | | | |
| | 6 | T20 | 4 | 2 | 8 | 852 | 150 | 457 | | | | |
| | 7 | R10 | 2 | 4 | 8 | 567 | 202 | 600 | | | | |
| | 8 | R10 | 1 | 5 | 5 | 400 | st | | | | | |
| | 9 | R25 | 3 | 4 | 12 | 150 | st | | | | | |
| | 10 | R16 | 7 | 3 | 21 | 220 | 205 | 600 | | | | |
| | 11 | R16 | 6 | 32 | 192 | 1515 | st | | | | | |
| | 12 | R8 | 4 | 1 | 4 | 458 | st | | | | | |

Figure 7.4 A reinforcing schedule

### Requisitioning

This is the process after scheduling where all the schedules and material requests are submitted in larger companies to the buying department. Alternatively, this can be done internally within the buying department. A requisition states what is required and when it is needed.

### Ordering

Ordering is best accomplished as a head office function. In this way, requisitions can be collected together to form full loads and obtain better discounts from suppliers by purchasing in bulk. Ordering from site should be limited to a small amount. Orders can be placed such that if the site has limited space available, then parts of the order can be called off in small deliveries to site. The quoted prices must be checked against the estimator's tender figures to establish whether the price is within the contractor's budget. In this way, costs can be controlled.

### Receiving and checking

When material or a piece of plant is delivered to the site, there will be documentation called the 'delivery ticket' accompanying it. The delivery ticket may state the amount and type of material delivered to the location specified. It is the responsibility of the the contractor's representative receiving the goods to check the delivery and note any shortfalls on the delivery note. A copy is normally given to the site from the supplier. If you fail to check the quantity of a material and have signed the delivery note, then any discovered shortfalls are at the contractor's cost.

### Site handling

The management function in this process would be in the selection of the materials handling equipment for distribution around the construction process.

Height, reach and the ground conditions will need taking into account with the distribution equipment that is hired, along with checking that the hire rate is in line with what the estimator placed in the tender. The supervisor must ensure that the driver they appoint has the required level of competency and licence to use that vehicle.

### Storage and security issues

High-value materials must be stored under lock and key on site as there would be a time delay as well as a loss if these materials were stolen. Security box containers are just one solution to this problem along with a night security person. Materials need clean and tidy storage areas so they do not become damaged. **Just-in-time deliveries** that have detailed scheduling can avoid theft and damage during storage. With this method materials are delivered just as they are needed and therefore do not require storage and are less prone to theft.

## Key Term

**Just-in-time deliveries** Materials ordered to be delivered just before they are required on site.

### Labour management techniques

#### ■ Work and method study

Work and method study is the application of science to the movement and efficiency of site operations. In essence, it is a time and motion study. You can analyse an operation involving labour to seek ways of improving its efficiency on site. This increases production and hence the contractor's profit margins. Work and method study, if applied correctly, will save financial resources. For example, you notice on site that labour is being used to barrow by hand concrete into an awkward part of the site. Having undertaken a study of this involving timing each employee, you have calculated that changing the method – using a concrete pump – would save both time and labour costs.

Sometimes work and method study causes resentment among the labour force, who believe they are being unfairly 'watched'. This may cause them to behave differently and work more efficiently until you stop 'watching'. Unobtrusive methods have to be employed to undertake work and method study effectively.

## ■ Control and organisation of labour

Labour can be controlled in several ways:

- Through gangers in labour teams, each being in charge of a labour gang which reports to the general foreperson, who then reports to the construction site manager. In this way, effective supervision and control of the labour is in place
- Through forepersons in their trade area of joinery, brickwork and finishes, each reporting to the site manager, and each controlling the subcontractors in their area.
- Through direct supervision in small groups. This would be undertaken on small sites with the site supervisor working directly with the labour force.
- Through subcontractors controlling their own labour. Often large construction sites do not directly employ labour as all the construction work is subcontracted out.
- By labour meetings at head office between all contracts managers, where labour requirements for each site are discussed and labour movements directed between sites.
- By written instructions on job cards. These contain what is required to be done and the location for each labour resource – when one is completed another is issued.
- Through the main contract programme planning, where the labour resource is 'programmed' into the master programme and labour reports can be run and issued.
- Through time sheets to control hours against each job. Each person submits their time sheet weekly to show where they have worked and for how long. Head office can total the hours against what was expected for each work activity on the programme.

**SIMTOP BUILDERS**

| | | | |
|---|---|---|---|
| Name | Trade | | Week ending / / |
| Employee code | | | Passed for payment |

| Vehicle cost | Description of work (Location) | PART 'A' To be completed by operative | | | | | | | | | | | | | | | | | PART 'B' For office use only | | | | | |
|---|---|---|---|---|---|---|---|---|---|---|---|---|---|---|---|---|---|---|---|---|---|---|---|---|
| | | MON | | | TUE | | | WED | | | THURS | | | FRI | | | SAT | | SUN | | | | | |
| | | 1 | 1½ | 2 | 1 | 1½ | 2 | 1 | 1½ | 2 | 1 | 1½ | 2 | 1 | 1½ | 2 | 1½ | 2 | 2 | JOB No. | Basic hours | Overtime @ 1½ | Overtime @ double | Job bonus | Expenses taxable | Expenses non tax |
| | | | | | | | | | | | | | | | | | | | | | | | | | | |
| | | | | | | | | | | | | | | | | | | | | | | | | | | |
| | | | | | | | | | | | | | | | | | | | | | | | | | | |
| | | | | | | | | | | | | | | | | | | | | | | | | | | |
| | | | | | | | | | | | | | | | | | | | | | | | | | | |
| | | | | | | | | | | | | | | | | | | | | | | | | | | |
| | | | | | | | | | | | | | | | | | | | | | | | | | | |
| | | | | | | | | | | | | | | | | | | | | | | | | | | |
| | | | | | | | | | | | | | | | | | | | | | | | | | | |
| | | | | | | | | | | | | | | | | | | | | | | | | | | |
| | | | | | | | | | | | | | | | | | | | | | | | | | | |
| | | | | | | | | | | | | | | | | | | | | | | | | | | |
| | | | | | | | | | | | | | | | | | | | | | | | | | | |
| | | | | | | | | | | | | | | | | | | | | | | | | | | |
| Vehicle details | Basic hours | | | | | | | | | | | | | | | | | | | TIME SHEET TOTAL | | | | | | |
| | Overtime @ 1½ | | | | | | | | | | | | | | | | | | | BROUGHT FORWARD | | | | | | |
| | Overtime @ double | | | | | | | | | | | | | | | | | | | TOTAL CLAIM | | | | | | |
| | **TOTAL** | | | | | | | | | | | | | | | | | | | | OFFICE USE ONLY | | | GENERAL BONUS | | |

▲ **Figure 7.5 A time sheet**

▲ Plant needs to be utilised effectively to ensure maximum use

## ■ Hire

Most construction sites of a short duration (16–20 weeks) hire in construction plant. It is often more cost effective to hire plant for several reasons:

- It would cost more to purchase than the total hire charge over the period of use on site. Always check this to see if money can be saved in the long run, especially if the piece of plant can be used on the next contract.
- Plant is always delivered fit for use and is tested. (Plant associations have to operate under the Provision and Use of Work Equipment Regulations (1998).)
- There are no maintenance costs involved as these are borne by the plant hirer.
- If plant breaks down, the hirer carries the cost of repair and not the contractor, except for punctures on site.
- It can be off hired (the hire terminated) when not in use, whereas the contractor's own plant would have to stand idle.

## ■ Lease or purchase

Leasing a piece of plant is similar to hiring but under an agreement with a finance company. In this method, the contractor 'hires' the piece of equipment for a number of years, usually three, and pays back the 'hire' as rent per week or month. Sometimes there are restrictions, for example the number of miles the contractor can do with the equipment per year, and it is often difficult to end a lease agreement early.

To purchase a piece of equipment is sometimes the best and most efficient method. The construction company needs to establish whether it will make full use of the equipment and not have it standing idle for long periods as this will not be an effective use of its investment. Before deciding to purchase equipment, the company will need to answer the following key questions:

- How will the purchase be paid for – through a bank loan or from the company's profits?
- How much maintenance and servicing will the equipment require and what are the likely costs?
- Will an operator need to be trained to use the equipment?

- How much will the equipment depreciate in value per year?
- What percentage productivity a year will the equipment attain?

Once the company has the answers to these basic questions, it will be able to establish how much a piece of plant will cost the company to buy, run and maintain, which can be compared with the cost of hiring the plant to see which is cheaper.

## Remember!

The decision to lease, hire or purchase must take into account the productivity gained, the labour savings made and the **opportunity cost** lost.

## Key Term

**Opportunity cost** An economics term which means what else could you have spent the money on, that is, what opportunity have you lost?

## ■ Utilisation and control

Utilising plant, whether it is hired, leased or purchased, for only 10 per cent of the time it is on site is not cost effective. We saw earlier that 100 per cent utilisation cannot be achieved. However, maximum utilisation can be achieved by transporting plant from site to site such that **down time** is kept to a minimum and full use of the plant is maintained. Highly trained and experienced operatives will be more productive than inexperienced ones and this factor must be taken into account.

Plant can be controlled by

- ensuring that, if it is not in use, the plant is off hired
- transferring it to another site where it can be used
- using short-wave radios to speed up communication and avoid delays

- using trained and qualified operators
- listing items on site using plant sheets
- ensuring the correct equipment is in place for the work in hand.

## Key Term

**Down time** When equipment is not being used.

## Assessment practice

The managing director has just returned from a surprise site visit to one of the company's construction sites. They are far from happy, muttering that it is organised chaos there. You have been asked to identify and explain the techniques commonly used to monitor and control resources on the company's sites, such that the managing director's opinion can be changed. List and discuss one control technique against the labour, plant and materials resources.

After the managing director's negative comments and your report, it has come to light that your site and office are in fact undertaking some very effective resource management techniques. The managing director has been shown these and is quite impressed. They have asked you to continue this valuable research. Compare and evaluate the following techniques, outlining the advantages and disadvantages of each.

- Long-term contract programmes.
- Receiving and checking material deliveries.
- Work and method study.
- Sorting waste into skips.

# General functions

## Forecasting

There are several items that require some form of forecasting. They include the following:

- Labour requirements – this will be required by the contracts manager from each construction site under their control so they can work out when to bring in additional labour or transfer labour from one site to another.

- Cash flow – this will be undertaken by the construction company's quantity surveyor or the financial manager. This is necessary to predict how much revenue and expenditure is entering and leaving the business, as a positive cash flow is preferable to a business overdraft.

- Plant requirements – if the company owns several pieces of plant, then the utilisation for key items like a concrete pump or an excavator needs to be forecast so that the plant can be used on each site at the correct time and maximum utilisation achieved.

- The weather – the pouring and finishing of concrete outside has to be timed with good weather. Concrete can be damaged if it is rained upon or is subject to excessive cold or dries out too quickly.

## Planning

Contracts of some duration are normally controlled by a contract programme. The only two dates expressed within the contract between the client and the contractor are the commencement and completion dates. The contractor is required to produce a main contract programme illustrating how the construction site activities have been planned and linked. This is used to monitor progress at each site meeting. Look at the contract programme in Figure 7.10 (page 307), which shows how the contract has been subdivided into activities with time operating left to right.

## Organising

The organisation of the site as a whole is paramount. This is achieved through a sequence of line managers, from the general foreperson to the site agent and, ultimately, the contracts manager or director. Communication is the key, both verbally and written, so that everyone on site knows who is doing what and when. 'Tool box talks' involve a five-minute discussion of key issues with supervisors who then inform the rest of the workers. Discipline is therefore essential and must be monitored.

## Monitoring

Progress on the project needs to be monitored through use of the contract programme on which progress is plotted to establish if work is on time, in front or running behind predicted progress. If work is falling behind on any activity, monitoring will act as an alarm bell so that resources can be directed to the lagging activity to bring it back on schedule.

The financial side of the project must also be closely monitored to ensure that the predicted profit for the contract is met and that a positive cash flow is maintained. This monitoring is called 'coat value reconciliation', and involves adding up all the costs against revenue at a particular time interval – to show a profit or a loss!

## Controlling

Resources will need controlling to avoid wastage, which is equivalent to a loss of profit to a contractor. High wastage cannot be maintained for long. Controlling is again undertaken by the supervisors on the site and may be aided by computer software solutions that identify what needs to be there and when. Control must be effective and directed at the site resources – anything beyond the supervisors' control is serious and should be avoided. Discussion at site meetings where items can be recorded is a very effective method of controlling the programme and progress.

## Coordinating

Subcontractors and the main contractor's labour activities require coordinating in terms of health and safety. For example, it would be dangerous to have the roofer working above the floor layer. Coordination will be needed especially with the building's services. Where services will be run within roof voids, which cable or pipe work needs to go in first will need to be coordinated.

## Reviewing

Reviewing involves looking at all the above and establishing whether it has worked. For example, a risk assessment has to be reviewed to check the required resources have been allocated to the work and that the control measures are working effectively. Reviewing provides feedback so a more viable solution can be implemented.

# Organisational aspects

## Site layout plan

Figure 7.6 shows a typical area within which the contractor would construct the building. The contractor would not be allowed to work outside the boundary; the area within it would be their responsibility. The site is fairly tight in two areas and would require some logical thinking on how best to prepare the site layout plan. The plan would be drawn to scale and, once complete, passed to the site supervisor to place all the site accommodation, box containers, traffic routes, etc. as shown on the plan. The contracts manager would need to be consulted.

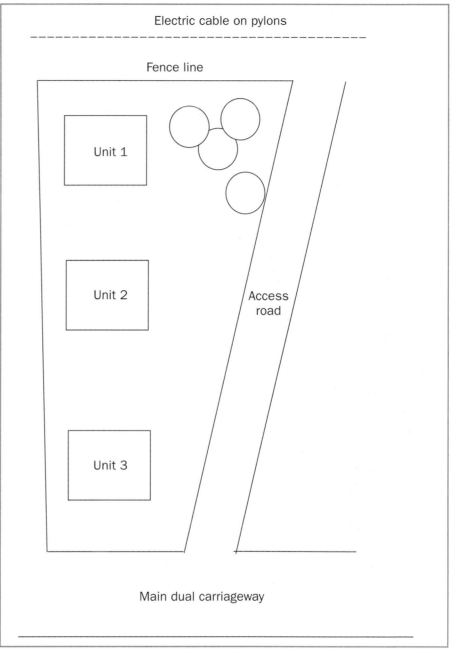

▲ **Figure 7.6 A site layout plan**

When detailing a site layout plan, the following need to be considered:
- traffic routes
- labour movement
- materials and plant location
- **access** and **egress**
- site accommodation
- storage and security.

## ■ Traffic routes

On a congested site it may not be possible to have two-way traffic, and a one-way system may have to be implemented, with traffic lights to control the flow of delivery and construction vehicles. Traffic routes should have a pedestrian walkway to separate operatives from moving plant and machinery, a cause of fatal injury every year. Ideally, they should be fenced walkways.

Traffic routes should be established using well-compacted hardcore such that the surface does not become muddy and a hazard. Routes that run off site onto the highway may have to have lorry wheel washes installed to prevent mud, soil and other materials being deposited along the public highway causing a hazard. This can be often resolved by employing a road sweeper to control dust and debris.

## ■ Labour movement

Regular labour resource meetings held at head office enable individual construction site requirements to be planned using each site manager's labour forecasts. The contracts manager can then decide where to use and relocate the labour to make maximum use of individual skills, training and experience.

Similarly, the movement of labour on site should be directed to ensure that activities critical to the overall programme are staffed sufficiently to ensure that they do not fall behind programme. Moving labour on site must go with skill levels, for example a joiner could not lay bricks.

### Materials and plant location

The temporary storage of materials and plant before they are required to build the project needs careful planning. Often there is insufficient space on site and arrangements may have to be made with suppliers to deliver smaller quantities as they are required. Materials need to be located close to the work area to avoid too much handling or double handling which increases the incidence of damage and wastes resources.

The location of lifting equipment, especially **crainage**, depends on the size of the structure and the point of furthest reach required. Tower cranes are often placed within the centre of a project, often within the lift shaft, as this is the central point.

## ■ Access and egress

Access and egress can either be to the place of work or the site entrance and exit. Traffic routes have been discussed above. Access on construction sites is generally through the use of temporary works such as scaffolding, which is wrapped around the building and can be raised and lowered as required. Mobile elevated platforms and scissor lifts are another method of controlled access to certain points of construction; for example, steel erectors use them to fasten the bolted connections together safely. Access can be gained by the use of scaffold mobile towers that are climbed and incorporate a working platform.

## Remember!

You will also need to refer to The Work at Height Regulations 2005 when considering access and egress. These regulations apply to all work at height where there is a risk of a person falling and being injured. You will need to consider whether an alternative method of work avoiding working at height can be employed, and if not, how work may be safely accessed by operatives working at height.

## ■ Site accommodation

This includes supervisors' offices, canteen or mess room, drying room, client's offices, and toilets. Larger long-duration sites may have whole banks of offices as several head office functions are moved onto site.

▲ Cabins provide onsite accommodation

The amount of space available on site may be limited and you might need to consider using site accommodation in a stackable format with external stairs. Cabins can be delivered in two formats: those with wheels or jack leg units. With some, a crane may be required to place them in position. You will also need to organise the connection of temporary services of electricity and water and bottled gas to provide heating, lighting and cooking facilities.

## ■ Storage and security

On large sites security personnel should be placed next to the entrance gates, so they can see everyone who enters and leaves the site and also direct deliveries. On smaller sites the site manager's accommodation would be located at the gates for the same reason. This would help to reduce the incidence of theft from the site.

Storage organisation concerns the size of box containers to suit the size of materials that are being stored, whether they need to be kept in a heated environment, and what level of locking security is required to the container. Tool safes enable equipment to be securely stored overnight to prevent theft.

### Health, safety and welfare

For more information, see Unit 1 Health, safety and welfare in construction and the built environment.

### Method statements

There are two types of method statement:
- The first gives a detailed description of how a task is carried out. It lists the resources required – labour, plant and materials. By undertaking this process, you can identify the hazards associated with the work and the control measures that will need to be put in place to minimise the risks.
- The other type is compiled by the estimator. For a known task, the estimator will list what labour, plant and machinery have been used in producing the rate for the work that has been included in the tender document. This system is written into a method statement which will be used by the contracts manager to establish what construction plant will be required on the project and how much it will cost.

## Progress monitoring

The monitoring of work on site is essential to obtain a clear picture of progress on the master construction programme. Tracking progress will establish if the project is on schedule. If the project is ahead of schedule, then there are too many labour or plant resources assigned to it, but there may be cost savings in time-related costs on site, for example the hire of cabins which are paid for per week on site. Behind programme is more of a cause for concern as this can lead to large financial penalties, both in **liquidated damages** paid to the client and the cost of increasing resources to pull back the lost time.

## Key Term

**Liquidated damages** Financial penalties paid by the contractor to the client when the project overruns the agreed completion date through no fault of the client.

Progress is plotted on the main contract programme (bar chart) by showing two bars for each task or activity. The top one is the actual point in time that the project should be at and the one below is the percentage of work completed. Therefore, if the contractor is half way through a task, the progress bar should be 50 per cent – less than 50 per cent highlights an issue.

## Site meetings

On large projects site meetings are generally held once a month. They provide an opportunity for all the parties to the contract to discuss certain key issues. The meeting is normally held on site so a walk around may be arranged to look at certain problems either before or after. Typical topics for discussion include:
- information required
- clerk of works' report
- progress to date against the programme
- variations
- architect's instructions
- mechanical and electrical queries
- health and safety issues.

The site meeting has a set agenda that is sent out before the meeting. A set of site meeting minutes is taken, usually by the architect or designer. The minutes are used as a true record of what was discussed, and can be referred to if disputes arise.

## Subcontractor liaison

This is an important aspect of organisation as a large proportion of work on site is subcontracted. Regular liaison needs to take place between the subcontractors and the main contractor, who will organise weekly site meetings with the subcontractor's main site contact ensuring that all key subcontractors attend. This will avoid any issues over services coordination between several subcontractors. Health and safety can be coordinated where one subcontractor is working above another. Access and egress issues, the use of crainage, waste disposal and storage are just some items that need controlling.

## Site resources documentation control

There are several ways to document the control of resources on a construction site as listed below.
- Daywork sheets – where there are any contract variations, these sheets record the additional resources utilised (labour, plant and materials). The contractor's quantity surveyor will then use the sheets to work out the cost of the additional resources and produce a price for the final account to be paid by the client.
- Daily report sheet – this records the labour, e.g. type and number, utilised on site each day as well as any instructions received and a record of what progress was made. This helps to control the level of labour on the site as numbers present have to be recorded daily.
- Time sheets – these allow workers who travel from site to site to record their hours against each contract so that the cost of their time is allocated fairly.
- Materials requisition sheets – these may be submitted by the site supervisor or the estimator to the purchasing manager in order for them to raise an order for the materials required on site. The sheets will specify the estimator's price, so a comparison can be made with a supplier's quoted price and savings made, the delivery time and the quantity required. From this information, an order can be placed.

## Daywork sheet — SIMTOP BUILDERS

| Client | Job no. | Date | Sheet no. 2516 |
|--------|---------|------|----------------|

**Job description & site location**

| Labour | | | | | Schedule | | | Amount | |
|--------|-------|---------|----------|------|---|---|---|---|---|
| Name | Trade | Time on | Time out | Unit | A | B | C | £ | p |
| | | | | | | | | | |
| | | | | | | | | | |
| | | | | | | | | | |
| | | | | | | | | | |
| | | | | | | | | | |
| | | | | | | | | | |
| | | | | | | | | Labour total | |

| Plant and description | | | Unit | Quantity | Rate | + | % | | |
|-----------------------|--|--|------|----------|------|---|---|--|--|
| | | | | | | | | | |
| | | | | | | | | | |
| | | | | | | | | | |
| | | | | | | | | | |
| | | | | | | | | Plant total | |

| Materials and description | | | Unit | Quantity | Rate | + | % | | |
|---------------------------|--|--|------|----------|------|---|---|--|--|
| | | | | | | | | | |
| | | | | | | | | | |
| | | | | | | | | | |
| | | | | | | | | | |
| | | | | | | | | Material total | |

| Signature for client | Comments | | |
|----------------------|----------|--|--|
| Signature for Simtop builders | | | TOTAL |

▲ **Figure 7.7 Daywork sheet**

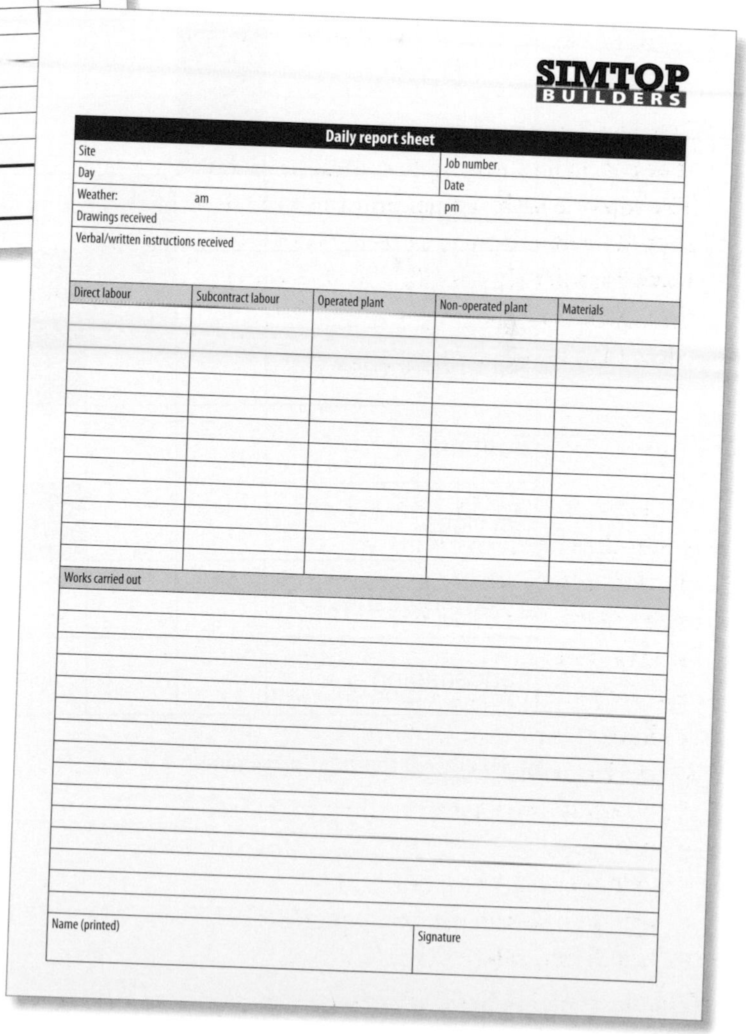

## Daily report sheet — SIMTOP BUILDERS

| Site | | Job number |
|------|--|------------|
| Day | | Date |
| Weather: am | | pm |
| Drawings received | | |
| Verbal/written instructions received | | |

| Direct labour | Subcontract labour | Operated plant | Non-operated plant | Materials |
|---------------|--------------------|----------------|--------------------|-----------|
| | | | | |
| | | | | |
| | | | | |
| | | | | |
| | | | | |
| | | | | |
| | | | | |
| | | | | |

**Works carried out**

| Name (printed) | Signature |
|----------------|-----------|

For more information on resource allocation documentation, see page 309.

Figure 7.8 Daily report sheet ▶

These become vital in the management of the project during the production phase. The most commonly used programme of work is a bar chart. Figure 7.9 illustrates how the contractor can see from week to week where progress should be on site.

Networks and schedules are discussed in section 7.4.

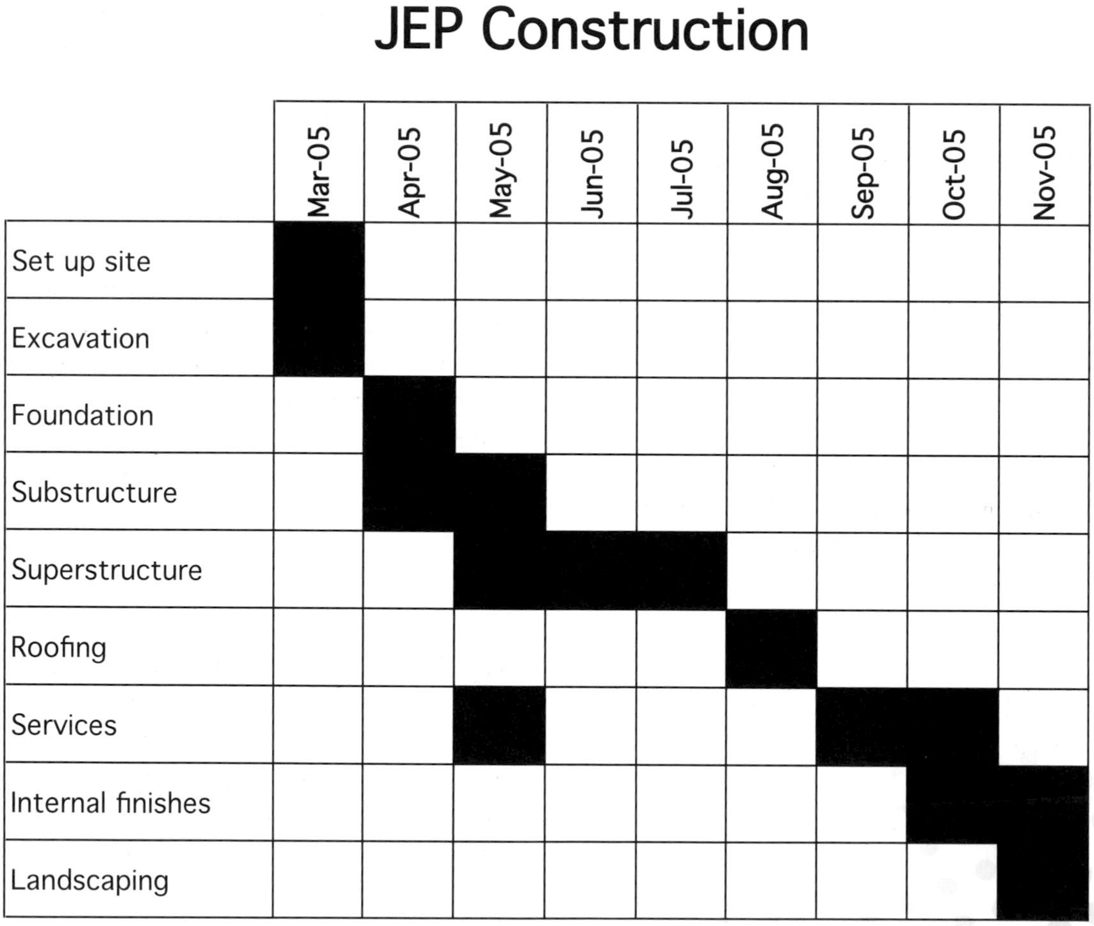

# JEP Construction

| | Mar-05 | Apr-05 | May-05 | Jun-05 | Jul-05 | Aug-05 | Sep-05 | Oct-05 | Nov-05 |
|---|---|---|---|---|---|---|---|---|---|
| Set up site | █ | | | | | | | | |
| Excavation | █ | | | | | | | | |
| Foundation | | █ | | | | | | | |
| Substructure | | █ | █ | | | | | | |
| Superstructure | | | █ | █ | █ | | | | |
| Roofing | | | | | | █ | | | |
| Services | | | █ | | | | █ | █ | |
| Internal finishes | | | | | | | | █ | █ |
| Landscaping | | | | | | | | | █ |

▲ Figure 7.9 Contract programme

# Variables and the unforeseeable

## Weather

Some types of weather can hamper the progress of a project. For example, concrete working can be seriously affected by rain, wind and excessive sunshine, while brickwork can be so badly damaged by rain and frost that it has to be rebuilt.

**Remember!**

The UK Met Office offers weather forecasting services for the building and construction industry, including wind speeds and wind direction for those working with tower cranes.

Construction companies use various methods to provide protection from the weather, including:

- the use of timber-framed housing – the structural part of the building can be completed and then the brickwork outer skin laid when weather permits
- covering up of brickwork with hessian or insulation during frosts
- insulation of concrete to protect it from frosts
- the complete enclosure of a building project using scaffolding and sheeting
- sheeting over concrete works using tent structures
- changing specifications, e.g. pre-cast concrete.

## Availability of skilled labour

This is becoming an increasing problem as availability often depends on the type of work involved. Highly skilled operatives are rarely out of work; for example, there are few people in the UK who have the skill to thatch the roof of a listed building. Recent labour shortages have been as a result of the cyclical nature of the construction industry which is linked to the

growth of the UK economy. To obtain skilled labour, construction companies sometimes make use of labour-only agencies that supply operatives for hire on an hourly basis. Alternatively, companies may retrain directly employed, semi-skilled labour as a stop-gap measure to allow them to make maximum use of their skilled trades people.

**Remember!**

Highly skilled trades people are in great demand! They will need plenty of notice to ensure that their services are secured and programmed into the work.

## Labour disputes

Strikes are now largely a thing of the past due to government legislation. However, labour disputes about pay and conditions on site sometimes lead to unofficial strikes. The manager has to walk a tightrope from making sure that the workforce is happy, that the company is not held to ransom and that productivity is maintained.

## Confined access

Confined access may occur unexpectedly when temporary structures need to be erected around the permanent structure. Often, these will restrict access and the site manager may have to organise an alternative, safer access point. Stairway towers should be used to gain access to upper floors and the roof of a construction project.

**Safety tip**

Ladders, as a means of access, should not be used if there is a safer alternative.

## Late design changes

On traditional contracts most of the design is completed before the award of the contract to the main contractor. However, on design and build projects this may not be the case and late design changes may have to be accommodated into the main contract programme. To avoid this, the programme needs to be designed with enough flexibility so it can accept design changes without too much disruption to the other activities.

## Late construction information

Late drawings or specifications can have a knock-on effect on the programme of works. Managers must make sure that all requests for information are recorded. These can then be confirmed at site meetings within the site minutes (see above). The manager will need to regularly chase the designer or architect for outstanding information. Communication is the key to avoiding lengthy delays to this process.

### Remember!

It is the manager's responsibility to explain the effect that late construction information will have on the programme and progress on site.

## Material shortages

These often occur when a certain material is in such high demand that the manufacturer is unable to supply sufficient quantities. If this occurs, the buyer may have to advise the architect or designer and request that an alternative material be sourced and accepted as a specification change. In times of shortages the contractor may have to collect the material from anywhere it can be supplied in order to reduce the amount of time delay on site.

## Assessment practice

The managing director of your company sees site documentation as reams of paperwork that serves no purpose. You have been asked to sort through the different types of documentation and have found examples of management documentation and resource planning as listed below. Decide which of the following are useful under these headings and explain how the ones you have selected achieve this.

- Drawing register
- Material requisition sheet
- Daywork sheet
- Confirmation of verbal instruction sheet
- Job card
- Site meeting minutes

## Case study

You have started employment at a local construction company in your home town. It is a traditional family-run construction business that is privately owned and has no external shareholders. The managing director, Colin Sherlock, makes all the company's financial and commercial decisions. Unfortunately, he falls ill very suddenly and has to take extensive leave in order to fully recover. In his absence, the other less senior partners agree to appoint a temporary managing director and elect another family member, who happens to be the firm's accountant.

After a settling-in period, the organisation and communication over important decisions starts to break down with little or no direction being given by the new managing director. The contracts manager is of little help, the estimator does not know what percentage profit to add to tenders and the quantity surveyor has no understanding of the company's cash flow or its finances.

In desperation, you have been called in as an external consultant to try to organise everyone's roles and responsibilities within a manual that will also be used for obtaining a quality award under the ISO scheme.

Discuss and identify the roles of the people mentioned above and establish what their responsibilities should be in a normal structured environment.

# Programming techniques

## Bar charts

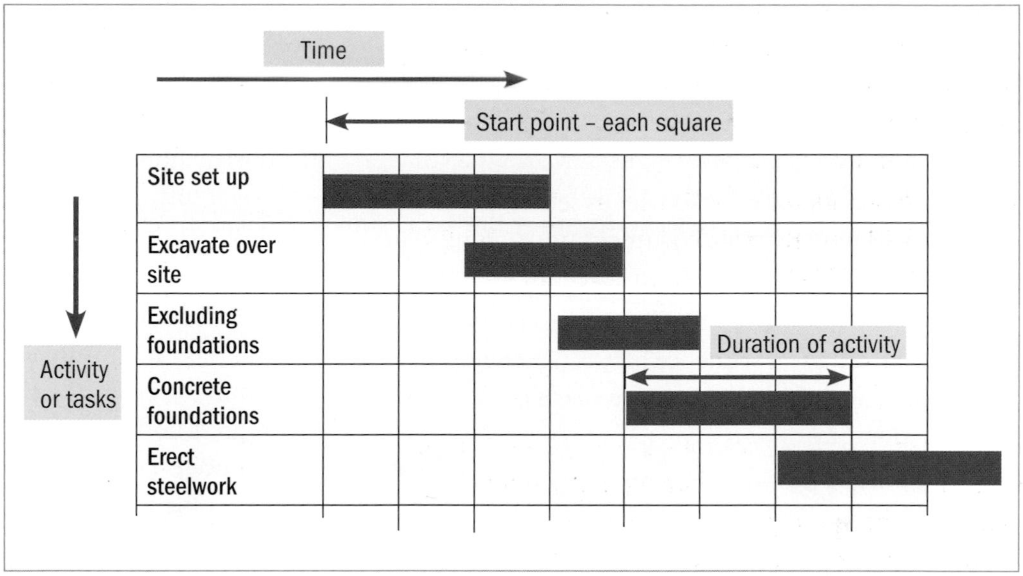

The length of each horizontal bar on the chart in Figure 7.10 represents a duration on site and its relationship to the other bars represents the logical sequence of work on site. For example, you could not concrete the foundations before excavating them – this is impossible! This type of bar chart was developed by Henry Gantt in the early twentieth century and is still one of the most popular methods used to produce contract programmes on site.

▲ Figure 7.10 Contract programme bar chart

To produce a simple bar chart, you will need to follow this sequence:

1   Analyse the contract drawings and specification and establish how many activities you will need for the master programme, e.g. site clearance, site strip, excavations, concrete works. On average, a medium-sized construction site will have 20 activities.

2   Find the length of each activity as set out by the estimator in the tender document. You will need to choose a suitable time unit to cover all the activities, e.g. number of days or weeks.

3   Record the logical sequence between activities so you have a working link between each.

4   Establish which activities are critical to the overall programme.

5   Plot each activity on a rough outline bar chart, starting each at their earliest start point.

6   Establish the critical path through the bar chart. This is the link between construction activities that are crucial to the contract completing on time.

Some activities can float within the critical activities, which means that their start or finish times can be delayed as they will have no overall effect on the completion date; others will not be able to float and are said to be critical to the overall programme – any slippage will affect the end date.

7   Adjust the non critical activities to suit the labour resources on site.

8   Produce the final bar chart for issue to site.

To read the bar chart, you will need to understand that time runs from left to right and the commencement of the programme is the first activity, with completion and subsequent handover of the project, the last. To monitor progress, place a string line across the programme at the current date, which will show you the percentage of each bar that should be completed. This will highlight which activities are ahead or behind schedule.

## Networks

These are more complicated than simple bar charts as Figure 7.10 shows. Time still works from left to right, with the first activity representing the commencement of the programme. This network can be referred to as an arrow diagram. Each arrow on the network represents an activity, just like the bars on the bar chart. The description of the activity is placed above the arrow, with the duration of the activity below it.

To produce a simple network, you will need to follow this sequence:

1 Analyse the contract drawings and specification and establish how many activities you will need for the programme.

2 Find the length of each activity as set out by the estimator in the tender document. You will need to choose a suitable time unit to cover all the activities, e.g. number of days or weeks.

3 Record the logical sequence between activities so you have a working link between each of the activities.

4 Draft out the network diagram using nodes and arrows.

5 Write on the description and durations of each activity.

6 Calculate the left-hand side of the circles' earliest start times right through the network; where two arrows finish at one node, take the highest value calculated starting at zero.

7 Work backwards from the completion node, taking the lowest value where two arrows enter a node until you arrive back at zero at the commencement.

8 Identify the critical path and mark this in red – this is the path where the left-hand and the right-hand figures in the circles are the same value.

9 Produce the final network for issue to site.

# Software applications

## Availability and use of software for programming and monitoring

Information technology has been a growth industry over the last decade and has influenced the way in which construction programmes can be written. There are several software systems available that will produce a construction programme, but in order to use them, you will require the data from the estimator's tender.

Construction programme software allows you to undertake many functions. You enter plant and labour resources and costs, and a variety of reports that track progress both in time and in financial cost can be produced. The software requires a certain amount of training which is offered as part of the package. To monitor a construction programme, you simply enter the progress against each activity and a report is produced visually illustrating the current position. For large programmes, however, you will need a plotter to produce A3-size (or larger) paper-based programmes.

## Assessment practice

The chief planner of the company you work for is keen to upgrade the existing manual programming methods to a more modern computer-based approach. Undertake some research on the Internet and examine the software systems that are available.

When you have found an example explain how this may be able to make easier the planning, organisation and control of the construction processes on the company's sites. **D1**

## Assessment practice

Produce and interpret bar charts, networks and schedules for typical low-rise domestic or commercial projects. Refer to your tutor who will print out the data required to produce a solution to the network and bar chart tasks. **P6**

# Resource allocation documentation

**Use of head office and site documentation to organise, control and monitor the movement, cost and allocation of resources**

The following are some of the more common types of resource documentation that is often completed on site and then used within the head office to control costs.

## ■ Goods received sheets

These are used on site to record each material that is delivered (see Figure 7.11). Any short deliveries or discrepancies are recorded on the sheet, which is then sent to head office for processing. When a supplier's invoice arrives it is checked against the site record to ensure that the quantity is correct. If there is a problem with the delivery, then a credit notice can be requested against the invoice. In this way, costs from suppliers can be controlled and a check kept that goods received are of an acceptable standard.

## ■ Plant sheets

This works in a similar way to goods received sheets. The on and off hire dates of plant are inserted, so allowing the period off hire to be checked against the invoice to establish if it is correct. Any discrepancies can be justified with the supplier.

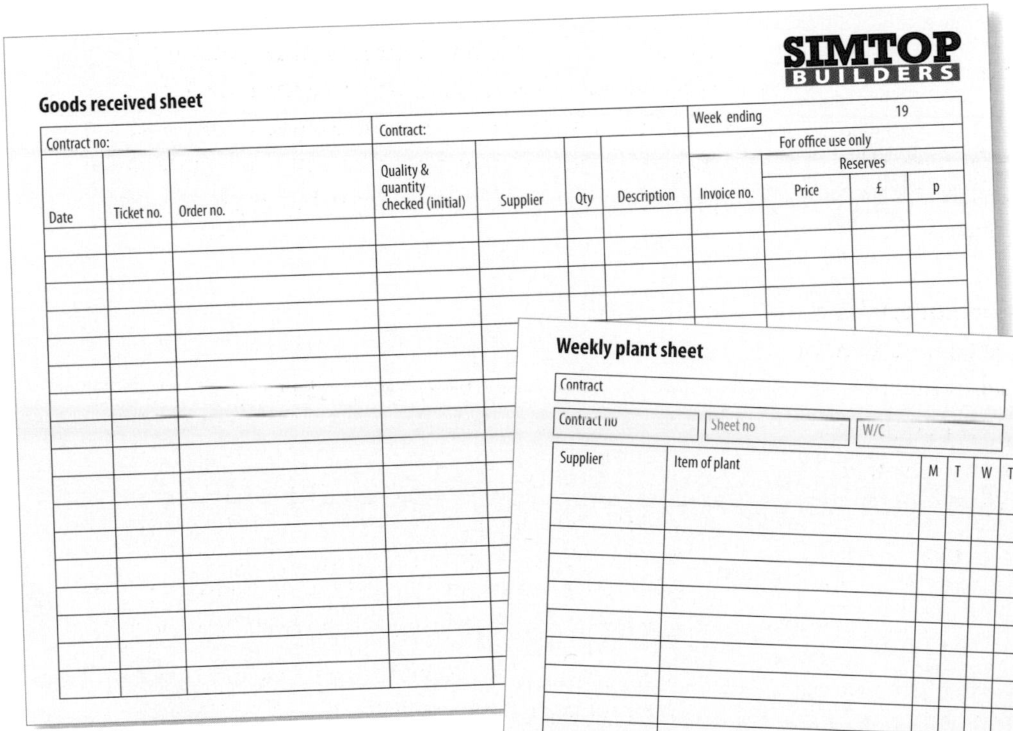

SIMTOP BUILDERS

Goods received sheet

Contract no: | Contract: | Week ending 19

| Date | Ticket no. | Order no. | Quality & quantity checked (initial) | Supplier | Qty | Description | For office use only: Invoice no. | Reserves: Price | £ | p |
|---|---|---|---|---|---|---|---|---|---|---|

▲ Figure 7.11 Goods received sheet

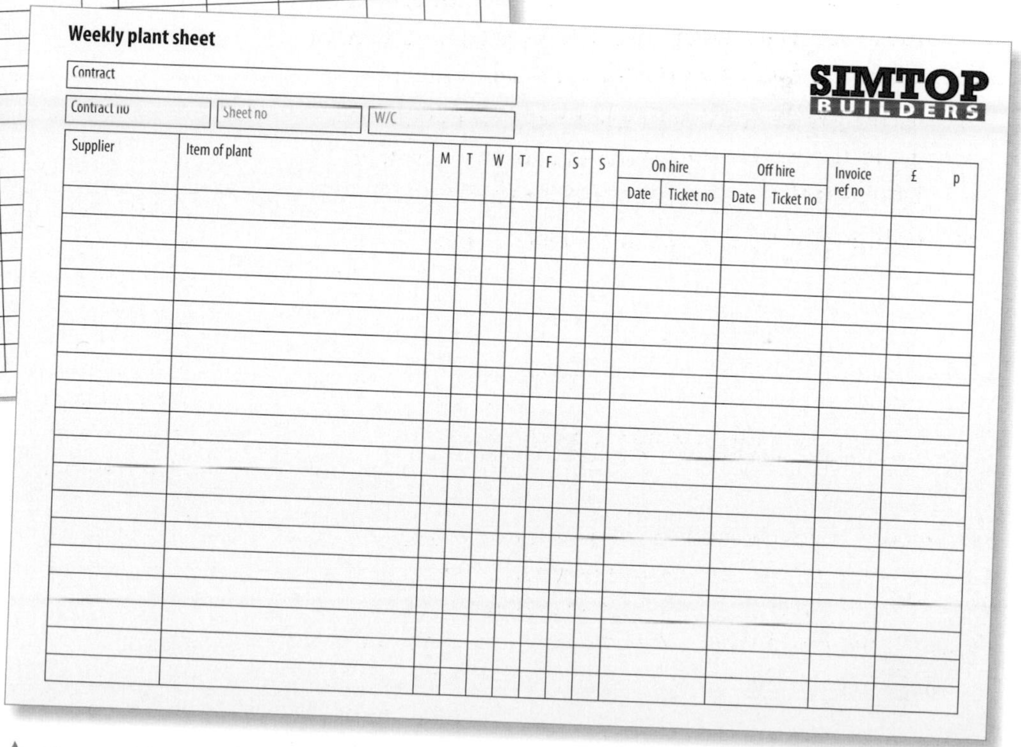

Weekly plant sheet

Contract

Contract no | Sheet no | W/C

SIMTOP BUILDERS

| Supplier | Item of plant | M | T | W | T | F | S | S | On hire: Date | On hire: Ticket no | Off hire: Date | Off hire: Ticket no | Invoice ref no | £ | p |
|---|---|---|---|---|---|---|---|---|---|---|---|---|---|---|---|

▲ Figure 7.12 Plant sheet

## ■ Job cards

These are issued to the operatives and each card states what task has to be undertaken on site. The operative records the hours they have worked on the job card, which can then be used to establish rates for the estimator to price future works, to monitor actual hours against planned to see if they are correct and whether the workforce needs motivating to recover lost hours.

## ■ Vehicle allocation sheets

These are used to track the hours of each company vehicle and apportion it against the contract on which the vehicle was employed.

## Assessment practice

Take a closer look at the documentation and control techniques covered in the previous pages and undertake an evaluation of three of these planning, organisational and control techniques in terms of utility (helpfulness) and efficacy (usefulness). **D2**

# Preparation for assessment

You have just been awarded a project for the construction of a single-storey, small factory unit comprising six identical units in total. Identify and describe the various stages of the construction process for one unit. **P1**

The construction team has been put together for this project. Investigate and explain the roles and inter-relationships of those members of the building team that will be involved in the resource management, planning and production phase of the project. **P2**

Identify the physical and human resources required to complete a single factory unit building. **P3**

The resources for the factory units require controlling and monitoring. Identify and explain the techniques commonly used to monitor and control resources. **P4**

The chief planner has handed you some examples of resource planning and management documentation. What could these be? Explain three examples so an uninformed person could understand. **P5**

Produce and interpret bar charts, networks and schedules for typical low-rise domestic or commercial projects. (For more information, refer to your tutor.) **P6**

The planner has asked you to produce organisational charts to explain the group dynamics of team working for the factory units. Draw up a site organisation chart to include links to the head office functions. **M1**

Looking at the three items that you have explained in P5, compare and evaluate the advantages and disadvantages of each resource management technique. **M2**

Things are not going well on site. Discuss the factors that may have had an adverse impact on the planning and organisation on site that have obviously not been taken into consideration and explain how they have caused delays on site. **M3**

The chief planner is keen to adopt new technology on site. Examine the software systems which facilitate the planning, organisation and control processes. **D1**

Looking at your three answers to P5, evaluate the planning, organisational and control techniques you have identified in terms of utility and efficacy. **D2**

# Grading tips

**M1** You will need to produce charts that show the supervisory structure of a company or construction site. They should show the hierarchy of the site management right down to the operative, using lines and boxes to illustrate the direct relationship. Links can be made between onsite and offsite roles on these charts, so that they show how team dynamics work in this direction.

**M2** You will need to select at least three resource management techniques, e.g. materials requisition sheets, and compare them, listing the advantages and disadvantages of each. A clear answer to this would use a table format so that a direct comparison can be made.

**M3** You are asked to discuss some of the factors that will have an effect on the planning and organisation of a project if they are not taken into account. Produce a good range and explain how each has a bearing upon the planning and running of the contract in question.

**D1** This will require some research. You could search the Internet for examples of planning software packages and then explain how they might help, assist or facilitate the planning process for the company or construction site.

**D2** The words 'utility' and 'efficacy' are key words here. Explain, making sure you include a range of control techniques in terms of what value they have, how useful they are – are they any good? Finally, look at the efficacy, i.e. the effectiveness, efficiency, worthiness or the benefits of each.

# Knowledge check

1. Name four principal members of the construction phase team.

2. What interaction would occur between the contracts manager and the site supervisor?

3. List the phases of a construction project.

4. Name the three ways in which maintenance can be undertaken.

5. What does procurement involve?

6. Identify the four principal resources needed to fulfil a construction contract.

7. What factors will affect the plant requirements on a typical project?

8. What factors will need to be taken into account when producing a construction programme?

9. What affects the output of a piece of construction plant?

10. What would influence the layout of the temporary organisational structure on site?

11. What decisions need to be made when a piece of plant is to be hired or purchased?

12. What functions do management undertake during the project?

13. In what way does a goods received sheet control materials?

14. How can the labour workforce on site be controlled effectively?

15. How can wastage on a construction site be minimised?

## Grading criteria: Unit 7

| To achieve a pass grade the evidence must show that the learner is able to: | To achieve a merit grade the evidence must show that, in addition to the pass criteria, the learner is able to: | To achieve a distinction grade the evidence must show that, in addition to the pass and merit criteria, the learner is able to: |
| --- | --- | --- |
| **P1** identify and describe the various stages of the construction process for a low-rise domestic or commercial building **Assessment practice pages 281, 311** | **M1** produce organisational charts to explain the group dynamics of team working **Assessment practice pages 278, 311** | **D1** evaluate two software systems that can facilitate planning, organisation and control processes **Assessment practice pages 308, 311** |
| **P2** investigate and explain the roles and inter-relationships of those members of the building team involved in resource management, planning and production **Assessment practice pages 278, 311** | | |
| **P3** identify the physical and human resources required to complete a building project **Assessment practice pages 288, 311** | | |
| **P4** identify and explain the techniques commonly used to monitor and control resources **Assessment practice pages 297, 311** | | |
| **P5** recognise and interpret examples of resource planning and management documentation **Assessment practice pages 306, 311** | | |
| **P6** produce and interpret bar charts, networks and schedules for typical low-rise domestic or commercial projects **Assessment practice pages 308, 311** | **M2** compare and evaluate the advantages and disadvantages of a range of resource management techniques **Assessment practice pages 297, 311** | **D2** evaluate a range of planning, organisational and control techniques in terms of utility and efficacy **Assessment practice pages 310, 311** |
| | **M3** discuss the factors that may adversely impact on planning and organisation if not taken into consideration and explain their possible effects **Assessment practice pages 291, 311** | |

# Graphical detailing in construction and the built environment

## Introduction

Communication of information is crucial to the successful design and construction of building and civil engineering projects. One of the primary means of communicating design information is by the use of drawings. You will need to know how to correctly read drawings and how to produce them. A drawing consists mainly of graphical information, its purpose being to show by means of lines, symbols and dimensions the size, shape and location of the designed elements and their various parts.

Throughout the early stages of the design, it is important to provide an overview of the construction project including a site plan, elevations or perspective views. As the elements of the design are developed, more detailed drawings are needed so that the construction details can be understood. Written information regarding the workmanship and quality of materials will also be required, either on the drawings themselves or in a separate document called the 'specification'. Other documents that may also be produced are materials lists or component schedules which also assist in the specification process.

Contract documents for any construction project are legally binding, and drawings and specifications form a part of these contract documents. It is therefore important that this drawing information is clear and accurate. Poorly produced or presented information may result in mistakes or errors being made on site and the original designer who produced the information may be held liable for any delays or additional cost to the project!

### How you will be assessed

This unit is internally assessed by your tutor. A variety of activities is included in this unit to help you understand all aspects of producing and using manual drawings and specifications.

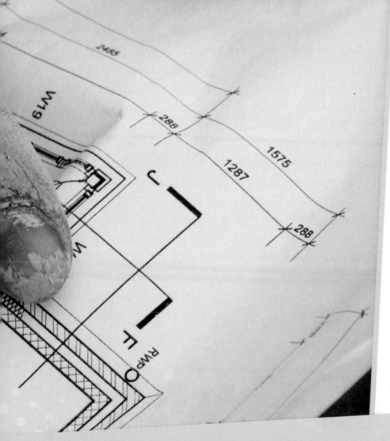

# Thinking points

There are many different forms of communication used in construction. Examples include written descriptions of materials and product information, numerical calculations, methods statements and tabulated lists of quantities and costs. However, the one form which it relies on most heavily is visual or graphical communication. Think about how you would describe the layout and organisation of spaces in your own home using just written words. It would be quite difficult if you lived in anything but a one-roomed flat and certainly confusing without any visual prompts to aid you. The majority of the graphical detailing today is done on computers using specialised detailing software packages. However, it is crucial that all professionals in the industry can sketch and draw manually. The importance of learning manual detailing skills cannot be overestimated. You need to appreciate the layout of drawings, the choice of scale and proportion, the types of views used, the use of correct line widths, conventional graphic symbols and the appropriate use of annotation; and this is best learnt using traditional methods.

Graphical detailing is at the heart of good design work and follows a gradual process of designing, reviewing and revising drawings and linked information. At the design stage, these drawings can take the form of free-hand sketches to show outline proposals for the scale, mass and size of the project. These drawings are then refined and developed to form technically detailed hard line plans, elevations, cross-sections or perspectives drawings.

If you are to be successful in your construction career, no matter what discipline you choose to follow you must be able to read, understand and produce graphical information. Can you produce a 1:50 plan on a detached house showing all the correct drawing conventions and symbols? Or a two-point perspective sketch of a simple building?

After completing this unit you should be able to achieve the following outcomes:

1 Know the main equipment, media and techniques used in the production of manual and CAD graphical information
2 Understand the use of CAD and its benefits in the production and management of graphical information
3 Be able to read and understand a variety of graphical drawings, details and schedules
4 Be able to produce graphical drawings, details and schedules using traditional manual drafting techniques.

## Equipment for manual detailing

The equipment needed for manual detailing is shown below.

### Parallel motion drawing boards

When drawing technical drawings a firm, smooth surface is necessary. There are a number of board types available, but the most common is the standard parallel motion type. This is usually on a free-standing frame or can be fitted with a ratchet mechanism to sit on a desk. Both boards are free to tilt. Some students still opt for the more traditional T-square and flat board, but these are not used in commercial design offices.

### Media

This is the name given to the material that is drawn on. In traditional forms of drafting there are four basic types:

- Paper – the quality of paper is given by its weight in grams per square metre ($g/m^2$). Very light 'layout' paper is around 60 $g/m^2$ while ordinary, cheap photocopy paper is about 80 $g/m^2$. A thicker 'letter' quality paper has a noticeably different 'feel' when it is around the 90–100 $g/m^2$ range, and thicker cartridge paper is around 120–150 $g/m^2$. Paper drawings can be reproduced in black and white or colour by electrostatic photocopying machines called plain paper copiers which can now handle larger paper sizes – see below.

- Tracing paper – this is semi-transparent medium and comes in various grades for draft work at around 80 $g/m^2$ up to 110 $g/m^2$ for master copies. Generally, pencil construction lines are drawn on tracing paper and inked in later with drawing pens. Tracing paper in the past was copied using a two-stage process ammonia copier or dyeline copier which needed the transparent nature of that medium in order to work. Dyeline copies were excellent at copying pencil shading or any other subtle toning methods but faded in sunlight. Dyeline copiers can still be found in some design offices although plain paper photocopiers are now more popular.

## Remember!

Tracing paper is susceptible to changes in moisture content and can stretch unevenly if left taped down to a drawing board overnight, so beware.

- Drafting film – this appears to be similar to tracing paper, but is easily recognisable by its waxy, silky feel, and its high static electricity content as it is made from polyester. It has the advantage of being

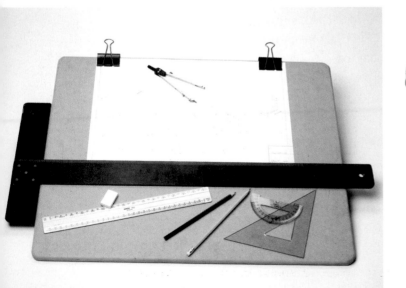

▲ Timber component drawing

strong and virtually tear-proof and resistant to moisture. The copies can be reproduced like tracing paper.

- Linen cloth – this is not used today but you may come across these drawings if working on historic buildings when the existing plans were often drawn in ink on a lacquered linen cloth.

## Remember!

Drafting film needs special ink because ordinary ink will take much longer to dry and be non-permanent. Also, ordinary pen nibs will wear out very quickly on polyester paper and so tungsten-tipped nibs are required.

All drawing media are supplied using the international paper size standard, ISO 216, which is based on the metric system. The sizes are based on the A0 sheet which has an area of 1 m² with the sides of the rectangle in the ratio 1:√2.

The range of paper sizes is shown in Figure 8.1.

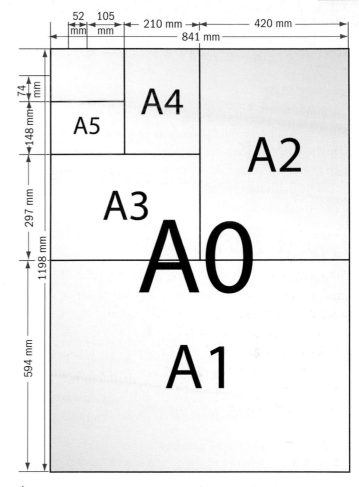

▲ Figure 8.1 Paper sizes – from A0 to A4

### Pencils, erasers and erasing shields

Pencils are the main working tool of the draftsperson and come in a range of different hardnesses. For technical drafting purposes, Table 8.1 shows the five most used with B being the softest and 2H the hardest.

Pencils must be kept sharp at all times and have regular, smooth points. This is aided by gently turning the pencil in your fingers as you draw the line.

For rubbing out pencil lines, a soft rubber eraser is used. It may be necessary to mask off parts of the drawing by

using a thin metal or plastic erasing shield. Pencil can be used on cartridge paper or tracing paper.

## Remember!

Always use the back of your hand to brush away erased shavings. If you use the palm of your hand, it may be sweaty and you will smudge your work!

**Table 8.1 Most used pencils in technical drafting**

Darkest ──────────────────────────────────────── Lightest

| B | HB | F | H | 2H |
|---|---|---|---|---|
| Shading and texturing | Rough sketching | Printing and general line work | Dimension lines and hatching | Construction lines |

When using plastic film, high polymer leads are used. These are usually available for use in clutch pencils with leads ranging from 0.2 mm to 0.9 mm.

## Scale rules

Drawings are generally produced to a scale which will conveniently fit onto the drawing sheet. You very seldom will need to produce drawings which are actual size, i.e. 1:1. The main tool to help you draw scaled drawings is a pre-marked scale rule with the most common scales included, such as 1:2500, 1:1250, 1:1000, 1:500, 1:250, 1:200, 1:100, 1:50, 1:20, 1:10 and 1:5.

## Pens

These are used for ink drawing and allow for a range of line thicknesses depending on the purpose of the line drawn. There are four standard common pen widths which are typically 0.25 mm, 0.35 mm, 0.5 mm, 0.7 mm. These produce lines which are of different character and are used for different purposes as shown in Table 8.2.

**Table 8.2 Pens for different purposes**

| Pen thickness | Type of line |
|---|---|
| 0.25 mm | Dimension line<br>Hatch line |
| 0.35 mm | General printing and linework details<br>Hidden details |
| 0.5 mm | Section lines<br>Titles |
| 0.7 mm | Titleblock and drawing borders |

Ink lines can only be drawn on non-paper media such as tracing paper or plastic film, and if you need to correct a mistake, then the ink line has to be gently scraped away with a safety blade and resealed with a rubber eraser.

### Remember!

Never use ink pens on paper as they become clogged and damaged.

## Adjustable set squares

These are used mainly to draw vertical lines at 90° to the parallel motion arm, but they can produce a line at any angle on the paper by adjusting the protractor scale. These are far more versatile than the traditional '30°/60°/90°' and '45°/45°/90°' fixed set squares.

## Compasses

These are used to draw circles and arcs. There are two main types: a traditional spring bow type and a longer horizontal beam compass for use in plotting traditional linear land surveys.

## Templates, stencils and flexible curves

These are useful aids to the draftsperson. Templates provide common outlines of objects at a range of typical scales, for example toilet cisterns and pans. Ink stencils help provide a guide for producing standard text on drawings and curves can be drawn smoothly with the aid of French curves or a 'Flexi-Curve'.

## Drafting tape

In order to secure the medium to the board, drafting tape is applied at its four corners. You must remember to remove the tape every night, otherwise the medium will not be able to expand and contract as the temperature changes.

# Equipment for CAD detailing

## Computer hardware

The essential current hardware required for computer-aided design (CAD) work comprises:

- a central processing unit (CPU) whose speed is at least 3 Giga-Hertz (GHz), e.g. an Intel™ or Celeron™ microchip, with a compatible operating system, e.g. Microsoft™ Windows™ XP

▲ **Typical work station for a CAD operator**

- an operating disk capacity of 2 Giga-Bytes (GB) RAM and at least 2 GB free disk space on the hard drive
- for presentation purposes a visual display unit (VDU) monitor with a resolution of 1280 × 1024 pixels and display adaptor capable of 32-bit colour 128 MB or greater
- a mouse and keyboard, although some professionals prefer using digitisers and digitiser pads or light pens
- a networked plotter capable of minimum A1 size plots in three pen colours/thicknesses.

In addition, the CPU should have capabilities to be networked (wired or wireless) to a local area network (LAN) and also have Internet and email access through a broadband connection.

### Intranets and project extranets

Three are three typical hardware configurations for a CAD system in a design office and they are dependent on how each configuration is networked and where the data is stored. More information is included later in this chapter. The three typical hardware configurations are as follows:

- Standalone single user – this is where the CAD software and drawing information is held within a **private domain**. Information is issued by plotting off drawings and sending them by post or sending electronic copies of the drawing files by email.
- Small office-based intranet set up using a local area network (LAN) – this is where the CAD and licensing software, together with drawing and document information, is held within a **project domain** which physically may be located in a separate computer server which itself is linked to the company plotting device. The server may also contain a plot management function to prioritise the work from, say, Architect B's work in preference to Architect A's work if there are important deadlines to meet. Companies may also use project management software on this system to track drawings, record revisions and control the electronic issuing of information.
- Large multi-location extranet set up for a wide area network (WAN) – this is where drawing information is uploaded or 'published' to a **public domain** on the Internet which is accessible to all the various members of the project team with users in different geographical locations. This internet web domain is provided by subscription from the CAD software company and uses its project management software to monitor and flag up when and what changes are being made. It also allows the user to search for the most up-to-date drawings themselves.

## General techniques used for manual and CAD detailing

When deciding the best way to represent this dimensional and constructional information the draftsperson needs to consider what the drawing's main purpose is and who is going to be reading it.

A drawing is used to provide information about the size and layout of buildings and their elements. They can also provide detailed information about the specification of the quality of materials and workmanship required. They form part of the contract agreement between two people – the client and the contractor – and at various stages throughout the design and construction process different graphical forms of information are used.

Above all else, the drawing must have the following qualities whether produced manually or by CAD:

- enough information to be useful for its purpose, but not cramped or too busy
- the construction information is clear and unambiguous
- all individual details on the drawing are clearly referenced and labelled, such as section marks and individual titles
- a clear system of cross referencing between drawings and other relevant documents is present.

In any design office there should be a consistent 'house style' that meets all these requirements and is applied to all drawings and documents. There may also be a need to set up a series of standard templates for drawings, word documents and spreadsheets which can be flexible enough to apply to large and small jobs alike.

### Projection methods

Drawings are essentially a two-dimensional (2D) representation of a three-dimensional (3D) element of a building which could be a wall, a staircase or perhaps a whole ground floor layout. There are a number of geometrical techniques for showing 3D objects on 2D media, that is, flat paper. The following are the most popular projection methods and they are illustrated with regard to one particular house:

#### ■ Orthographic projection

This is where individual views and plans are drawn in flat profile. There are two basic types of orthographic projection: 1st angle or 3rd angle. In construction, we generally use 3rd angle projection to show a building's external elevations and roof plans. This is useful for showing the general arrangement of the features of a house and the relative positions of windows and doors.

In Figure 8.2, the main view is the south elevation with the plan of the roof shown above, that is, a bird's eye view. The side elevations are the east and west elevations and these are drawn next to the south elevation, the

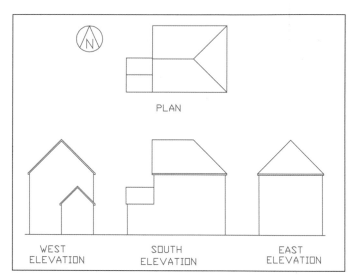

▲ **Figure 8.2 Orthographic projection in 3rd angle**

west elevation drawn next to the west side of the building, etc.

#### ■ Isometric projection

This projection gives a 3D image with all lines drawn at the same scale and at an angle of 30°. Note that all the receding lines are parallel. Therefore, this is not a perspective view.

This is often used to show the overall mass of smaller construction elements such as stone window cills or special brick plinth constructions as shown in Figure 8.3.

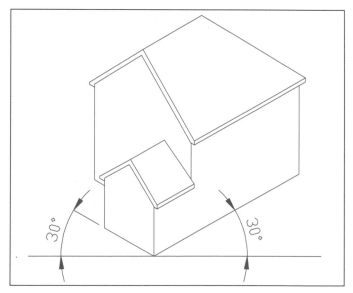

▲ **Figure 8.3 Isometric projection**

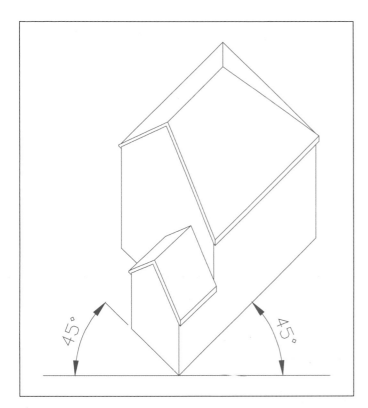

Figure 8.4 Axonometric projection

## Axonometric projection

This is similar to isometric but with all lines drawn at 45°. This method is easier to construct because it uses the true plan view but simply rotated by 45°.

It is most suitable for interior and office or kitchen layouts as it appears to give a higher view point than isometric, that is, it lets you see inside a box.

## Perspective

This gives the most realistic view and is particularly good for elevations and external views. For a two-point perspective, all lines converge on to two vanishing points fixed at eye level on the horizon. Perspective drawings can be drawn to scale but are quite complicated to construct. The one shown in Figure 8.5 has been generated from a computer model, Google SketchUp™.

## Exploded views

Often in product manufacture and particularly in building services exploded diagrams are provided to show clearly how the various component parts fit together These drawn elements are relatively simple to construct as a 3D model and can be linked to schedules for specification of materials. An example of an exploded diagram used in a water pump is shown in Figure 8.6.

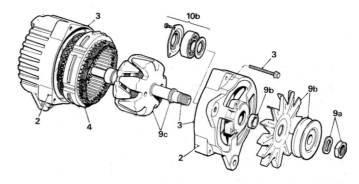

Figure 8.6 Exploded view

Figure 8.5 Perspective drawing ▶

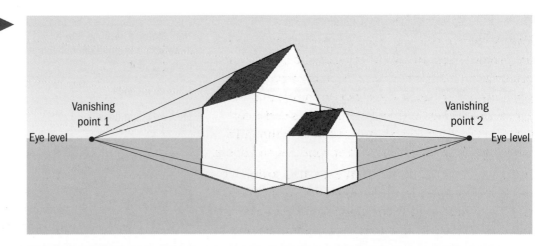

**Table 8.3 Types of drawing line**

| Type of Line | Function of line | Typicalluse |
|---|---|---|
| ———————— thick | Site outline or new building | Site drawings |
| ———————— medium | General details | |
| ———————— thin | Reference grid, dimension lines, leader lines and hatching | |
| ———————— thick | Primary functional elements in horizontal or vertical sections (e.g. loadbearing walls and structural slabs) | General location drawings |
| ———————— medium | Secondary elements and components in horizontal and vertical sections (e.g. non loadbearing partitions, windows, doors); also components etc., in elevation | |
| ———————— thin | Reference grids, dimension lines, leader lines and hatching | |
| ———————— thick | Primary functional elements in horizontal or vertical section (e.g. loadbearing walls, structural slabs) | Assembly drawings |
| ———————— medium | Secondary elements and components in horizontal and vertical section (e.g. non loadbearing partitions, windows, doors); also components etc., in elevation | |
| ———————— thin | Reference grids, dimensions lines, leader lines and hatching | |
| — — — — — — | Medium broken line. The purpose and position of the line should be noted in relation to the plane of section. The line begins with a dash cutting the outline adjoining, and all lines should meet at changes in direction | Work not visible Work to be removed |
| —————⁄\—————— | Thin line with break in it or if necessary a thin continuous line with a zig zag in it | Breaks in continuity of drawings |
| ▬·▬·▬·▬·▬·▬ | Thick chain lines | Pipe lines, services, drains |
| ▬·▬·▬·▬·▬ | Medium chain lines | |
| –·–·–·–·–·– | Thin chain line | Centre and axial lines |
| –·▬·▬·▬·▬·○ | Indicated by a circle at the end of the line | Controlling line, grid line |

## Techniques used for manual detailing

### ■ Text and font styles

General notes should not be scattered over the drawing but should be neatly arranged in panels of regular shape and provided with a clear printed text heading. They should be broken up into paragraphs for ease of reading, and should not be cramped nor become so widely spaced as to become illegible. It is important to avoid over stylised or italicised fonts as these can be difficult to read. A simple, open print text style provides the clearest form of communication. Ideally, text should be in block capitals with plenty of open space inside the characters, e.g.

THIS DRAWING SHALL NOT BE SCALED

not *THIS DRAWING SHALL NOT BE SCALED*

Upper case or lower case is acceptable depending on the house style of the organisation. In each case, the height of the text should range from 3 mm high for general text up to 5 mm high for titles of individual sections and plans.

### ■ Types of drawing line

The three most common types of line are continuous, dashed and chain-dotted and each line has three relative thicknesses: thick, medium and thin. These various conventions are combined to indicate specific construction elements or controlling information, the functions of which are described in Table 8.3.

### ■ Dimensioning

There are a number of ways in which dimension lines can be shown, two examples of which are shown in Figures 8.7 and 8.8.

For horizontal dimensions, it is normal to print the dimensions along the dimension line with the ends of the line marked with arrowheads or thick oblique strike lines. For vertical dimensions, the dimension numbers are printed to the left-hand side of the dimension line. The dimensions are always taken to be in millimetres and as such do not need to have the abbreviation 'mm' printed after the dimension figures. If the units represent a different unit, like metres, then the abbreviation 'm' has to be shown after the dimension figure.

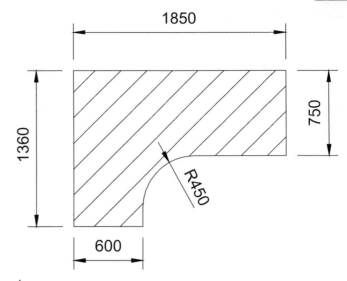

▲ Figure 8.7 Dimension lines with arrowheads

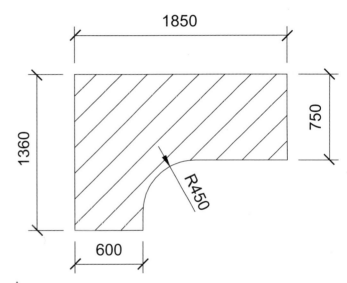

▲ Figure 8.8 Dimension lines with oblique strike lines

It is also important that there is a gap between the dimension lines and the detail element as this could lead to confusion.

### ■ Use of standard hatch patterns and symbols

Where detail elements are being cut through as in a cross-section in plan or elevation, it is appropriate to show cross hatching to denote the material from which they are made. Typical hatching patterns are given in Figure 8.9.

The most common hatching are brickwork and blockwork. Another common convention used to save

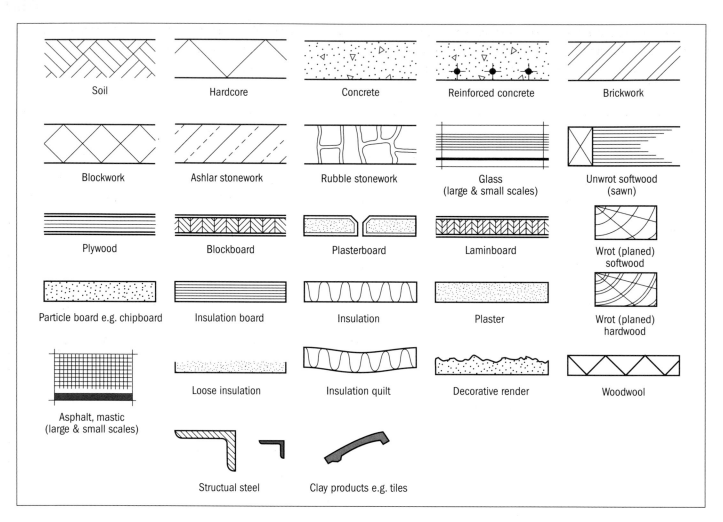

▲ Figure 8.9 Hatching patterns

Table 8.4 Standard abbreviations

| Item | Abbreviation | Item | Abbreviation | Item | Abbreviation | Item | Abbreviation |
|------|------|------|------|------|------|------|------|
| Airbrick | AB | Foundation | fnd | Cast iron | CI | Rainwater pipe | rwp |
| Asbestos | abs | Hardboard | hdbd | Cement | ct | Reinforced concrete | RC |
| Bitumen | bit | Hardcore | hc | Column | col | Satin chrome | SC |
| Boarding | bdg | Hardwood | hwd | Concrete | conc | Satin anodised aluminium | SAA |
| Brickwork | bwk | Insulation | insul | Cupboard | cpd | Softwood | swd |
| Building | bldg | Joist | jst | Damp-proof course | DPC | Stainless steel | SS |
| Damp-proof membrane | DPM | Mild steel | MS | Polyvinyl acetate | PVA | Tongue and groove | T&G |
| Drawing | dwg | Plasterboard | pbd | Polyvinyl chloride | PVC | Wrought iron | WI |

time and aid clarity is the use of various symbols for common constructional features like door, windows and light switches. Common symbols used are shown in Figure 8.10.

A number of abbreviations are also commonly used on drawings to aid clarity and expression. Some standard ones are shown in Table 8.4.

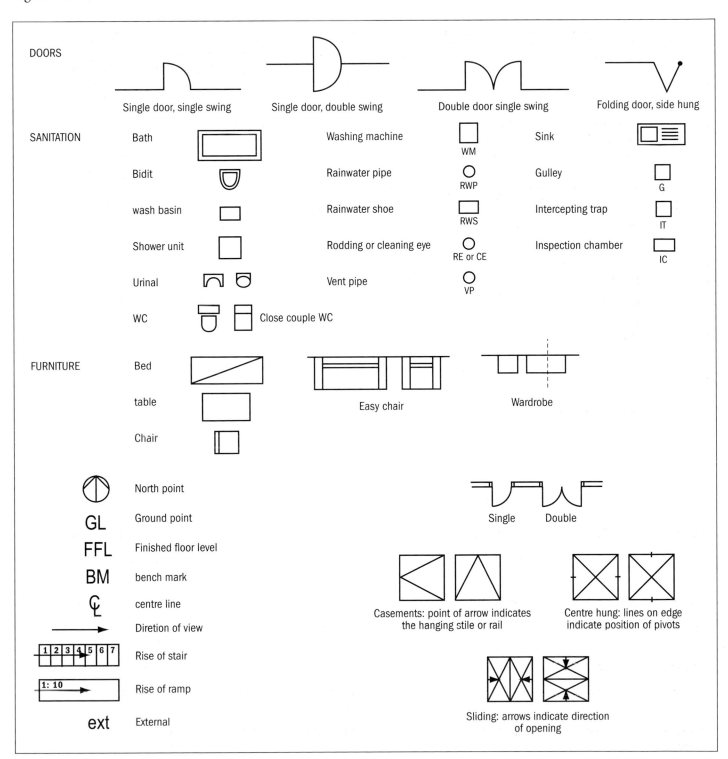

▲ **Figure 8.10 Constructional features symbols**

A construction project's **specification** communicates in written or tabular form the nature and quality of each construction element required, as distinct from providing visual information about geometry, size, shape and arrangement which is shown on the drawings.

## Key Term

**Construction specification** Written information prepared by the design team for use by the construction team, the main purpose of which is to define the products to be used, the quality of work, any performance requirements and the conditions under which the work is to be executed.

On small jobs like a 'room-in-the-roof' house extension, all the specifications notes can usually be contained on the drawing without being confusing and also allow the work to be priced accurately by the contractor.

On larger jobs, like a small housing development with a number of drawings, there should be enough information written on the drawing to identify the components and their size but not too much information as this could be quite confusing. The detailed information, such as how it is to be constructed or the quality of the materials, is usually contained within other contract documents like the specification or the bill of quantities, and it is important to note that for tendering purposes the detailed **bill of quantities** should provide very clear information as to what the contractor is expected to provide for the proposed project, and the drawings and bills must tie up.

## Key Term

**Bill of quantities** A document that quantifies the amount of materials and components in a building.

### Coordinated project information

In order to ensure that information in drawings, specifications and bills of quantities is the same, the construction industry has used a number of specification systems for defining building products and materials in the UK. This has been very important for large projects where there are a large number of drawings produced. The first coordinated project information system to be widely used was the CI/SfB – Construction Index system – of Swedish origin, but lately, due to problems both with introducing new categories and computerisation, a new all encompassing classification scheme for the construction industry is currently being implemented known as the Uniclass system. It has been developed by the National Building Specification (NBS) on behalf of the Construction Project Information Committee (CPIC). This organisation represents the following major sponsoring organisations:

- Construction Confederation
- The Institution of Civil Engineers
- Royal Institute of British Architects
- Royal Institution of Chartered Surveyors
- Chartered Institution of Building Services Engineers.

Uniclass comprises 15 tables, each of which represents a different broad area of construction information. Each table can be used as a stand-alone table for the classification of a particular type of information but, in addition, terms from different tables can be combined to classify complex subjects. This system is very useful in large projects where there is a lot of information that needs to be communicated.

The full list of classification tables includes:

A  Form of information
B  Subject disciplines
C  Management
D  Facilities
E  Construction entities
F  Spaces
G  Elements for buildings
H  Elements for civil engineering works
J  Work sections for buildings
K  Work sections for civil engineering works
L  Construction products
M  Construction aids
N  Properties and characteristics
P  Materials
Q  Universal Decimal Classification.

The one with direct relevance to the production of drawings for the construction industry is 'Table G Elements for buildings' and for the civil engineering Industry there is 'Table H Elements for civil engineering works'.

Table G is further broken down into more detailed classifications known as the Common Arrangement of Work Sections (CAWS) from which bills of quantities can be produced using the **Standard Method of Measurement of Building Works, seventh edition (SMM7)**. An example of the way CAWS breaks down the work into sections is shown below:

Level 1: Group, e.g. M Surface finishes

Level 2: Subgroup, e.g. M1 Screeds/trowelled flooring

Level 3: Work section, e.g. M13 Calcium sulfate based screeds.

In this way, detailed definitions are provided in order to reduce possible variations and conflicts between documents – even within the same document, and in practice it ensures that gaps and overlaps between different work sections are eliminated.

## Key Term

**Standard Method of Measurement of Building Works (SMM7)** A clearly defined method of calculating the materials needed for a project using a systematic and clear measuring procedure based on the dimensions shown in the contract drawings.

## Theory into practice

In order to explore the specification of building works in small and large projects, visit the CPIC website at www.productioninformation.org and look at the examples it provides for specifying building works. Copy out a specification clause for a building element. In particular, see 'Documentation for a small project', 'Performance specification' and 'Prescriptive specification' examples.

1  What is a performance specification?

2  What is a prescriptive specification?

Essentially, these systems enable the information on the drawing to complement the information in the written specification and vice versa. This is covered in more detail later in this chapter when we look at reading and producing drawings.

## An overview of CAD techniques

An understanding of computer-aided designing is an essential requirement for today's design office. There are many advantages over traditional methods when using CAD. These include, for example, the:

- production of high-quality graphics in a relatively short time
- facility to reuse standard 'house' style details
- ability to easily amend and reissue revised drawings/ details
- ease of archiving and saving electronic drawings
- improved management and tracking of work.

Most CAD programmes today also offer other advantages by combining highly powerful databases to prepare lists of materials, specifications, and cost data. Details of the specialist design and detailing software are included later in this unit in Section 8.2 Understanding the use of CAD and its benefits in the production and management of graphical information.

## ■ Specific CAD techniques

Drawing with a computer requires a different attitude as well as a different set of skills from the traditional approach to drawing. To illustrate this, we will now look at using a 2D CAD package such as AutoCAD LT™.

### Setting up the drawing

At the start of the drawing, the 'real' size of construction project is set up on the screen, known as the 'limits' of the drawing. The limits are the $x$- and $y$- coordinates of the size of the 'drawing area' and the zoom enables you both to magnify small parts of the drawing and also to see an overview of the whole drawing. CAD drawings are always drawn real size, that is, at a scale of 1:1. How you move around the drawing is controlled by the 'limits' of the drawing and the 'zoom' controls. The screen area could detail the elevation of an electrical plug socket or the complete plan view of a football stadium; it would depend on what limits were set.

## Drawing and editing commands

One of the main differences between manual drafting and CAD is the way in which lines and shapes, called 'entities', are created. Essentially, the drawing area is gridded up into $x$- and $y$- coordinates which define the exact positions of the drawn entities. This method is known as vector-based drawing where you need to specify the end point of say a line relative to its starting point. For example, to draw a horizontal line 3 metres long, the command would be LINE @ 3000,0 where the '@' indicates the chosen start point of the line and the 3000 and 0 the $x$- and $y$- coordinates respectively from that starting point.

Once you have created some entities, you can use a variety of different editing commands to copy, rotate and mirror the existing entity, for example. Most CAD software comes with its own set of pre-made entities which can be loaded into the drawing as 'blocks', such as items of furniture, people or cars, or you can create your own standard blocks.

## Layers and controls

Layers are another useful feature of a CAD drawing. Different constructional elements can be shown on different 'layers' which can be visualised as separate transparent overlay sheets containing grouped or linked objects. For example, one layer would contain all the electrical trucking and duct work and switches, etc. which would overlay the floor plan drawn on another separate layer. These separate layers can have their own colour, line thicknesses and line styles all preset, and they can be turned off or on to aid drawing and also can be plotted separately. Often hatching is shown on a separate layer so as not to slow the computer down and also to make selection and editing of line work easier. Typical layer name conventions are shown in Table 8.5 using Uniclass elements. The layer reference is made up of four separate fields, as shown in Table 8.5; for example, A-25-D-intwall, which means the 'architectural dimensions of the internal walls'.

## Plotting methods

As most drawings are larger than A3 size, a plotter is used instead of a printer. These can produce drawing plots up to A0 size from a drawing roll, of quality of around 90–100 grams, which is fed through a series of rollers. The plot is produced by a range of different pens that move against the direction of the fed roll of paper. The loading of the plotter rolls into the plotter needs careful alignment to ensure that the rolls run smoothly, usually there are guides marked on the feed loading

Table 8.5 Standard abbreviations for CAD layers

| 1 | | 2 | 3 | 4 |
|---|---|---|---|---|
| **Discipline** | | **Element (from Uniclass Table G or H)** | **Type of presentation information** | **User description** |
| A | Architect | G2 = Building fabric<br>G13 = Groundworks<br>G21 = Foundations<br>G22 = Floors<br>G23 = Stairs<br>G24 = Roofs<br>G25 = Walls<br>etc. | D – Dimensions<br>G – Graphics<br>H – Hatching<br>T – Text<br>M – Model Graphics<br>P – Page, Plot related | Optional e.g.<br>int-walls = internal walls<br>wall conc = concrete walls<br>roof timb = timber roof<br>etc. |
| B | Building Surveyor | | | |
| C | Civil Engineer | | | |
| D | Drainage, Highways Engineer | | | |
| E | Electrical Engineer | | | |
| F | Facilities Manager | | | |
| G | GIS, Land Surveyor | | | |
| H | Heating, Ventilation Designer | | | |
| I | Interior Designer | | | |

bay to assist in this tricky manoeuvre. The plotter pens will run an automatic check on their operation prior to starting a plot but you will need to ensure that plotter pen reservoirs are full and the right colour.

Many popular CAD software programs use a 'model space' or 'model view' to construct the building as a virtual 2D or 3D representation, which is then selectively transferred to a flat paper space or paper view 'layout' from which it is plotted. It is only when the drawing is plotted that the virtual drawing model is scaled down from 1:1 to fit onto the plotting paper space 'layouts'.

These layouts contain the company's title block, borders and standard notes. In this way, these standard details can be reproduced at the same time that the drawing entities are plotted and there is no need for a pre-printed title block/company logo on the drawing paper.

Also, with the increased use of CAD plotting techniques, there is no longer the need to store hard copies when drawings can be stored digitally without the need for climate-controlled storage areas that are required for paper and film based media.

## Assessment practice

For each of the following situations describe the equipment, media and techniques that would be used to produce the graphical detailing information. For each, clearly describe the use and function of the equipment and the media used:

a   You have been asked to produce some creative ideas for a proposed landscaping/planting area and patio for a communal garden in medium-sized apartment accommodation.

b   A student assignment to show a draft house floor plan and cross-section prior to producing an inked presentation copy.

c   A self-employed architectural designer uses his computer to generate some planning drawings for a proposed bungalow development.

d   A large architectural practice working on a major regional shopping centre development together with five other separate design consultants.

# Production of CAD drawings

The development of information and communication technologies (ICT) over the past decade has revolutionised the process of building design and construction. Now computers have greater capacity, work faster, and by means of the world wide web (www) can communicate a vast amount of information securely to all interested parties in any one construction project.

The development of CAD software for personal desktop computers was the impetus for almost universal application in all areas of construction. Initially, with 2D in the 1970s, it was typically limited to producing drawings similar to hand-drafted drawings. Advances in solid modelling involving wire-frames and surface area treatments in the 1980s allowed more versatile applications of computers in design activities. Autodesk™ was founded in 1982 which led to the 2D system AutoCAD™. Further software developments in the early 1990s led to solid 3D modelling linked to database features. These could capture information about material properties and product specifications of the drawn objects, and not just treat them as a series of lines. Currently, there are many CAD software products on the market, the most popular ones being Autodesk's AutoCAD™, with its derivative programs based on its DWG file format system, Bentley's Microstation™ suite of programs and Graphisoft's ArchiCAD™ software system. All of them offer capabilities for managing building data to provide secure, clear and timely management of design and construction documents known as Building Information Modelling (BIM) systems.

Today, CAD programs have become highly visual with intuitive interfaces which help make the software easier to use. The keyboard and mouse are still the main input devices (although light pens and digitisers are also used in some design offices) but with less focus on dialogue or instruction boxes and more emphasis on designing directly in the virtual model space.

## Remember!

Originally, CAD stood for computer-aided drafting as it was merely a tool to mirror the traditional manual drafting techniques but with increased speed and increasing functionality, it became an important design tool in itself – where CAD came to represent computer-aided design. However, you may also come across the term CADD which stands for computer-aided design and drafting!

## Basic CAD concepts

There are essentially two methods of producing computer-aided design depending on the nature of the construction project.

Small-scale domestic projects such as house extensions and alterations would use 2D CAD systems which, as stated above, mimic the processes involved in creating hand-drafted drawings, and to some extent many design practices still use this for the majority of their work. This method uses similar conventions to manual drafting in representing real 3D architectural elements through a series of flat 2D graphical images, typically consisting of plans, sections, and elevations (see Figure 8.11). Often, to provide a more realistic 3D effect traditional geometric techniques are created such as 'two-point perspectives' and isometric views.

The second process for producing CAD drawings or plots utilises powerful hardware systems and complex software programs to produce a set of virtual architectural 'objects'. These objects behave as complete architectural elements and not just a geometric pattern of lines or a wire framework as in the previous 2D method. These objects when combined form a virtual 3D model of the construction project such that they not only contain location and spatial information but also can hold information about the physical specifications

Designer's conceptual design sketches for the building

2D model file containing elevation data viewed from South

2D model file containing section and elevation data viewed from East

2D files can be plotted off or emailed to client/contractor, etc.

▲ **Figure 8.11 A 2D model**

of the 'objects'. This is known as a Single Model Environment (SME).

For example, in Figure 8.12 the Column Layout Model specifying the steelwork frame of the building, the Grid Model showing the setting out framework for the building and the mechanical services Ducting Model are brought together to form a composite model of the building. This system has a number of

powerful advantages over the 2D CAD systems which include:

- flagging up clashes where one 'object' interferes with another, e.g. where the column positions clash with ducting layout, which is invaluable in checking for errors and speeding up the design process
- improving design productivity and efficiency because 'objects' behave according to the specific properties that these elements have in the real world. For example, a window has a relationship to a wall that contains it; if you move or delete the wall, the window will also be deleted, just as in reality a window could not exist in that location without a wall to support it
- embedding information about the 'objects' in the form of linked schedules which provide details of their material properties, finishes and manufacturer's details which can then be used for costing and procurement purposes. In addition, these intelligent architectural objects can maintain dynamic links. For example, when someone deletes or modifies a door in the model, the door schedule document will be automatically updated

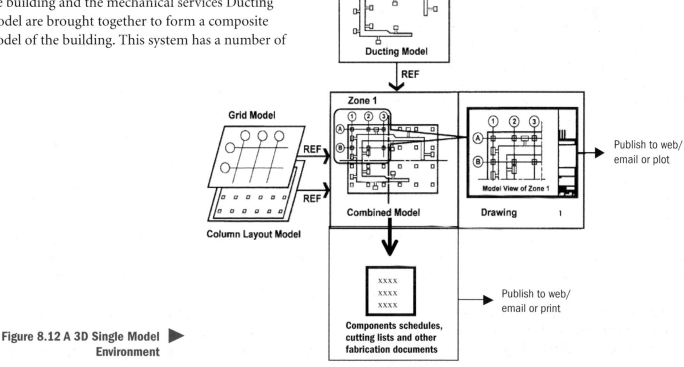

**Ducting Model**

REF

**Grid Model**

REF

REF

**Column Layout Model**

**Zone 1**

**Combined Model**

**Model View of Zone 1**

**Drawing**

Publish to web/ email or plot

xxxx
xxxx
xxxx

**Components schedules, cutting lists and other fabrication documents**

Publish to web/ email or print

**Figure 8.12 A 3D Single Model Environment** ▶

- enabling easier and more efficient methods of specifying components and materials direct from subscription services like the National Building Specification (NBS).

Figure 8.13 A 3D virtual model

## Theory into practice

Go to the National Building Specification (NBS) website at www.thenbs.com/products/nbsBuilding/default.asp and investigate the demo provided that illustrates the content and use of the NBS.

Briefly list the features of the NBS specification.

What do you think are the benefits of using this method to create specification notes for a building project?

From this model of the construction project, specific cross-sections, elevations and plans can be selected and automatically generated and plotted, as well as schedules printed. This is obviously more than just a simple graphical detailing operation as it is combining different 'objects' of pre-existing spatial and technical data to form a new design solution as a Single Model Environment.

## Presentation techniques used in CAD

As CAD software has become more powerful and computer hardware has evolved greater storage capacity and speed, so the virtual representation of construction and civil engineering projects has become increasingly realistic.

## ■ Rendering and photo-realisation

What used to be just wire frames with solid faces have now become realistic structures with natural textures giving the impression of real materials. It is not just the designed elements that appear to be real, with the development of powerful surveying software and

equipment the 3D surfaces of the 'natural world' can be accurately mapped and realistically represented with bright sunlight and shadows and wind-rippled foliage. In addition, some programs offer the capability to map photographs of buildings and people into 3D virtual models. A typical rendered elevation for a major retail refurbishment project which illustrates this type of presentation is shown in Figure 8.13.

Thus CAD enables projects to be brought to life for impressive client presentations at any stage of the design with integrated rendering and photo-realisation. The streamlined visualisation capabilities make this type of presentation stand out by visually communicating richer design information than mere 2D perspectives drawings or physical 3D architectural models. They also help the client to appreciate how the proposals works on a human scale.

## ■ Walk-throughs

Sometimes realistic textures combined with photographic montages in 2D are not enough for some clients who wish to experience a real physical presence of the proposed building and how you can move around the spaces that are envisaged. In these cases, animated sequences as seen from a person walking through the property, known as walk-throughs, are ideal. A good example of an architectural walk-through is given in the following Activity based on the famous 'Falling Water' house in America.

## Theory into practice

Watch the walk-through clip that was produced of the famous Kaufmann House 'Falling Water' that was designed by the American architect Frank Lloyd-Wright in Pennsylvania:

digitalurban.blogspot.com/2006/08/frank-lloyd-wright-architectual.html

As you follow the walk-through, list all the different surface textures that have been created.

Identify at least three other techniques used to create a very realistic presentation.

# Management of CAD drawings

In the previous section on equipment needed for CAD work we looked at the hardware requirements for three different CAD systems based on where the drawing/model information was held and they were:

- the stand-alone private domain – typically a sole designer who uses CAD more as a drafting aid than a design tool
- the small office project domain
- the collaborative team public domain.

The second two types of corporate CAD user relate mainly to larger companies with project and public domain systems where there is facility for electronic management and communication. These methods are explored in more detail below.

### CAD file systems – DWG/DXF/DWF formats

There are many software companies that produce CAD programs. However, currently the three major CAD systems used for construction are Autodesk's AutoCAD, Bentley's Microstation and Graphisoft's ArchiCAD, and the CAD drawing files used by these companies come in different formats. The leading CAD file format is Autodesk's '.DWG' (DraWinG) file system. Microstation

uses '.DGN' (DesiGN file) types but can also read and write a variety of other formats including '.DWG'. ArchiCAD uses a slightly different system which stores information in a drawing database depending if it is a 2D or 3D model as '.2DX' or '.3DX', but it can import and read '.DWG' files as well.

Another common file format is the '.DXF' (Drawing Exchange Format) file which was originally developed by Autodesk to enable their competitors to import AutoCAD files. However, as CAD programs in general have become more powerful, this format has waned, and many commercial CAD software developers have chosen to support DWG as their primary drawing format for CAD data. Autodesk also offers its DWG read/write technology for licence, in a developer toolkit called 'RealDWG'.

The '.DWF' (Design Web Format) format is the latest file format system that allows electronic drawing information to be accessed by anyone who needs to view, review, or print files of CAD information, without the need for having the specific CAD software. It is particularly beneficial for uploading onto an Internet server where many different organisations need to access information quickly and efficiently.

### Workflow, tracking and reporting

Until about 10–15 years ago, most design companies when issuing drawings for consultation would produce hard copy prints, which would be sent by post, arrive a couple of days later, be marked up by hand showing the required amendments, and then posted back to the design company which received the amended drawings about a week after it initially sent them out. The designer would then revise their original drawing and re-issue it … and the process would start again!

Throughout this process, the designer had to keep on file the drawing issue slips which stated what drawings were sent, their current revision number and who it was sent to, and perhaps a plea to get the revisions looked at as quickly as possible!

It didn't get a lot better when email started to be used to attach drawing files. Time was saved through no longer having to rely on the post, but there was still the problem of how to mark up amendments and return them, probably resulting in posting back the marked up hard copy drawing – that is, assuming that the recipient had the same version of CAD that the designer had, to enable them to open the attached file in the first place. Furthermore, this process was probably monitored by an *ad hoc* inspection of the designer's 'Sent Items' to see what they had requested and when they wanted it done by. If there were more than one or two people in the office working on the same project, then error or duplication of work was highly probable.

This is just a small insight into the problems of tracking and monitoring work. Over the last five years, running parallel to the development of the various CAD packages, there has been the development of powerful CAD management software. This has been necessary because of the increasing speed with which drawings can be altered, amended and issued via increasingly powerful drafting/modelling software and Internet communication. For example, a typical information management software application enables all the latest CAD drawings to be uploaded or published in a DWF format onto a third-party Internet server.

Then if a revision is made by someone in the design team or a drawing is **red lined**, the coordinator of the project can receive an automatic email providing information of who, when and how data was taken and changed. This can work not only within the design company (working from different locations) but also with colleagues working on the project in other companies, for example the structural engineers can locate the current architect's floor plans to see if there is clash in their steel column layout. Also, the customer or contractor can search or mine for the latest published drawings, specifications or details from the Internet server, and throughout this period the coordinator would be able to keep track of what changes are being made.

## Key Term

**Red lining** This indicates where CAD drawings have been marked up to show proposed or amended details, just as you would annotate manual drawing in red ink.

## Real time mark-up and reviews

All the major CAD software programs have systems which allow project data to be shared with remote colleagues and customers to review or amend details. Most programs utilise DWF Viewer and DWF Writer programs or similar, which are used like the commonly available Adobe™ Acrobat for text documents.

The '.DWF' file system is a major improvement in the communication of design and construction information. The main advantages of DWF files is that architects, engineers, project managers, or any of their colleagues can communicate design information without needing to have CAD software installed on their computer network, or knowing how to use CAD software. Using a DWF writer, anyone working on the project can view, review, comment on or print out the design drawings or information through a variety of standard wordprocessing, spreadsheet, presentation or web-browsing software.

Some software management systems also enable joint online design review meetings with a range of people dispersed throughout the country or indeed the world, where electronic drawings are discussed, marked up or red lined and reviewed in real-time.

## Sharing/security and back-up issues

Drawing information like any important data needs to be kept secure and safe. Some information will be

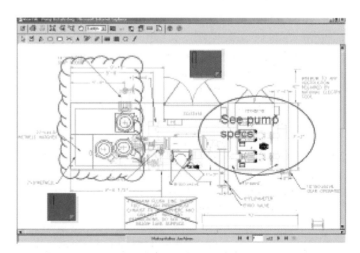

▲ **Figure 8.14 A red lined CAD drawing**

confidential to, say, the main directors of the project due to its sensitive nature, for example a contentious planning proposal. Where this is the case, it may be necessary to restrict access to certain files through a technique known as folder level permissions, that is, all files that are sensitive are kept in a digital folder which can only be accessed by certain people with the appropriate user permissions and passwords. Furthermore, the system creates a log of all actions and the name of the persons who carried them out.

A further security measure would be where the system detects when files are checked out and checked back. This importantly prevents two users revising the same document at the same time and protects old revisions

overwriting newer revisions – similar to 'Read-Only' files in Microsoft Office.

Another security issue is the distribution and licences for a given software product. Within companies with a 'project domain' set-up, the licensing software is held on the local server. This licensing software is registered and authorised at the time of purchase. For the company with a 'public domain' set-up, the server is located at the software company's own web-based servers, and it controls the licences directly.

As with all electronic data systems, making regular back-up copies of files is essential. If there were to be a fire, flood or other catastrophe where the server became damaged, then thousands of hours of work

## Case study

The British Airport Authority (BAA) Terminal 5 (T5) at Heathrow is a major architectural and civil engineering project worth more than £4 billion and is due to open in March 2008. The main terminal building, crowned by a distinctive waveform roof, is set to be one of the largest single-span structures in the UK with a span of over 150 metres. It was conceived by the Richard Rogers Partnership together with a fully integrated design and development team of nearly 30 individual design consultants and is currently being built with Laing O'Rourke as the principal contractor.

At the start of the project BAA set itself a target to reduce the cost and programme risks by carrying out the design and development of the project fully utilising the benefits of the Single Model Environment. BAA approached a company called Asite to develop a comprehensive CAD management tool. Part of the solution was to provide a platform to create a single graphical, spatial model that covered the full extent of the programme and was divided into model files. All plans, elevations as well as sections, where possible, were spatially located and orientated relative to the global origin and ordnance datum.

This model, with data organised in both 2D and 3D space, enabled design coordination to be carried out

between disciplines on and between each floor level. One example was the ability for the services engineers to ensure that the vertical drops of the services were fully coordinated. The processes allowed for the data to flow through the design and production/manufacturing processes such that the resultant program model resembled the final virtual construction model.

At one stage, there were 473 CAD document users working on the design SME producing 85,945 CAD drawings, 16,124 2D model files and 12,335 3D model files.

Carry out some Internet research into the BAA T5 Project at Heathrow to find out:

a  the names of the key design and contracting companies

b  the range of different application software used on the project. (*Hint*: see website article at www. excitech.co.uk/DPJ/articles.asp?Art_id=245)

c  the estimated cost savings that this Single Model Environment would achieve for the T5 Project. (*Hint*: see Asite's website detailing the collaborative work undertaken with BAA, which can be found at www. asite.com/casestudies.shtml) may be lost with serious consequences for all current projects. Companies with project domains should back up their local server at least once a week, usually onto a separate removable hard drive which is then kept safe at a separate location. For companies who subscribe to a public domain extranet, then that subscription should include back-up routines as standard and appropriate insurances, although it is always wise to undertake a manual back-up by downloading your current projects onto a separate local server at your own offices.

## Assessment practice

Contact a local design practice that uses CAD as part of its design and production processes. Conduct a structured interview with the company's CAD manager or a senior partner and undertake the following:

**a** Identify and describe the CAD systems that they use and the formats of their drawing files.

**b** Describe the organisational and management factors that led them to choose this system. **P2 P3**

Identify a list of features which good drawing systems should possess.

Using the above list as a starting point, prepare a report which compares the use of a CAD system in comparison to manual systems. Clearly state the advantages of where each system could be successfully used, and arrive at a reasoned conclusion. **M1**

# Drawings and details

## Planning and surveying drawings

At these early stages of the design process, a great deal of information has to be researched to confirm if the proposed building will be technically, functionally and financially feasible. Drawings are sought of the existing site and buildings from historical drawings, reports and records; and also from measurements carried out onsite.

This involves carrying out a detailed survey of the layout and levels of the site. A plan of the site is then produced showing the physical positions of existing site features – this is called the site survey drawing.

Figure 8.15 shows a typical site survey drawing for a medium size building plot. It shows existing boundaries, trees and buildings. It also shows spot heights as crosses which indicate the slope of the land. Although the drawing is produced to scale, overall dimensions are also included.

## Design drawings

In consultation with the client during the outline and scheme design stages, the building designer uses preliminary sketches to develop design ideas and help the client to understand the proposals and contribute to the design. These drawings are by their very nature sketches and unrefined but provide sufficient visual and dimensional information to appreciate the proposal.

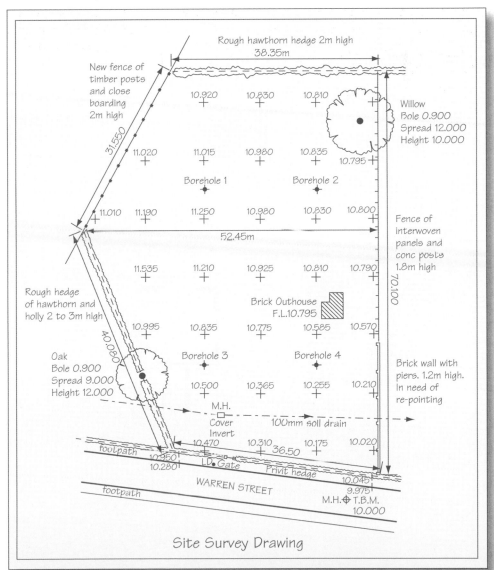

**Figure 8.15 A site survey drawing** ▶

▲ **Figure 8.16 A free-hand design sketch for a bungalow**

A typical example of a free-hand design sketch (for a proposed bungalow) is shown in Figure 8.16. This enables both the designer and client to explore possible elevations and window/door positions, including the massing, symmetry and scale of the building.

There are a number of intermediate stages in the design process, for example architects follow the RIBA Plan of Work which details a number of evolving design stages (see Unit 5 Construction technology and design in construction and civil engineering). It is during these stages that the design is refined and filtered according to the needs and demands of not only the client, such as a particular requirement for the type of finishes they would like, but also other design team specialists such as structural or building service engineers.

At these early design stages, it is prudent to consult with the local authority planning department to check what its preferences and constraints for the project might be. This can be done informally meeting with the local planner or formally through making an initial 'outline'

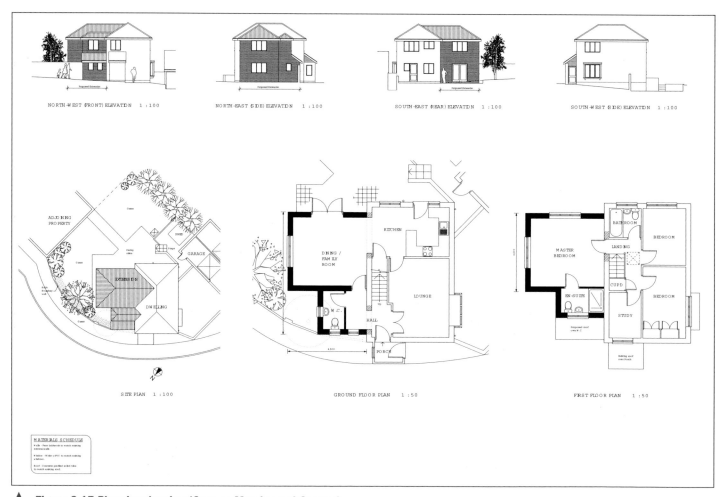

▲ **Figure 8.17 Planning drawing (Source: Munday and Cramer)**

planning permission application. However, before the scheme can proceed it must acquire full approval from the local authority through consultation with both the planning and building control departments. The local authority has the responsibility to ensure that all the requirements of the various Town and Country Planning Regulations and Building Regulations are being followed (see Unit 6 Building Technology in Construction).

Typical views provided for a planning permission application include an Ordnance Survey tracing of the area, a site plan and proposed elevations. The information typically provided includes the setting out dimensions of the proposed building, surface finishes, positions of external doors/windows and any permanent vehicular access that is required.

Figure 8.17 contains the proposed plans and elevations for a two-storey side extension to accommodate a dining room and toilet on the ground floor, and a master bedroom and ensuite on the first floor.

During the final stages of the design process when the technical issues are being resolved, the drawings are checked for compliance with building regulations by the local building control inspector. They require far more detailed information to check for compliance than the planners required. For example, sufficient information needs to be provided to show the provision for thermal or sound insulation, the dimensional layout required for disabled access or the minimum headroom requirements for staircases.

## Production drawings

Once the final design details are resolved and agreed between the design team, the local authority and the client, the production stage drawings can commence.

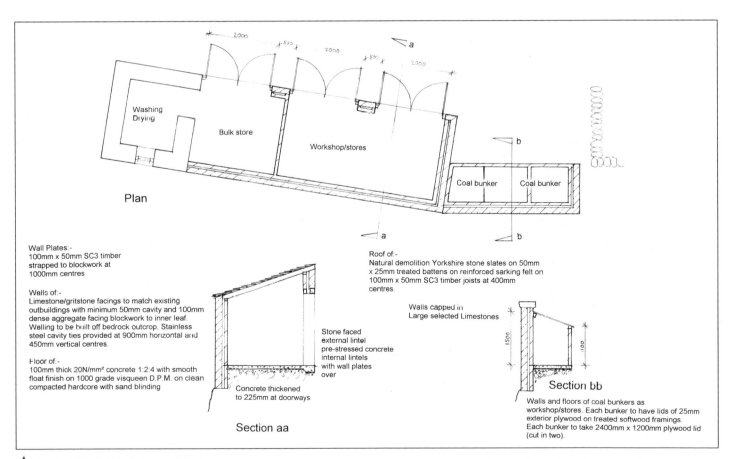

▲ **Figure 8.18 Simple GA drawing**

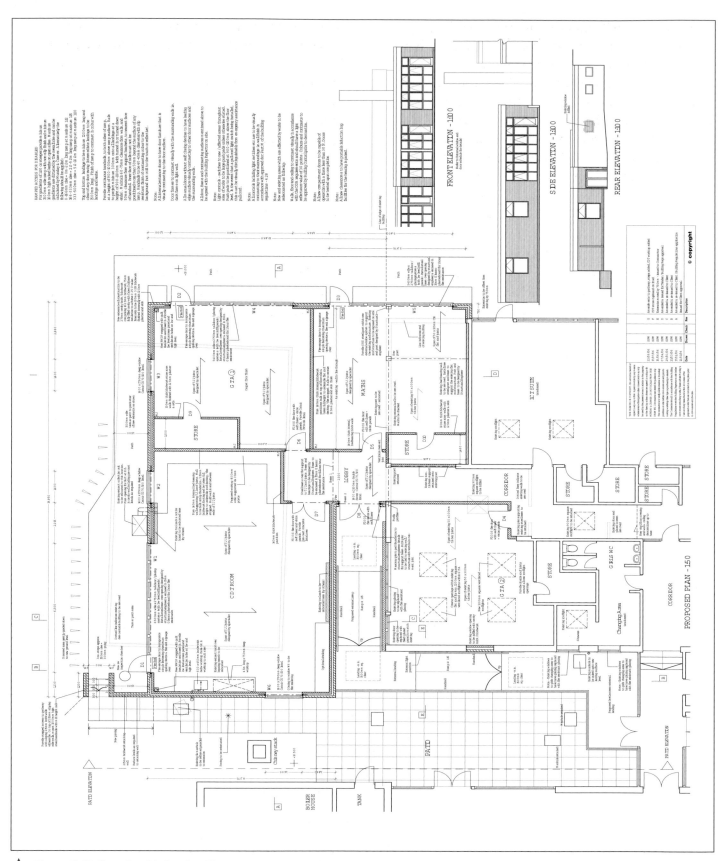

▲ Figure 8.19 Complex GA drawing (Source: Munday and Cramer)

These drawings will ultimately form the 'working drawings' and contain the detailed information of how the building will be constructed in terms of the quality of materials, the type of fixings and the workmanship requirements. The drawings are structured working from the 'whole to the part', where in this case the drawings firstly provide an overview of the project (its location, layout, overall size, and general form of construction), then show a detailed breakdown of the project via larger more detailed scale drawings that zoom in on specific areas like the construction of walls, floor and roofs, etc.

The drawings that provide the overview are called location drawings or general arrangement drawings (often abbreviated to GA). These show the relative positions of the proposed works and may also include written specifications. An example of a GA for the construction of a workshop and storage building is shown in Figure 8.18. In this case, because the project is relatively simple, the specification for the materials and construction is supplied on the drawing itself.

When drawings become more complex it is difficult to put a great deal of written text on the drawing without causing it to be too cramped and difficult to read. It can also lead to duplication and errors. In the example in Figure 8.19 involving various extension and alterations to a school complex the annotation is kept to a minimum with separate drawings for the sectional elevations and enlarged details.

The many specialist members of the design team also may produce their own drawings which show their

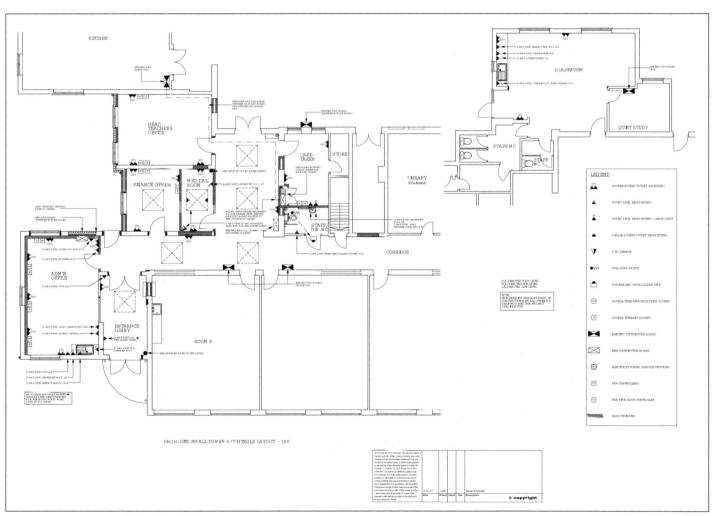

▲ **Figure 8.20 A building service drawing (Source: Munday and Cramer)**

contribution to the project. The structural engineer may include plans and cross-sections of the foundations such as the piling layout or location information about the structural steel framework. While the building services engineer will want to show the positions, fixings and materials needed for the various building services fittings and these too form part of the 'working drawings'.

Figure 8.20 shows part of the layout and positioning of the power and control units to be installed. Note the use of clear symbols and a legend to identify all the different controls.

Where there is more detailed information about components and their installation or fixing methods, these are often shown on a larger scale drawing called a detail or assembly drawing. The larger scale facilitates a clearer view of more complicated parts of the project and how they fit together. Depending on the element being drawn, ideally a good detail drawing should clearly show:

- shape and geometry
- position and orientation
- dimensions.

It may also include specification information such as fixings, materials to be used and manufacturer's references, or these may be included in a separate specification – see later in this chapter.

The working drawing details taken through an end external wall showing the foundation and wall/window details are shown in Figure 8.21.

Similarly for civil engineering projects, various detail drawings are produced which identify, for example, the construction layout and the position of steel reinforcement. In the following example regarding a raised walkway platform, Figure 8.22 shows the general setting out details that the formwork contractor would use to construct the overall shape of the walkway, while Figure 8.23 identifies to a larger scale the exact type of steel reinforcement and where it should be positioned by the steel fixer. Note that numbers shown refer to a coded bar reference which would be used in the steel bar bending schedule.

## Component drawings

The largest scale drawing is the component drawing (1:5, 1:2 or 1:1). This enables the fabrication of complicated bespoke offsite or onsite elements such as steel beams, stair flights, sash windows or built-in furniture. These drawings are often used in conjunction with a materials lists, bolt lists or cutting list which are essentially tables of exact lengths and sizes of the sections and the jointing/connection treatment required for each section.

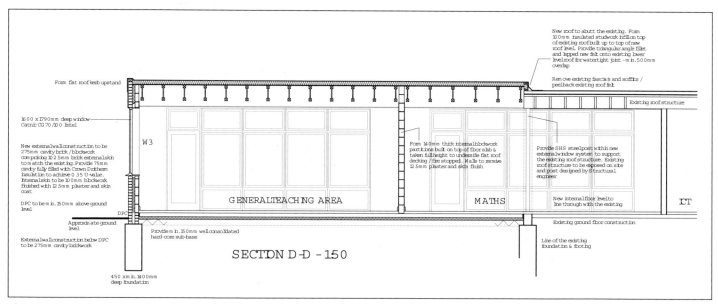

▲ Figure 8.21 A sectional drawing of wall/window details (Source: Munday and Cramer)

BTEC National | Construction

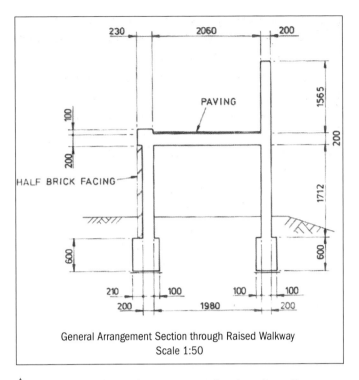

General Arrangement Section through Raised Walkway
Scale 1:50

▲ **Figure 8.22 General arrangement drawing of a walkway**

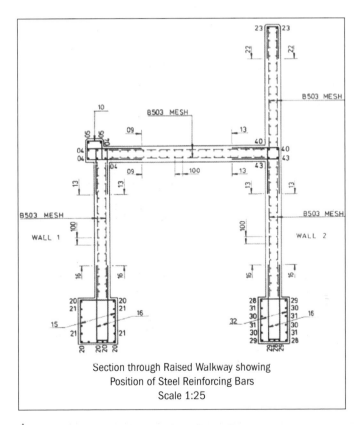

Section through Raised Walkway showing
Position of Steel Reinforcing Bars
Scale 1:25

▲ **Figure 8.23 Detailed section of a walkway**

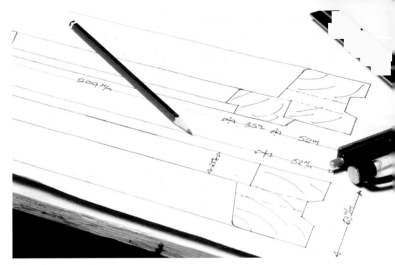

▲ **Equipment required for manual detailing**

| Timber cutting list | | | | | | |
|---|---|---|---|---|---|---|
| **Job description:** Two panel door | | | **Date:** 8 Sept 2006 | | | |
| Quantity | Description | Material | Length | Width | Thickness | Remarks |
| 2 | Stiles | S wood | 1981 | 95 | 45 | Mortise/groove for panel |
| 1 | Mid rail | " | 760 | 195 | 45 | Tenon/groove for panel |
| 1 | Btm rail | " | 760 | 195 | 45 | Tenon/groove for panel |
| 1 | Top rail | " | 760 | 95 | 45 | Tenon/groove for panel |
| 1 | Panel | Plywood | 760 | 590 | 12 | |
| 1 | Panel | " | 600 | 590 | 12 | |
| | | | | | | |
| | | | | | | |

▲ **Figure 8.24 Timber cutting list**

The photo above shows an example of a component drawing or 'rod' in the process of being drawn up to fabricate a timber window frame, together with its cutting list which gives the lengths and cross-sectional sizes of timber required to make up the parts of timber window.

## Key Term

**Timber joints** The method whereby pieces of timber are joined together by cut joints such as mortice and tenon or dovetail joints.

# Schedules

## Component schedules

Where a set of components is mostly the same but in detail have minor variations, component schedule or just schedule is used. This is the most efficient method of providing this type of information.

A good example of the use of schedules is the specification of doors. These can be specified for internal or for external use, they may be flush or panelled, large or small, made of timber or some other material, pre-finished or they may need to be painted or varnished. Add to this the different glazing possibilities and the various ironmongery variations of different locks, hinges and handles and it can be seen that there are many permutations possible. The best way to specify this information is using a door schedule which is a tabular form of collating information.

A typical door schedule is shown in Figure 8.25 where all the minor variations regarding size, finish, fixing, etc. are clearly tabulated. In addition, each component has a unique reference which is also cross-referenced to the appropriate location plan.

SITE: Cedar Hall School Hart Road Thundersley Benfleet Essex

| WINDOW / DOOR NO. | PLAN VIEW | DOOR TYPE | DESCRIPTION | SIZE | IRONMONGERY | | DOOR CLOSER | COMMENTS |
|---|---|---|---|---|---|---|---|---|
| D1, D2, D3 | | | Refer to external window and door schedule for D1, D2 & D3 combined with window screens (smart systems) | | Furniture | N/A | | Refer to drawing number - D745/15 |
| | | | | | Locks | N/A | | |
| | | | | | Butts | N/A | | |
| | | | | | Kick plate | N/A | | |
| D4 D5 D6 | | | FD30 solid core door. Intumescent strips, smoke seals & acoustic seals. Plywood veneered to both faces. Doors finished on all edges with 5mm plywood lippings. FD30 Vision Panels. | 926mm wide x 2040mm x 44mm thick. (min. 800mm clear opening req.) | Furniture | Levers - Albro 316 19mm satin stainless steel safety levers and plate (pair) | GEZE TS 4000 DA | Check & match existing locks on site to allow keys to be suited to master key. 6mm pyroshield clear vision panels with intumescent glazing material and screwed beads. Door ironmongery available from ironmongery direct (Tel. 0845 450 0020 |
| | | | | | Locks | ASSA Union sash lock to match existing keyed cylinder with keys both sides | | |
| | | | | | Butts | 1 & 1/2 pair heavy duty SAA ballrace hinges per leaf door | | |
| | | | | | Kick plate | 150mm high SAA to both sides | | |
| D7 | | | FD30 solid core double rebated doors. Intumescent strips, smoke seals & acoustic seals. Plywood veneered to both faces. Doors lipped on all edges with 5mm plywood lippings. FD30 vision panels. | 1500mm wide x 2040mm high x 44mm thick Leading leaf to be 948mm wide (Rebated door leaf) | Furniture | Levers - Albro 316 19mm Satin Stainless Steel safety levers & plate (pair) Flush bolts to small leaf top & bottom | GEZE TS 4000 DA | Check & match existing locks on site to allow keys to be suited to master key. 6mm pyroshield clear vision panels with intumescent glazing material and screwed beads. Door ironmongery available from ironmongery direct (Tel. 0845 450 0020 |
| | | | | | Locks | ASSA Union rebated sash lock set to match existing keyed cylinder with keys both sides | | |
| | | | | | Butts | 1 & 1/2 pair heavy duty SAA ballrace hinges per door leaf | | |
| | | | | | Kick plate | 150mm high SAA to both sides of both doors | | |
| D8 | | | Refer to external window & door schedule for details of door. (Smart systems) | | Furniture | N/A | | Refer to drawing number - D745/15 |
| | | | | | Locks | N/A | | |
| | | | | | Butts | N/A | | |
| | | | | | Kick plate | N/A | | |
| D9 D10 D11 | | | Cupboard doors - FD30 solid core door. Plywood veneered to both faces. Doors lipped on all edges with 5mm plywood lippings | 838mm wide x 2040mm x 44mm thick. | Furniture | Satin stainless steel ball knob set on rose and round rope for lock | None | Check & match existing locks on site to allow keys to be suited to master key. 6mm pyroshield clear vision panels with intumescent glazing material and screwed beads. Door ironmongery available from ironmongery direct (Tel. 0845 450 0020 Also 'Fire Door Keep Shut' sign |
| | | | | | Locks | ASSA/Union deadlock. Keyed cylinder with key to one side only | | |
| | | | | | Butts | 1 & 1/2 pair heavy duty SAA ballrace hinges per door leaf. | | |
| | | | | | Kick plate | 150mm high SAA to both sides | | |

▲ Figure 8.25 A door schedule (Source: Munday and Cramer)

Other components which readily utilise schedules for providing building production information are bar bending schedules which specify the exact length and shape of individual steel reinforcing bars for reinforced in situ concrete construction. An example of a simple bar bending schedule for a series of six identical ground beams is given in Figure 8.26. Note that there are only seven different types of bar in each beam and that each has its exact diameter and steel grade noted. For example, bar mark 03 is 'T25' which means high yield steel (T) with a diameter of 25 mm. Its length is 2400 mm long and it is a straight bar as '20' is its code. A 'U' shaped bar has a 38 code and an overlapping link is a shape code 61.

Similarly, steel-framed buildings constructed from individual universal beam and column steel sections have their own set of tabulated schedules and component drawings for fabrication purposes, such as steel section 'Materials lists' and steel 'Bolt Lists'.

### Remember!

For more information on the scheduling of reinforcement, refer to BS 8666:2005 'Scheduling, dimensioning, bending and cutting of steel reinforcement for concrete'.

| Company Name: | *Bestend Consultants plc* | Bar Schedule Reference: | *8/ 1289* | | |
|---|---|---|---|---|---|
| Job Reference: | *1298/07* | Date Prepared: | *12/03/07* | Date revised: - | |
| Job Title: | *Express Foodmarket, Kings Lynn.* | Prepared By: | *mjh* | Checked By: | *jfs* |

| Member | Bar Mark | Type & Size | No. of Members | No. of Bars in Each | Total No. | Length of Each Bar | Shape Code | A | B | C | D | E/R |
|---|---|---|---|---|---|---|---|---|---|---|---|---|
| *Ground Beams* | *01* | *T20* | *6* | *2* | *12* | *7600* | *20* | | | | | |
| *On Gridlines* | *02* | *T20* | *6* | *2* | *12* | *5400* | *20* | | | | | |
| *A to F* | *03* | *T25* | *6* | *2* | *12* | *2400* | *20* | | | | | |
| | *04* | *T25* | *6* | *3* | *18* | *5600* | *20* | | | | | |
| | *05* | *T20* | *6* | *3* | *18* | *3125* | *99* | *1450* | *400* | | | *125* |
| | *06* | *T20* | *6* | *2* | *12* | *2875* | *38* | *1300* | *425* | | | |
| | *07* | *R12* | *6* | *37* | *222* | *1550* | *61* | *450* | *250* | | | |
| | | | | | | | | | | | | |
| | | | | | | | | | | | | |
| | | | | | | | | | | | | |
| | | | | | | | | | | | | |

▲ **Figure 8.26 A reinforced concrete bar bending schedule for a ground beam**

The written specification, together with drawn details or assembly drawings, should define the quality of the construction systems, products, workmanship and finished work such that:

- the designer's (and client's) detailed requirements will be met
- the contractor (when quoting for the project) can estimate the costs with certainty and accuracy
- the contractor (when managing the project) can plan, execute and supervise the work in an efficient and controlled manner
- the manufacturer's products can be ordered correctly and in good time
- within the design and construction team misunderstandings and unintended variations are minimised.

Therefore, a good specification should be specific to the project, with no irrelevant material and cover every significant aspect of quality to an appropriate level of detail. It should be technically correct and up to date and reflect current good building practice and legal requirements. It should be well coordinated with the drawings and not conflict or have irregularities with other contract documents. Examples of typical specifications that would be placed on a drawing or in a separate specification document are given in the next section.

## ■ The procurement of the contractor and the works onsite

These specifications and drawings together with the bill of quantities form the bulk of the production information documents, and under traditional rules of **procurement**, these are used to select the principal or main contractor. This information, stamped 'Issued for Tender', needs to be sufficiently detailed and specified to enable the contractors to tender fairly for the construction works.

Drawings may also be issued to specialist manufacturers known as nominated suppliers to supply designed components for the project. This information is in drawing or schedule format to help them prepare proposals for the design and installation of a particular element of the project, such as the internal metal partitioning systems or timber staircases. The information supplied would specify the layout and location required as well as details about the proposed materials or possible fixing points for the particular element. It is important to note, however, that this information may be unsuitable to build from.

All these contract documents form the basis of the legal agreement between the client and the selected contractor and are referred to as 'Issued for Contract', particularly where there have been negotiated changes between the tender drawings and the contract drawings.

Drawn information and written specifications should be complementary and the relationship between the two should be kept simple and clear.

The drawings and specification provide the contractor with documentation to build from. These are commonly referred to as the 'working details/drawings' but does not necessarily mean that no changes will occur in the future. The designer or the client may want to make changes to the original design, in which case, the drawings are amended and a revision reference appended to the drawing number. It is vitally important that at all times the contractor is working to the latest set of drawings to avoid any possibility for error.

## Key Term

**Procurement** The process of finding and acquiring the expertise, labour, plant and materials resources needed to build a construction project.

## Assessment practice

Contact the same design practice as previously contacted in the last section and ask if you may borrow a selection of drawings based on those previously described above. Alternatively, your college may hold a selection of current graphical information drawings, specifications and schedules that you could use.

Review the drawings and comment on whether the standard detailing conventions have been met under the following headings:

- Title block information provided
- Selection of views and scales used
- Range of line thickness/hatchings used
- Clarity of printing and labelling
- Specification uses
- Coordinated project references
- Cross-referencing between other documents

As part of your written response, take appropriate copies of parts of the drawings studied and clearly label them with your findings. **P4**

Using the drawings and schedules from **P4**, describe in words the proposed works. Clearly explain what you understand about the technical issues contained within the drawing and specification. Select one cross-sectional detail and using the National Building Specification or similar provide an alternative specification. Justify your choices. **M2**

Describe how errors in graphical information, and mistakes in how it is managed, can lead to problems during construction. Comment on where responsibilities lie and evaluate how these issues can be resolved. **D1**

# Graphical drawings and details

## How do you set up the drawing?

On larger projects, the titling and numbering of a set of drawings has a big influence on how easy it is to locate and retrieve construction information. In general, the larger and more complex the project, the more important is the titling and numbering of the production drawings. On smaller projects with up to, say, 15 drawings, this is far less important, particularly if the titles of the drawings are specific and clear and include cross-referencing from general arrangement drawings to details drawings or cross-sections.

The first thing to do when starting a manual drawing is to tape your drawing paper or film onto your parallel motion drawing board with masking tape. A border is drawn around the paper using your set square and parallel motion slider. The width of the border should be 10 mm. Then you need to construct the title block and notes section, which is drawn usually to the right-hand side of the drawing (see Figure 8.27). Typical dimensions for the title block contents and layout are given in EN ISO 9431:1999 'Construction drawings – spaces for drawing and for text, and title blocks on drawings sheets' and summarised below.

The information contained within the title block and notes is described as follows:

- Explanations – this provides guidance in reading the drawing such as abbreviations used, or special symbols or the dimension units used. Conventionally all dimensions should be in millimetres unless stated otherwise.
- Instructions – this provides general information such as the drawing should not be scaled and it may also include instructions regarding the inspection of works by the architect, local authority or design engineer prior to them being covered up.

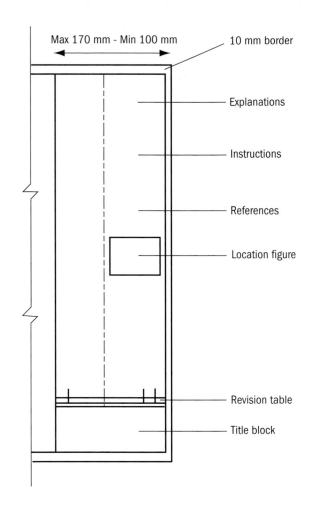

**Figure 8.27 Title block layout**

- References – in this section reference should be made to other relevant drawings, specifications and other documents.
- Location figure – this is a small 'key' plan to help identify the physical area that the drawing covers in comparison with the whole project. The location figure should be placed so that it remains visible after the drawing has been folded.
- Revision table – this part of the title block is used to record all revisions such as corrections and/or amendments following the issue of the drawing. The revision should clearly state the date and designation

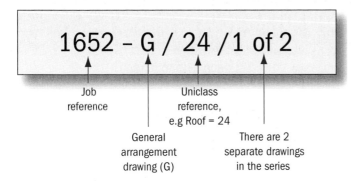

Job reference

General arrangement drawing (G)

Uniclass reference, e.g Roof = 24

There are 2 separate drawings in the series

▲ **Figure 8.28 The drawing reference number**

of the revision as indicated by an alphanumeric reference, e.g. 'A'. It should also describe briefly the details concerning the revision. It should also indicate who made the revision, with suitable initials.

- Title block – this should include separate boxes for the title of the drawing, the address of the project location, the client's name, the company logo panel. Details of the scales used and who drew the drawing should also be indicated.
- The drawing reference number – the drawing should be numbered as simply as possible to facilitate easy filing and retrieval. A typical example is shown in Figure 8.28.

Note: Assembly Drawing is denoted (A), Component Drawing is denoted (C)

The details of the drawing are entered on the Register of Drawings which is a record of the drawing title, numbers, issue dates and any revisions. A typical copy is shown in Figure 8.29.

## How do you choose the correct views and the right drawing scale?

Once the drawing border and title block information are in place, the scales of the drawing are selected. When planning what view to show you need to consider the purpose of the drawing and what information you want to show. The types of view have been covered earlier in this chapter (see page 00); the most common views used in construction are orthographic projections and cross-sections.

The next item to consider is how big each view will look on the final drawing and this is based on the scale that you choose. Typical scales for the various types of drawing are given in Table 8.6.

When you have decided on the scale and type of views to be included the various elements need to be set out on the paper or film. The different views need to sit in the drawing in a well-balanced way and allow for areas of specification text if they are to be included on the drawing.

In order to plan how the views will be set out, draw a rough sketch of your drawing sheet with the proposed

**DRAWING REGISTER AND ISSUE SHEET**

| Co. | | Project No. 02000 | Drawing No. Drgs 8/G/300 Series | Sheet No. 1 of 1 |
|---|---|---|---|---|

| Origination **Structural Engineer** |
|---|

| We enclose copies of the drawings etc listed below | Date of issue |

| Project Title **New Project Substructure** | Day | 05 | 23 | 30 | 05 | 13 | 04 | | | | | | | |
| | Month | 07 | 07 | 07 | 08 | 08 | 09 | | | | | | | |
| | Year | 06 | 06 | 06 | 06 | 06 | 06 | | | | | | | |

Date of receipt

| Received by | Day |
| | Month |
| | Year |

| Description | Ref No. | Ammendments |
|---|---|---|
| G.A. Foundations - sheet 1 of 2 | 301 | P1 | P2 | P3 | P4 | P5 | A |
| G.A. Foundations - sheet 2 of 2 | 302 | | P1 | P2 | P3 | P4 | A |
| G.A. Ground Floor - sheet 1 of 2 | 303 | P1 | P2 | P3 | P4 | P5 | A |
| G.A. Ground Floor - sheet 2 of 2 | 304 | | P1 | P2 | P3 | P4 | A |
| Foundation & Ground Floor Sections | 305 | | P1 | | P2 | P3 | A |

▲ **Figure 8.29 The Register of Drawings**

**Table 8.6 Typical drawing scales**

| Type of drawing | Purpose | Typical scales used |
|---|---|---|
| Site location plans | A map to show the location of the site | 1:2500, 1:1250, 1:1000 |
| Layout of block plans | A plan showing the proposal in relation to the boundaries of the site | 1:500, 1:200, 1:100 |
| General arrangement (location) drawings | Plans, elevations, perspectives and cross-sections to show the relative position of construction elements | 1:100, 1:50 |
| Assembly/Detail drawings | Plans and cross-sections of individual parts of the building showing detailed construction information | 1:20, 1:10 |
| Component drawings | Large scale plans and views showing fabrication information of construction components | 1:5, 1:2 |

views shown as control boxes, which are rectangles which enclose the proposed views – see the example in Figure 8.30.

If you are going to use a scale of 1:50, then measure the overall width and height of the drawing area to a scale of 1:50. Then knowing the widths and heights of the control box, you can add these up in any direction to get the total. This is then subtracted from the overall width and height of the drawing area to give the total amount of free space available; this can then be divided by two or three depending on how many equal spaces are required as shown on the sketch in Figure 8.30.

The control boxes can be pencilled in on the paper to give you a starting point for each individual view, be it the plan, elevation or section.

When drawing a 'plan view' it is conventional that the height at which the horizontal cross-section is taken is at 1.2 m above the finished floor level. In this way, all the main doors and window positions will be picked up together with the positions of staircases and partitions. When selecting where to take a suitable 'cross-sectional view' through a building it is important to select a position that shows the most typical cross-section which applies to the majority of the proposed new work. It is important that plan views and cross-sectional views are connected by the correct use of titles and section marks.

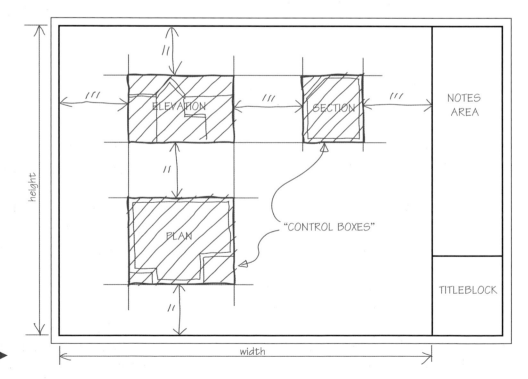

**Figure 8.30 Setting out sketch** ▶

## Remember!

Always draw to scale as accurately as is possible. Even though contractors should never scale from the drawings, it will give you confidence that you are working accurately and with precision. In this way, you can always double-check as the design is progressing that your calculated dimensions are the same as your scaled dimensions.

## What should the drawings contain?

Each project will have different needs and objectives, but all projects will have a high technical content that will rely heavily on your understanding of construction technology and processes. It is therefore essential that you are confident in your construction technology knowledge and understanding, as this is ultimately what you are trying to communicate to the reader.

As a guide, here are examples of indicative content of various types of construction drawing. The list is not exhaustive but provides help in knowing the scope of detail that you need to know and ought to include:

### ■ General

A sequential order of drawings, detail sheets and schedules linked to an itemised register of drawings.

Drawing notes and specifications that provide an appropriate level of information tailored to the audience/reader of the drawing.

Ensure that all work complies with appropriate British Standard, Euro-codes, Building Regulations and Town and Country Planning Regulations.

Use standard abbreviations, hatching patterns and symbols.

Ensure that dimension lines and dimension text are clear and there is agreement between separate and overall dimension.

Title blocks should be complete with correct information and scales shown.

Doors, windows and other fixtures, etc. referenced to relevant schedules.

All work is checked by a second person to avoid errors prior to issuing.

### ■ Presentational sketches/details

Presentational sketches can help the client fully appreciate the proposed design. There are a number of options open to the designer that have been briefly mentioned earlier in this chapter. These can be produced free-hand to aid creativity, or in a hard line technical format. The most common projections are:

- Isometric – good for showing a 3D aerial type view which looks down onto the building, but because of the rigid box into which the object is placed it appears unnatural as it has no convergent lines of perspective.
- Axonometric – this is good for showing an aerial view of an object but from a higher viewing point than the isometric projection. Very useful for showing internal fitting out to kitchens and retail areas as the projection is based on a true plan shape.
- Perspectives – the most complicated to do but often produces the most realistic and natural view with all lines converging to points on the horizon.

### ■ Block plan/layout plan

Ordnance Survey map view/references provided to locate site.

North point clearly shown.

Vegetation/trees to be removed/retained.

Vehicular access and sight splays dimensioned.

Setting out dimensions of all new work clearly referenced to identifiable existing features, e.g. rear kerb line/existing building line.

Site datum clearly identified together with all site levels to be achieved, retaining wall positions.

New drainage layout for soil, waste and storm water including location of inspection chambers/soakaways if applicable. Invert levels and cover levels of inspection chambers also shown. Location and levels of public sewers.

Details of the proposed external works, e.g. identify accurately areas of hard/soft landscaping/planting areas and boundary constructions.

## ■ External elevations

Site slope in relation to proposed development.

Levels of floors, windows, roofs and other features.

Type of external treatment or finish to walls and roof.

Position and size of windows and types of openings, position and type of doors.

Retaining wall profiles, boundary wall heights and positions of movement joints.

Heights of adjacent existing properties/trees.

## ■ Building plans: general arrangements/location plans

Plans are orientated to block plan with entrances/front of building clearly indicated.

Grids are shown on centre lines of structural frames, with numerical/alphabetic grid references.

Foundation sizes and layout clearly set out about centre-lines of superstructural elements/grids.

Wall construction is correctly hatched with cavities closed at reveals and damp proof membranes/insulation shown, etc.

Door and window positions set out, with door swings shown as arcs.

Direction of stairs indicated by an up or down arrow, numbering of risers. Balustrades/railings identified. Direction of ramps and gradient stated.

Position of services, including:

– gas, electric and cold water intakes

– all service metering devices

– sanitary fittings to be plumbed

– electrical consumer unit, luminaries, light switches, power sockets, kitchen appliances and smoke detectors

– heating appliances such as boilers/flues and radiators, also location of hot and cold water tanks

– soil and vent position and associated above ground drainage runs

– telecommunications/optical cabling sockets.

Finished and structural floor levels referenced to site datum. Direction of floor spans if suspended, positions of lateral restraint straps and strutting (first floor). Trimming details around staircase. Floor finishes specified.

Roof plans should show direction of falls for flat roofs. Position of outfalls, gutters and rainwater downpipes (rwp). Direction of span of roof trusses, lateral and diagonal bracing. Water tank supports, roof lights and loft hatch positions noted. Type of roof covering noted.

## ■ Sectional elevations/detail sections

Construction details of the proposed development with elements clearly cross-hatched to identify materials.

Smaller scales used for general arrangement purposes to show inter-relation between the different elements; larger scales to show construction details and specifications, e.g. position of ground floor slab and sub-base in relation to damp proof course (dpc) and insulation materials, etc.

Size and position of stepping of foundations on slopes.

Changes in floor levels, staircase/ramp cross-sections, balustrades/railings.

Long sections along the length of a proposed sewer and formation and pavement levels of a road gradient, both should use exaggerated vertical scales (see Chapter 10 Surveying in construction and civil engineering).

### Why is producing good linework and printing important?

All drawings must be clear to those who will read them. Some drawings may be complicated and so need to be made as simple as possible for the design team members, main contractor and subcontractors.

Various techniques are used to make views easier to understand and that is the use of different line thicknesses, hatching and shading. With ink pens on tracing paper or film, achieving the correct thickness is relatively easy providing you have a range of nib sizes, usually three from 0.25 up to 0.5, with 0.35 being the most used for text and general linework. However, with pencil on paper, this effect is more difficult and requires practice.

Thicker lines indicate primary information; for example, a cross-section where members that have been cut through are shown with a thicker outline than those that have not been cut but appear in the same view. Where views are titled, they are printed in thicker lines than the normal specification notes that are printed on the drawing. Section line markers should also be drawn with thicker lines so that they easily stand out from the rest of the view and can be located quickly. Thinner lines are not only used for shading or hatching but also for showing dimension lines as these should not obscure or detract from the main outlines of the physical parts of the constructed element.

# Written specification information

## Detailed specification notes

On large projects with many drawings produced by many people, inconsistencies may easily occur. Therefore, it is better to have drawings just identifying the elements of construction with brief labels and dimensions together with one definitive specification from which to source all the detailed information about the product/material and how it should be fixed. For these larger projects a full 'specification' is a separate written document that provides clear and concise requirements and describes exactly the quality of *materials* and *workmanship* to be used in the proposed work.

Each sentence in the specification is known as an individual clause, and should be concise and direct; using verbs to instruct the contractor/subcontractor such as 'excavate', 'pour', 'nail', etc. Essentially, each clause should be prefaced by the words 'The Contractor must' and it should state what is to be supplied and then what is to be done with it. The specification should also be supported by the relevant British Standard. For example, a specification for the fixing of natural roof slates:

> 'The Contractor shall fix natural slates to BS 680-2 with 3.35 mm shank copper clout nails to BS 1202-2 to sawn softwood battens to BS 5534-1. Moisture content at time of fixing of battens to be a maximum 20%. Setting out of battens to be to true lines and regular appearance, with neat edges, junctions and features. Ensure that gutters and pipes are kept free of debris and cleaned out at completion.'

## Schedule of work

On small to medium projects for both the estimating and management of the construction project, the primary documents are the **schedule of work** and the drawings. These complement each other to give an overall appreciation of the project, which includes notes about the location, materials and dimensions of the construction elements and assembly details.

## Key Term

**Schedule of work** A separate written contents list of the operations to be carried out for the job which includes a brief written specification, often called a reference specification, which describes the product/material to be fixed and how the fixing will be carried out.

For small jobs, such as a single house, where only a few drawings are needed to cover the whole project, then the written notes that form the specification may be printed on the drawing itself, provided that it is set out clearly and the notes do not obscure the drawing's individual plans, sections and elevation views.

The choice of whether to provide a full and separate specification, a schedule of work and drawings, or just drawings will vary from job to job, but it is important that the amount of information included is consistent and can be revised without causing discrepancies between documents. The design team needs to carefully consider the structure of the information at the earliest stages in the design process.

## Materials schedule

As seen in the previous section, a schedule is a way of presenting information where there are variations in size and specification for a certain element of construction, for example doors schedules, windows schedules, steel bending reinforcement schedules, steel column schedules and drainage schedules.

Typical column headings for some of these schedule formats are shown below:

1 Door Schedule
Reference/Size/Description/Frame/Threshold/Hanging/Lock and Latch/Handle/Other

2 Steel Bar Bending Schedule
Member/Bar Mark/Type and Size/No. of Members/

No. of bars in each/Total No. /Length of each Bar/Shape Code/A–E (individual measurements relating to shape code)

In this way, a great deal of information can be collated in an easy to handle table without unnecessary and confusing drawing work.

## Assessment practice

You are employed in a small, traditional architectural company and have been given the job of producing some of the architectural and construction drawings for a new residential site consisting of three townhouses designed by and sold for the Bestend Housing Association. The small site is located close to the town centre's popular high street with a road frontage of 18 metres and a depth of the plot of 20 metres. The building line is 2 metres from the rear of the front kerb.

The aim of the development is to create three twin-bedroom townhouses with the following features:

- Ground floor – integral garage, w.c., hallway, and access stairway to first floor
- First floor – kitchen/diner, living room with small balcony to rear
- Second floor – two bedrooms, bathroom and airing cupboard.

The site is to be built using traditional materials and techniques but still reflect contemporary design in its layout and internal features. There will be space for a small communal garden to the rear of the building.

Undertake research into the construction of the development using:

- examples of similar housing projects in your area
- construction technology and design notes
- British Standards/building regulations
- Identify a physical location for this site in your local town and locate it on a large scale Ordnance Survey map of the area.

Produce simple 2D and 3D graphical drawings using traditional manual drafting techniques by producing drawings for all those listed in Table 1.

**Table 1**

| Drg. | Graphical information to be produced | Purpose |
|---|---|---|
| 1 | Preliminary sketches | Free-hand sketches of development to show all floor layouts and overall massing of development and elevations |
| 2 | Site location plan | To locate site |
| 3 | Block plan | To orientate site and show setting out dimensions, access to rear garden and external works/landscaping |
| 4 | General arrangement plan at 1st or 2nd floor for one town house | To show layout of walls, doors, windows and fittings |
| 5 | Elevations of town house development building | To identify the materials and massing of the building |
| 6 | Typical cross-section drawing | To show an overview of one of the house's structure and construction details |
| 7 | 3D isometric view of whole townhouses development | To provide a visual 3D impression of the development |
| 8 | Wall details cross-section | To show wall, window and lintel constructions |

Produce in tabular form a window and door schedule for the development to identify the size, type, opening and ironmongery required for the houses, and a suitable specification for the timber first floor and staircase construction using the National Building Specification or similar. **P6**

In addition to the drawings produced in Table 1, you are to select and apply manual techniques and resources to produce complex graphical drawings as outlined in Table 2. **M3**

In order to achieve the distinction criteria, you must demonstrate a professional level of competence in the production of the drawings listed in Tables 1 and 2. Your work should show technical skill, neatness and accuracy, and include a full specification for drawings 10 and 11 using the CAWS/Uniclass coordinated project information. **D2**

**Table 2**

| Drg. | Graphical information to be produced | Purpose |
| --- | --- | --- |
| 9 | 3D scaled perspective view of whole townhouse development | To provide a realistic visual 3D impression of the development |
| 10 | Roof plan and cross-sectional details at eaves and verge | To show general roof structure, fixings, insulation, drainage and bracing |
| 11 | Foundation details | To show foundation and ground floor construction |
| 12 | Suitable 3D kitchen layout as an axonometric view | 3D view of fitted units in kitchen area |

# Preparation for assessment

Using a range of drawings obtained from your tutor or from any construction-related work experience that you have undertaken, write a brief account of each drawing identifying and describing the equipment and media used to produce the drawing and related information.　**P1**

Research the CAD systems that your college provides for student use on its IT computer systems together with any freeware CAD programmes available on the Internet.

**a** Identify and describe the types and formats of CAD information systems available.

**b** Identify the factors in the organisation and management of the CAD software on the system.　**P2** **P3**

Examine the drawings used in P1 and describe orally to your tutor how the standard detailing conventions shown have been met for the following parts of the drawing studied:

**a** Title block information provided

**b** Selection of views and scales used

**c** Range of line thickness/hatchings used

**d** Clarity of printing and labelling

**e** Uses coordinated project references

**f** Cross-referencing between other documents　**P4**

In order to prepare simple 2D and 3D graphical drawings using traditional manual drafting techniques, sketch out the layout of your ideal studio flat within a volume measuring 5 m wide by 5 m long by 5 m high. The walls are to be brick/block cavity with timber floor/flat roof. Make reasonable assumptions for any information not supplied.

Include a bathroom area, food/preparation area, sleeping area and lounge area.

From your design sketches produce the following labelled detail drawings at a scale of 1:50:

**a** Floor plan

**b** Front elevation

**c** Vertical cross-section

**d** Cross-section through a window sill and lintel

Set the drawings out clearly using the appropriate drawing conventions, title block and layout.　**P5**

Produce in tabular form a window and door schedule for the studio flat you sketched out in P5 using standard conventions.　**P6**

Look over the research undertaken in P1, P2 and P3, and compare the use of manual and CAD techniques in the production and presentation of graphical information. Clearly state the advantages of where each system could be successfully used.　**M1**

Using the drawings and schedules studied in P1, describe in words the proposed works. Clearly explain what you understand about the technical issues contained within the drawing and specification. Select three elements shown in the drawings, such as the roof covering or first floor structure, and using a product library or other technical resource, find and reproduce an alternative specification for each chosen element.　**M2**

Discuss with relevant examples the statement 'Badly drawn and set out drawings will result in badly constructed buildings'. Write your answer as an essay explaining the implications for both the designer and the contractor.　**D1**

You are to select and apply appropriate manual techniques and resources to produce the following complex graphical drawings for the studio flat in P5 and P6:

**a** A one-point scaled perspective view of the inside of the studio flat

**b** Suitable internal view of the kitchen units/area as an axonometric view

Your work should be of the highest quality demonstrating a professional level of competence and skill.　**M3** **D2**

## Grading tips

Manual and CAD techniques have different strengths and weaknesses. Give a balanced view and back up your case with specific examples of good practice. **M1**

Understanding the context of drawing information enables you to have a better grasp of the fundamental factors that need to be communicated in any project. Ensure that your work demonstrates this fact by appraising a range of information sources for their fitness of purpose. **M2**

Applying manual techniques and resources to produce complex graphical information will involve you producing a range of different projections and views. Plan the work carefully and show neat construction lines. You will be expected to demonstrate a sound knowledge and understanding of current drawing standards and conventions. **M3**

You need to explain how clarity, neatness, accuracy and consistency of drawings influences the quality of the completed project. Ensure that you make reference to examples of coordinated project information such as CAWS, Uniclass or CISfB systems. **D1**

You will need to produce drawings that would not look out of place in a professional office; therefore your preparation, planning and execution needs to be thorough and complete. Remember to check your work for errors, including spelling mistakes! **D2**

# Knowledge check

1 What type of pencil would be used for drawing dimension lines?

2 Describe how CAD drawings are reproduced.

3 What type of projection would be used to give a realistic 3D view of a building?

4 Explain why it is important to get the right balance between too much information and not enough information on a drawing.

5 Suggest for each of the following two companies the type of CAD system each would require:

   a A small architectural company employing two technicians whose main work involves small domestic and commercial buildings and extensions.

   b A large sized, multi-disciplinary design and development company with two regional offices, one in London the other in York.

6 Explain the difference between DXF and DWF file formats in CAD.

7 List five reasons why CAD can be more efficient at producing drawings than manual methods.

8 Describe the main security issues that need to be considered when using a CAD system.

9 What are the main purposes of the designer's preliminary sketches done at the early stages of a project?

10 Explain with examples the difference in content between general arrangement drawings and detail drawings.

11 What are the advantages of using a 'schedule' when specifying window components for a small housing development?

12 What is the function of the 'specification' notes?

13 Explain the use of the 'revisions' section in the title block of the drawing.

14 In the following cases state the typical drawing scales that would be used:

   a The block plan for a pair of detached houses.

   b The GA drawing for a proposed industrial unit that measures 15 m by 25 m.

   c A section through a standard trench fill foundation and floor slab.

15 List five construction features that would be shown on a plan view of a new retail shop building.

16 A proposed hotel complex will require the production of around 50 drawings in total. What would be the best way to organise the specification of the proposed works?

## Grading criteria: Unit 8

| To achieve a pass grade the evidence must show that the learner is able to: | To achieve a merit grade the evidence must show that, in addition to the pass criteria, the learner is able to: | To achieve a distinction grade the evidence must show that, in addition to the pass and merit criteria, the learner is able to: |
|---|---|---|
| **P1** identify and describe equipment and media used to produce manual and CAD drawings and information<br>**Assessment practice pages 329, 356** | | |
| **P2** identify and describe the types and formats of CAD information<br>**Assessment practice pages 336, 356** | **M1** compare the use of manual and CAD techniques in the production and presentation of graphical information<br>**Assessment practice pages 336, 356** | **D1** evaluate how the quality of graphical information relates to the quality of the final constructed project<br>**Assessment practice pages 347, 356** |
| **P3** identify and describe the main factors in the organisation and management of CAD information<br>**Assessment practice pages 347, 356** | | |
| **P4** identify and describe correct drawing standards, conventions, layouts and presentation techniques<br>**Assessment practice pages 347, 356** | **M2** extract and relate clear, accurate and valid information from a range of graphical sources, details and schedules<br>**Assessment practice pages 347, 356** | |
| **P5** produce simple 2D and 3D graphical drawings using traditional manual drafting techniques<br>**Assessment practice pages 354, 356** | **M3** select and apply manual techniques and resources to produce complex graphical information<br>**Assessment practice pages 355, 356** | **D2** demonstrate a professional level of technical skill, neatness and accuracy in the production of manual graphical information<br>**Assessment practice pages 355, 356** |
| **P6** produce graphical information in the form of simple specifications and schedules<br>**Assessment practice pages 355, 356** | | |

# Measuring, estimating and tendering processes in construction and the built environment

## Introduction

Measuring, estimating and tendering are an essential part of a construction company's business activities. The estimator is the first key person to become involved in pricing the tender for the client, using measurement to produce quantities, estimating to produce prices and the tendering procedure to submit their tender.

This unit looks at the processes associated with measurement, the purpose and processes of estimating, the production of costs estimates, cost modelling and, finally, the tendering procedure.

Measurement encompasses the physical act of using a tape measure or scale rule to produce a value that can be used to produce a meaningful quantity. Although it is also used in surveying and setting out, measurement is primarily used in the quantity surveyor's role in the construction process.

### How you will be assessed

This unit is internally assessed by your tutor. A variety of activities is included in this unit to help you understand all aspects of the measuring, estimating and tendering processes in the construction industry.

After completing this unit you should be able to achieve the following outcomes:

1. Be able to record dimensions and descriptions of construction work in a methodical way and process these into final quantities for varying purposes, e.g. bills of quantities, variations, final account, interim payments, claims, etc.

# Thinking points

Modern-day measurement is used to provide a clear set of rules that are applied to the process. These rules are listed within the *Standard Method of Measurement of Building Works Version 7* (SMM7) and provide a basis that is equal to everyone who adopts them so that a level playing field is presented to the principal contractors who are tendering for the work.

Think about the following key questions as you work through this chapter:

- What would happen if there was no rule book?
- If there was no standard for setting out tenders, how would the client faced with several different tenders select a suitable contractor? Would this be fair to the client?
- How can the client achieve a fair and reasonable price, and one that is within budget, for the project works?
- How does a client procure a contractor to undertake the project works? Remember, it has to be someone that can be trusted to complete the work on time and within budget.
- What tendering methods are available for different types of work?
- How does a client select the most appropriate method of tendering?

2  Understand the purpose of estimating and the common techniques used to price construction work
3  Be able to calculate all-in costs of materials, labour and plant, together with unit rates, for a variety of construction work
4  Be able to derive approximate quantities and costs to determine the approximate value of building projects at varying pre-contract development design stages and to understand the limitations on the accuracy that might be achieved
5  Understand the purpose of tendering, the common techniques used and the relevant documentation and explain the factors that can affect the level of tenders

# Applications of measurement

## Detailed measurement and production of quantities and descriptions for bills of quantities

This is where the **SMM7** rule book comes into force. It consists of several chapters that cover aspects of the construction of a project, and the measurement rules that apply to each item. Detailed measurement is undertaken from the contract drawings and specification and, using dimension paper or a software program, quantities are **taken off** and calculated for each item. The descriptions for the items that are produced for the bill of quantities must follow the rules set out within SMM7. These should contain all the necessary information for the estimator to know what they are pricing, for example fixed with screws rather than nails is more expensive as it takes longer to do.

## Key terms

**SMM7** This is the standard method of measurement (seventh edition) and is published by the Royal Institution of Chartered Surveyors (RICS).

**Taken off or taking off** The process of taking dimensions from drawings and producing a quantity.

## Remember!

The SMM7 provides a clear set of rules that can be applied fairly, so that all contractors bidding for work do so on an equal basis that is fair to all, that is, every contractor will be pricing the same set of items.

## Theory into practice

Find out more about the RICS by visiting their website, www.rics.org.

In general terms, the rules contained within SMM7 follow the following structure:

- the item's classification, e.g. excavation
- size restrictions, e.g. maximum depth less than 0.25 m
- the unit of measurement, e.g. cubic metres ($m^3$)
- the measurement rule for that item, e.g. quantities are measured in bulk before excavation
- the definition rule for that item, e.g. site vegetation includes hedges, scrub, trees and stumps
- the coverage rule for that item, e.g. works include removing tree roots
- any supplementary information, e.g. describe filling materials that will be used.

## Interim payments

Interim payments occur at a regular time intervals during a project's life – usually every 30 days. The client's quantity surveyor will, in agreement with the contractor's quantity surveyor, measure all the work accomplished on site to date. This is called the gross valuation and from this all the previous payments are deducted to give the net valuation, which represents the work achieved that month. The valuation is prepared using the percentage of work done against each item within the **bill of quantities**. Simple multiplication and summing up gives the value of the total amount of work achieved to date.

## Key term

**Bill of quantities** A document produced as a result of the taking off of dimensions. It represents the whole of the project measured as items, square metres, cubic metres, all broken down into the SMM7 sections, and is used to place prices in as rates against the quantity measured, then totalled.

## Key term

**Provisional and prime cost sums** These are sums of money placed within a tender for unforeseen works or items that cannot as yet be measured. They are subsequently omitted and the agreed rate and price is put back when the work is completed. These can also be sums of money for nominated suppliers or subcontractors.

### Final account work

A final account is the summation of all the variations that have occurred on a typical contract and this is adjusted against the original contract sum that was agreed at the commencement of the project. It is the final total that the client has to pay the contractor less the previous payments they have received.

In compiling the final account, an architect's instruction may require carrying out measurement on site and then valuing against the bills of quantities rates that the contractor entered within their **tender**. All the contract variations are worked through and the final account is then prepared for agreement by the contractor and the client.

## Key term

**Tender** The estimate that is submitted by the contractor to the client containing the price for the work.

### Variations

These are changes to the construction works on site as a result of, for example:

- errors in the design
- errors in the specification
- the expenditure of **provisional and prime cost sums**
- design changes by the client.

These may need to be measured in order to ascertain how much the client has to pay the contractor for the variation. For example, if you have been asked to increase the length of a brick wall, then you would physically measure the length on site or from a revised drawing. This would establish the quantity of wall in square metres ($m^2$); looking up the bill of quantities' rate for this gives the value of the additional work.

### Claims and disputes

Claims and disputes items often arise on construction projects and are principally between the client and the contractor. They can lead to losses and expenses for the contractor and a delay to the project handover for the client. Many factors start disputes such as:

- adverse weather conditions
- late receipt of information from the designer
- a vast number of design changes
- cancellation of some part of the construction work.

Measurement may be needed to substantiate some of the claims and dispute items in order to provide evidence for an adjudicator to decide who is right in the dispute. Any record supplied in evidence will help to determine who is to blame and, ultimately, who will pay for the additional resources used.

### Thinking points

When the Wembley Stadium project ran into delays and additional costs associated with several design changes, the contractor and the Football Association eventually settled out of court.

# Processes

This process involves the use of dimension and abstraction paper. Dimension paper is used to take off quantities and record their dimensions, size, shape and description, so a bill of quantities item can be produced. Figure 9.1 shows part of a piece of dimension paper. Each column has a particular function – we have named each column from A to I, and each column's function is described below.

Dimension paper is unique as each page contains two pages of dimension paper, as we shall see from the numbering of the following columns.

- Column A – the binding column, used to bind or staple or tag together all the other sheets of dimension paper. No figures or writing go into this column. It is used only to fasten together the other sheets.

- Columns B and F – the 'timesing' columns, used to multiply one particular quantity by several factors above one.

- Columns C and G – the dimension columns where the dimensions are entered. Single dimensions indicate a linear dimension, e.g. metres; two dimensions indicate a squared dimension, e.g. m²;

three dimensions indicate a cubic dimension, e.g. m³. A single integer in this column indicates a number.

- Columns D and H – the summing up or squaring columns where the final solutions from the dimensions are placed and tallied up.

- Columns E and I – the description columns where the item being measured is described.

The first step in the procedure is to prepare a **take-off list**, which lists all the items that require to be taken off in a logical sequence. Once the project has been completely taken off, then the process of abstraction follows. Each item of work is recorded on the top of an

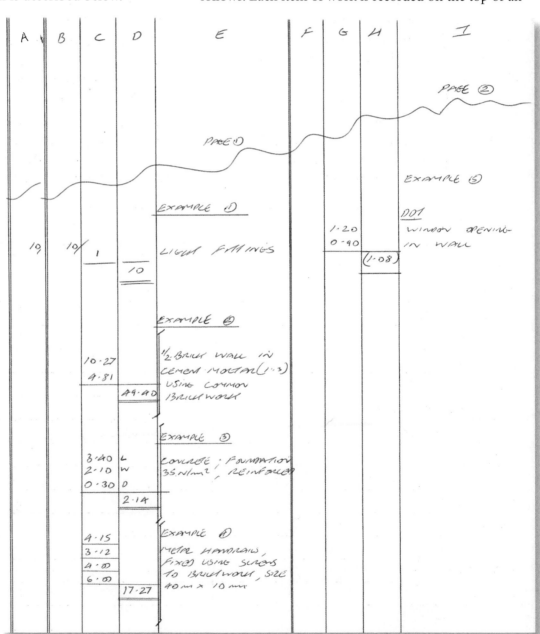

**Figure 9.1 Dimension paper**

## Key term

**Take-off list** A list prepared by the estimator or quantity surveyor which they use to check that all the items required have been covered. They tick off each item as the measurement is worked through.

abstract sheet. From each dimension sheet, the totals are listed under each heading of the abstract sheet. When all have been added, the final value quantity can be obtained by adding up the column of figures on the abstract sheet, taking across any deductions that occurred. From this, the final figure can be placed into the bill of quantities which is then prepared for the tender process.

Further down the dimension paper are some examples of how dimensions are taken off:

Example 1 is for numbered units, e.g. light fittings – there are ten of them. You always start with one in the dimension column and then times that by ten.

Example 2 is the dimensions for a metre squared take-off, e.g. the SMM7 states that brickwork is measured in square metres with the thickness specified. You always round up to two decimal places in taking off.

Example 3 is for a cubic dimension, say, concrete which is measured in cubic metres.

Example 4 uses linear dimensions, e.g. handrails to a staircase.

Example 5 illustrates how we deal with deductions. There are often voids that will need removing from the dimensions, or voids from within shapes such as window openings.

This example shows how to deal with a window opening that requires deducting from the brickwork measurement earlier; you often highlight this by putting brackets around it.

Looking at the dimensions illustrated, you should notice a strange s-type shape that is drawn just inside the description column. This is used to group sets of the same dimensions together so they can be added up.

| Tender Schedule | June | | | | July | | | |
|---|---|---|---|---|---|---|---|---|
| | wk1 | wk2 | wk3 | wk4 | wk1 | wk2 | wk3 | wk4 |
| Check documents | ▓ | | | | | | | |
| Prepare timetable | | ▓ | | | | | | |
| Mark up documents | | | ▓ | | | | | |
| Photocopying | | ▓ | | | | | | |
| Copy drawings | | | ▓ | | | | | |
| Send out s/c enquiries | | | | | | | | |
| Send out material enquiries | | | ▓ | | | | | |
| Send out plant enquiries | | | | ▓ | | | | |
| Site visit | | | | | ▓ | | | |
| Prepare method statements | | | | | | ▓ | | |
| Compile estimate | | | | | | ▓ | | |
| Pricings | | | | | | | ▓ | |
| Insert s/c sums | | | | | | | ▓ | |
| Tender adjudication | | | | | | | | ▓ |
| Submit estimate | | | | | | | | ▓ |

▲ Figure 9.2 Abstract sheet

## Remember!

Dimensions are always entered on the dimension paper in the following order: length, width and, finally, depth (look at the annotation on example 3) and are always rounded to two decimal places.

### Cut and shuffle

This method is no longer used as software applications for taking off have made it redundant. It involved the use of take-off dimension paper that had a perforated centre. Only one item at a time was placed on each sheet. When the take-off had been finished, the sheets were separated and the sheet for each separate item taken off collected together. This was the shuffle process. When all the same sheets were added up together, a total for each item could be established. This avoided the abstraction traditional process but, as you can see, was very complicated to operate.

# Production of accurate descriptions and quantities

### Compilation of descriptions for works

Descriptions are compiled from the SMM7 interpretation rules. For example, looking at brickwork in section F, the classification table gives you useful titles to contain within a bill of quantities description.

The first column states the type of wall, for example isolated piers; the second column gives descriptions on thickness, whether the work is face work; the third column gives descriptions on shape, for example vertical. These general headings must be used to reference the work in the order that SMM7 dictates from the first page to the end, so

preliminaries go first in a bill of quantities followed by the other sections.

Descriptions for quantities are often taken from the contract specification and drawings, where the architect has supplied a detailed specification. **NBS** produces specifications that can be used to describe building materials in detail. Architects and designers can then use these to specify materials for the contract.

## Key term

**NBS** The publisher of National Building Specifications which can be used in bills of quantities or specifications with drawings.

## Theory into practice

Find out more about the role of the NBS by looking at their website: www.thenbs.com.

## Remember!

Descriptions for quantities need to contain sufficient detail so the estimator has enough information to produce a price for that item. They should contain detail on the materials and any method of fixing or alteration that may be required, for example fixing to brickwork with screws is harder than nail gunning.

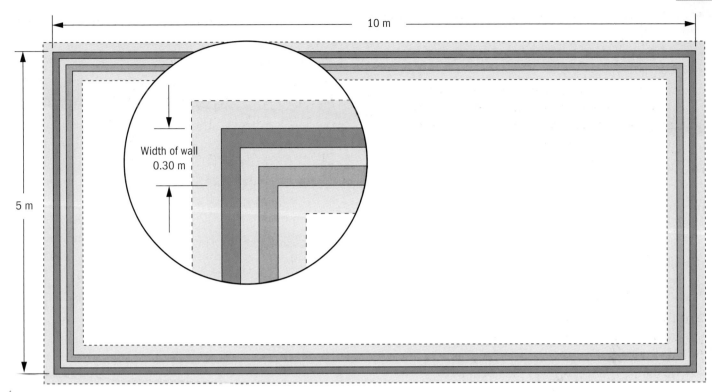

Width of wall
0.30 m

10 m

5 m

▲ Figure 9.3 Centre line method

## ■ Centre line calculation

This is a basic **mensuration technique** that can be used on closed buildings, that is, ones where the walls rejoin at the start in a closed loop as illustrated in Figure 9.3. The basic method involves the following:

1. Calculate the perimeter from the designer's dimensions – this is the total length of the outside walls measured on the face from start to back at the point you started.

2. Work out the complete wall thickness, in this example it is 0.30 m.

3. By taking off four full wall thicknesses, which equals 1.20 m (4 × 0.30 ), from the total perimeter, you will arrive at the centre line of the foundation trench, which is the red line of the diagram.

## Key term

**Mensuration technique** The process of producing quantities that can be used to make this simpler and more efficient.

This method can be used to find the centre line of any material within the wall's construction, but you must look at what dimension you take off or add on to move the intended centre line to or from. For example, if you want to find the centre line of the outside skin of brickwork, you would deduct four times the wall thickness of 100 mm (400 mm) from the original perimeter dimension.

# Application of standard methods of measurement

## Standard Method of Measurement for Building Work (SMM7)

As we have seen, this is the application of a set of rules to the building quantities measurement. It differs from the Civil Engineering Standard Method in that it covers a lot more complex construction works above ground, including services and finishes in some detail. The index to the SMM7 contains the following major items:

- preliminary items
- demolition
- groundworks
- concrete
- masonry
- structural carcassing
- claddings
- waterproofing
- linings
- windows/doors/stairs
- finishes
- furniture and equipment
- sundries
- external works
- drainage
- mechanical and electrical (SMM7).

## Civil Engineering Standard Method of Measurement (CESMM3)

This is the standard method of measurement or take-off rules for the civil engineering industry. It covers much of the **heavy-side engineering**, for example earthworks and pipework which would be used in reservoir construction. It has a similar purpose to SMM7, providing a level system for each contractor to price the work against. There is very little above-ground building work included within CESMM3. The only other major differences are that the first three columns are called divisions, whereas in the SMM7, they are classifications.

The index to the CESMM3 includes the following major items:

- definitions, principles and application
- ground investigations
- demolition and clearance
- earthworks
- concrete
- pipework
- structural steelwork
- piling
- roads
- rail tracks
- tunnels (CESMM3).

As you can see, it differs from the building measurement in that it deals with large infrastructure projects such as railways, drainage and roadways.

## Key term

**Heavy-side engineering** Construction work that requires heavy machinery to undertake it, e.g. roadways, highways, mass concrete dams, earthworks.

# Assessment practice

Figure 9.4 illustrates a typical cross-section through a modern-day foundation, which uses a concrete foundation with concrete trench blocks and two skins of engineering brickwork.

Using basic mensuration techniques, calculate and accurately record the following:

a the centre line length from the plan drawings of the foundation

b the volumes of concrete and excavation (ignoring any backfill)

c the area of the earthwork support to the sides of the excavation

d the total square metres of engineering brickwork

e the length of the damp-proof course that will be placed on top of the engineering brickwork. **P1**

In undertaking your take-off to the activity P1, ensure that you apply the rules of the Standard Method of Measurement to the production of the accurate quantities and descriptions listed in items b to e. Ask your tutor for a copy of the relevant sections from SMM7. **M1**

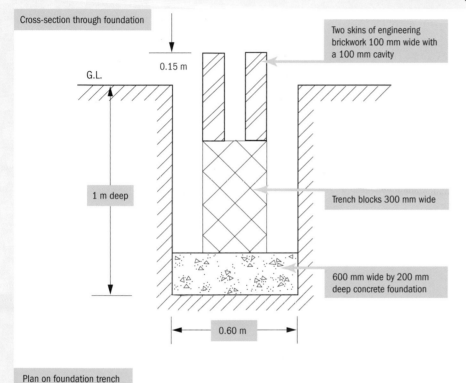

Cross-section through foundation

Two skins of engineering brickwork 100 mm wide with a 100 mm cavity

0.15 m

G.L.

1 m deep

Trench blocks 300 mm wide

600 mm wide by 200 mm deep concrete foundation

0.60 m

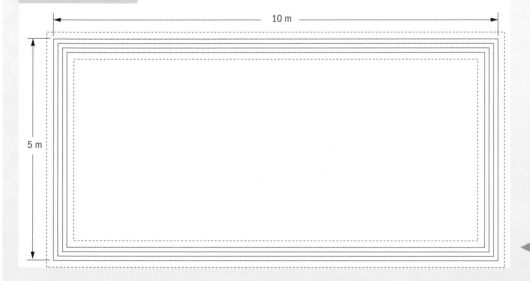

Plan on foundation trench

10 m

5 m

Figure 9.4 A foundation plan and cross-section

# Purposes of estimating

## Estimating net cost

The contract documents that the estimator receives may take two forms:

- a set of drawings with a specification – from these, the estimator will have to take off their own quantities
- a set of drawings and a bill of quantities.

From these, the estimator will prepare against each quantity a rate. Multiplying the rate by the quantity gives the total price for each taken off item. When all these are summarised, the estimate is said to be the **net costs**, that is, it only contains the cost of labour, plant, materials, preliminary items and subcontractors. The **gross estimate** contains the items that require to be added to the **net estimate**. These are:

- profit
- overheads
- risk and uncertainty items.

## Key terms

**Net costs** Basic prices of labour, plant, materials and subcontractors plus preliminary items.

**Gross estimate** The net estimate plus overheads and profit and risk items.

**Net estimate** Net costs.

## Pricing of preliminaries, profit and general overheads

### ■ Preliminaries

Preliminaries tend to be time-related costs that cannot be easily priced or included within a bill of quantities

bill rate. Since it is a requirement of SMM7 to produce preliminary items, they are priced within this section. Typical preliminary items would be:

- management and supervision costs
- employers' requirements, e.g. accommodation
- services and facilities, e.g. temporary water supply
- mechanical plant, e.g. a tower crane
- temporary works, e.g. scaffolding
- site accommodation
- transport.

A typical pricing of preliminaries calculation is shown in the worked example below.

### Worked example

All the preliminaries are time-related charges and so you will need to produce durations on site for these items.

From the following data, calculate the cost of the tower crane price which has to be included in the preliminaries.

*Data*
Cost of delivery of crane = £1200
Number of weeks on site = 20
Cost of erection and dismantling = £2500
Hire charge per week = £5500

*Calculation:*

| | |
|---|---|
| Delivery | £1,200 |
| Hire: 20 × £5500 | £110,000 |
| Erect/dismantle | £2,500 |
| Total | £113,700 |

### ■ Profit

Construction companies do not consider profit to be measurable and so do not include this within a typical contract. However, businesses have to make money in order to survive, and profit can be included in an estimate by adding a percentage to each of the rates within the bill of quantities, or placing it within the preliminary section by adding to each of the items contained.

The level of profit that is applied to a cost estimate may vary and depends on the following factors:

- the amount of work that the construction company currently has on its order books
- the level of competition in the location of the work
- the amount of risk associated with the project
- the complexity of the work undertaken
- the nature of the **procurement route**, e.g. **partnering agreements**
- the payments terms of the contract.

In essence, there is no set level of profit that can be applied to an estimate. Each tender that is returned should undergo an **adjudication process**. This is where the senior managers of the company discuss the factors listed above and arrive at the level of profit that will be applied to the estimate, based on sound judgement.

## Key term

**Procurement route** The method or route that a client uses to select a contractor to construct the project.

**Partnering** A method of procuring a contractor which enables cost sharings on savings between client and contractor.

**Adjudication process** A meeting held by senior management to decide what level of risk and profit requires placing on the net tender or estimate.

### ■ Overheads

A company's overheads are those costs that have to be met in order to run the head office, and include such items as:

- departmental costs, e.g. the buying department, the finance department
- insurances – public and employer's liability

- company cars
- IT equipment.

Again, these costs have to be met from somewhere, so a percentage is often recovered from additional costs added into the estimate. To calculate this percentage, you need to ascertain the total value of the company's overheads per year. Then take the turnover for the year (the amount the company takes in receipts) and divide this by the overhead costs × 100 per cent. This gives the percentage that needs to be applied to future estimates as long as the turnover does not drop below this level.

$$\frac{\text{Overheads}}{\text{Turnover}} \times 100\% = \text{Percentage to add to tender}$$

There are a number of ways of **reconciling** the overhead costs and recovering these against tendered works. Overheads can be costed in several ways:

- by not including them, but using an increased profit margin to cover their cost
- by establishing their cost divided by the total turnover and adding this percentage to tender submissions
- on larger projects, by moving head office functions onto site and recovering these costs through the preliminaries.

## Key term

**Reconciling** The settling up of costs so their value is known.

## Assessment practice

The estimator has just finished an important tender, and the senior managers of the company are meeting to undertake adjudication before submitting the price. Describe the items that make up the on-costs (overheads and profit) that must be added to the net price and explain how a percentage for on-costs and overheads might be calculated for the company. **M3**

Very small projects, for example less than £10,000, can be estimated simply by calculating the number of days' labour required plus materials or plant in order to produce a cost or quotation for the work. Much larger, complex projects, for example £1 million, will require more thorough techniques of measuring and rating each item to produce a final cost estimate. This is because they are very complicated and contain several different installations by specialist subcontractors, each project being a one-off design.

A client's budget will need to be accurate when the project costs run into millions of pounds and have to be financed through loans. There are several techniques that can be employed to achieve this as follows.

# Estimating techniques

## ■ Unit or number method

This is where cost estimates are prepared on a unit basis, for example a seat in a cinema or a bed in a hospital. Very simple calculations then produce a cost for a potential project by using previous contract final accounts and the unit number of occupancy. Obviously, this method may be very inaccurate and takes no account of the complexity of the design.

## ■ Area method

Taking previous historical contracts, square-metre cost rates can be produced and compiled, often by the Royal Institution of Chartered Surveyors. These can then be used to produce cost estimates. This is undertaken by measuring the total floor area of a project and multiplying it by the rate plus or minus any adjustments. This method produces a fairly accurate estimate for the new project.

## ■ Cubic method

This is where the volume of a historical project (that is, its length, width and depth calculation) is measured and the original cost divided by this volume. This produces a rate per cubic metre that can then be applied to a new project volume in order to produce a cost estimate for the client's budget. This method does not provide an accurate estimate.

## ■ Approximate quantities

This method uses sketch designs from the architect to produce some approximate quantities from this small amount of information. The experience of the estimator needs to be called on here to include the items of work that will be required for the final design. By using current cost rates or **price books**, a realistic estimate can be prepared for the client's budget.

### Key term

**Price book** A published book that contains current prices and rates for items of work based on the SMM7.

## ■ Elemental estimating

This involves breaking down the proposed design into elements, for example foundations, ground floor construction, first floor construction, structural frame, roof finishes. Cost estimates can then be prepared against each element and a final budget prepared.

## ■ SMM7 quantities

This method is undertaken as part of the preparation for tendering and the procurement of a contractor to carry out the contract work. It is the most accurate stage of the measurement process compared to the above methods.

The accuracy of all the methods will vary greatly. Preparing area unit or cubic estimates will depend on two things: the accuracy of the drawn information from the architect and the historical cost information used to produce a unit rate, e.g. the effects of inflation on prices.

Once a detailed design is approved, accurate quantities can be taken off and a better cost estimate refined from the initial studies.

## Key term

**Method statement** This is prepared by the estimator to illustrate how they perceived the build up of the rate in the estimate and the labour and equipment used.

## Assessment practice

The client has queried a cost estimate which appears to have risen by a large amount from the initial feasibility studies undertaken by the designer. Explain to the client the reasons for the differences in the accuracy of the measurements for different applications and stages of work during the various budget preparation processes. **M2**

- Unit rate pricing, e.g. the compilation of the unit rates to be applied to the tender.
- Provisional sums, e.g. percentage rates and attendances including dayworks.
- Overheads, e.g. the percentage or calculation of overheads.
- Completing the estimate, e.g. final calculations.
- Final review, e.g. the tender adjudication summary.
- Feedback, e.g. whether the tender was won or lost.

The code sets out a structured management of the tendering and estimating procedure that contractors can follow. It is similar to a quality system in that it provides checks to ensure no items are missed or mistakes made. It is a very useful guide for the estimator to follow.

# Documentation

## Code of estimating practice

The code of estimating practice is produced by the CIOB (Chartered Institute of Building) and provides guidance on estimating procedure on the following topics:

- The selection of contractors to undertake the tenders, e.g. through advertising, methods of selection and compiling the tender list.
- The decision to tender, receipt, acknowledgement, e.g. contract conditions, tender documentation and the resources needed to complete the tender.
- The management of the estimate, e.g. timetables and workloads of the estimator, site visit, checking the tender documentation and information required.
- Subcontract enquiries and material enquiries, e.g. how these will be sent out, scheduling material requirement and timetable for receipt.
- Estimate planning, e.g. the process of **method statements**, the pre-tender programme.

## Assessment practice

The architect has prepared several sketch designs for you, as the estimator, to prepare a budget for each. Identify several methods you could use to provide an estimate and describe the purpose of each.

The estimate for one of the designs has been completed, but the estimator has explained that it is net as opposed to gross. What does this mean?

The estimate now requires the final stage where preliminaries, profit and overheads are added to the net estimate. What do these include and mean? **P2**

# Materials costs

**Calculation of materials quantities and costs of construction works based on unit costs of materials**

Let's consider the calculation involved with a common construction material, as this will explain the process involved in the production of a material unit cost.

## Remember!

When calculating the cost of materials, break down each item into common units, so they can all be added together to establish a unit rate for the material delivered to site.

## Worked example

The site production of brickwork mortar involves three materials: cement, sand and an additive. Calculate the unit rate for this brickwork mortar using the following data handed to you by the estimator.

▲ Mortar

*Material data:*

Mortar is mixed in the proportion specified by the architect or engineer, which is usually a ratio of 1:4 for load-bearing brickwork.

Cement is delivered in a 25 kg bag, which costs £4.25.

Sand is delivered in 20-tonne wagons costing £80 per load.

Additive for workability is £9.00 for 2.5 l; 300 ml covers 100 kg of cement.

*Unit rate calculation:*

Each 1 m³ of mortar will weigh approximately 2 tonnes. Therefore, we require:

$$\frac{2000 \text{ kg}}{5 \text{ sets of units per 1 m}^3 \text{ mortar}} = 400 \text{ kg per unit}$$

Cement = 1 unit × 200 kg = 400 kg

$$\frac{400}{25} \times £4.25 = £68.00$$

Sand = 4 units × 200 kg = 1600 kg

$$\frac{£80}{20 \text{ tonnes}} = £4 \times 1.6 = £6.40$$

$$\text{Additive} = \frac{£9.00}{2500 \text{ ml}} = 0.003 \times 200 \text{ kg} = £0.60$$

Therefore, the total cost of 1 m³ brickwork mortar is £75.00.

# Labour rates

The basis of undertaking these calculations is to establish a rate that the estimator can use to price the tender works which recovers all the costs involved in employing labour directly.

If you employ an operative on a construction site for £12.00 per hour, is this all that it will cost the construction company? The answer is no, because there are several factors that need to be taken into account when calculating the all-in cost of labour. These are:

- the basic rate of pay per hour that has been agreed between the employer and the worker
- annual holiday entitlement and public holidays
- employer's national insurance contribution
- the weather (possible loss of production)
- staff sickness
- CITB (Construction Industry Training Board) levy
- travelling time
- bonuses.

## Application of labour costs in unit rates

To apply the labour cost per hour that we calculated above, one further piece of information is required, that is, output rates for the labour. For example, how fast can a bricklayer lay bricks? If you can establish this, then you can calculate the unit cost of labour per unit of brickwork and apply this to the tender prices. Output rates can be established in two ways:

- timing bricklayers working using **work study**
- using output tables from historical works or price books, which will provide information on how long things took to construct or unit output rates.

Once you have established how many bricks can be laid in an hour, it is possible to calculate the output rate for labour costs.

## Key term

**Work study** This involves the timing of work so that a rate can be established and involves watching the bricklayers work on a known quantity and seeing how long they took.

## Worked example

Calculate the annual cost of labour for this general operative using the following data

*Data:*
Basic salary = £15,000.00
Holiday pay: 4 weeks at £288 per week = £1152.00
Employer's national insurance contribution at 12.5% = £1875.00
Lost production time, say, 2 weeks at £288 = £576.00
Public holidays: 8 days at £58 = £464.00
Sick pay, say, 2 weeks at £288 = £576.00
CITB levy at 2.5% = £375.00
Travelling, say, 2 weeks at £288 = £576.00
Bonuses, say, £30 week × 48 weeks = £1440.00
Total annual cost = £22,034.00

*Unit rate calculation:*
In order to calculate a unit rate of labour, we need to establish the total number of productive hours on site.
Total hours in one year:
4 days per week × 8 hours + 1 day × 7 hours for
    Friday × 52 weeks = 2028 hours
Less holidays: 4 weeks × 39 hours = 156 hours
Less public holidays: 7 × 8 + 1 × 7 = 63 hours
Less sickness 2 weeks × 39 = 78 hours
Total = 1731 hours

The hourly rate of labour is a simple calculation, as follows:

$$\frac{£22,034.00}{1731 \text{ hours}} = £12.73 \text{ per hour}$$

This is the labour rate that you would use as an estimator to price the works contained within a tender.

## Definition of prime cost of daywork and comparison with 'all-in' rates

Every year or following price increases, the BCIS (Building Cost Information Service) publishes daywork rates for the various specialist trades. These daywork rates are hourly rates for different trades, for example bricklayers or plumbers. The bill of quantities will have costs inserted by the client for **dayworks**. However, there may be occasions where a rate for variations cannot be used from the bill of quantities and instead dayworks which calculate labour, plant and materials costs can be used instead as the agreed method of payment. The contractor inserts a percentage against each of the daywork schedules for labour, plant and materials in the tender to cover for profit and overheads. The quantity surveyor can then convert any dayworks into a measured item if there is a rate in the bill of quantities.

## Key term

**Dayworks** Unforeseen works that may involve variations to the contract. This is a historical arrangement within a contract in that contractors undertake variations to the project works on a daywork basis. This records the labour hours and any plant or materials used against this item and is signed by the client's representative.

In order to present a level playing field, nationally agreed rates produced by the BCIS are used for the base rate on which the contractors add a percentage to cover all their on-costs, which is added to the tender document.

# Plant rates

## Calculation of fixed and operating costs

Fixed plant costs are those that are not time-related and would cover for example:

- delivery costs – low loader and tractor
- erection costs – crane to erect a tower crane
- removal costs – transport for piling rig.

In calculating delivery and removal charges, these could be obtained from the plant supplier. So, if delivery was £35 for a dumper, this would be multiplied by two and added onto the total duration time-related costs on site, and then divided by the number of hours to give an hourly rate. For example:

Delivery collection charges = 2 × £35 = £70

Time on site = 150 hours × £9 = £1350

$$\text{Total cost} = \frac{£1420}{150} = £9.47 \text{ per hour}$$

Variable or operating costs are those that are time-related to the length of hire on site and would cover for example:

- the cost of fuel – to calculate this you will need to establish the consumption rate of the plant when working
- puncture repairs – these will occur randomly and a certain percentage can be added in to recover the costs
- operator costs – the number of hours that an operator is required specifically to use the plant will need to be established.

## Calculation of hourly rates

Construction plant can be very expensive to own and operate. There are generally two methods of providing plant for construction sites:

- purchase, service, operate and maintain
- hire in the plant either externally or internally.

The unit rate calculation for an item of construction plant will depend on several factors, including:

- the ground conditions
- trained operators
- productivity
- height and reach
- breakdowns and reliability.

## Worked example

Calculate an hourly rate for a 1.5-tonne dumper using the data provided.

*Data:*

Hire rate= £150 per week

Driver costs = £300 per week (50% driving, 50% working on tasks)

Fuel requirements = 150 litres per week at £1.50 per litre

Working week = 39 hours

*Unit rate calculation in hours:*

Hire $= \dfrac{£150}{39 \text{ hours}} = £3.85$ per hour

Driver $= £300 \times 50\% = \dfrac{£150}{39 \text{ hours}} = £3.85$ per hour

Fuel $= 150 \text{ l} \times £1.50 = \dfrac{£225.00}{39 \text{ hours}} = £5.76$ per hour

Total cost per hour = £13.46

## Remember!

There is often a hidden cost associated with large pieces of construction plant – the cost of delivery to site using alternative transport such as a low loader.

### Application of plant costs in unit rates

The application of plant costs within unit rates for bill of quantity or measured quantity items must be carefully considered. This is because some plant items are used for several different measured items, activities and operations on site and so cannot easily be included within unit rates. They are therefore often placed within the appropriate section of the preliminaries section of the bill of quantities or specification section (see page 370).

Examples of types of plant that would be included within preliminary items are:

- rough terrain loadall
- tower cranes
- vans
- skips for rubbish removal
- temporary lighting
- scaffolding.

Examples that would be included within the relevant unit rate would be:

- concrete pumps
- diamond drilling equipment
- compressors and breakers
- screed pumps.

# Calculation of unit rates for various classes of construction work

To undertake the calculation of unit rates for use in estimating, you need to know the output rates for two constituent factors – labour and plant. Output rates, as we have seen, can be obtained by actual measurement or from historical work study tables. It is worth looking at the factors that affect the output of labour on a construction site. The following is a list of identified factors that would contribute to a lower output from the workforce:

- poor motivation
- excessive breaks
- wet weather
- dirty conditions
- excessive cold
- excessive heat
- dangerous and complicated work
- poor wages
- lack of supervision
- a complicated bonus scheme.

Similarly, the output of plant and equipment on site is affected by:

- the type of ground conditions
- ground or surface water levels
- the height to be reached
- the distance to move
- the skill of the operator
- the age of the plant
- whether it is hired or owned
- the amount of maintenance and servicing
- the correct capacity of plant for the work undertaken.

To calculate a unit rate for construction work, you need to break down the rate into the three main constituent parts of:

- labour
- plant
- materials

and calculate each element before totalling the unit rate. If we use a typical bill of quantities description for each of the following examples, it will show the process of compiling the rate that would be applied to each item. Finally, profit can be applied to the rate against each bill of quantities item.

## Excavation work

## Worked example

Calculate the following unit rate for the brickwork using the data provided.

Excavate to reduced level, maximum depth not exceeding 1 m (unit: m³)

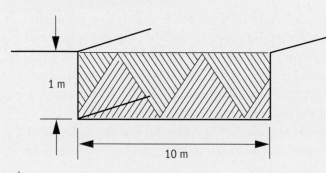

▲ Figure 9.5  Sketch of excavation

▲ Excavating a site

*Data:*
Excavator with operator = £35 per hour
Output = 6m³ per hour, which includes loading the dumper, waiting for it to tip and then starting the cycle again
4-tonne dumper with driver = £55 per hour
One dumper is required and tips spoil 10 m away

*Unit rate calculation:*

Cost of excavation = $\frac{£35}{6 \text{ m}^3}$ = £5.83 per m³

Cost of dumper = $\frac{£55}{6 \text{ m}^3}$ = £9.17 per m³

Total cost to excavate and tip = £15.00 per m³

## Remember!

Always break down your calculations into each of the resources of labour, plant and materials and then total these to obtain the unit rate per quantity. That way you won't miss anything!

## Worked example

Facing brickwork one side half brick thick in cement mortar 1:4 built in stretcher bond (unit: m²)

▲ Brickwork

*Data:*

Brickwork gang (two bricklayers/one labourer):

    Bricklayer rate per hour = £12.50

    Labourer rate per hour = £9.50

Output per bricklayer = 45 bricks per hour

1 m² of brickwork contains 60 bricks

Brick costs = £335 per 1000

Wastage = 5%

Mortar delivered to site = £52.50 per 1 m³ tub

Mortar use = 0.04 m³ per m² of brickwork

*Unit rate calculation:*

- Labour (2+1 gang cost):

  Bricklayers × 2 × £12.50 = £25.00

  Labourer = £9.50

  Total hourly rate = £34.50

  $$\text{Output} = \frac{60 \text{ bricks per m}^2}{2 \times 45 \text{ bricks per hour}} = 1.5 \text{ m}^2 \text{ per hour}$$
  for the gang

  $$\text{Unit rate} = \frac{£34.50}{1.5} = £23.00 \text{ per m}^2$$

- Materials:

  $$\text{Bricks} = \frac{£335 \times 60}{1000} = £20.10$$

  Add wastage at 5% = £1.01

  Mortar 0.04 × £52.50 = £2.10

  Total cost = £23.21

  Unit rate = £23.00+£23.21 = £46.21 per m²

## Worked example

Calculate the following unit rate for the concrete foundations using the data provided.

 **Concrete foundations**

Foundations Gen 1 grade, 10 mm aggregate 75 mm slump, thickness not exceeding 450 mm (unit: m³)

*Data:*

Concrete will be delivered ready mixed in 6 m³ trucks

Cost of concrete = £82.50 per m³

Wastage = 2%

Part load charges = £15.00 per m³ not delivered in the wagon

Volume required in the foundation = 22 m³

Two ground workers will be required to place and compact the concrete:

  Output of one ground worker = 6m³ per hour

  Cost of ground worker = £12.00 per hour

Compaction will be by hand tamp

*Unit rate calculation:*

- Labour:
  Ground workers 2 × £12.00 = £24.00 per hour
  Output = 2 × 1.5 m³ per hour = 3 m³ per hour

  $$\text{Cost per m}^3 = \frac{\text{£24.00 per hour}}{3 \text{ m}^3 \text{ per hour}} = \text{£8.00 per m}^3$$

- Materials:
  Basic cost of concrete = 22 × £82.50 = £1815.00
  Add wastage × 2% = £36.30
  Part load charge = 2 m³ × £15 = £30.00
  Total cost = £1881.30

  $$\text{Unit rate} = \frac{\text{£1881.30}}{22 \text{ m}^3} = \text{£85.51 per m}^3$$

  Concrete rate = Labour + Materials
  $$= \text{£8.00} + \text{£85.51}$$
  $$= \text{£93.51 per m}^3$$

## Remember!

It is acceptable to calculate the cost of the concrete as in the worked example, but this relies on the fact that when the ground workers have completed their work, they must have other work to move on to or their cost will exceed the amount of labour included within the unit rate. Careful site management of resources is therefore essential.

## Drainage

### Worked example

Calculate the following unit rate for the drainage using the data provided.

100 mm diameter upvc pipes in trenches, jointed using collars (unit: linear metres)

*Data:*
pvc-u pipes 6 metres long cost £65.78 each
pvc-u pipe coupler costs £ 9.95
Silicone lubricant 1 kg per 100 m pipe work costs £25.00
Pipelayer = £15.00 per hour
Output of pipelayer = 20 m per hour

*Unit rate calculation:*
- Labour:

$$\text{Cost per metre} = \frac{\text{£15.00 per hour}}{\text{20 m per hour}} = \text{£0.75 per metre}$$

- Material:

$$\text{Pipe} = \frac{\text{£65.78}}{\text{6 m each}} = \text{£10.96}$$

$$\text{Couplers (one required every 6 m)} = \frac{\text{£9.95}}{6}$$

$$= \text{£1.66 for each metre run}$$

$$\text{Lubricant} = \frac{\text{£25.00}}{\text{100 m}} = \text{£0.25}$$

Total cost per metre = Labour + Materials = £0.75 + £10.96 + £1.66 + £0.25
$$= \text{£13.62 per metre}$$

▲ **Laying drainage pipes**

## Timber floors

Calculate the following unit rate for the timber floors using the data provided.

Floor members, 225 × 38 mm softwood, treated with preservative, built into block walls (unit: linear metres)

*Data:*

Joiner and labourer to fix joists
    Joiner = £18 per hour
    Labourer = £9.50 per hour
Output = 8 metres per hour
Joists = £3.50 per metre
Wastage = 5%

*Unit rate calculation:*
- Labour:

$$\text{Joiner + labourer} = \frac{\text{£18 + £9.50}}{\text{8 m per hour}} = \text{£3.44 per m}$$

- Materials:
Joists = £3.50 + 5% waste = £3.67 per m

Total cost = £3.44 + £3.67
Unit rate per metre = £7.11

## Assessment practice

Calculate the following 'all-in' labour rates, plant rates and 'unit rates' from the following data.

*Labour data:*
Basic salary = £20,000
Working weeks = 42 weeks
Hours per week = 39 hours
Employer's national insurance contribution = 12%
Holidays = 5 weeks
Sick pay = 2 weeks
CITB levy = 3%
Bonus = £35 per week

### Remember!

To calculate the weekly rate for holidays and sick pay, divide the basic salary by the number of working weeks, add up all your costs for a total, then divide by the number of weeks, then the number of hours per week to find the hourly rate.

*Plant data:*
Type: compressor and breaker
Rate per week = £85

Fuel at 1.5 litres per hour = £2.50 per litre
Operator = £250 per week
Productivity per week = 65%
Oil = £9 per week
Working week = 39 hrs

*Unit rate data:*
Brickwork gang (two bricklayers/one labourer):
    Bricklayer rate per hour = £14.50
    Labourer rate per hour = £10.00
Output per bricklayer = 55 bricks per hour
1 m² of brickwork contains 60 bricks
Brick = £455 per 1000
Mortar delivered to site = £62.50 per 1 m³ tubs
Mortar use = 0.04 m³ per metre squared of brickwork

### Remember!

The following classes of construction work are nearly always contracted out on larger projects as they are specialist works, so they have not been included here: structural steelwork, roof coverings, painting and decorating, plumbing work, electrical installation and glazing.

# Traditional cost modelling

## Approximate estimating techniques

### ■ Cost per unit

This method of approximate estimating for budget preparation uses a physical unit, for example a hospital bed, a school pupil place or a workstation. The method relies on the fact that there is some relationship between value and the number of units. Look at the following two examples:

1.  A 250-bed hospital costs £350 million to construct. This has been taken from historical information on the cost of building a hospital.

    $$\frac{£350,000,000}{250} = £1,400,000 \text{ per bed space}$$

    Proposed hospital
    300-bed space × £1,400,000 = £420,000,000

    There can be a vast difference between actual cost and estimated costs and this method does not have a high degree of accuracy. An experienced estimator would need to look at the provisional design against the historical design from which the bed unit rate was obtained in order to ensure some degree of consistency.

2.  A 76,000-seater stadium cost £37 million to construct. Estimate the cost of a proposed 60,000-seater stadium using similar construction methods and design.

    $$\frac{£37,000,000}{76,000} = £486.84 \text{ per seat}$$

    New stadium = 60,000 × £486.84 per seat
    = £23,210,400

## Cost per unit area

Calculating the cost per unit area, for example square metres of gross floor area or square metres of functional space, again involves using historical rates on a similar project, increased in line with inflation, in order to produce a realistic rate for a new building project's floor area. This can be illustrated using the following example:

Historical cost of building A = £300,000

Floor area = 40 m × 20 m = 800 m²

$$\text{Area rate} = \frac{£300,000}{800 \text{ m}^2}$$

$$= £375 \text{ per m}^2$$

Proposed new building B of similar design floor area = 650 m²

$$= £375 \text{ per m}^2 \times 650 \text{ m}^2$$

$$= £243,750$$

## Cost of functional element

This involves breaking down the estimate into functional elements, or small packages of work. Unit rates per square metre, metre or number can then be applied to produce a cost estimate. This method relies on the knowledge and experience of the estimator to apply historical element costs from previous work and upgrade these to the new proposal. It provides a budget plan from which further work can be developed. A typical element cost estimate is shown in Table 9.1.

This method allows costs to be taken from different historical works to produce a reasonably accurate budget figure.

| Element | Quantity | Element unit rate | Totals |
|---|---|---|---|
| Substructure | 150 m² | £50 | £7500 |
| Structural frame | | | £20,000 |
| External walls | 2500 m² | | £137,500 |
| Roof construction | 1500 m² | £55 | £67,500 |
| Internal partitions | 2000 m² | £45 | £56,000 |
| Windows and doors | 40 | £28 | £10,000 |
| Wall finishes | 1500 m² | £250 | £18,000 |
| Floor finishes | 1500 m² | £12 | £37,500 |
| Plumbing | | £25 | £30,000 |
| Electrical | | | £50,000 |
| External works | 2000 m² | | £40,000 |
| Drainage | | £20 | £25,000 |
| Total | 1000 m | £25 | £499,000 |

**Table 9.1 A typical element cost estimate**

## Approximate quantities

This method provides additional detail compared with the other methods described above. It involves the use of dimensions or sketch proposals on the proposed design. From these, approximate quantities are measured and historical bill of quantity rates applied to produce a reasonably accurate cost estimate. For example, the following small building has been taken off to produce approximate quantities and historical rates applied to give a cost estimate. (For the purposes of the example, the building is much slimmed down in order to simplify the concept of approximate quantities.)

### Remember!

These quantities are approximate as the detailed design drawings from which the accurate quantities are taken are not available at this stage.

*Design data:*
Single storey building 10 m long × 5 m wide × 2.4 m high

*Approximate quantities take-off:*

| Description | Quantity | Rate | Totals |
|---|---|---|---|
| Concrete foundations | 4 m³ | £65 | £260 |
| Trench blocks | 5 m² | £25 | £125 |
| Engineering brickwork | 2 m² | £23 | £46 |
| External solid walls in blockwork | 72 m² | £45 | £3240 |
| External render | 72 m² | £15 | £1080 |
| Roof joists | 125 m | £9 | £1125 |
| Plywood | 50 m² | £6 | £250 |
| Three-layer roofing felt | 50 m² | £22 | £1100 |
| Total | | | £7226 |

# Application

## Feasibility studies

These are undertaken as part of the RIBA Plan of Work, and follow the initial brief taken from the client. At the early stage of a contract, the client must be advised if the contract is feasible, that is, whether it is possible, practical and economical to proceed with the detailed stages of the design, or whether it is better to halt the project now. Measurement can help by taking a brief outline from the client in the form of a sketch and, by using historical cost data, produce a reasonably balanced idea of what the projected costs for the project would be in order to make an informed decision.

The application of measurement also enables comparison between several project proposals such that the benefits of one against another can be compared, and a decision made in favour of one or a combination of parts to push the feasibility through to detailed design.

## ■ Links to stages of RIBA Plan of Work

The cost planning of the project is an essential item to incorporate within the early stages of the RIBA Plan of Work. Cost planning is undertaken for several reasons:

- To ensure that the client's financial limit, i.e. budget, is not exceeded.
- To produce the right quality for the project.
- To ensure that the project will return value for the financial investment.

The amount of effort put in at this stage should equal the requirement that is expected from it, so that:

- the tenders received do not exceed the client's budget
- there are no unforeseen or hidden costs – all is transparent
- the amount of financial wastage is reduced, for example **cost value engineering**, when the project overspends the budget.

It is far better to use a lot of resources at this vital stage of the project in order to control the budget of the project. For example, the client may prefer a low-maintenance building, so feasibility costs will be required on alternative maintenance-free materials in order to make an informed decision.

## Key term

**Cost value engineering** The reduction of costs by changing specification, methodology quantities, omitting items or other works to reduce costs.

## Remember!

Measurement only plays a small part in pre-contract cost planning. Other costs that must be considered may be the cost of finance, consultants' fees, the purchase of the land, etc.

# Processes

Historical cost data is invaluable in preparing budgets and costing future designs. It requires great care on the part of the estimator undertaking this task, as a client who overspends considerably will not be pleased. Similarly, a completed design that is well under budget that has not realised its full potential will also displease a client. So, is this process an exact science? The answer is no, and a percentage plus or minus will have to be discussed with a client so that they are well-informed.

Historical cost data can be obtained from many sources, such as:

- in-house company analysis of tender submissions
- work study methods
- published price books
- BCIS (Building Cost Information Service) and the BMI (Building Maintenance Information).

## ■ In-house data

This is historical data established over a period of time by the estimating department. It contains suppliers' discounts, measured output rates for plant, suitable subcontractors to use, and an estimating data base from which can be drawn sufficient information from previous projects to assist in pricing future projects. Previous bills of quantities are also a source of current information and rates. This is very valuable data and assists the competitive edge of the construction company.

## ■ Work study data

This involves the physical measurement of the company's labour force to establish historical output data that is then used to complete current estimates. For example, if you know how many bricks are contained within a wall and how long it took to build and the costs involved, you can calculate a rate per square metre. This data is, therefore, a realistic output picture on sites and accurately reflects the current situation.

▲ Cost modelling can help determine the approximate value of planned building projects

## ■ Published price books

These are published works that contain the SMM7 rates often divided into major and minor works. They provide a rate per item that can be used or adjusted to reflect certain circumstances. However, they are global figures and tend to be a little generous in the output rates used.

## ■ BCIS and BMI

This is cost data that is compiled and published each quarter by the Royal Institution of Chartered Surveyors. It enables the estimator to look closely at a particular product such as a hospital, school or factory and examine the complete breakdown of elements, areas, specification and rates. These can then be used to prepare a pre-tender estimate.

**Application of tender price indices and location factors**

Historical cost data, as its name suggests, is collated over a period of time that may be over several years. Current cost data will, therefore, require to be updated to take account of the following:

- rate of inflation
- local labour rates
- delivery and transport costs
- geographical location of the work.

In order to establish future tender prices, tender price indices are available. These are sets of figures that enable inflation and increased costs to be taken into account when predicting future work costs. Each index has a base rate, usually 100, and prices can then be set above or below the base rate. Therefore, in simple terms, indices are applied as follows for an item:

Cost per m$^2$ of element A in 2001 was £245.50. Indices for 2001: 171

Proposed project to commence in year 2009. Indices for 2009: 195

Calculation is as follows for item A:

$$£245.50 \times 195 = \frac{£279.87}{171} \text{ per m}^2$$

This can be applied similarly to the different geographical locations around the UK, as tender prices in the London area will be greater than in other areas. This is particularly so for the cost data used to provide price books, which is mainly based on London prices, and so adjustments have to be made.

## Principles of wall-to-floor ratios

Look at the two buildings A and B in Figure 9.6. Their perimeters and floor areas differ in size and shape. Using the small calculations given, you will see that the wall-to-floor ratio becomes smaller with the increased floor area. It is often more cost effective to add something extra to the project at the tender stage rather than in the future when increased costs would make it expensive.

### Remember!

The designer does not often have a free hand to design the plan shape as economically as possible, as design aesthetics and site constraints often play a part in the process.

## Window-to-floor ratios, plan shape, number of storeys

This exercise can also be done to window and floor ratios. Openings in buildings can be costed against the full wall construction. It is necessary to establish a balance between the amount of daylight and cost savings established. Building regulations, however, govern the percentage of windows applicable to a building's elevations.

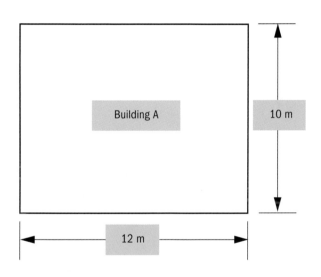

Building A — 10 m, 12 m

Floor area = 120 m$^2$
Height 3 m
Perimeter = 44 m
Wall area = 132 m$^2$

$$\text{Ratio} = \frac{\text{Wall}}{\text{Floor}} = 1.10$$

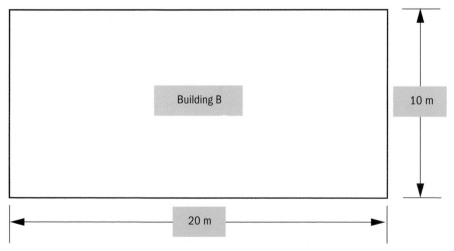

Building B — 10 m, 20 m

Floor area = 200 m$^2$
Height 3 m
Perimeter = 60 m
Wall area = 180 m$^2$

$$\text{Ratio} = \frac{\text{Wall}}{\text{Floor}} = 0.90$$

▲ Figure 9.6 Wall-to-floor ratios

Square shapes are obviously the most economical as they present the lowest floor-to-wall ratio when comparing buildings of the same height. Economies can be obtained by joining two buildings together, for example by saving one external wall. Every economy should be considered when designing the plan shape to maximise the potential within the site boundaries. Using one element for two buildings saves money.

Storey height must be considered when constructing multi-storey buildings. For example, look at the comparison of buildings C and D:

*Building C:*
Plan area = 25 m × 25 m
Height = 59.50 m
Storey height = 3.5 m

Number of floors $= \dfrac{60}{3.5} = 17$ floors

Total floor area = 17 × 25 × 25 = 10,625 m²

*Building D:*
Plan area = 25 m × 25 m
Height = 59.50 m
Storey height = 2.98 m

Number of floors $= \dfrac{60}{2.98} = 20$ floors

Total floor area = 20 × 25 × 25 = 12,500 m²

By designing a much smaller storey height, it is possible to increase the gross floor area, which boosts the amount of rental revenue.

## Purpose, aims and objectives of tendering

### For main or principal contractors, subcontract and supply packages

The main purpose for the main contractor and, ultimately, the subcontractors and suppliers is to win contract work on a competitive basis and to ensure that the profit margin placed within the tender is maintained or exceeded. If the reverse occurs, and a loss is made, then this can be made up during the trading period of the company with other projects, but large losses cannot be maintained indefinitely and could lead eventually to the closure of the company.

### Thinking points

In order to survive, subcontractors and suppliers require construction contractors to operate healthy businesses.

## Common methods of tendering

### Methods of tendering relevant to the scale, size and value of the construction works, and to the type of work

#### ■ Scale, size and value

The method of tendering chosen to select a contractor for a project will depend on some of or all the following:

- The size of the project – the Channel Tunnel could not have been built if a consortium of several civil engineering companies had not pooled resources.
- The geographical location of the project – construction works operated within continental Europe differ from those in the UK.
- The financial stability of the construction company tendering for the work.
- The competency of the contractors with regard to health and safety – firms with high accident rates will need to be carefully considered before placing them on a tender list.
- The physical resources of labour, plant and facilities of a company.
- The reputation and references of a company.

Construction works vary in many aspects, and in terms of physical and financial size. Small construction works of less than £10,000 can be run locally using a contractor in the area; larger multi-million-pound projects will require contractors from much larger organisations that may be further away.

The type of work also has an effect. Large civil engineering projects may require a consortium to be put together, in order to pool resources from several contractors so that the work can be completed. In this type of project, a single contractor would be unlikely to be able to sustain the resources required.

High-value projects will require the financial accounts of a prospective tenderer to be checked over a number of years in order to ensure that they have the capacity to take on a high financial burden and the associated cash flow requirement and financial stability.

### Types of tendering

#### ■ Single stage selective

This method involves pre-selecting contractors, usually six, and asking them to submit tenders for the project.

The list from which the contractors are selected will have been compiled using several factors:

- references
- health and safety record
- experience
- value of the work
- resources of the companies
- type of work.

Local authorities also use selective tender lists for different values and categories of work, for example highways and building services.

The benefits of using this method are as follows:

- Contracts are pre-checked and poor performing ones removed from the list.
- Lists can be rotated to provide a constant pool of different contractors.
- The tender procedure is competitive.

## ■ Two stage selective

Where time is of primary importance to the client, potential contractors may be invited to initial discussions before any design has been commenced in order to provide input to the project. This is to canvas ideas, and from these interviews a second stage commences. This covers the project in more detail, and may include the final selection of a contractor, with a bill of quantities submitted as part of a final tender process using previously agreed rates. This process is complicated to conduct but the client may benefit from the knowledge and experience and ideas gained from the successful contractor.

## ■ Open tendering

Open tendering is simply an open invitation to tender, normally in response to an advert placed by the client in a newspaper. Such contracts tend to be for services, for example local council road cleaning or waste collection. They generally ask for expressions of interest to be placed, and from this a shortlist of prospective candidates is prepared.

The disadvantage is that open tendering attracts contractors of which you have no knowledge regarding quality, costs and reputation. References will be requested and checked.

## ■ Serial tendering

Serial tendering, as the name suggests, is tendering to agree to a series of works set out in the initial offer. For example, a contractor prices the full documents for the first project. These are then used to price the second, and so on. This type of tendering could be used for works of a similar nature, for example a series of schools, community projects, community police stations.

There are several benefits to this system. The chosen contractor will learn about the complexity of the first job which can then be used as valuable experience on the next one. The client will also have a long-term commitment ensured.

## ■ Target cost

This basis of tendering is very similar to a partnering agreement. The client sets out a final budget or target costs that must not be exceeded. Any savings made under this maximum are split 50/50 between the contractor and the client, but should the contractor overspend, then this is at their risk and not the client's. The benefits are efficiency savings that are shared, less risk for the client, a less confrontational relationship and a development of trust.

## ■ Measured term

Measured term tendering involves the use of a standard specification and bill of quantities or a national measured schedule of rates. The rates are already priced by the client. The prospective tenderer has to apply a plus or minus to this national schedule, which is then converted into a total tender sum. The winning contractor undertakes a piece of work that is measured against the agreed rate and payment is made on this basis. This process involves a lot of administrative work in order to control each small job. Measured term contracts would be used on pre-paint repairs on housing, for example.

## ■ Fee bidding

These are sometimes called cost reimbursement or cost plus contracts because they contain a fee element. The contractor agrees to undertake the basic cost of the work plus a fee payable on top of the basic costs. There are several variations to this method:

- Cost plus a percentage as a flat rate – this is charged on the construction work.
- Cost plus a fixed fee – this is an amount stated in the tender submission.
- Cost plus a flexible fee – this varies under certain constraints.

This method of tendering involves a degree of trust as the awarded contractor has to prove the costs paid out on the contract in order to claim a fee on top of the work.

## Assessment practice

The levels of tenders submitted to the client's estates department are widely fluctuating. The procurement manager is keen to establish why. Is it the method of tendering or something else? Describe the common methods of tendering for main contractors, subcontractors and supply package contractors and explain how different objectives for each might affect the tender price. **P5**

A client has asked you to undertake an evaluation of what methods of tendering could be employed on the future workload. Explain how the method of tendering selected matches the nature of the project **M4**

Evaluate and justify the selection of tendering methods available for the following range of project scenarios:

a   A series of six school 850-pupil projects.
b   Highly specialised and complex projects.
c   A project where the client is keen to stay within budget.
d   A pre-painting repair programme for council housing. **D2**

# Documentation

## Functions of different documentation used for each method of tendering

### ■ The enquiry form

The estimating team, contracts manager and managing director use the enquiry form to find out details of the tender proposed by the client. From this, they can then make a decision whether to proceed with the tender or not. Normally, the initial enquiry from the client arrives in the form of a telephone call, asking if the contractor would like to tender for the work. It is good practice to make a decision quickly so that the client has an option to add another contractor to the tender list.

### ■ The tender information form

This provides all the information that can be extracted from the tender documents, so it can be placed in one form and used during the tender adjudication process.

**TENDER ENQUIRY FORM**

Client: _____

Address: _____

_____

_____

Tel: _____

Description of Project _____

_____

_____

_____

_____

Value _____

Time scale _____

Tender return date _____

Decision _____

Decline: _____   Accept: _____

Sign: _____   Dated: _____

 Figure 9.7 Enquiry form

## ■ Tender drawings

The set of drawings received with the tender should provide sufficient information for the estimator to price the unit rates within a bill of quantities, or if the tender contains drawings and specification only, to provide information for the take-off of quantities.

It is advisable to stamp the drawings with the wording 'tender drawing' and a date. This provides a record reference set of the drawings that accompanied the tender and upon which the contractor's price was based. These can then be checked against the contract revised drawings during the final account stage of the project in order to highlight changes and hence contract variations.

## ■ Schedules

These are often prepared for certain material elements and may be issued with the tender documentation. A typical schedule would include:

- windows
- doors
- ironmongery
- joinery
- internal finishes
- reinforcement for concrete.

Schedules are an easy way of counting up similar specified items, using the one document which saves you having to look through several drawings as the window schedule in Table 9.2 illustrates.

## ■ Specifications

Drawings and specifications are a common form of tender documentation. Often, they do not contain

| | WMCC | | £ | p |
|---|---|---|---|---|
| **Item** | | | | |
| A | **SUBSTRUCTURE** Excavate to remove hardstandings or turf, and to reduce levels average 250 mm deep, and cart away (approx. 23 m³) | Item | | |
| B | Excavate to reduced level for foundation trench not exceeding 1.00 m deep, 600 mm wide, and cart away surplus spoil, level and ram bottom to receive concrete, part backfill trench with hardcore internally in 150 layers, and with spoil externally to level of existing ground (12 m³) | Item | | |
| C | Provide and lay ground floor complete on prepared ground, comprising 150 mm thick consolidated hardcore, well rolled, 25 mm sand blinding, 1200 gauge visqueen damp proof membrane turned up wall at edges and lapped into dpc, 100 mm thick A 252 mesh reinforced concrete slab, tamped finish Gen 1 concrete – 20 aggregate, 100 thick Kingspan insulation laid butt jointed, floor overlaid with laminate flooring (approx. 45 m²) | Item | | |
| D | Provide and lay concrete Gen 1 foundations poured against face of excavation 250 mm deep (approx 8 m³) | Item | | |
| E | Provide and lay 300 wide dense 7n/mm² concrete foundation blocks, in cement mortar (1:3) (approx. 25 m²) | Item | | |
| F | Provide and lay three course class B engineering bricks 102 mm wide, in sand lime cement mortar (1:1:6) (approx. 4 m²) | Item | | |
| G | Provide and fix hy-load dpc 100 mm wide, including all necessary laps at joints, steps, etc. (approx. 15 m) | Item | | |
| | To Collection | £ | | |
| | 4.3 | Section – schedule of works | | |

 **Figure 9.8 A specification**

| Description | W1 | W2 | W3 | W4 | W5 | W6 |
|---|---|---|---|---|---|---|
| 1200 x 1200 upvc window in white with trickle vents to top, including upvc window board and cill, Pilkington K glass double glazed units with 20 mm air gap. | √ | | | | | √ |
| 2400 x 1200 upvc window in white with trickle vents to top, with two side opening lights 600 mm wide a 1200 mm high, including upvc window board and cill, Pilkington K glass double glazed units with 20 mm air gap. | | √ | | √ | | |
| 900 x 1200 upvc window in white with trickle vents to top, including upvc window board and cill, Pilkington K glass double glazed units with 20 mm air gap. | | | √ | | √ | |

**Table 9.2 Window schedule**

quantities, and the estimator will have to prepare these in order to price the tender. Specifications often use all-encompassing descriptions followed by the unit of 'item' against each work activity. The risk element of taking off accurate quantities is the responsibility of the contractor's estimator and not the client's quantity surveyor who would normally prepare a bill of quantities.

## ■ Bills of quantities

These are similar to specifications, but follow the rules set out under the Standard Method of Measurement. The whole project is measured and unit quantities placed within the bill of quantities. The exceptions are:

- contingencies – amounts of money for unforeseen items, e.g. obstructions in the ground
- dayworks – amounts of money for time-related charges levied by the contractor for variations that cannot be measured
- provisional sums – amounts of money included for works not fully designed or specified.

Bills of quantities are included within the tender documents to cover items that have not been measured. A bill of quantities will have section totals which are carried to collections which summarise each section and total them, and to a final summary which adds up the tender price.

## ■ Subcontractor and supplier enquiries

It is advisable for the contractor to keep a record of information sent to a supplier and subcontractor which can be used as evidence in the event of a dispute over prices. This information is normally recorded on an enquiry form – see Figure 9.9. The enquiry form will also be passed to the person who copies the drawings and pages from the bill or specification that are sent to the subcontractor or supplier.

A covering letter (with the company's letterhead) should be attached to the enquiry packages sent out to the subcontractor and supplier. The letter must include a date by which the subcontractor/supplier will need to respond – this should allow the estimator sufficient time

| Tender supplier | Drawing nos | Specification pages | BoQ pages |
|---|---|---|---|
| Aggregates Ltd | 2007/01/a | P23 item 1 | |
| | | P23 item 3 | |
| **Tender subcontractor** | **Drawing nos** | **Specification pages** | **BoQ Pages** |
| Topliss Electrical | 2007/21/a | | P47 items 1–8 |
| | 2007/22/b | | |
| | 2007/23/c | | |

▲ Figure 9.9 A subcontractor enquiry form

to finish compiling the tender for submission before the due date. Contractors usually contact subcontractors by phone initially to ask if they are interested in giving a quotation for the works instead of sending out an enquiry unannounced, as this saves time and valuable resources.

## ■ Activity schedules

These are programmes that can be used to visually control the tendering and estimating procedure. They enable other tenders to be coordinated on a master programme, so that the estimator can control the workload. They act as a programme and can assist the process by enabling monitoring to be established if one item lags behind. Where more than one tender is being priced at a time, a master estimating schedule may have to be produced to control the whole process within the estimating department.

### Remember!

The average time you have to compile a tender is normally three to four weeks. Planning during the estimation stage is essential to meet the tender deadline (see Unit 7 Planning, organisation and control of resources in construction and the built environment).

| Description | Latest date | Month | April | | | | | | | | | | | | | | | May | | | | | | | | | | | | | |
|---|---|---|---|---|---|---|---|---|---|---|---|---|---|---|---|---|---|---|---|---|---|---|---|---|---|---|---|---|---|---|---|
| | | Date | 11 | 12 | 13 | 14 | 15 | 18 | 19 | 20 | 21 | 22 | 25 | 26 | 27 | 28 | 29 | 2 | 3 | 4 | 5 | 6 | 9 | 10 | 11 | 12 | 13 | 16 | 17 | 18 | 19 | 20 |
| | | Latest date | M | T | W | T | F | M | T | W | T | F | M | T | W | T | F | M | T | W | T | F | M | T | W | T | F | M | T | W | T | F |
| Project appraisal | | | | | | | | | | | | | | | | | | | | | | | | | | | | | | | | |
|   Check documents | | | ■ | | | | | | | | | | | | | | | | | | | | | | | | | | | | | |
|   Tender information sheet | | | ■ | | | | | | | | | | | | | | | | | | | | | | | | | | | | | |
|   Tender timetable | | | ■ | | | | | | | | | | | | | | | | | | | | | | | | | | | | | |
| Document production (d & b and drg & spec) | | | | | | | | | | | | | | | | | | | | | | | | | | | | | | | | |
|   (Drawing) | | | | | | | | | | | | | | | | | | | | | | | | | | | | | | | | |
|   (Specification) | | | | | | | | | | | | | | | | | | | | | | | | | | | | | | | | |
|   (Bills of quantities) | | | | | | | | | | | | | | | | | | | | | | | | | | | | | | | | |
|   Code bill items and enter computer bill | | | | ■ | ■ | ■ | | | | | | | | | | | | | | | | | | | | | | | | | | |
| Enquiries | | | | | | | | | | | | | | | | | | | | | | | | | | | | | | | | |
|   Abstract, prepare, despatch – subs | 18 Apr | | | ■ | ■ | ■ | | | | | | | | | | | | | | | | | | | | | | | | | | |
|   Abstract, prepare, despatch – mate | 20 Apr | | | | | | ■ | ■ | | | | | | | | | | | | | | | | | | | | | | | | |
|   Date for receipt of quotations – mate | 4 May | | | | | | | | | | | | | | | | | | | ■ | | | | | | | | | | | | |
|   Date for receipt of quotations – subs | 9 May | | | | | | | | | | | | | | | | | | | | | | ■ | | | | | | | | | |
| Project appraisal | | | | | | | | | | | | | | | | | | | | | | | | | | | | | | | | |
|   Site visit | 19 Apr | | | | | | | | ■ | | | | | | | | | | | | | | | | | | | | | | | | |
|   Tender method statements | | | | | | | | | | ■ | | | | | | | | | | | | | | | | | | | | | | |
|   Tender programme | 12 may | | | | | | | | | | | | ■ | | | | | | | | | | | | | | | | | | | |
| Pricing | | | | | | | | | | | | | | | | | | | | | | | | | | | | | | | | |
|   Labour and plant | | | | | | | | | | | | | ■ | ■ | ■ | ■ | ■ | ■ | | | | | | | | | | | | | |
| Materials | | | | | | | | | | | | | | | | | | | | | | | | ■ | ■ | | | | | | | |
|   Sub-contractors | | | | | | | | | | | | | | | | | | | | | | | | | ■ | ■ | | | | | | |
|   PC and provisional sums | | | | | | | | | | | | | | | | | | | | | | | | | | | ■ | | | | | |
|   Project overheads | | | | | | | | | | | | | | | | | | | | | | | | | | | | | | | | |
| Reports | | | | | | | | | | | | | | | | | | | | | | | | | | | | | | | | |
|   Checking procedures and summaries | | | | | | | | | | | | | | | | | | | | | | | | | | | ■ | ■ | | | | |
| Tender | | | | | | | | | | | | | | | | | | | | | | | | | | | | | | | | |
|   Review meeting(s) | 17 may | | | | | | | | | | | | | | | | | | | | | | | | | | | | ■ | | | |
|   Submission documents | | | | | | | | | | | | | | | | | | | | | | | | | | | | | | ■ | | |
|   Submission | 19 May | | | | | | | | | | | | | | | | | | | | | | | | | | | | | | ■ | ■ |

**Project**
Horizon Laboratories

**TENDER TIMETABLE**

**Simtop Construction**

Figure 9.10 An activity schedule

## Codes of procedure for tendering relevant to main and principal contractors, subcontract and supply packages

The CIOB code of estimating practice referred to earlier in the chapter once again provides guidance on the procedures for dealing with estimates and enquiries to subcontractors and suppliers. You should refer to a copy of this document for more information.

The key to getting a response to enquiries is to send as much information as possible with the enquiry. This should contain the following as a minimum:

- Tender drawings – these should be relevant to the sections of work you want the subcontractor/supplier to price.
- Specification pages relevant to the subcontractor/supplier's work area – the standards that will be required.
- Bill of quantity pages – the pages with the items you want priced.
- Preliminary items – any useful information contained with the client's enquiry.
- Conditions of contract – what type of contract will operate.
- Return date for enquiry – when you want the price by.
- Insurance level required – the amount or indemnity required as a minimum.
- Any site restrictions – for example restricted access or hours on site

- A provisional programme – to inform the subcontractor/supplier of a start and finish date on site.
- A schedule stating what has been sent to the contractor/supplier.

It is useful to maintain a database of subcontractors and suppliers to refer to on future tenders.

## Remember!

It can cost a lot of money to prepare a typical estimate for a tender. With an average success rate of one in six, these costs have to be recovered from the company's overheads.

# Factors affecting the level of tenders

**Impact on value, price or level of a tender for main and principal contractors, subcontract and supply packages**

## ■ Main and principal contractors

Value has a great effect on the level of a tender. Small value tenders would tend to have a lump-sum overhead and profit element added to them as applying a percentage would mean a small return on investment. Multi-million-pound projects require a large financial commitment by the estimating department. For example, design and build tenders can cost thousands of pounds to complete with no obvious return if the company does not win the contract.

Generally, in a competitive tendering situation a company is competing against five other contractors, so the chances of winning the contract are 1:6. There are several factors that can affect the level of tenders received by the client, as follows:

- The economic climate of the country – a buoyant economy also means higher tender prices and enquiries.
- The base rate of interest set by the Bank of England – this affects the cost of borrowing required to finance initial stages of contracts and the client's budget.
- The geographical location of the work – tender prices within the London area tend to be much higher than the rest of the UK due to the higher cost of living in the capital.
- The level and quality of the competition – large organisations may benefit from **economies of scale** and also have regional offices to cover the whole of the UK.
- Specialism – e.g. a major contractor specialising in stone work will have more demand for their services due to a shortage of contractors within this field.

## Key term

**Economies of scale** The ability to buy in bulk, thus receiving greater discounts.

## Remember!

The factors of economic supply and demand also work for construction. A shortage of reliable contractors will have an effect on tender prices.

## ■ Subcontractors

The tendering methods we have looked at tend to be the common methods adopted in order to secure a main contractor for a project, but there are also subcontractors and suppliers to consider.

Subcontractors can be appointed in two ways:

- As a domestic subcontractor to the main contractor.

- As a **nominated subcontractor** engaged by the client in prior negotiations and who is then instructed to be engaged by the main contractor.

## Key terms

**Nominated subcontractor** A subcontractor who is appointed by the client and has already tendered for the work package for the client. The main contractor is then instructed to appoint this subcontractor and the value is offset against a provisional sum placed within the main tender documents, including profit and **attendances** by the main contractor.

**Attendances** The items that will be required by the nominated subcontractor such as a crane, rubbish removal, water, electricity and other items.

Subcontractors tender for the work mainly in a selective way by the main contractor who will send out enquiries for the specialist works that they cannot undertake. Sometimes the contractor has to use subcontractors who are approved by the client and, in these cases, a list accompanies the tender.

Subcontractor prices are influenced by:

- how busy the subcontractor is
- their historical relationship with the main contractor
- the level of main contractor's discount
- how long the main contractor takes to pay the subcontractor
- the location of the work
- how specialist the work is.

### ■ Suppliers

Suppliers do not undertake subcontract works involving installations. They only provide a material or a piece of equipment. Therefore, they are asked to provide material quotations from schedules prepared by the estimator. When the work is won, these are purchased from the supplier using a purchase order. Suppliers' prices and rates are affected by the following factors:

- the payment terms negotiated

- nationally agreed rates by the contractors' buying departments
- the level of discount negotiated
- the location of the supplier
- how quickly the materials are required.

Suppliers can also be 'named' by the client, for example a work of art is ordered and paid for by the client but installed by the main contractor. In this case, the price is already agreed, the main contractor is paid a percentage profit as stated in the tender document plus attendances such as the use of a crane to position the artwork.

### Profit element factors

The estimator will prepare a net estimate. This contains the basic prices of labour, plant, materials, subcontractors and preliminary items. To this net value are added the overheads and profit items. The amount of profit applied to a contract will vary depending on the following factors:

- the level of competition where the proposed works is located
- the current and future workload or capacity of the company tendering
- the current resources of the company
- the level of risk associated with the proposed works
- the complexity of the project
- whether the potential client or their representative is confrontational
- the payment history of a client
- the financial position of a client
- the size of the contract.

These matters are normally discussed at a tender adjudication meeting where senior team members decide on what level of profit to place on the tender.

### Potential variations

Poor quality tender documents tend to lead to a higher level of contract variations. Similarly, a tender containing a high level of provisional sums indicates to a contractor the potential for a high level of variations. From these variations, profit can be generated as the contract proceeds. Therefore, a lower than expected level of initial profit can be placed with the submitted tender as this will be made up in the long run.

### Quality of tender documents

Poor quality tender documents provide an opportunity for an astute contractor's quantity surveyor to exploit any loophole and force a contract variation from the client along with any additional payment. The types of mistakes that may be made are:

- poor quality drawings
- incorrect setting out information
- missing bill of quantity items
- poor specification clauses.

Any of these may lead to a contract variation and a potential to increase the level of profit for the contractor.

### Standard form of contract, amended standard form and bespoke contract forms

Standard contracts contain many clauses that have been included over several years of legal litigation. The JCT (Joint Contracts Tribunal) series of contracts are 'fair' and reasonable as they have been devised by both representatives from the employers' and the main contractors' associations.

Standard forms of contract are produced by the JCT for many types of work. For example, the JCT 98 standard form shares the risk fairly equally between the parties, whereas the JCT standard contractors design and build form sways more risk towards the main contractor. To allow for this, a premium may be included in the tender that is submitted.

Clients may choose to use bespoke contracts drawn up by their legal departments. These types of contract are worded in the client's favour. In order to counteract the risk that is placed on the main contractor, a premium is included in the tender to allow for onerous contract conditions.

## Assessment practice

The client of a large property developer is concerned about the level of fluctuating tenders that are been received for its property development projects. Identify and explain the factors that may be affecting percentage profit margins applied to submitted tenders.

The main contractor's estimator is concerned that the labour and plant outputs that they are using to price the tenders may be increasing the value of the submitted estimates to the property development client.

Identify those factors that affect the output of labour and those that affect the working hourly/idle rates for a variety of plant items for the estimator to make an informed decision. **P4**

The managing director of the construction company you work for is keen to establish computer-based electronic tendering and estimating system. Undertake some research for the managing director and examine some of the software systems that are available which may make it easier for the estimating and tendering process. **D3**

# Preparation for assessment

Using the sketch for the foundation cross-section in Figure 9.4 (p. 369) and applying this to the perimeter dimensions of the proposed building, which is 20 m × 15 m, accurately calculate the centre line of the foundation trench, the volume of concrete and the concrete foundation blocks. **P1**

The new estimating technician has just commenced employment with your company. Explain in simple language what the following mean, so they can grasp a basic understanding of these concepts:

**a** the purpose of different estimating methods

**b** net pricing

**c** the content of the preliminaries section

**d** general overheads and profit. **P2**

Calculate the 'all-in' labour rates, plant rates and 'unit rates' from the following data:

*Labour data:*
Basic salary = £18,500
Working weeks = 40 weeks
Hours per week = 39 hours
Employer's national insurance contribution = 12.75%
Holidays = 6 weeks
Sick pay = 4 weeks
CITB levy = 2.5%
Bonus = £55 per week

*Plant data:*
Type: JCB 3CX
Rate per week = £355
12.5 litres of fuel per hour at a cost of £2.50 per litre
Operator cost = £300 per week
Productivity per week = 85%
Oil and grease = £9 per week
Working week = 39 hrs

*Unit rate – supply and fix doors:*
Labour: to fit and hang a door = 4 hours
Joiner cost per hour = £15.50

Door = £65.00
Hinges 1.5 pair cost £1.75
Door closer 1 nr = £35.00
Lock 1 nr = £15.00
Handles 1 set = £12.75
Intumescent strips 5 m at a cost of £1.50 per metre
Kick plates = £3.00 **P3**

The managing director is looking closely at the estimating and tendering strategy of the company and has asked you to look at the following factors that are having an effect on winning work:

- percentage profit margins
- output of labour
- hourly/idle rates for a variety of plant items.

Identify and describe how these factors will have an effect on the competitiveness of the company. **P4**

Describe the common methods of tendering for:

**a** contractors

**b** subcontractors

**c** supply package contractors.

Explain what different objectives might affect the tender price submitted from each. **P5**

Identify the factors that influence the levels of tenders for the:

**a** main contract

**b** subcontract works

**c** supply packages.

Explain how these factors may have an effect on the pricing strategies of each. **P6**

Apply the rules of the Standard Method of Measurement to the production of accurate quantities and descriptions to P1 above. **M1**

The chief estimator for the company has asked you to analyse and explain the reasons for the differences in the accuracy of the measurements for different applications and stages of work. Produce a short report on this topic of no more than 300 words. **M2**

At several tender adjudication meetings, the managing director has stated that the level of company overheads is not helping the competitiveness of the bids submitted. Describe the items that contribute to on-costs and overheads and explain how to determine accurately the percentage on-costs and overheads for the company. **M3**

The following projects are now at the detailed design stage and the method of tendering has to be selected for each. Explain how the tender method used matches the requirement of each project.

**a** A series of four community police stations – serial tendering

**b** A complex project with design input from the contractor – two stage tendering

**c** A project where the client is keen to stay within budget – target cost fee

**d** A pre-painting repair programme for a housing association – measured term **M4**

The following estimating methods are to be used to provide a budget for the client:

**a** Approximate quantities method

**b** Cubic metres unit method

**c** Floor area method

**d** Unit of accommodation method

Evaluate and justify the selection of each used to price this construction work for the budget. **D1**

Taking your answers to M4, evaluate and justify the selection of the tendering methods outlining the advantages and disadvantages of each method. **D2**

There are several estimating and tendering software systems available to assist in the preparation of tenders. Do an Internet search to find one such system and, in a short report, examine and evaluate its performance. **D3**

## Grading tips

**M1** You will need a copy of the Standard Method of Measurement. Open the relevant section that is applicable to the items that you are taking off, and read all the rules contained within the columns. Use this information and the rules from the knowledge of using dimension paper and accurately produce the quantities required.

**M2** You need to look closely at the various stages of the construction process from the preparation of the client's budgets to the final account. Identify when measurement will take place and explain the reasons for the accuracy in the measurement at the different stages.

**M3** You need to place yourself in the shoes of a construction managing director who has to recover the office overheads and on-costs through the tendering process by winning work. You need to identify what are on-costs and overheads and give some description of these. You then have to identify a method of determining these on-costs and overheads for a given organisation, that is, how you are going to calculate these.

**M4** You need to identify why the selected tendering method matches the requirements of the proposed project, that is, why that particular method is better than the others.

**D1** You need to look closely at the estimating methods that have been identified and undertake an evaluation of them, justifying (giving good reason for the selection of each) for producing, say, budgets for a client.

# Grading tips

# Knowledge check

1 State three reasons for undertaking measurement?

2 What is the sequence for dimensions in the dimension column?

3 What is a bill of quantities?

4 What do SMM7 and CESMM3 stand for?

5 What would you find contained within the preliminary section of a bill of quantities?

6 What would be costed within a company overhead?

7 What does daywork mean?

8 What items of plant would you include within the preliminaries section?

9 Name five factors that affect the output rates of labour.

10 What affects the output of construction plant?

11 Name the elements that need to be included in general within a unit rate.

12 What documents would you send out in a tender enquiry?

13 What factors affect the return level of tenders?

14 What is the difference between net and gross?

15 What is a nominated supplier or contractor?

| To achieve a pass grade the evidence must show that the learner is able to: | To achieve a merit grade the evidence must show that, in addition to the pass criteria, the learner is able to: | To achieve a distinction grade the evidence must show that, in addition to the pass and merit criteria, the learner is able to: |
|---|---|---|
| **P1** use basic mensuration techniques to calculate and record accurate dimensions, volumes, areas and lengths from drawings **Assessment practice pages 369, 398** | **M1** apply the rules of the Standard Method of Measurement to the production of accurate quantities and descriptions **Assessment practice pages 369, 398** <br> **M2** explain the reasons for the differences in the accuracy of the measurements for different applications and stages of work **Assessment practice pages 373, 399** | |
| **P2** explain the purpose of different estimating methods and the meaning of net pricing, the content of the preliminaries section of a project and general overheads and profit **Assessment practice pages 373, 398** | | **D1** use, evaluate, and justify the selection of an appropriate estimating method for a tutor-specified scenario **Assessment practice page 372** |
| **P3** calculate all-in labour rates, plant rates and unit rates **Assessment practice pages 382, 398** | | **D2** use, evaluate, and justify the selection of an appropriate tendering method for a tutor-specified scenario **Assessment practice pages 391, 399** |
| **P4** identify and explain those factors that affect percentage profit margins, those that affect the output of labour and those that affect the working hourly/idle rates for a variety of plant items **Assessment practice pages 397, 398** | **M3** describe the items that contribute to on-costs and overheads and explain how percentage on-costs and overheads might be determined for a given organisation **Assessment practice pages 371, 399** | |
| **P5** describe the common methods of tendering for contractors, sub-contractors and supply package contractors and explain how different objectives might affect the tender price **Assessment practice pages 391, 398** | **M4** explain how the method of tendering selected matches the nature of the project **Assessment practice pages 391, 399** | **D3** examine and evaluate the use of a tutor specified software system for facilitating the estimating and tendering processes **Assessment practice pages 397, 399** |
| **P6** identify the factors that influence the levels of tenders for the main contract, sub-contract works or supply packages and explain how these factors may affect pricing strategies **Assessment practice page 398** | | |

# Surveying in construction and civil engineering

## Introduction

Surveying involves measuring distances, heights and angles. These are used to correctly position physical features correctly during the design and construction phases, and play a major part in the development of the built environment.

Before a new house can be built, a thorough measured survey of the existing site needs to be undertaken. This maps the existing natural or manmade features and is known as land or geometric surveying. This dimensional information can be presented in the form of a two-dimensional plan or three-dimensional CAD model, which is used to help a building designer produce designs for the new building and its situation on the site.

Then, as part of the construction process, the new building is positioned on the 'plan' of the site with exact dimensions showing its location, size and shape. These key setting-out dimensions fix the new building relative to the existing site features and are used to peg out the positions of the new foundations, walls and other elements of the building. The work of marking out the position of these new features is the task of the surveyor or engineer and is known as 'setting out'.

In both land surveying and setting out surveying accuracy is very important. Therefore, all surveyors need to adopt a methodical way of recording their measurement and carrying out suitable checks to make sure no mistakes have been made, and where there are errors, these must be examined to check if they are within acceptable limits.

This unit introduces you to the practical aspects of going to a site and measuring distances, levels and angles of features, then returning to the office to plot these features on a scaled plan. The final section looks at the process of setting out, which is taking an architect's scaled drawing for a new building and physically marking out the positions on the ground to enable the foundations and walls to be constructed.

### How you will be assessed

This unit is internally assessed by your tutor. A variety of activities is included in this unit to help you understand land and setting out surveying. You will need access to a range of

# Thinking points

Surveyors have a lot of responsibility in their job. They need to be numerate, organised and methodical, and be able to produce and understand technical drawings. If they ever get their calculations wrong and set out a structure or building incorrectly, then the whole project would suffer.

Would you be able to check whether two walls were correctly set out at right angles to each other? Or would you know how to find out the height of an inaccessible point? By the end of this chapter, you should understand these basic surveying techniques and be able to confidently book, record and check your measurements.

Think about some of the major civil engineering projects built during the last 15 years or so, like the Channel Tunnel or the new Wembley Stadium. Both these projects required pin-point accuracy in the measurement of the existing terrain/features and the setting out of the new works. The now-famous Wembley arch that supports the Wembley Stadium roof has a height of 133 metres, weighs 1750 tonnes and has a span of 315 metres. The individual segments of the arch were carefully aligned, positioned and welded together before being lifted into position in a series of four key stages – these being at approximately 30, 65, 100 and 112 degrees to the horizontal. During this whole process, the setting-out surveyors carefully monitored the arch's progress by recording angles and distances to track its movement until it was finally anchored at 112 degrees to the horizontal. Of course, not every surveyor's job is as prestigious as the Wembley arch, but the same competence and accuracy is required whether you are setting out the foundations for a small house or the structure for the biggest single-span roof in the world!

You can investigate further the construction of Wembley Stadium by looking at the website – www.wembleystadium.com.

basic surveying equipment as well as appropriate personal protective equipment (PPE); you should seek guidance and support from your tutor in obtaining the appropriate kit.

After completing this unit you should be able to achieve the following outcomes:

1 Understand surveying terminology and be able to use the equipment and instruments typically used to perform linear surveys, record the measurements in a standard form and produce drawings
2 Be able to use the equipment and instruments typically used to perform levelling surveys, record the measurements in a standard form and produce drawings
3 Be able to use the equipment and instruments typically used to measure angles, record the measurements in a standard form and produce results from calculations
4 Be able to perform the setting out of small buildings

## Methods of measurement

An early method of measuring distances was developed by Edmund Gunter in the seventeenth century, which involved the use of a standard-length metal chain, 22 yards long, with links of a known length. In order to measure **horizontal distances**, these chains would be pulled taut, to reduce sagging and slack, and in instances of measuring up a slope, the surveyor might have to 'break' the measurement, that is, raise the rear part of the tape upward, and plumb from where the last measurement ended. In today's fast moving construction industry, with the use of complex electronic measuring devices, these basic principles and methods are still valid. In fact, the principles that are used in these instruments have not changed since Gunter's time.

### Key term

**Horizontal distances** The flat distance that would be plotted on a two-dimensional drawing plan.

## Linear measurements

In order to understand how linear measurements can be accurately taken, let's now have a look at the two basic methods of measurement for linear methods only:

- offset measurement
- trilateration

The best way to understand how each of these different methods operates is to consider an example. So, with reference to Figure 10.1 , we can fix the position of a brick wall XY in relation to an aerial mast at Z by measuring distances only, as shown below.

### Measurement by offset

This method relies on being able to locate the point P which is at right angles to the aerial mast. Once this point is found, then the linear distances along the wall can be recorded together with the offset distance PZ. Finding the position of point P is not difficult. When measuring with a tape, the 'zero' is placed at Z and held taut, then the tape is swung in an arc and where it just

**Figure 10.1 Measurements by offset and trilateration** ▶

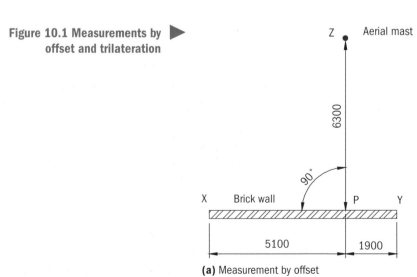

(a) Measurement by offset

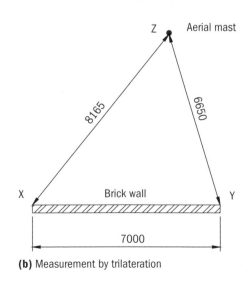

(b) Measurement by trilateration

touches the wall is the shortest distance, and will be the point P. PZ is also known as the perpendicular offset.

Then, back in the drawing office, the three distances 5100 mm, 1900 mm and 6300 mm can be plotted to a suitable scale to represent the wall and mast positions, with the 6300 mm dimension drawn at 90° to the wall. This is a traditional method for measuring details in linear surveys.

## Measurement by trilateration

This method relies on measurement of the three sides of a triangle. It is important to note that for accuracy this method should only be used where **well-conditioned triangles** are present, i.e. they are not too acute or too obtuse but roughly equilateral. Back in the drawing office, the length of the wall of 7000 mm can be plotted to a suitable scale with two arcs constructed of 8165 mm and 6650 mm radii centred on point X and Y respectively. Where these two arcs cross will be the correct position for the aerial mast at Z. This method of using two **tie lines** is often used in traditional linear surveys where offset would be too long, generally over 10 metres.

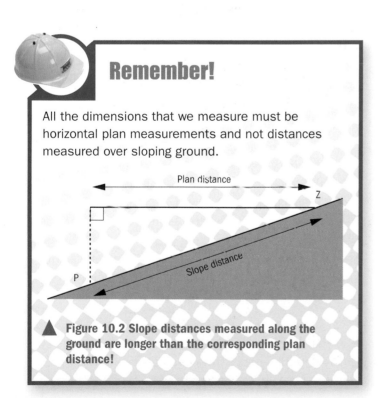

## Remember!

All the dimensions that we measure must be horizontal plan measurements and not distances measured over sloping ground.

**Figure 10.2 Slope distances measured along the ground are longer than the corresponding plan distance!**

## Key term

**Well-conditioned triangles** Triangles which are roughly equilateral in shape with no small internal angles.

**Tie lines** A pair of horizontal plan measurements used to fix the position of a point

# Carrying out a linear survey

## Equipment required

The equipment required to carry out a traditional linear survey is shown in Figure 10.3.

### ■ Measuring tapes
#### Synthetic tape

These tapes are made from fibreglass or nylon and are coated with PVC. They are a cheaper option than steel tape, but they are only graduated down to the nearest 5 mm and can become permanently stretched if pulled too hard. They have a metal prong on the end to hook the tape into position, but care should be taken to avoid bending this flat. The tape should be wiped before being re-wound, and care should be taken that the tape does not become twisted and get jammed into the case.

#### Steel tape

Graduated at every millimetre, steel tapes are durable and more stable than synthetic tapes and can be enamelled or plastic coated for added protection. They are available in 30-metre or 50-metre lengths and are calibrated to read true lengths at a standard temperature and pull, both of which are printed on the tape at the start, and are typically 20°C and 50 Newtons force respectively. With the demise of the traditional metric land chain, featuring solid 200 mm links, steel tapes are used throughout industry for a variety of land surveying and setting-out tasks. As with the synthetic tapes, steel tapes have a metal prong on the end to hook the tape into position. Ideally, the tape should be dried and wiped with an oily rag before being re-wound into its case.

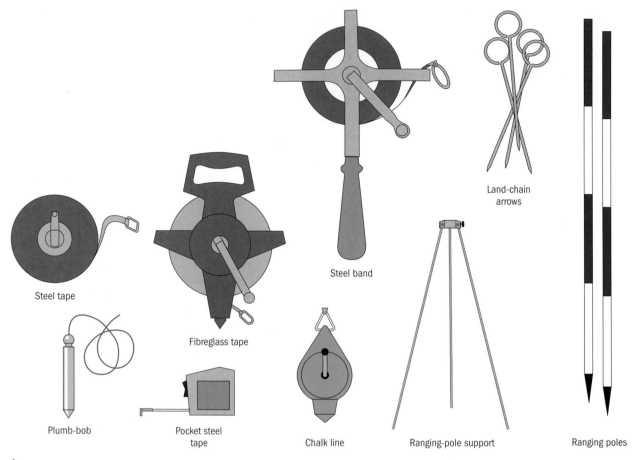

Steel tape

Plumb-bob

Fibreglass tape

Pocket steel
tape

Steel band

Chalk line

Land-chain
arrows

Ranging-pole support

Ranging poles

▲ **Figure 10.3 Equipment required for a linear survey**

**Steel band**

The steel or surveyor's band can still be found in use today by some surveyors. It is similar to the steel tape but is carried on a four-arm, open-frame winder and has oval handles connected directly to the tape. It functions like a traditional metric chain.

## ■ 25-mm folding wooden rules

These are two main types: the one-metre long boxwood folding rule with its characteristic swivel hinge or the longer two-metre multi-lath rule. Both are graduated to the nearest 1 mm and are used mainly for internal building surveys but can also be used for short offsets. Care must be taken when opening or closing the hinges to ensure that they are not bent into the wrong position.

## ■ Ranging rods or poles

These are circular timber poles, usually 2.5 m long, coated with distinctive red and white bands 500 mm in length.

The points are encased in steel shoes which allow them to be pushed into soil or they can be used with lightweight stands for surfaces such as concrete or tarmac. They are only used to mark survey stations and for ranging lines.

## ■ Arrows

These are 400 mm long steel pins with a point at one end and a ring at the other to aid carrying. A strip of red cloth or plastic tape is attached to the ring so that the arrow can be easily observed. They can be used for marking out points on the ground or for marking survey station positions prior to fixing with a stout wooden peg. A variation on the normal arrow is the dropping arrow which has a weighted point in the form of a plumb bob and is used in step measurements of slopes.

## ■ Chalk-line marker

This is a useful device which can quickly and easily imprint a straight line on any hard surface. A tight string is impregnated with chalk which is held within the case of the wound string line. This line is pulled out and held between the two points that need a marked line drawn between them, e.g. setting out a tile gauge line on a roof. The string line is pinged against the hard surface leaving a thin chalk line.

## ■ Abney level

One of the most convenient instruments for quickly finding the angle of elevation or depression of a slope, and hence the horizontal plan distance. It comprises a sighting tube, a spirit level and a scale graduated in degrees By the use of a prism, the instrument can be levelled and the angle of the line of sight recorded.

▲  **An abney level**

## ■ Electro-distance measuring device

These are a very popular method of measuring and recording distances. The hand-held instruments are quick and accurate with a range approaching 100 m with an accuracy of + or – 2 mm. Some, like the Leica Disto™, have a continuous reading which allows maximum

▲  **Electro-distance meter**

distances for measuring room diagonals, and minimum distances for finding right-angle distances or offsets distances.

## ■ Personal protective equipment

When carrying out surveying work it is important that you (the surveyor) carry out risk assessments on the possible hazards that may be present at the site location to minimise the probability of harm to yourself and others while undertaking the work. The current minimum statutory requirements for site workers' personal protective equipment (PPE) are to wear a hard hat, high visibility jackets and safety boots or shoes and this applies to site engineers and surveyors. Even when undertaking land surveys prior to any construction work being carried out, you should always wear PPE and it is advisable to keep an appointments dairy so office staff can track where you are and know your return time. When surveying existing buildings you should always carry out a thorough risk assessment for possible hazards. Typical hazards are the presence of asbestos, unstable floors, trip hazards, untethered guard dogs and pigeon droppings!

### Safety tip

- Always wear suitable personal protective equipment when carrying out a survey.
- Keep an appointments diary so office staff know where you are.

### Procedure for carrying out a linear survey

## ■ Reconnaissance

The first stage of any survey involving linear, level or angular measurements is to carry out a full reconnaissance of the area to be surveyed. The basic process involves creating a **survey framework** that covers the whole area, which in itself can then be broken down into smaller parts to record all the small but necessary details and features of the area. This process is commonly known as **working from the whole to the part**, that is, taking an overview of the whole extent of the survey area and thinking carefully how it could be split up into manageable parts. You, the surveyor, should walk over the site to select the most suitable positions for key reference points, which are known as survey stations. These stations should be clearly marked and referenced so that their positions can be found at any time in the future. This process of recording the positions of the stations is called 'witnessing' and consists of drawing sketches of the point with clear dimensions to at least three existing fixed features such as the corner of an inspection chamber or a steel fence point.

The best survey framework for accuracy comprises a network of strong well-conditioned triangles. Also, to ensure high accuracy, there should be one main **baseline** from which all the other triangles are linked. There should also be secondary **check lines** which can be used as further check on the survey framework.

## Key terms

**Survey framework** A triangular network of measured horizontal lines that fix the end points (survey stations) of those lines.

**Working from the whole to the part** Taking an overview of the survey area and working out how it could be split up into manageable parts.

## Key terms

**Baseline** The main survey line or 'back-bone' on which to form all the other survey triangles.

**Check lines** An additional measured line to check the accuracy of the survey framework.

## Remember!

Always consider the accuracy of the survey!

The reconnaissance must also take into account the purpose of the final survey drawing and the accuracy of the final survey plot. In manual plotting the thinnest line width that can be plotted by a sharp pencil or ink pen is approximately 0.25 mm. If the final plot of the survey is to be 1:200, then the smallest dimension that can be measured during the survey and accurately plotted will be:

0.25 mm × 200 = 50 mm

When deciding the positions of the stations and survey lines that form the surveying framework, the following should be considered:

- Survey lines should be as few as possible, but sufficient to form a triangular framework over the site.
- The location of the baseline from which to form all the other survey triangles.
- The triangles should not have small internal angles.
- Check lines should be used.
- Survey lines should pass close to the boundary and any features of the site.
- Survey lines should be positioned over the more level ground.
- Stations in any triangle should be intervisible.
- Obstacles to ranging and chaining should be avoided, e.g. trees and ponds.

The measured data should be recorded in a special field book, traditionally known as the chain book, which has two thin tramlines drawn down the centre of the page These represent the tape line laid out between the survey stations and either side of these double lines are drawn the features that are to be measured with offsets or tie lines.

You, as the surveyor, should walk down each survey line and note exactly what physical features are on either side of the line and sketch them. Do not start measuring anything until after you have drawn all the features that you are going to measure first – you must develop this methodical and clear system otherwise you will miss detail or make errors when you do measure. In this way, you are concentrating first on what and how you are going to measure and then, and only then, you can go on to devote all your energies to measuring and correctly recording your measurements.

### Remember!

Don't start measuring anything until *after* you have drawn all the features that you are going to measure.

## ■ Measuring and booking the details

So now you have drawn all the features that you plan to measure on your booking sheet, you can record the running measurements or **chainage** along the tape from one station to the point on the line where the offset distances (at right angles) occur to selected features (for example, location of boundary of the site, paths, trees). The offset distances can be measured with a synthetic tape and the way to find the right-angle point is straightforward (see Figure 10.1 on page 404).

## Key term

**Chainage** The cumulative distances measured to specific features as fixed from one end of the survey line.

The main points to be considered when recording information in the booking sheets are as follows:

- Offset measurements should be as short as possible, and should not normally exceed 10 m. You can estimate a right angle by eye if the distance is less than about 3 m or by swinging the tape in an arc and taking the shortest measurement. The offset dimension lines should not be drawn in the book.

- Where offset distances are greater than 10 m, it is best to use a pair of tie lines as this is more accurate. Both tie line measurements should be shown in the booking sheet. (See the case study below on fixing the position of the oak tree.)

- All measurements should be recorded to two decimal places and an oblique stroke used, not a decimal point, for example 4/25 not 4.25. This avoids blobs of dirt from obscuring the decimal point and making the recorded figures unintelligible.

- Information need not be drawn to scale in the booking sheet, but should be clearly set out so that it can be understood when the survey is plotted in the office. It is best to write the offset distance close to the feature drawn in the booking sheet.

- Several pages of booking may be needed for long or complicated tape lines, and explanatory notes should be added where necessary. It may be very difficult and time consuming to return to the site to re-do a measurement or check up on information, especially if the site is a long way from the office.

- Straight line measurement may be continued beyond a station to the site boundary, if necessary, and the information recorded. This is so that detail in the corners of the site can be recorded.

- Circles should be drawn around the stations in the booking sheet, so they can be seen clearly, and the overall distance of the survey line included within the circle.

- The circumference or girth of a tree should be measured 1 m above the ground and recorded in brackets by the tree. The spread of the tree should also be recorded.

## Case study

An old factory and storage depot is being surveyed for redevelopment. A reconnaissance has been carried out and the sketch in Figure 10.4 has been produced showing the selected survey stations and survey lines. The longest line AF has been set up as the baseline for the survey and its bearing to magnetic north has also been noted with a magnetic compass. Survey line BC is acting as a check line but will also be used to measure survey details. To ensure that the survey stations can be found at any time, they are pegged out with a stout timber peg if on soil or fixed by a shot-fired nail into asphalt or concrete and marked with surveyor's spray paint.

The booking sheet for GC in Figure 10.5 shows clearly the layout and notation to be used for showing offsets, tie lines and chainage to a standard format.

## Key term

**Ranging a line**  The process of measuring a straight line between two points which are a long way apart.

### Ranging a line

Consider baseline AF. It is approaching 160 m long. This is far longer than any manufactured steel tape, the majority of which are around 50 m long. Therefore, we have to create a straight line between A and F using a technique called **ranging a line**. A ranging pole is set up in a vertical position at stations A and F. You stand behind the range pole at A. Your assistant holds a range pole in a vertical position at the other end of the tape and roughly in line with stations A and F. You then sight through A to F and direct your assistant to move the range pole to the left or right, until the range pole is in line with stations A and F. This new point is marked with a surveying arrow or marked with spray marker. This process is known as ranging a line.

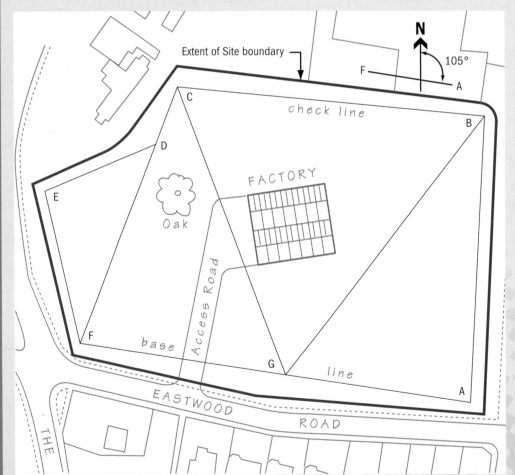

**Figure 10.4 Sketch of Eastwood Road**

Your assistant then gently ripples the tape up and down until the steel tape lies along the sight line between A and the end of the tape. Under no circumstances should the tape be pulled into position as it will stretch the steel tape. Further ranging and taping may be necessary to position the chain exactly in the direction of the stations A and F then the end of the tape is marked with an arrow.

The length along the tape is measured cumulatively from A right to the end at F. As you progress along the line, you record the offset distances to the features to be surveyed as before. As you move along the line, you must ensure that you collect up all the arrows until you finally reach station F.

1   **What other survey lines for this case study do you think would need to have a line ranged in?**

2   **The majority of the site is a grassed area. How would the survey stations be physically marked?**

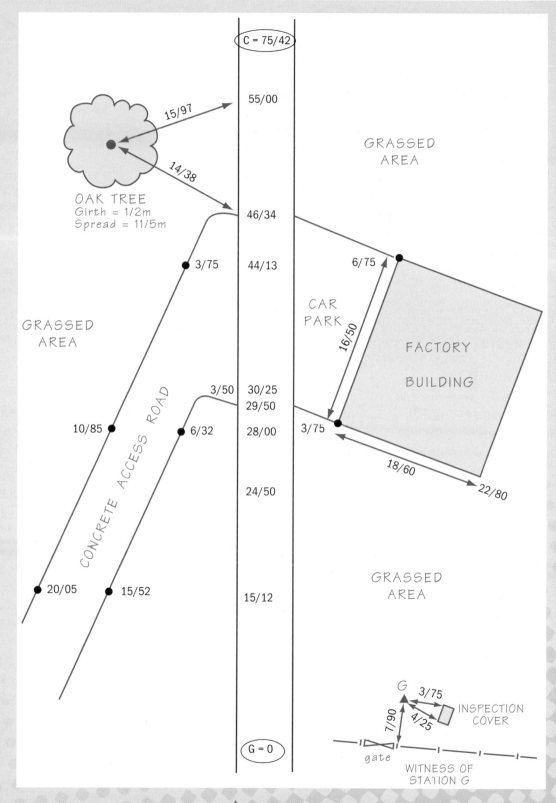

▲ **Figure 10.5 Booking sheet for the line GC**

## Errors in measurement and booking

Measurement of distances will always be prone to inaccuracies due to the continuous nature of the data. As a surveyor, you must be aware of where errors can occur and more importantly how they can be minimised. There are three basic classifications of errors:

- *Gross or human errors* – mistakes made in reading or booking measurements, such as miscounting or wrongly reading the tape, or writing down the wrong measurements in the booking sheet. These errors can be very large and can occur at any stage in the survey. If not picked up early on, they can cause the survey to be abandoned and redone. The best way to avoid making mistakes like this is to develop a clear method of reading and booking the results. For example, read the measurement on the tape, write the measurement in the booking sheet, then re-read the tape to check it is the same as what you have just written.

- *Systematic errors* – errors in the **calibration** of the equipment, for example using a plastic tape which has become permanently stretched. This inbuilt error will always give an under estimation of the true distance and will have a gradual cumulative effect on the survey. The only way to check for this type of error is to compare the tape against 'standard' steel tapes kept for that specific purpose. If the error is found after the fieldwork has been completed, the distance can be corrected by applying a suitable correction to the measured dimensions, so no information is lost.

## Key term

**Calibration** The process of ensuring that the measuring equipment is correctly adjusted to give true readings.

- *Random errors* – these are generally small errors that compensate each other and are due to the limitations of the surveyor or the equipment. For example, a person might have a slight visual impediment due to their short-sightedness which affects how they read

## Remember!

Full details of how to check the calibration of tapes is given in BS 7334: Part 2:1990 'Measuring instruments for building construction'.

the tape's graduations. Although these errors tend to be very small and can cancel each other out, they can be avoided by taking suitable check measurements and repeating readings.

## Accuracy in measurement and booking

In normal practice, linear surveys should try to achieve an accuracy of 1 in 5000, or 6 mm over a distance of 30 m. To do this, you must consider the following errors that might affect finding the true horizontal plan distances:

- *Slope* – where the measured distance was recorded along the sloping ground. If there is a difference of height between the ends of a 30-metre tape of less than 600 mm, then the accuracy above is achievable. Where the drop is greater than 600 mm, use other methods to find the true plan distance such as step measurements or measuring the slope angle (see box).

- *Sag* – where the measured distance was in an arc due to the weight of the tape. To obtain an accuracy of 1 in 5000, the centre of a 30-metre steel tape should not sag by more than 300 mm from the horizontal.

- *Temperature variation* – where the temperature of the steel tape caused it to expand where it was warmer than the standard temperature of 20°C, or to contract where it was cooler. If the temperature does not vary from the standard temperature by a maximum of 18°C, then an accuracy of 1 in 5000 for a 30-metre tape is possible.

- *Tension* – where a steel tape is pulled to reduce the sag but as a result is stretched because the steel is 'elastic'. These errors are generally very small and can be ignored.

## Step measurements

In this method, the chain is held in a horizontal position and the end of the chain is stepped down to the ground, using a drop arrow. It is easier to work downhill rather than uphill. The horizontal distance measured depends on the steepness of the slope of the ground, but generally should not exceed 10 m. The vertical distance should not exceed 1.5 m, for example eye-sight level.

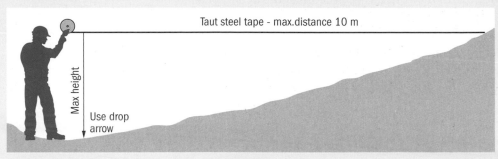

**Figure 10.6 Step measurement**

## Slope measurement

In this method, the slope distance is measured with the tape, and the angle of slope is measured with an Abney level (see Figure 10.7). The angle is measured by setting up a range pole at each end of the line. The surveyor stands by one range pole holding the Abney level against the range pole. The surveyor then sights a point at the same height on the other range pole. The angle measured is the angle of slope of the ground. Then the:

True plan distance = Slope distance × Cosine (measured angle of the slope)

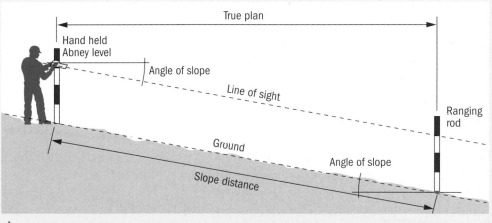

**Figure 10.7 Slope measurement**

## Plotting the survey

It is very important that your final survey drawings are accurate and neat. A great deal of effort and time will have gone into producing a comprehensive set of field notes and measurement data and this will be wasted if a survey drawing is badly presented. Your client will certainly not want to pay for a poorly presented and inaccurate drawing!

Just as the survey was progressed from the 'whole to the part' so is the final survey plot. The lengths of all the survey lines are taken from the booking sheets and the longest line, known as the baseline, is plotted first to the desired scale. By striking arcs with a large radius compass, the other survey stations are established and the network of triangles drawn. Check lines are scaled off and compared with actual distances.

Once the framework has been plotted, the details of all the features of the site can be plotted. Offsets and ties are systematically plotted in the same order in which they were booked, that is, working from the beginning to the end of each line. The right angles for offsets may be set out by set square.

The ranges of available scale are given in Table 10.1.

| Small-scale maps | Large-scale maps | Site plans | Detail plans |
|---|---|---|---|
| 1:1 000 000 | 1:10 000 | 1:500 | 1:20 |
| to | to | to | to |
| 1:20 000 | 1:1000 | 1:50 | 1:1 (full size) |

**Table 10.1 Preferred scales**

When plotting the survey manually, it is good practice to draft out the survey lines on tracing paper so that by overlaying this on the paper to be used, the survey may be properly centred on that sheet. The 'North' point should always be shown and preferably pointing towards the top of the sheet.

After the points are plotted, the detail is drawn in, using standardised symbols, some of which are shown in Figure 10.8. The drawing is then inked in, the North point drawn and any necessary lettering, including a suitable title block, scales and annotation, carried out. The conventions for showing landscape features are given in BS EN ISO 11091:1999.

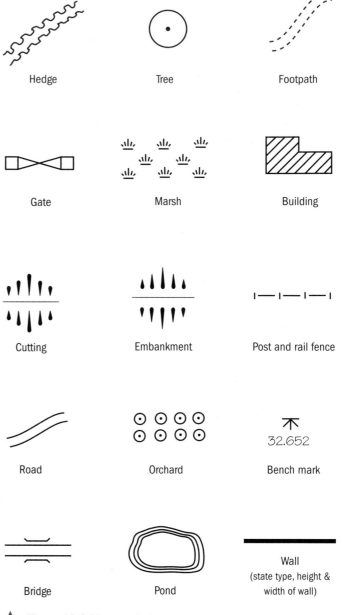

▲ **Figure 10.8 Map symbols**

## Knowledge check

1  Describe what working from the 'whole to the part' means when carrying out a survey reconnaissance.

2  Define each of the following terms and illustrate with labelled diagrams: (a) baseline, (b) survey line, (c) detail line, (d) check line, (e) offset, (f) tie line.

3  An initial site sketch has been made of a small farmstead and the surveyor has started setting out the survey stations as shown in Figure 10.9, with the baseline AB and detail lines BC and AC.

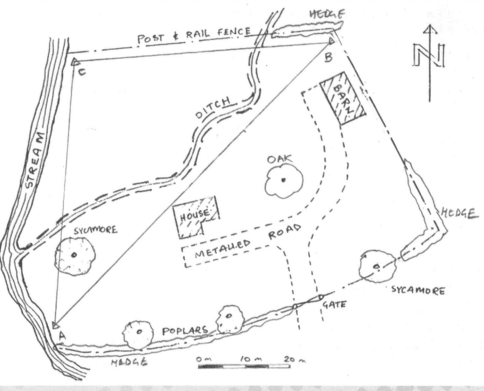

▲ **Figure 10.9 Site sketch of farmstead**

**a**  Take an enlarged photocopy of the sketch and then complete the reconnaissance sketch clearly showing all the survey lines and check lines needed to cover the whole site.

**b**  Produce a booking sheet using standard methods for line AB showing clearly how:

(i)  the ditch running across the site could be plotted

(ii)  the oak tree's position could be accurately fixed from baseline AB.

## Assessment practice

Practical site survey using linear measurement:

**a**  Select a small area of land close to your place of study.

**b**  Working in groups of three, undertake a reconnaissance of the site and select/witness your survey stations.

**c**  By practical application and use of tapes or bands, record the features of the site and book them using a recognised procedure.

**d**  From your field notes produce a drawing to a recognised scale showing the main site features.

Analyse the methods for improving the accuracy of linear surveys and reducing errors. **D1**

# Key terms used in levelling

Levelling is a process that compares heights of points on the earth surface. In carrying out a level survey, reference has to be made to a fixed point or datum of known height. On large civil engineering projects, such as roads, railways and bridges, levels are linked to the system of Ordnance Survey Bench Marks (OSBM) which are referenced to the height of mean sea level at Newlyn in Cornwall. These heights appear on a range of maps and small-scale plans published by the Ordnance Survey. On smaller local construction projects, it is usually sufficient to relate all heights to an arbitrary fixed point established on site called a Temporary Bench Mark (TBM).

The act of levelling and height control has the following purposes:

- Measuring vertical heights of points or stations located on the ground.

- Setting out profiles on site to give the heights of new construction works, such as depths of foundation relative to the ground slab level or damp-proof course height.

- Producing a grid of spot heights to give an indication of the ground surface. This information is often shown on maps and plans as a series of contour lines, where a contour line joins points of equal height.

- Producing a cross-sectional drawing, often called a 'long' section, to help plan the construction of underground services, such as setting out sewer gradients.

**Figure 10.10 Main parts of an optical level** ▶

# Levelling equipment used in land surveying

Levelling instruments are very versatile and can be used for both setting out points and for recording heights of existing features. They are accurate and, if properly maintained, should provide a long and useful service.

All levels comprise two basic parts:

- a high-resolution telescope with magnification of around ×20–×24 which rotates around a vertical axis

- a spirit bubble tube which is set parallel and horizontal to the telescope.

If the level is in good adjustment, the line of sight through the telescope – the line of collimation – is parallel to the horizontal level line given by the spirit bubble tube, and both these lines are at 90 degrees to the vertical axis of the level. A simple test known as the 'two-peg test' should be undertaken to check that both line of collimation and level line are parallel (see below).

The basic set up of these main elements and linked terminology is shown in Figure 10.10.

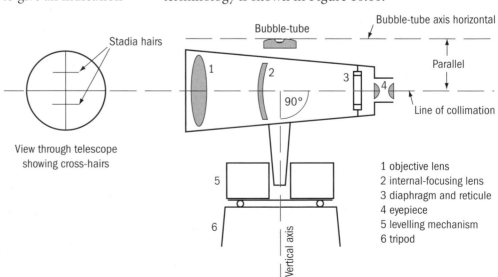

View through telescope showing cross-hairs

Stadia hairs

Bubble-tube

Bubble-tube axis horizontal

Parallel

Line of collimation

Vertical axis

1 objective lens
2 internal-focusing lens
3 diaphragm and reticule
4 eyepiece
5 levelling mechanism
6 tripod

## Setting up the level

1  Whenever possible, locate the instrument where all stations to be sighted can be viewed.

2  Extend the legs on the tripod so that it is at shoulder height, and fix the level to the tripod using the centre screw. Make sure the legs are spread wide to form a stable support to the level.

3  Level the instrument according to the type of level and its controls (see below).

4  Once the instrument is level, locate the levelling staff on top of the datum, either the TBM or if available the OSBM. You may have to adjust the main telescope focus knob on the side of the level to see the staff.

5  Once you have located the staff, make sure that the cross and stadia hairs are sharp by adjusting the eyepiece focus ring. This corrects for the phenomenon known as parallax where the cross-hairs move relative to the image of the staff.

6  The level is now ready to use. Another person will be needed to hold the staff as upright as possible to ensure an accurate reading can be taken.

## Reading the surveying staff

In order to take full advantage of the accuracy and range of the optical level, a special staff known as the 'E' staff is used. These are lightweight, aluminium, telescopic staffs available in 4-metre and 5-metre lengths and graduated in distinctive 'E' shaped black, red and white blocks where each horizontal bar is equal to 10 mm, making the height of the 'E' as 50mm. Staffs are generally used to measure the distance up to the level line of sight. However, they can just as easily be turned upside down to record the heights of bridge soffits or gable walls by measuring the distance down to the level line of sight. These readings are known as inverted staff readings and are booked as

▲ Metric 'E' staff

negative values in a level booking form.

With good eye-sight, you should be able to estimate the staff reading to the nearest 1 mm, that is one tenth of one of the 10 mm coloured blocks.

To help the person holding the staff to keep it vertical, there is usually a circular spirit bubble on the back face of the staff. However, with older staffs, this can often get damaged or knocked and so may not be all that reliable. An alternative is to gently sway the staff backwards and forwards in line with the instrument, and the surveyor observing the staff reads the minimum distance observed on the staff.

## The dumpy level

This is the traditional optical level that is levelled by three foot-screws and a single plate or tube spirit bubble, a common device used extensively in theodolites and total stations (see page 00). The dumpy level can give an accurate reading up to a tolerance of 3 mm over a distance of 150 m.

▲ Automatic level with dumpy levelling mechanism

## ■ Setting up the dumpy level

1  Ensure the instrument is stable, the legs are spread and at the right height for viewing.

2  Ensure the top of the tripod is reasonably level to receive the instrument. This is because the screw adjustment has only limited travel.

3  Ensure the screws of the instrument are approximately in the middle of the thread.

4  Position the barrel of the telescope and therefore the levelling bubble parallel to any two screws – 2 and 3 in Figure 10.12 (a).

5  Adjust 2 and 3 screws at the same time, either both away from or both towards each other at the same rate. The bubble will move in the direction your *left thumb* is moving. By this method centre the bubble.

## Case study

The following readings were sighted through the telescope of an optical level A, B, C and D. The reading for A is 1.033 m and B is 0.635 m.

What are the readings for C and D?

Did you know that you can also use a level to measure plan distances? This method is known as stadia tachemometry, where the:

Plan distance = 100 × Distance recorded on the levelling staff between the top and bottom stadia hairs

For example, if the top stadia hair reads 2.255 m and the bottom hair reads 2.105 m, then the direct plan distance between the instrument and the staff positions would be:

Plan distance = 100 × (2.255 m − 2.103 m)
$\qquad$ = 100 × 0.152 m
$\qquad$ = 15.2 m

For optical level staff readings, calculate the distances for B, C and D.

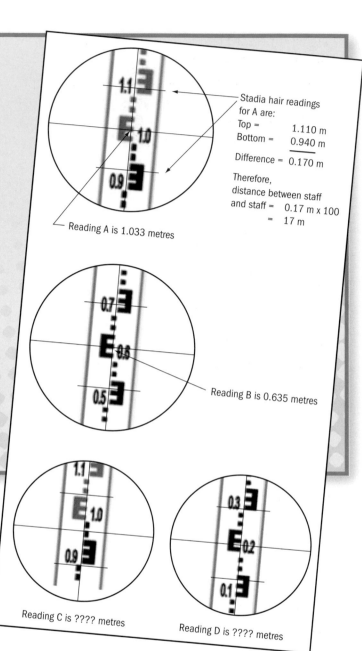

Stadia hair readings for A are:
Top = 1.110 m
Bottom = 0.940 m
Difference = 0.170 m

Therefore,
distance between staff and staff = 0.17 m x 100
$\qquad$ = 17 m

Reading A is 1.033 metres

Reading B is 0.635 metres

Reading C is ???? metres

Reading D is ???? metres

**Figure 10.11 Reading a levelling staff** ▶

6   Now turn the barrel through 90 degrees so that it lies over the third screw 1, as shown in Figure 10.12 (b).

7   Adjust that screw *only* to centre the bubble.

8   Repeat the process on the two original screws to ensure fine accuracy.

**Figure 10.12 Setting up the** ▶
**dumpy level**

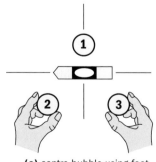

**(a)** centre bubble using foot screws 2 and 3

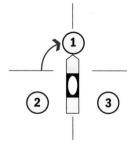

**(b)** centre bubble using 1 after turning through 90°

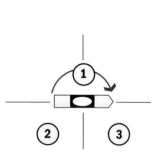

**(c)** turn bubble through 180° in plan and if it stays central it will do so for all positions

9 Finally, rotate the level so it is 180 degrees from its starting position as shown in Figure 10.12 (c).

10 If the bubble remains in the centre, then the instrument will be level in all directions; if not, then the bubble tube will need to be reset according to the manufacturer's instructions.

## The tilting level

These levels are most often used for high accuracy work but can be used in all types of level surveys. The main difference between tilting levels and the dumpy level is the levelling mechanism. The rough levelling of the tilting level is sometimes done by a circular spirit bubble; thereafter, every time the instrument is pointed in a new direction, it is accurately levelled by centring a plate bubble with a fine vertical adjusting screw. This does not affect the line of collimation. Tilting levels can also be used to assist in setting out slopes and sewer gradients with the aid of the tilting screw.

## The automatic level

The automatic level has a mechanism which allows the instrument to be levelled automatically provided that it is roughly levelled by using a small circular spirit bubble located on the body of the instrument.

The method by which this bubble is levelled varies from instrument to instrument. Some favour a central knuckle joint while others have a pair of sliding circular wedges; some also use three foot-screws such as used in a dumpy level, as shown in Figure 10.13.

▲ An automatic level

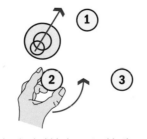

**Figure 10.13 ▶ Automatic levelling**

A circular bubble is centred in the same way as a tube type. A bubble will always move in the same direction as the surveyor's left thumb

## The digital level and bar-coded staff

These are automatic levels which read the 'bar-coded' staff electronically. This is a relatively new development and although more expensive than normal optical automatic levels, they are quicker to read and (when used properly) are less prone to human errors.

After aiming and focusing on the bar-coded staff using optical sights, the reading is taken electronically and displayed. It can also be set for tracking continuous measurement for use in setting out height.

They also incorporate facilities to store levelling measurements and download them to a variety of computer software programs for working out cross-sectional areas and volumes.

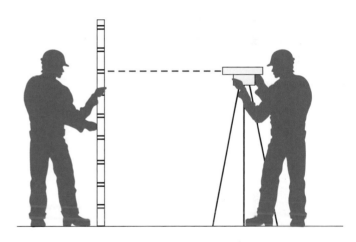

(a) A bar-coded level in use

(b) View through telescope

(c) Electronic display of difference in height and reduced level

▲ **Figure 10.14 Surveyor using bar-coded staff**

# The principle of levelling

The basic method of undertaking levelling with an optical, digital or laser level is that the line of collimation forms a horizontal level line from which vertical measurements are recorded. The example below shows a level set up correctly and sighted on to five points on the ground and a TBM of known height. We can work out the **reduced level** of *any* of these points so that *all* their heights can be compared. For example, the reduced level of:

point A = 15.0 m + 0.9 m − 1.5 m = 14.4 m
point B = 15.0 m + 0.9 m − 1.2 m = 14.7 m
point C = 15.0 m + 0.9 m − 1.7 m = 14.2 m
point D = 15.0 m + 0.9 m − 2.2 m = 13.7 m
point E = 15.0 m + 0.9 m + 0.8 m = 16.7 m
point F = 15.0 m + 0.9 m − 1.4 m = 14.5 m

Note that point E has the level staff turned upside down, which is known as an 'inverted' staff reading; thus the reduced level of the underside of the footbridge is obtained by adding the staff reading to the height of the instrument.

## Key term

**Reduced level** The height of a point or horizontal line that is relative to a given point of known height (datum)

## The two–peg test for optical levels

The main source of error in optical levelling is when the line of collimation of the levelling instrument is not parallel to the horizontal level line. This error can be detected and adjusted using the two-peg test. This test should be carried out before any major level survey. The method for carrying out this test is as follows:

1   Select two points X and Y approximately 60 m apart and set the level up midway between them. Take readings for the staff at point X and at point Y. The readings when subtracted will give the true difference in height between the points as the collimation error will cancel itself out.

2   Move the level beyond point X as close as its minimum focusing distance and take readings on points X and Y again. If the level has no collimation error, the difference between the readings of the two points should be identical to that previously measured.

3   If the result of this test shows a difference of more than 5 mm, the level instrument should be returned for a calibration service. (BS 5606: 'Guide to Accuracy in Building' states that the error should be less than 5 mm over 60 m.)

## Remember!

Keep the distance of backsights and foresights approximately equal as this will reduce collimation errors. It is easier to estimate the staff reading to the nearest 1 mm if you keep staff readings to less than 30 m distance.

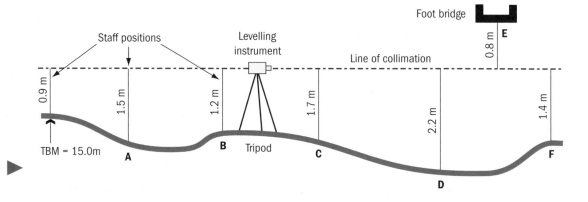

**Figure 10.15 The principles of levelling**

# Traditional methods of booking levels

There are two methods for booking level readings to enable the reduced levels of points to be found:

- the height of the plane collimation (HPC) method
- the rise and fall method.

Each method requires the use of standard booking sheets, which can be purchased in pre-printed, bound, note books, or can be drawn up on squared paper.

Both methods use similar terms. The headings of the booking sheets are shown below.

Repeated individual staff readings have different names depending on the order in which they are taken. The basic definitions for the different staff readings are shown in Table 10.2.

| Backsight (BS) | First staff reading of a levelling operation or the first reading after the instrument has been moved |
| --- | --- |
| Foresight (FS) | Last staff reading of a levelling operation before the level is moved |
| Intermediate sight (IS) | Any staff reading taken between the backsight and foresight readings |
| Reduced level (RL) | Height of any point relative to the datum used for the survey |
| Change point (CP) | A known point on the ground in which a foresight and then a backsight is taken |

Table 10.2 Definitions of staff readings

**The HPC method booking form**

Job description ..............................................  Surveyor ..............................................

Name of site ..............................................  Job reference ..............................................

Address ..............................................  Date ..............................................

| Backsight (BS) | Intermediate sight (IS) | Foresight (FS) | Height of plane of collimation (HPC) | Reduced level (RL) | Distance | Remarks |
| --- | --- | --- | --- | --- | --- | --- |
|  |  |  |  |  |  |  |
|  |  |  |  |  |  |  |
|  |  |  |  |  |  |  |

**The rise and fall method booking form**

Job description ..............................................  Surveyor ..............................................

Name of site ..............................................  Job reference ..............................................

Address ..............................................  Date ..............................................

| Backsight (BS) | Intermediate sight (IS) | Foresight (FS) | Rise | Fall | Reduced level (RL) | Distance | Remarks |
| --- | --- | --- | --- | --- | --- | --- | --- |
|  |  |  |  |  |  |  |  |
|  |  |  |  |  |  |  |  |
|  |  |  |  |  |  |  |  |

Often the levelling instrument needs to be moved during the levelling circuit. A point on the ground is selected to be a 'change point' (CP) at which the staff reading is taken. A foresight is read with the staff held on this change point, the staff remains at the change point and the level is moved and set up again. A backsight is then read to the change point and the survey continues. In this way, the reduced levels relative to the original bench mark can be transferred around the circuit.

The method of recording the staff readings is the backsight reading in the left-hand column, intermediate sight in the second column and foresight in the third column. It is important to remember that the staff reading for any new point on the ground needs a new line in the booking table, and the only time two staff readings will appear on the same line is at a change point (CP). This is where the foresight from the previous level position and the backsight from the new level position coincide.

If the misclosure is outside the allowable value, then the survey should be repeated; if it is within the allowable error, the error should be distributed equally between the readings.

### Remember!

The construction and setting out of the Channel Tunnel in 1991 had to achieve an accuracy of 100 mm in level over a distance of 18 km.

In order to understand the process of carrying out a level survey using the HPC and rise and fall methods, let's now consider the following case study.

### Remember!

When booking the levels in the field, always use a '/' instead of a decimal point '.' because decimal points can become easily obscured by mud or dust.

### Remember!

Keep clear and neat booking entries for all your readings, and always carry out your booking in the field before you return to the office as it is easier and quicker to check and, if necessary, repeat your readings.

The levelling operation is undertaken as a circuit of levels between points of known height, usually a bench mark such as a TBM or OSBM. A circuit will start and return to the same point – a closed level survey – or it will go between two different bench marks of known height. Either way, the series of levels can be checked for accuracy such that the closing errors between the first and the final transferred levels can be determined. This survey error is called the 'misclosure' and can be compared against an allowable value given in BS 5606: 'Guide to Accuracy in Building' which is often quoted as:

$\pm$ 20 mm$\sqrt{}$(No. of kilometres travelled around circuit)

or for small surveys less than a kilometre

$\pm$ 20 mm$\sqrt{}$(No. of instrument positions).

# Case study

A sewer is to be constructed to a new industrial warehouse. Part of the initial design work requires the profile of the existing ground level to be found. Therefore, a series of levels is taken along the length of the proposed sewer at regular intervals.

Details of the fieldwork that has been undertaken are shown in Figure 10.16. There were three instrument positions to pick up the ground levels at 15-metre chainage intervals, and the circuit of levels started from an OSBM on an existing building. The individual staff readings that were taken are shown on the sketch.

## Using the HPC method

The HPC method uses the horizontal line of sight through the level instrument as a reference for all the individual staff readings. This horizontal line of sight is called the plane of collimation and the height of this can be found from:

| Height of plane of collimation (HPC) | = | Given bench mark height (BM) | + | Backsight reading (BS) |

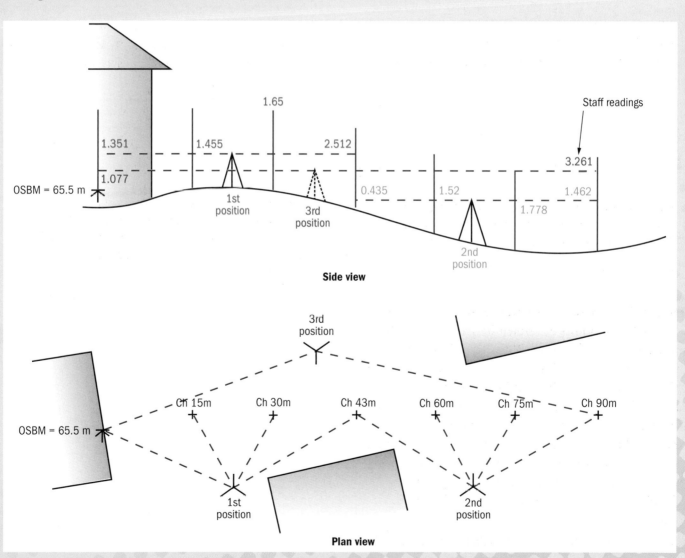

▲ **Figure 10.16 Premiere Industrial Estate plan**

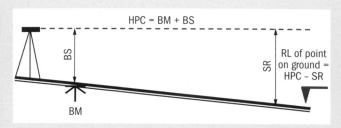

HPC = BM + BS

BS

SR

RL of point on ground = HPC – SR

BM

▲ **Figure 10.17 The HPC method**

From then on, the reduced levels (RL) of the ground are found from:

Reduced level of ground (RL) = Height of plane of collimation (HPC) − Any staff reading (SR)

This is shown in Figure 10.17.

Let's now book the levels for the Premiere Industrial Estate level survey using the HPC method. The staff level recordings that were carried out as shown in Figure 10.16 are placed in the HPC booking table shown in Figure 10.18. In the table the readings have been colour coded to help you understand how each value was calculated:

Red is the calculated reduced levels of the ground.

Blue is the 1st level instrument position staff readings and the HPC height is found:

HPC = 65.5 + 1.351 = 66.851 m

and the RL at 15 m chainage = 66.851 − 1.455 = 66.396 m etc.

Green is the 2nd level instrument position staff readings and HPC height.

e.g. New HPC = 64.339 + 0.435 = 66.774 m

and RL at 60 m chainage = 64.774 − 1.52 = 63.254 m etc.

Purple is the 3rd level instrument position staff readings and HPC height.

e.g. New HPC = 63.312 + 3.261 = 66.573 m

and RL at measured back onto the OSBM = 66.573 − 1.077 = 65.504 m etc.

| Job Description...Ground levels along sewer line..................... | | | | Surveyor...MJH............ | | |
| Name of site......Premiere Industrial Estate.................. | | | | Job Reference...11/19-11 | | |
| Address.......................... | | | | Date......15th Sept 06..... | | |

| Backsight BS | Intermediate sight IS | Foresight FS | Height of Plane of Collimation HPC | Reduced Level RL | Distance | Remarks |
|---|---|---|---|---|---|---|
| 1/351 | | | 66/851 | 65/500 | - | OSBM 65/500 |
| | 1/455 | | " | 65/396 | 15 m | |
| | 1/650 | | " | 65/201 | 30 m | |
| 0/435 | | 2/512 | 64/774 | 64/339 | 45 m | Change Point (CP) |
| | 1/520 | | " | 63/254 | 60 m | |
| | 1/778 | | " | 62/996 | 75 m | |
| 3/261 | | 1/462 | 66/573 | 63/312 | 90 m | Change Point (CP) |
| | | 1/077 | " | 65/496 | - | OSBM |
| | | | | | | |
| 5/047 | | 5/051 | | 65/500 | | |
| | | 5/047 | | 65/496 | | |
| | | 0/004 | | 0/004 | | |
| | | | | | | |
| Booking Checks | | | | | | |
| Difference in BS – FS = Difference between 1st & last RL | | | | | | |
| Therefore Levels have been booked correctly however | | | | | | |
| there is a misclosure of 4mm | | | | | | |
| | | | | | | |
| & Allowable Misclosure | | | | | | |
| The allowable misclosure for this small level survey is | | | | | | |
| ± 20mm √(No. of change points) = ± 20mm x √2 | | | | | | |
| | | = ± 28 mm > 4mm THEREFORE ACCEPTABLE MISCLOSURE | | | | |

▲ **Figure 10.18 The HPC booking table**

## Booking checks for the HPC method

Once all the reduced levels have been calculated for the whole circuit of staff readings, a check has to be carried out to make sure that they have been booked correctly and that the arithmetic is right! If the arithmetic is correct, then:

| The difference between the sum of the backsights and the sum of the foresights | = | The difference between the first and last reduced level |
|---|---|---|

So, totalling up all the backsights and all the foresights and finding their difference gives an answer of 4 mm. Then finding the difference between the first and last reduced levels also gives 4 mm. Therefore, the backsights and foresights have been correctly booked.

## Using the rise and fall method

This method does not use the height of collimation but instead compares the difference in height between adjacent staff readings that have been measured. In the example below the staff reading at the TBM is 1.56 m and the next staff reading at point A on the ground is 1.75 m.

The difference between these two readings is found by subtracting the second reading from the first reading, i.e. 1.56 m – 1.75 m = –0.19 m. Because it is a negative value, it is a 'fall'.

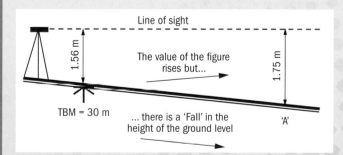

| Job Description...Ground levels along sewer line.................... | | | | | | Surveyor...MJH........... | |
|---|---|---|---|---|---|---|---|
| Name of site......Premiere Industrial Estate............................ | | | | | | Job Reference...11/19-11 | |
| Address........ | | | | | | Date......15th Sept 06..... | |

| Backsight BS | Intermediate sight IS | Foresight FS | Rise | Fall | Reduced Level RL | Distance | Remarks |
|---|---|---|---|---|---|---|---|
| 1/351 | | | | | 65/500 | - | OSBM 65/500 |
| | 1/455 | | | 0/104 | 65/396 | 15 m | |
| | 1/650 | | | 0/195 | 65/201 | 30 m | |
| 0/435 | | 2/512 | | 0/862 | 64/339 | 45 m | Change Point (CP) |
| | 1/520 | | | 1/085 | 63/254 | 60 m | |
| | 1/778 | | | 0/258 | 62/996 | 75 m | |
| 3/261 | | 1/462 | 0/316 | | 63/312 | 90 m | Change Point (CP) |
| | | 1/077 | 2/184 | | 65/496 | - | OSBM |
| | | | | | | | |
| 5/047 | | 5/051 | 2/500 | 2/504 | 65/500 | | |
| | | 5/047 | 2/500 | | 65/496 | | |
| | | 0/004 | | 0/004 | 0/004 | | |

Difference in BS – FS = Difference in Rise & Fall = Difference between 1st & last RL
Therefore Levels have been booked correctly however
there is a misclosure of 4mm

▲ **Figure 10.20 The rise and fall booking table**

If the TBM is at a known height of, say, 30 m, then the reduced level of point A is 30 m – 0.19 m = 28.1 m.

This can be seen clearly from looking at the staff readings in comparison to the level line of sight. The figures recorded on the staff 'rise', but the ground levels actually 'fall'.

### Remember!

A quick way to remember if the difference is a 'rise' or 'fall' is to say 'If it's a rise in the book it's a fall on the ground'.

The process is repeated for each new staff reading, where each adjacent staff value is compared to see if it is a rise or a fall. The reduced level of these points is then calculated by adding the rises or subtracting the falls from the previous point's reduced level.

Using the same recorded staff readings for the Premiere Industrial Estate survey, let's now study the 'rise and fall' method of booking (see Figure 10.20). Note that the coloured arrows have been added to show which staff

Line of sight

1.56 m

TBM = 30 m

The value of the figure rises but...

... there is a 'Fall' in the height of the ground level

1.75 m

'A'

▲ **Figure 10.19 The rise and fall method**

readings are being compared, to give the rise or fall value and the calculated reduced level.

The first readings to be compared are the backsight to the OSBM and the staff reading at the 15 metre chainage:

1.351 m – 1.455 m = –0.104 m 'fall'

giving a reduced level of the ground at the 15-metre chainage as:

65.5 m – 0.104 = 65.396 m

The next two figures to be compared are the 15-metre and 30-metre chainage:

1.455 m – 1.65 m = –0.195 m 'fall'

which when added to the reduced level of the 15-metre chainage:

65.396 – 0.195m = 65.201 m, etc.

At the change point you cannot compare figures written on the same line as these are by definition the same point on the ground. You must compare staff readings written on different consecutive lines, such that at the 45-metre chainage point you have to compare the 0.435 m backsight with the 1.52 m intermediate sight at the 60-metre chainage:

0.435 m – 1.52 m = –1.085 m 'fall'

which then gives the reduced level of the ground at the 60-metre chainage as:

64.339 m – 1.085 m = 63.254 m

This process is repeated until the last staff reading has been compared which, in this case, is the difference between the backsight at the 90-metre chainage and the final closing foresight onto the original OSBM.

## Booking checks for the rise and fall method

As with the HPC method, there are checks that can be carried out to make sure the booking arithmetic is correct. The rise and fall method has an extra check whereby the total rises and total falls are summed up and the difference between the two calculated. This calculated difference should be the same for:

- the difference between the sum of the rises and the sum of the falls
- the difference between the sum of the backsights and the sum of the foresights
- the difference between the first and last reduced level.

If this is true for all three checks, then the levels are correctly booked.

We see from our example that all the differences equal 4 mm. Finally, the misclosures checks are compared with the allowable value in exactly the same way as with the HPC method.

1  **If in the above rise and fall method none of the booking checks equalled each other, what would you conclude?**

2  **If in the above rise and fall method all the booking checks equalled 35 mm instead of 4 mm, what would you deduce and how would you proceed?**

## The rise and fall method v. the HPC method

The height of collimation method requires less calculation but does not have a built-in check on the intermediate sights, as does the rise and fall method. The rise and fall method is best suited when a level is being transferred over a distance via a number of change points where no intermediate sights are used – this is known as flying levelling. The height of collimation method is best used when a large number of readings are being taken from the same instrument position, such as plotting or setting out a small levelling grid

# Typical levelling applications

## Flying levels

This is the transferring of levels from one point to another using only backsight and foresight readings. It is a quick and convenient way to establish a new TBM from an existing bench mark, but the flying levels must be returned to close back at the original bench mark, i.e. the levels will need to fly back to close the survey and to carry out all the necessary checks.

## Remember!

Make sure that you position the instrument so as not to block access on any footway or make it vulnerable to being knocked. When reading the instrument, do not lean on the tripod or the level, and also be careful when moving around it. Finally, do not leave the instrument unattended – opportunist thieves may steal your equipment, and your prize level may end up at the local boot sale!

## Grid levels

These can be used for contouring an area and also for calculating the volume of earthworks. A rectilinear grid is set out on the ground and marked with pegs or arrows. The levelling instrument is set up in the middle of the points with a backsight to a bench mark. The levels of the ground at each of the grid points are then read and reduced. These grid levels can be manually manipulated to give contour levels at regular vertical intervals or used to calculate volumes of excavation using a variety of formulae and techniques. Alternatively, with the use of digital levels the data can be downloaded directly into a range of software packages for producing virtual three-dimensional (3D) models. These can then be manipulated for contours and volumes as required. A typical example is shown in the NRG Surveys example of a contoured site in Figure 10.21.

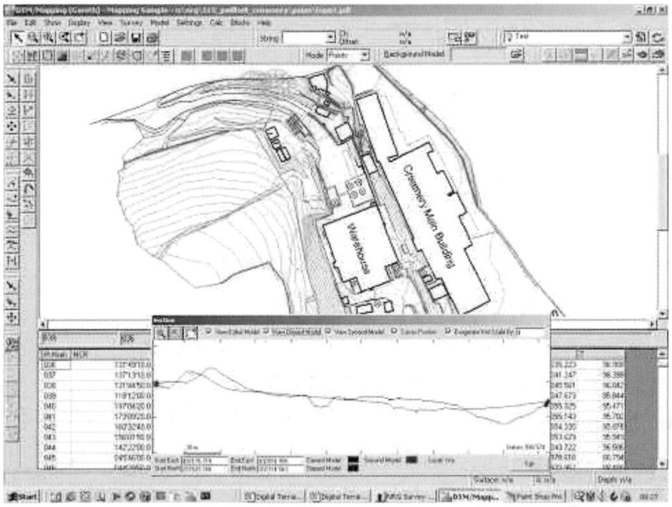

## Long sections

These are vertical cross-sections taken along the length of proposed sewer or road construction, and because these forms of construction are often very long compared to their depth, they are plotted with an exaggerated vertical scale to clearly show the slope and changes in height relative to the length. For example, a new sewer may be 800 m long, but the levels throughout may only vary by 5 or 6 m. Plotting these to the same scale would give no impression of the gradient and how it may change along its length. Therefore, a typical long section will have a vertical scale ten times the horizontal scale, for example 1:500 horizontally and 1:50 vertically.

Numerical information is tabulated below the long section for the new sewer and will include the cumulative distance or chainage, as well as the reduced levels of the ground, the **invert level** of the sewer, the **cover level**, the **formation level** of sewer excavation and the sight rail heights that aid the setting out. A typical long section is shown in Figure 10.22.

## Key terms

**Invert level** The reduced level of the lowest part of the internal diameter of the sewer (see Figure 10.22).

**Cover level** The reduced level of the top of the inspection chamber cover (see Figure 10.22).

**Formation level** The reduced level of the bottom of the excavated sewer trench (see Figure 10.22).

▲ **Figure 10.21 Contoured site**

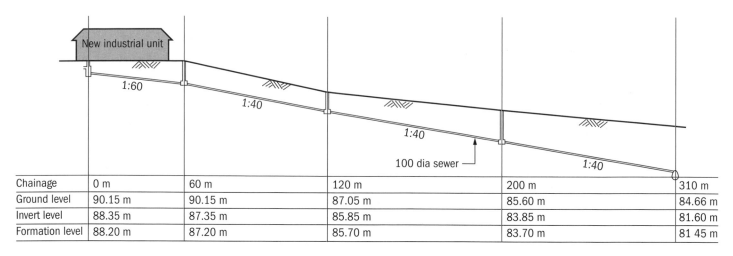

| Chainage | 0 m | 60 m | 120 m | 200 m | 310 m |
|---|---|---|---|---|---|
| Ground level | 90.15 m | 90.15 m | 87.05 m | 85.60 m | 84.66 m |
| Invert level | 88.35 m | 87.35 m | 85.85 m | 83.85 m | 81.60 m |
| Formation level | 88.20 m | 87.20 m | 85.70 m | 83.70 m | 81 45 m |

**Long section on sewer**
scales – horizontal 1:1250 – vertical 1:200

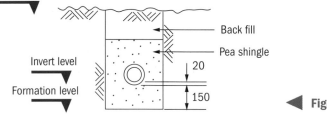

Figure 10.22 Long section of a sewer

## Knowledge check

1   Define the following terms used in levelling: backsight, intermediate sight, foresight, bench mark and reduced level.

2   The standard metric staff uses the 'E' motif to denote the measured height. How high is the letter 'E' and what is the minimum value that can be estimated in good conditions?

3   A sketch of a level survey cross section undertaken at St Bernard's Farm is shown in Figure 10.23. Book the reduce levels for the survey using the rise and fall or HPC method and carry out all the necessary checks. Then using your results:

a   Identify the change points in the survey and state their reduced levels.

b   State the difference in height between Point A and Point H.

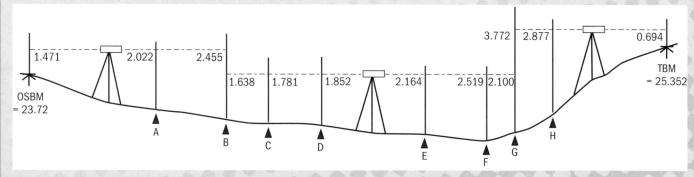

Figure 10.23 Ground level survey at St Bernard's Farm

# Assessment practice

Undertake a practical levelling survey using the levelling equipment provided by your college.

**a** With the permission of your tutor, select a small area of land close to your place of study.

**b** Working in groups of three, peg out a straight line a minimum 40 m long over undulating land. This represents the line of a proposed sewer. Set out pegs or arrows at regular intervals to take account of the changes in the slope of the ground.

**c** Establish a suitable point for a TBM and using this, undertake a level survey of the ground marked by the pegs using an optical or digital level. Use one of the two available methods of booking levels. Remember in your group to take turns in holding the staff and taking/booking the readings.

**d** Carry out all the booking in the field and all necessary arithmetic and accuracy calculation checks.

**e** From your field notes and booking sheet produce a long section in a standard format showing the variation of ground level with chainage. **P2**

Undertake further levelling work.

**a** Re-survey the line using a different booking method to the one used in P2 above and undertake all the necessary booking checks.

**b** The new sewer that is to be constructed starts from a point at the end of the line, with a reduced level of 1 m below the existing ground level at that point. Calculate the invert levels of all the chainage points survey along the ground assuming that the sewer falls at gradient of 1 in 40.

**c** Add the reduced levels of both the invert of the sewer and the formation level of the sewer trench to the long section produced above in P2 (e) in a standard format. **M1**

# Angular measurement

So far we have looked at linear and height measurement; the final form of measurement involves angular measurement. In order to understand how angular measurements can be accurately taken, let's now look at the two basic methods of measurement using angular methods:

- polar measurement
- triangulation.

The best way to understand how each of these different methods operates is to consider an example. So, with reference to Figure 10.24, we can fix the position of a brick wall XY in relation to an aerial mast at Z by using angles, as shown below.

## Key terms

**Whole circle bearing** An angle measured clockwise from a reference point, usually North, with a value ranging from 0° to 360°.

**Traverse survey** An interlinked polygon of survey stations with known easting and northing coordinates.

The plotting of these measurements is straightforward, with the angle and distances marked out on paper as recorded; alternatively, the coordinates of Z relative to X can be worked out using simple, right-angle trigonometry and plotted manually or by using computer-aided design (CAD).

### Polar measurement

Polar measurement requires an angle to be measured in relation to a reference direction, and in our example it is the angle of 51 degrees relative to the wall. Then, to fix the position of the aerial mast at Z, we need to measure the distance XZ which, in our example, is 8165 mm.

This form of measurement is commonly used in navigation with the reference direction being 'North' and the relative angle known as the 'bearing' angle or '**whole circle bearing**'. This terminology continues to be used in **traverse surveys**.

### Measurement by triangulation

This method is ideal where the point to be fixed cannot be physically reached. In our example, it may be that the aerial mast and wall are separated by a deep excavation. The only requirement is that there are clear lines of sight

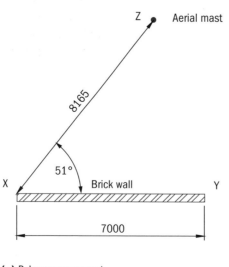

**(a)** Polar measurement

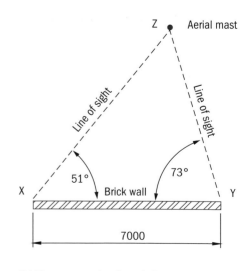

**(b)** Measurement by triangulation

**Figure 10.24 Angular methods of measurement** ▶

between the ends of the wall at points X and Y and the aerial mast at point Z. Only one linear measurement needs to be recorded and that is the length of the wall. In linear surveys this forms the backbone to the survey measurements and is called the baseline. In the drawing office, the length of the wall of 7000 mm is drawn first to a suitable scale, and then the two angles of 51 degrees and 73 degrees are plotted. The lines of sight can be plotted and where they intersect will be the position of the aerial mast Z.

# Using degrees, minutes and seconds

As we have already seen in Unit 3 Mathematics in Construction and the Built Environment, angles in the UK are measured using the sexagesimal system where there are 360 degrees in a whole circle. This system is very common in both land and setting-out surveys where a high degree of accuracy is needed.

All angles used in land and setting-out surveying use this system of measurement, so it is important to know how to add and subtract in the sexagesimal system, both manually and with a scientific calculator.

When doing manual calculations, you must always remember that you are using numbers up to 60. For example, 72' is written as 1°and 12' because there are 60 minutes in a degree. Let's do some manual calculation examples using the place values of 60:

This one is straightforward with no complications:

$$
\begin{array}{rrr}
192° & 30' & 20'' \\
62° & 20' & 10'' \\
\hline
130° & 10' & 10''
\end{array} -
$$

The one below, however, is more difficult because we have to subtract 50" from 30". This is done by borrowing 1' from the 28' from the next column and adding that 60" to 30" to make 90". The subtraction can then be carried out:

$$
\begin{array}{rrr}
 & +60'' & \\
 & \overset{\frown}{27'} & 90'' \\
75° & \cancel{28'} & \cancel{30''} \\
26° & 20' & 50'' \\
\hline
49° & 7' & 40''
\end{array} -
$$

Here's another one that needs careful consideration. Subtracting the seconds is fine; however, it is the minutes column which is not straightforward. We have to borrow 1° from the 273° and add those 60' to give 80' from which 30' can be subtracted.

$$
\begin{array}{rrr}
+60' & & \\
\overset{\frown}{272°} & 80' & \\
\cancel{273°} & \cancel{20'} & 40'' \\
102° & 30' & 10'' \\
\hline
170° & 50' & 30''
\end{array} -
$$

## Remember!

All good scientific calculators will be able to deal with these calculations by inputting the degrees, minutes and seconds directly (study the manual carefully to make sure you can do this). Then double check the result using manual calculations.

# The theodolite

The theodolite is a device for measuring horizontal and vertical angles. Its basic components are a telescope and two protractors which measure angles in the vertical and horizontal plane. Old instruments relied on physical protractors etched on brass protractors or 'circles' with a variety of circular scale rules known as vernier reading devices. However, these are no longer used.

Today, theodolites are fitted with either an optical or electronic system for reading both horizontal and vertical circles. You will need to familiarise yourself with the theodolites that your college has as these will be the ones that you will use for your practical work, and also seek the guidance of your tutor in the care and the use of this equipment. Figure 10.25 shows the essential parts of a theodolite together with its main controls and moving parts.

The theodolite has two horizontal circular plates that rotate independently of each other, called the upper and lower plates The lower plate of the instrument is calibrated in degrees, minutes and seconds in a clockwise direction and is either free to rotate, or it can be clamped to the base (tribrach). The upper plate has an indictor or pointer, thus enabling angles to be read optically or digitally depending on the type of instrument. Control knobs called clamps are provided with slow-motion screws for fine adjustment for both plates. These screws are often referred to as tangent screws. By adjusting these clamps, the theodolite's cross hairs within the telescope can be set to zero or any given angle and pointed at the required survey target. These same principles apply to the vertical circle also.

## Setting up a theodolite

The theodolite is set up correctly when:

- the instrument is *levelled* in all directions, which implies that it is truly vertical
- the instrument is *centred* over the desired survey station point.

This is achieved in two main stages as described below.

## ■ Rough levelling and centring

First, set up the tripod of the theodolite over the survey station, which can be a nail head or fine cross made with

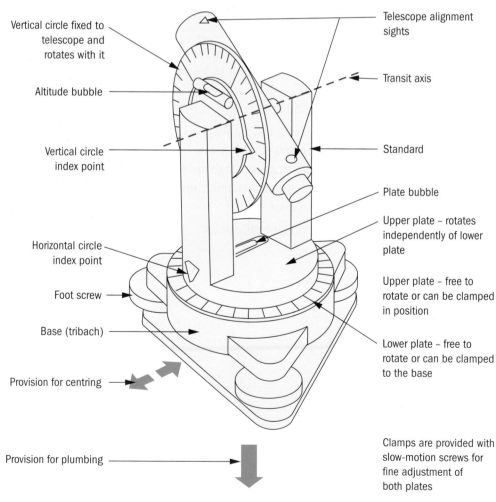

Vertical circle fixed to telescope and rotates with it

Altitude bubble

Vertical circle index point

Horizontal circle index point

Foot screw

Base (tribach)

Provision for centring

Provision for plumbing

Telescope alignment sights

Transit axis

Standard

Plate bubble

Upper plate – rotates independently of lower plate

Upper plate – free to rotate or can be clamped in position

Lower plate – free to rotate or can be clamped to the base

Clamps are provided with slow-motion screws for fine adjustment of both plates

**Figure 10.25 A theodolite** ▶

a site marker pen. Make sure that the tripod is pulled up to at least shoulder height and that the top of the tripod is roughly level and roughly centred above the nail. Screw the theodolite firmly to the tripod first checking that all the foot screws are at the mid-thread position. Then you need to check if the instrument is centred. Most theodolites have an optical plummet where you can look down the vertical axis of the theodolite. There you can see if the small circular target which represents the vertical axis is centred on the nail. If not, you can adjust the foot screws slightly to get the axis at its base to coincide with the nail, or if there is a large distance, two legs of the tripod can be lifted and moved while still looking through the optical plummet.

## Remember!

When taking the theodolite out of its carrying case, always look carefully at how it fits in its cradle within the case. Sometimes the most difficult thing about using a theodolite is getting it snugly back into its case!

### ■ Fine levelling and centring

Once the theodolite has been roughly levelled and centred, then the three foot screws are used to finely level the instrument. This operation is exactly the same as levelling a dumpy level (see page 418). Once the theodolite has been levelled on the foot screws, the optical plummet must be checked to see if the instrument's vertical axis has moved off the nail. If so, it can be brought back on centre by loosening the tripod screw and gently sliding the whole instrument across the top of the tripod while looking through the optical plummet. With this operation complete, it will be necessary to recheck the fine levelling by levelling the three foot screws again.

The theodolite is now centred over the survey nail, is levelled and is ready to use! You will need to practise this procedure if you are to master the use of the theodolite. Make sure you are confident of setting up the theodolite before you undertake a practical assignment.

### Reading an angle on a theodolite

Many modern instruments have direct reading electronic displays which state clearly the values of angles measured in degrees, minutes and seconds. However, if you are using an optical theodolite, you will need to know how to read its optical micrometer devices. These give the angles in two parts depending on the type of theodolite.

Different instruments have different displays, but they all work on the same principle. Figure 10.26 shows three sequential views of the optical micrometer reading for a particular sighting. The left-hand view shows that a reading has been taken on the horizontal scale between 210° and 211°. By adjusting the micrometer screw on

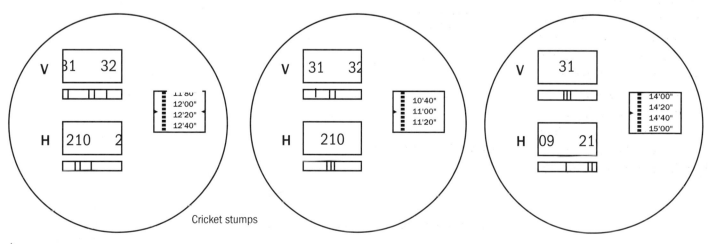

Cricket stumps

▲ Figure 10.26 Example of optical theodolite reading

the side of the instrument, the reading is brought round so that the moving double line coincides with the static single line, forming a 'cricket stump'. This produces a reading of 210° 11' 00", as shown in the middle view. The vertical angle can be read in a similar way by adjusting the micrometer screw for the 'cricket stumps' to give a vertical angle of 31° 14' 30" in the right-hand view.

You will need to check with your tutor as to the system of optical measurement that relates to your college's optical theodolites.

When using a theodolite, it is necessary tell what 'face' the instrument is on. This can be found by seeing on what side the vertical circle lies in relation to the telescope. When the vertical circle is to the left of the telescope, this is known as 'face left' and when it is on the right, it is known as 'face right'. Moving from face right to face left or vice versa is a simple matter of flipping the telescope over to point in the opposite direction, then turning the instrument 180° to get the telescope to point back to its original sighting. This is called transiting the telescope.

It is common practice in surveying to take at least two readings for a single angle, one on face left and one on face right. In this way, you are using the whole 360° circle and as such you are eliminating any miscentring error that may be present in the instrument. This is explained in more detail below.

## ■ Booking procedures for a single horizontal angle

It is important to note in the survey book the number or letter used to denote the survey station over which the instrument is placed and the number or letter of the two stations which are being sighted. It should also be noted whether the instrument is on face left or face right.

There now follows a worked stage-by-stage example to calculate on two faces the angle BAC as shown in Figure 10.27.

## Key term

**Horizontal angle** An angle measured between three fixed points within a horizontal plane (Figure 10.27).

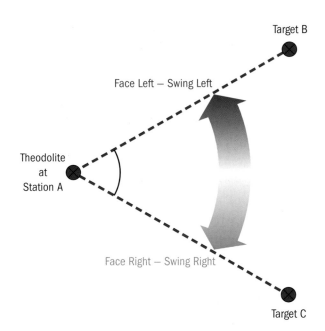

▲ **Figure 10.27 Plan on single angle survey measurement**

## Worked example

The standard booking table has five columns to show where the instrument is located 'At' and at what targets you are sighting 'To'. The next two columns are 'Face right' and 'Face left' and, finally, a place to note down the 'Mean angle' of the two angles.

Here are the readings from the above angular measurements and an explanation of how field work was done and the readings booked correctly:

| At | To | Face right | | | Face left | | |
|----|----|------|------|------|------|------|------|
| A | B | 0° | 0' | 0" | 180° | 00' | 15" |
| | C | 82° | 20' | 15" | 262° | 20' | 10" |
| | | 82° | 20' | 15" | 82° | 19' | 55" |
| | | | | | **Mean angle = 82° 20' 05"** | | |

1  Set up instrument levelled and centred over the required station A.

2  Using the lower plate clamps and tangent screws, set the index to a low value of angle, preferably 0° 00' 00", and put the instrument in the face right position.

3  Sight onto the first station B making sure that you always strike out in a clockwise direction. Using the lower plate clamps and its fine adjacent tangent screw, set the 0° 00' 00" on to station B.

4  Release the *upper plate clamp* – not the lower plate clamp – and swing right to the second station at C. Sight accurately onto C using the tangent screws with the upper plate clamps on and, after adjusting the optical micrometer (if it is an optical level), book the reading, which in this case was 82° 20' 15". The instrument is on face right and pointing at station C, so this is where the reading is booked in the booking table.

5  Calculate the angle made at A between C and B by subtracting the 'top from the bottom' to give a value of 82° 20' 15".

6  Transit the telescope by flipping it over and unclamping the upper plate – *but not the lower plate!* – and turn the telescope to point back to station C.

7  Sight on to C using the upper plate clamps and tangent screw, and accurately book the reading, which in this case is 262° 20' 10". The instrument is on face left and pointing towards C, so that is where this reading is booked in the booking table. Also note that, ideally, if there were no errors, this value should be 180° greater than the previous angle.

8  Release the upper plate clamp and swing left back onto the original station B and book the reading of 180° 00' 15" in the booking table. This reading is on face left and pointing at B, so this is where it goes in the booking table.

9  Calculate the angle made at A between B and C by subtracting the 'top from the bottom' to give a value of 82° 19' 55".

10 Where the difference between the angles measured is less than 30", the mean of the pair can be calculated and taken to be the true angle subtended at A measured between points B and C.

1  **What do you understand by the terms 'face right' and 'face left'?**

2  **Determine the mean horizontal angle XYZ given the following angular measurements on face right and face left.**

| At | To | Face right | | | Face left | | |
|----|----|------|------|------|------|------|------|
| Y | X | 0° | 0' | 0" | 179° | 55' | 45" |
| | Z | 79° | 50' | 30" | 259° | 40' | 15" |

## ■ Booking procedures for a single vertical angle

A similar procedure is used for measuring vertical angles, except that the zero is generally fixed in one position, either pointing straight up – known as the **zenith** – or set at the level horizon. Angles that dip below the horizon are often quoted as angles of depression while those that rise above the horizon are **angles of elevation.**

It is always good practice to record single vertical angles on both faces, but be aware that once the values go beyond 360°, they revert back to 0°, just as a clock hand moves from 12 o'clock to 1 o'clock.

### Accuracy in measuring angles

The theodolite can measure very small angles; some theodolites can read down to 1 second of a degree, which is equivalent to 1 in 216,000th of a whole circle. An error of just 60" of angle roughly equates to an error of about 15 mm over 50 m. To understand how to reduce errors, you need to know the main axes of the theodolite and these are shown in Figure 10.28.

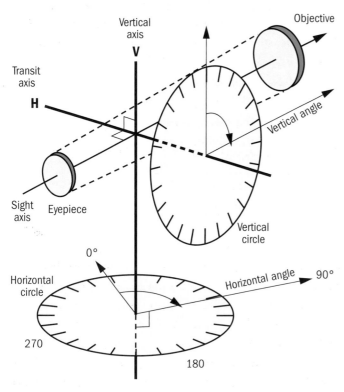

▲ **Figure 10.28 Main axes of the theodolite**

- The vertical axis – at right angles to the horizontal plane and transit axis, which is considered to be truly vertical when the theodolite has been levelled.
- The horizontal circle – at right angles to the vertical axis.
- The transit axis – at right angles to the line of sight and the vertical axis and forms the pivot for rotation of the telescope.

Errors in angular measurement originate from two main sources:

- *Instrument error.* The axes of a theodolite must be in good adjustment with each other to ensure that the instrument is level and rotates perpendicularly about its various axes. It is advisable to service the theodolite at the start of all major contracts and at frequent intervals by a certified calibration and testing company. The rough handling that these instruments may get over the period of a contract can be quite harsh, particularly under site conditions. There are three basic checks for errors:
  - Vertical axis check – after levelling the instrument on the three foot screws and all appears to be in good adjustment, simply rotate the instrument 180° and the plate bubble should stay central. If not, there is an error.
  - Transit axis is perpendicular to line of collimation – if you book readings on both face right and face left, this error, if any, will be cancelled out when the mean is calculated.
  - Spire check – this checks that the transit axis is truly horizontal and involves sighting a target high up like a church spire on one face which is then brought down to ground level by dipping the telescope and marking a point on the ground. The instrument is then changed onto a different face and the spire target is sighted once more. If this reading, when brought down, coincides with the first mark, then there is no error and the transit axis is horizontal. By booking readings on both face right and face left, this error can be eliminated, but it is always best to get the instrument checked and calibrated.
- *Human errors.* These are mistakes on the part of the surveyor caused by carelessness, tiredness or inexperience. For example, sighting the wrong target,

or adjusting the wrong clamp, or reading/booking the angle incorrectly. These errors can be very large and the only way to avoid them is to fully familiarise yourself with the theodolite's controls, practise setting up and checking the theodolite and using a standard methodical way to read and book your results.

There can also be small random errors such as minute human sight defects or by sunlight affecting the movement of the plate bubble. However, these tend to be very small and compensatory.

# Application of angular measurement

You have already studied the use of angles in Unit 3 Mathematics in Construction and the Built Environment. Before you move on, revise and review the section on trigonometry (see pages 118–124).

The main trigonometrical formulae you will be using here are:

- Pythagoras' rule and right-angle trigonometrical ratios – these are commonly used in all branches of land and setting-out surveying. It is important that you understand how to apply these in the various surveying tasks that you need to carry out.
- Non-right angle trigonometrical ratios (sine rule and cosine rule).
- Sum of angles within a closed polygon – this formula is very useful when setting up a control network of survey stations as part of a closed traverse survey to check the sum of internal angles.

# Practical applications of angular measurement

## Finding the height of a point

Often in surveying the height of fixed features is required. A common problem, particularly on civil engineering sites, is checking the headroom under existing bridges or power lines to enable plant and machinery to pass under.

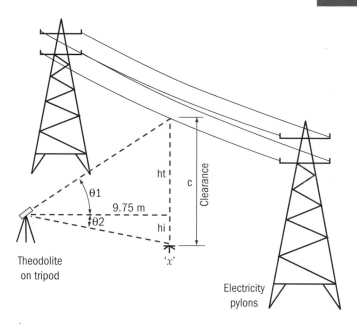

▲ Figure 10.29 Height of accessible point

This can be done by measuring a vertical angle to that point from a known distance away.

For example, in Figure 10.29 calculate the clearance c between the overhead power cables and the ground directly beneath it at $x$. The angle of inclination $\theta_1$ was measured as 42° 30' 20" to the overhead line and the angle of depression $\theta_2$ to point x on the ground was 6° 20' 50". The distance between the theodolite and point x was measured horizontally as 9.75m.

The clearance distance = $h_t + h_i$

where $h_t$ = 9.75 m × tangent 42° 30' 20" = 8.936 m

and $h_i$ = 9.75 m × tangent 6° 20' 50"= 1.085 m

Therefore, Clearance = 8.936 m + 1.085 m = 10.02 m, say, 10 m headroom.

## Finding the height of an inaccessible point

To measure distances to inaccessible points more complex triangulation is required. In the example in Figure 10.30 the height of the aerial mast is required, but there is a large drainage ditch preventing the horizontal distances from being measured, hence there appears to be no physical way of measuring the height $h_m$.

In order to solve the problem, one method is to establish a base line AB, in this case 50 m long, and record the vertical angle to the top of the mast from both ends of the line.

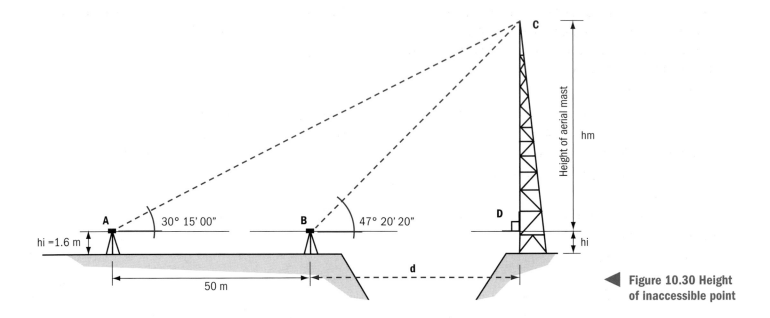

Figure 10.30 Height of inaccessible point

In right-angle triangle BCD, using the tangent ratio, we have:

$h_m = d \times$ tangent 47° 20' 20" (equation 1)

and also in right-angle triangle ACD we have:

$h_m = (50 + d) \times$ tangent 30° 15' 00" (equation 2)

But $h_m$ is the same in both equations 1 and 2. Therefore, we can write:

$d \times$ tangent 47° 20' 20" = (50 + d) × tangent 30° 15' 00"

Multiplying out the brackets on the RHS, we have:

$d \times$ tangent 47° 20' 20" = (50 tangent 30° 15' 00") + (d × tangent 30° 15' 00")

Work out all the known terms given:

$1.08512 \times d = 29.159 + 0.58319 \times d$

collecting up all the terms that are linked to the distance d and solving the equation

$$1.08512 \times d - 0.58319 \times d = 29.159$$
$$0.50194 \times d = 29.159$$
$$d = 58.093 \text{ m}$$

which we can now substitute back into equation 1 to find $h_m$.

$h_m = d \times$ tangent 47° 20' 20"

$h_m = 58.093 \times$ tangent 47° 20' 20"

$h_m = 63.04$ m

Therefore, the height of the aerial mast will be $h_m + h_i = 63.04 + 1.6$ m = 64.64 m

## Detail surveying by coordinate point fixing

A relatively simple method of surveying elevations of buildings just by recording horizontal and vertical angles is described below. All that is required is the theodolite to

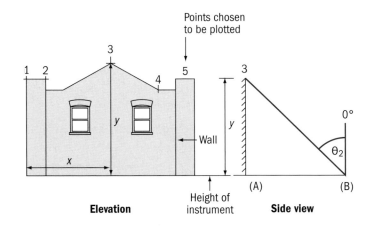

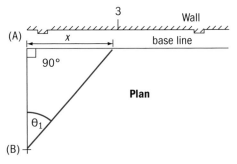

Figure 10.31 Use of angular measurement for surveys

be set up at a known right-angle distance from the left-hand side of the chosen building. Then, applying some right-angle trigonometric ratios, the coordinates x – and y – can be calculated and plotted.

The procedure is as follows:

1  Set up the theodolite on a tripod close to wall on baseline parallel to wall (point A).

2  Set out 90° angle to fix peg at point B.

3  Measure the right-angle distance from B to the wall, e.g. 23.5 m.

4  Set up theodolite at B and zero circle onto previous station on baseline (at A).

5  Draw sketch of the elevation to be surveyed showing target point to be fixed and plotted. Number these points on the sketch you have made – see above.

6  Measure both horizontal angle Hz ($\theta_1$) and vertical angle V ($\theta_2$) to each point and tabulate them in a suitable table:

| Target point | Hz ($\theta_1$) | V ($\theta_2$) | x (m) | y (m) |
|---|---|---|---|---|
| e.g. 3 | 6° 30' 00" | 81° 0' 00" | 2.677 | 3.722 |
|  |  |  |  |  |
|  |  |  |  |  |

7  Calculate the distance x and y and write in the table shown in red from the following:

$$x = AB \times Tangent\ \theta_1$$

$$y = \frac{AB}{Tangent\ \theta_2}$$

8  Plot x and y as coordinates to fix each point on graph paper or using a suitable CAD program to give the required elevational view of the building.

## Knowledge check

1  Briefly explain the main parts of a theodolite and its controls.

2  Describe the three main checks on a theodolite to ensure that it is in good adjustment.

3  State the difference between an angle of depression and an angle of elevation.

# Assessment practice

Carry out a practical site survey using angular measurement:

**a** Select a small area of land close to your place of study and peg out three points about 30 m apart in the shape of a triangle. On the top of each peg mark, draw a cross with a survey marker pen – these will be your survey stations.

**b** Set up the theodolite over one station and then measure on 'face right' and 'face left' the internal angle of the triangle between the two other stations.

**c** Record and book the angles using a standard method of booking.

**d** Measure and book the two other internal angles in the survey triangle.

**e** Work out your misclosure and comment on your accuracy. **P3**

Work out the height of an inaccessible object on a slope.

In a land survey of a coastal area the reduced level of the top of a cliff needs to be found as part of works to stabilise the cliff face. A baseline 35 m was set up on the foreshore area and the angles of inclination at the ends of the baseline were measured as shown in Figure 10.32. Also, with the theodolite telescope set horizontally at 0°, the heights of collimation of the instrument were found relative to the TBM, which are also shown in the diagram. (*Hint*: Use right-angle trigonometry and Pythagoras' rule to

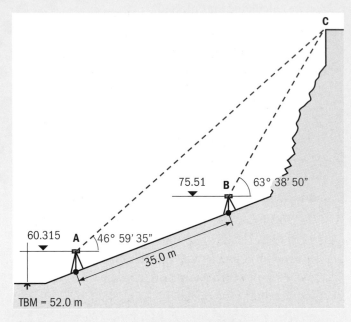

▲ **Figure 10.32 Section through cliff face**

help find the vertical height of point C above point A.) **M2**

Consider errors in angular measurement.

Undertake research to analyse methods used in angular measurement in terms of trigonometrical accuracy. Provide examples which clearly show the effect of increasing distance on angular error and the need for good intersection of lines of sight. **D2**

In the previous sections, we have only considered the operation involved in land surveying, that is, going to a site and measuring distances, levels and angles of features and returning to the office to plot these features on a scaled plan by manual or CAD methods. This section will look at the process of setting out, which is taking an architect's scaled drawing for a new building and physically marking out the positions on the ground to enable the foundations and walls to be constructed.

Setting out is an exercise in communication. The requirements of the designer are set out clearly on the drawings and other contract documents. The setting-out engineer or surveyor must interpret these and provide clear dimensional information to the craft operatives so that they can build the structure. This involves creating a clear system of temporary marks and physical profiles so that the layout of the building works can be monitored and controlled in terms of both the horizontal dimensions (referred to as 'line') and the vertical dimensions (referred to as 'level').

This process starts with a site layout drawing that shows the intended position of roads or buildings. A typical drawing for a site layout is shown in Figure 10.33 together with the main setting-out dimensions that are required.

# Reconnaissance and preparation

First, check with the architect or project manger that you have the latest setting-out drawings, usually noted by the date and revision number included in the title block. It is advisable to walk over the whole site before you start in order to familiarise yourself with the boundary positions and all existing features of the site, as well as the slope of the site and visibility issues, for example overhanging trees. Check that the drawing has sufficient dimensions that adequately locate the building on the site relative to two or three existing fixed points, called the **primary setting-out points** (SOPs). You should never scale off measurements from drawings or make other assumptions without first checking with the architect or project manager.

## Key term

**Primary setting-out points** These are existing identifiable, fixed features to which all new building work is related in terms of their setting out dimensions and angles.

The SOPs could be a pre-existing survey station from a previous control traverse or may just be dimension from the rear face of the kerb or from the centre-line of the adjacent road. In order to accurately position a building, there must be at least two accurately dimensioned points; a third point is good to act as a check. This should give the horizontal position, but there should also be information on the required reduced levels based on an established Temporary Bench Mark on site.

Before you arrive on site, you should have a clear idea of how you are going to set out the given dimensions and do as many calculations and sketches as possible. You may need to discuss with the project manager where he or she would like the profiles to be placed so that it does

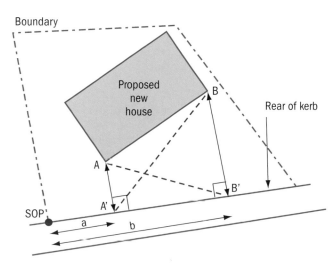

▲ **Figure 10.33 Site layout**

not interfere with the movement of vehicles, storage of materials, etc.

Make sure that all your setting-out equipment is correctly adjusted and in order. Typical equipment for a small domestic development includes:

- two measuring tapes (30 m or 50 m), preferably steel.
- levelling equipment (e.g. Cowley, optical, laser or digital level as appropriate)
- standard 20" theodolite or optical site square for establishing angles on complicated plan layouts
- various hand tools for setting up the corner pegs or constructing the profiles (lump hammer, claw hammer, hand saw, etc)
- selection of round-headed nails and/or cartridge gun
- string to line in wall positions
- spray paint to mark out stations and line in foundation trench positions
- personal protective equipment (hard hat, high visibility jacket and safety boots as a minimum).

You must look after your equipment by keeping it dry and clean at all times. Steel tapes should be lightly oiled and levels or theodolites if used when damp should be left to dry out before storing way in their boxes. Do not carry instruments attached to a tripod over your shoulder as this will distort the threads and bend the vertical axis of the instrument. Finally, never leave your equipment unattended as it can fall prey to opportunist thieves, particularly when used in public areas.

# Setting out the corners of the building

It is important that you take your time and do not rush. Pressure from site management and subcontractors can be great, but always remember that accuracy is more important than speed in setting out work. Locate the main SOPs and mark with spray paint and protect them with suitable fencing or barriers. These are your reference datum and must be protected from accidental damage and vandalism. Later you may have to re-set out some of the building positions and if you cannot locate the SOPs or TBM, then you will have problems.

## Remember!

When setting out, accuracy is essential! Don't rush – take your time to get the work right.

In the example in Figure 10.33, the corners of the building A and B are at right angles from the rear of the kerb to points A' and B'. These points are located from the SOP by given distances a and b.

To establish point A, you need to construct a right angle at point A'. This can be achieved using one of the following:

- A 3:4:5 builder's square, which is a triangle made from three lengths of timber in the ratio of 3:4:5.
- Two tapes and applying Pythagoras' rule, $X^2 = Y^2 + Z^2$, to determine the diagonal line X.
- A theodolite or site square to swing out an angle of 90° from the rear kerb line.

The cheapest and most convenient method is the second method. This is illustrated in Figure 10.34.

where:

$X^2 = Y^2 + Z^2$

$X^2 = 6.750^2 + 12.850^2$

$X^2 = 45.563 + 165.123$

$X^2 = 210.686$

$X = \sqrt{210.686} = 14.150$ m

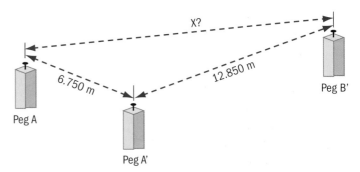

▲ **Figure 10.34 Setting out of a right angle by tape**

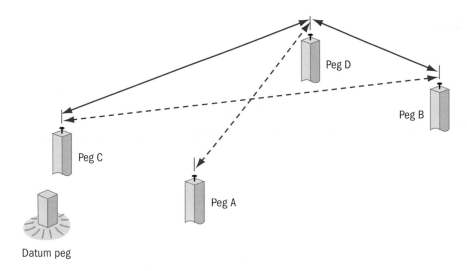

▲ **Figure 10.35 Step by step setting out of a small building: step 2**

(see Setting out the levels on page 444), placed at least 4 m away from the proposed construction works if machine dug.

Nails or saw cuts are used to mark out the face of the wall. You will find these positions by pulling string lines tight between the corner post nails and extending them to the profiles. Once the outside face of the wall is marked on the profile, other nails or saw cuts are marked out along the top of the profile showing the centre line of the wall/foundation or the positions of each individual leaf of the cavity wall. They also need to be painted in red and white chevrons so that they cannot be run over or mistakenly pulled up.

Therefore, two tapes can mark out peg A by pulling out a distance of 6.75 m from peg A' and a distance of 14.15 m from peg B'. Where these two tapes cross will give peg A at right angles to line A'B'. In a similar way, peg B can also be fixed.

## Step 2: Establish the other corners of the building by setting out a right angle

The remaining corners of the building can be positioned at right angles to each other by using Pythagoras' rule to calculate the diagonals. As a check measurement, the external perimeter measurements should also be checked. All measurements should be within 5 mm for every 10 m of length (see below).

## Step 3: Erect the profile boards

The profile boards will remain in place throughout the job as a permanent reference to fix the position of both the substructure and superstructure. They usually consist of a horizontal timber member fixed to two stout timber posts at a given height

## Step 4: Excavate the foundations

Using string stretched between the marks as a guide, apply spray paint to the ground. The excavator operator can then use this line to guide the bucket of the machine to pull out the strip footing or ground beam. The corner pegs will, of course, be lost, but with the saw cut marks on the profile boards, they can be re-established to find the position of the following brickwork walls, etc.

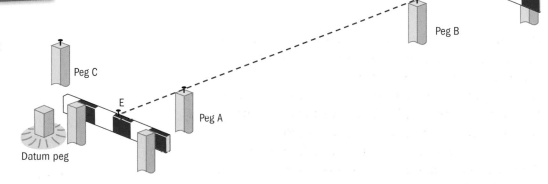

▲ **Figure 10.36 Setting out of a small building: step 3**

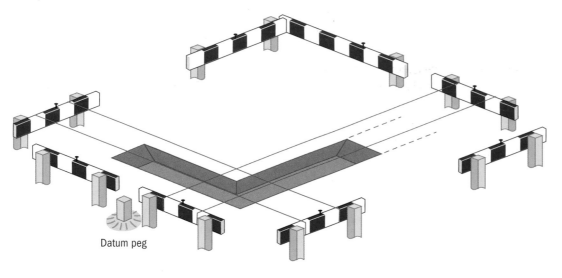

Figure 10.37 Setting out of a small building: step 4

or steel bolt cast into a concrete block and fenced off with suitably painted barriers or tape. It is given an arbitrary height value, but in some cases may be transferred from a local Ordnance Survey Bench Mark (OSBM). It has to be protected to make sure that it does not get knocked over for the duration of the construction project (Figure 10.38).

# Setting out the levels

Just as important as the horizontal positioning of the building is the vertical positioning. The heights of floor levels, window levels and roof ridges, for example, must be constructed exactly how they were planned. There have been cases where levels have been wrong and the height of the building contravened the planning restriction and so had to be demolished!

The vertical control is established on site by setting up a Temporary Bench Mark (TBM) to provide a fixed reference point for all levels on site. This is a timber post

## ■ Spirit level

The simplest form of transferring a level from one point to another is a spirit level and straight edge. This is very useful for small-scale craft operations such as setting out pegs for construction of a level area of timber decking, but it has its limitations as it cannot easily be used to transfer levels over longer distances more than about 4.5 m, and is difficult to set out gradients. It is shown in Figure 10.39.

## ■ Water level

The water level comprises a 15-metre long rubber hose filled with water with Perspex cylindrical end pieces and screw caps. This is a traditional method of transferring levels, particularly in brick-laying, which relies on water being able to find its own level. This is more useful than the previous method as the level can be transferred over much longer distances, and even taken onto other rooms within the building.

## ■ Cowley level

The Cowley level is more precise than the previous methods for transferring levels and can be used accurately to set out slopes and gradients quickly and efficiently. It comprises a system of pivoted mirrors that hang vertically held safely within a metal case (the

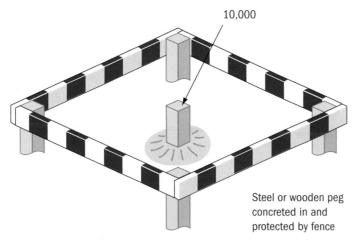

Figure 10.38 Temporary site bench mark

10,000

Steel or wooden peg concreted in and protected by fence

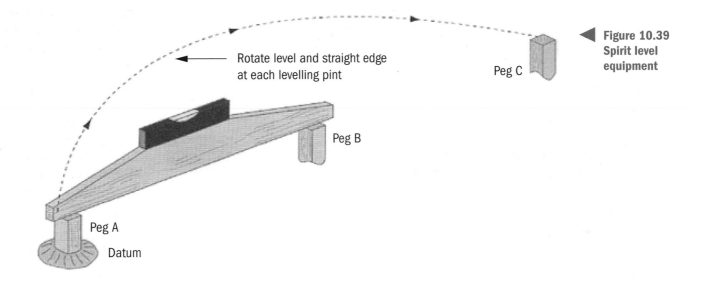

Rotate level and straight edge
at each levelling pint

Peg C

Figure 10.39
Spirit level
equipment

Peg B

Peg A

Datum

Cowley level), a lightweight metal tripod and a cross-bar target staff. The level swivels 360 degrees on a pin and is accurate up to about 30 m. It is also a considerably cheaper piece of kit when compared to more complex optical levels. The basic operation of the Cowley level is shown in Figure 10.40.

The procedure for levelling with a Cowley level is as follows:

1  Securely set up tripod and lower level onto pin.

2  Position staff on datum and observe through viewfinder.

3  Move site rail up or down to obtain image A or D.

4  Secure site rail with screw.

5  Place staff on peg A and rotate level to observe.

6  Adjust height of peg to obtain image A or D.

7  Peg A will then be level with datum peg.

Cowley levels are limited to a range of about 30 m with an accuracy over that distance of +/ −5mm.

## ■ Optical level and 'E' staff

These are some of the most useful pieces of equipment provided they are handled with care. Their operation and range have been covered earlier on pages 416–19 and are frequently used in setting out all types of levels in construction.

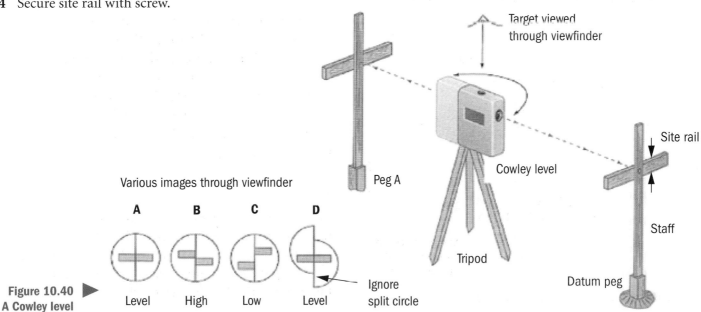

Various images through viewfinder

A       B       C       D

**Figure 10.40 ▶
A Cowley level**

Level    High    Low    Level

Ignore
split circle

Target viewed
through viewfinder

Site rail

Cowley level

Peg A

Staff

Tripod

Datum peg

## ■ Laser levels

Laser levels are increasingly being used for setting out in preference to the Cowley level. They are far more accurate with a much wider range – some as much as 300 m. They do not require any visual sightings to be taken and are easy to set up and use. Most instruments also provide an automatic warning signal if the laser gets knocked or is unintentionally moved.

There are many applications of laser levels in construction, including pipe laying lasers and rotating lasers. The rotating laser is fixed to a tripod, which when switched on automatically finds its level, then generates a red horizontal line that can be picked up by a suitable sensoring device to give an audible or visual reading of the height. A typical application is in the control of

excavation depths and grading level surfaces where the sensor is fitted to the excavating bucket or blade.

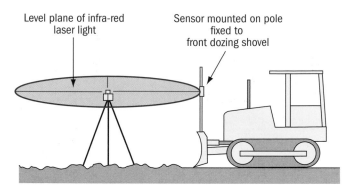

Figure 10.41 Use of the laser level for earthworks

## Case study

The proposed reduced levels of the foundations and floor slab of a house on a site are given on the architect's drawing as:

Finished floor level (FFL) 10.15 m
Finished ground level (GL) 9.85 m
Formation level of foundations (bottom of foundation) 9.00 m
Top of concrete strip 9.15 m

These are based on a site TBM with a reduced level of 10 m as shown in the cross-section in Figure 10.42.

## Theory into practice

Studying the reduced level, you can see that the depth of the foundation is:

9.85 m – 9.0 m = 0.85 m

What do you think is the thickness of the concrete strip?

The profile boards are located close to the building and need to be set at the correct height such that the

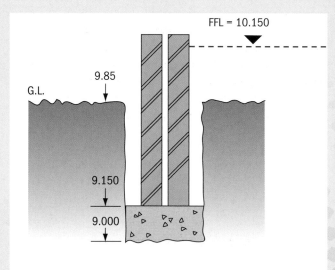

Figure 10.42 Use of reduced levels for setting out house foundations

top of the profile is at the same height as, say, the finished floor level (FFL), in this case 10.15 m. The level instrument is set up, and a backsight taken onto the TBM. This gives the height of collimation (HPC) of the level instrument, i.e. the reduced level of the line of

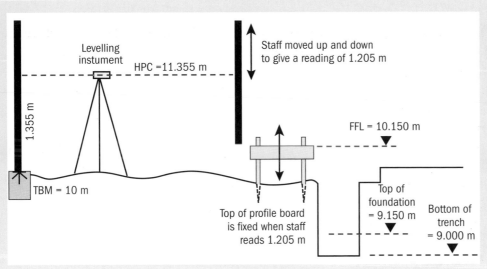

Figure 10.43 Setting out of house using the staff reading method

Levelling instument
HPC =11.355 m
Staff moved up and down to give a reading of 1.205 m
1.355 m
TBM = 10 m
Top of profile board is fixed when staff reads 1.205 m
FFL = 10.150 m
Top of foundation = 9.150 m
Bottom of trench = 9.000 m

sight. If the backsight reading was 1.355 m, then the HPC will be:

HPC = 10 m + 1.355 m = 11.355 m

Now to set up the profile board at 10.150 m, the value to be read on the staff needs to be:

Staff reading for FFL = 11.355 m – 10.15 m = 1.205 m

The staff is moved up and down by the assistant surveyor until 1.205 m is read on the staff, then the height of the bottom of the staff is marked off on one of the uprights of the profile. This is the finished floor level. The profile board is then nailed to the uprights so that the top of the board coincides with the mark on the upright. The profile can now be used to set out

all the required levels by using a spirit level, Cowley level or pulling out a string line between two profile boards set at the same height.

Alternatively, heights can be set out directly by reading the correct value off the staff, for example the staff reading needed to set out the bottom of the foundation is

11.355 m – 9.000 m = 2.355 m

You can use this technique with laser levels that have infrared sensors fitted to the staff. These sensors can be adjusted to the correct position on the staff, so that when the staff is raised or lowered a visual and/or audible signal tells you that you have found the required reduced level.

What would be the staff reading needed to set out pegs for the top of the foundation within the side of the trench?

## Knowledge check

1   Explain with the aid of neat labelled sketches three different methods of setting out a right-angled corner of a structure.

2   Explain the role site profiles have in the setting out of sewers.

3   In each of these cases select the most appropriate setting out equipment:

   a   Setting out the profile heights for a sewer

   b   Excavating the road base for a motorway construction.

# Assessment practice

Study the foundation plan for the small house shown in Figure 10.44. The walls are to be 300 mm cavity walls built centrally on a 600 mm wide strip foundation, and all internal walls are constructed from 100 mm thick concrete blockwork.

You are required to set out the corner points of this building both in plan and height using traditional methods.

1 As part of your preparation:

   a Make a copy of the plan clearly showing all the dimensions you intend to use to set out the corners of the building.

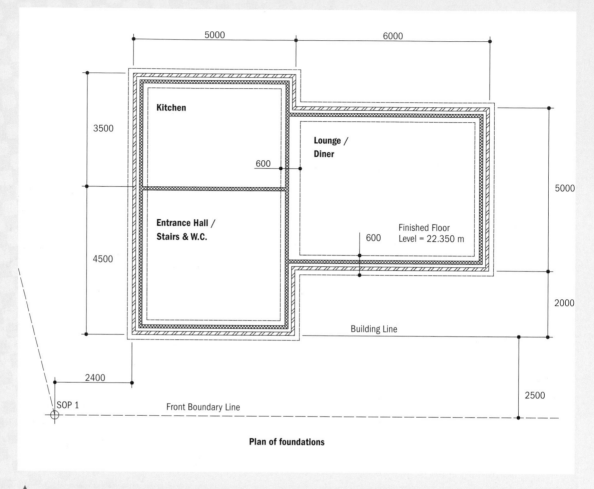

**Figure 10.44 Foundation plan of house**

   b Sketch on the plan the positions of all the required profiles.

   c Produce a checklist of all the equipment and materials needed to undertake the setting out, including personal protective equipment.

2 Select a level piece of land close to your place of study where you are permitted to undertake practical surveying work. In a group of three, set out a baseline approximately 15 m long marked out with ranging rods at each end. This represents the front boundary line of the small house shown in the drawing. One end of the line represents SOP 1 shown on the drawing.

3 Set out the corners of the building using steel tapes, pegs and nails.

4 Check the diagonals and external dimensions for accuracy and take a photographic record of your work. **P4**

Establish a suitable TBM close to the building set out above and take its value as 21.90 m. Then, using the corner positions set out previously, erect suitable timber profiles to construct all foundations and ground floor walls in both plan and vertical alignment. The tops of the profiles are to be at the height of the given finished floor level. Check your work for accuracy and take a photographic record of your work. **M3**

Produce a brief written report that explains the constraints on positioning and protecting the setting-out profiles. **D3**

# Preparation for assessment

For the pass criteria P1 to P4, you must actively participate in the planning, reconnaissance and fieldwork. You will be assessed not only on the final survey information/output (report, drawings, calculations, etc.) but also on observation of the practical work and the quality of your field notes and methodology.

Using surveying equipment is a practical skill that improves with practice. It is therefore advisable that you take every opportunity to get your hands on the equipment and use it. First, use it within supervised situations like class sessions with your tutor, but use it later on with your peers to undertake a variety of practical exercises in your private study time — remember the saying 'Practice makes perfect'!

It is important that your field notes are neat and in good order when you submit them as part of your final submission. All good surveyors must be methodical and organised in their survey work, and this means keeping accurate and legible field notes. Your plotted survey drawings should be to an appropriate scale with title blocks giving full information about the survey's purpose, authorship and scales/dates, etc. Don't worry if you are not a natural draftsperson; it is the clarity and accuracy of the work that is important (see Chapter 8 Graphical detailing in construction and the built environment).

Carry out linear surveys and produce clear and accurate drawings. Demonstrate in your planning that you can 'work from the whole to the part'. What errors are possible and how can these be reduced in practice? **P1**

Carry out levelling surveys using both the HPC and the rise and fall methods and produce clear and accurate drawings. Check that your level survey always closes back onto a known bench mark, and carry out arithmetic booking and misclosure checks. Reduce errors in your survey work, particularly with regard to collimation errors and booking errors. **P2**

Carry out angular measurements and produce accurate results from calculations. Provide suitable diagrams which show how you are approaching the problem, and how you are applying mathematical formulae. **P3**

Set out and check corner pegs for a small building. Identify the main controlling horizontal and vertical dimensions that fix a building's position and then calculate and set these points out. Produce and use check measurements. **P4**

## Grading tips

In order to achieve the merit criteria M1 to M3, you must be able to work semi-independently from your tutor in the application of applied maths to surveying contexts and problems. Your original 'in the field' booking sheets should be neat and accurate, that is, you have not had to copy out earlier scribbles to make sense of your last surveying practical! Ensure that you are thoroughly familiar with both right-angle and non right-angle geometry and trigonometry calculations (see Unit 3 Mathematics in construction and the built environment). Site-based engineers often have to work under a lot of pressure, so your mental maths will need to be good — practise doing a range of calculations and check your answers yourself, then consult your tutor.

# Grading tips

Your survey reports should emphasise the importance of neat and accurate fieldwork, and discuss strategies that could be used to correct results where errors have been found.

Carry out levelling calculations using both height of collimation and rise and fall methods.

You should be able to decide which type of level booking method would best suit a given task and be able to explain your choice. Your field work should include a working proficiency of all arithmetic checks and a suitable comment on the misclosure and overall accuracy. **M1**

Use angular measurements and trigonometry to calculate heights and distances.

You must be able to approach a trigonometric/geometric problem and create a mathematical solution illustrated with suitable sketches. It is advisable to go through as many angular calculation examples as possible so that you get better versed in their use. Make sure that you are comfortable adding and subtracting using angles in degrees, minutes and seconds, and that you get into the habit of laying out your calculations in a neat and logical way. **M2**

Set out and check profiles for a small building.

Careful planning is crucial if you are to achieve this merit criteria. Before you are assessed, undertake a practice assignment by setting out in 'line' and 'level' a house plan of your own making. Remember to demonstrate the checks that need to be done, such as diagonal distances and finding your levelling misclosure, and the allowable tolerances. **M3**

In order to achieve the distinction criteria D1 to D3, you must be able to relate your previous practical activities to a thorough knowledge of surveying 'good practice'. You should also demonstrate your ability to

research and apply your findings to your practical work independently from your tutor.

Analyse the methods used for linear survey in terms of accuracy.

You should carry out research into the types and size of likely linear errors and their effects on the final survey. You should demonstrate a clear understanding of the classification of errors into three main types, human, systematic and random errors, and be aware of the methods that can be used to reduce these errors. **D1**

Analyse the methods used in angular measurements in terms of trigonometric accuracy.

You need to be able to demonstrate an understanding of the principal reasons for errors encountered in carrying out angular measurement with a theodolite. In preparation for this assessment you should carry out research into the temporary adjustments needed to set up the theodolite and in the selection of the appropriate survey frameworks and survey stations. **D2**

Explain the constraints on the positioning of profiles.

To prepare for this it would be advisable to contact a local construction site and make an appointment with the project manager to discuss their strategy for setting out the site. Remember to plan your questions well in advance to maximise your time and take some photographs of what you are shown. You will need to demonstrate knowledge of the correct positioning of profiles in regard to a variety of real-life practical situations involving plant movements, storage of materials, health and safety issues, phasing of construction work, weather conditions, vandalism and inter-visibility between survey stations, bench marks and profile positions. **D3**

## Grading criteria: Unit 10

| To achieve a pass grade the evidence must show that the learner is able to: | To achieve a merit grade the evidence must show that, in addition to the pass criteria, the learner is able to: | To achieve a distinction grade the evidence must show that, in addition to the pass and merit criteria, the learner is able to: |
|---|---|---|
| **P1** carry out linear surveys and produce clear and accurate drawings **Assessment practice pages 415, 449** | | **D1** analyse the methods used for linear survey in terms of accuracy **Assessment practice page 415** |
| **P2** carry out levelling surveys and produce clear and accurate drawings **Assessment practice pages 429, 449** | **M1** carry out levelling calculations using both height of collimation and rise and fall methods **Assessment practice page 429** | |
| **P3** carry out angular measurements and produce accurate results from calculations **Assessment practice pages 440, 449** | **M2** use angular measurements and trigonometry to calculate heights and distances **Assessment practice page 440** | **D2** analyse the methods used in angular measurements in terms of trigonometric accuracy **Assessment practice page 440** |
| **P4** set out and check corner pegs for a small building **Assessment practice pages 448, 449** | **M3** set out and check profiles for a small building **Assessment practice page 448** | **D3** explain the constraints on the positioning of profiles **Assessment practice page 448** |

# Building surveying in Construction

## Introduction

Over 70 per cent of people in the UK either own their own home outright or have a mortgage. Investment in your first house is one of the major decisions that you will have to make in your life. Part of this decision-making process, not just for the housing market but also for the commercial purchasing of factories and offices requires the services of a building surveyor.

A building survey is often a mandatory requirement from financial lenders so that in the event of default, there is considered to be enough equity within the property to recover monies lent against it. All banks and building societies employ building surveyors to carry out this task.

A building surveyor has many skills and often has to locate the source of many deterioration problems within older properties. Attention to detail is essential in producing survey reports for clients, employers and individuals. A thorough technical knowledge of construction is also required in order to diagnose defects that appear within building structures.

Good communication skills are required both in writing and verbally between different organisations, members of design teams and contractors undertaking corrective and refurbishment work.

### How you will be assessed

This unit is internally assessed by your tutor. A variety of activities is included in this unit to help you understand all aspects of building surveying.

After completing this unit you should be able to achieve the following outcomes:

1 Be able to demonstrate knowledge and understanding of the role of the building surveyor, interaction with other professionals and the professional qualifications required

## Thinking points

Most of us at some time consider purchasing a home. It is one of the most costly single investments we shall make in our lives. So, with even the smallest of properties costing a large amount of money in today's market value, why should you spend even more on a house survey or other report?

**2** Understand the reasons for, and the processes involved, in surveying buildings

**3** Be able to carry out simple building surveys: measured, dilapidation and condition for low-rise domestic and commercial buildings.

**4** Be able to produce a survey report and schedule of maintenance and repair and distinguish between planned and unplanned maintenance for low-rise domestic and commercial buildings

# Role of the building surveyor

## Completion of measured surveys

Measured surveys are, in effect, dimensional surveys of buildings. These can be as simple as a sketch drawing with dimensions laid out on the drawing so that an architectural technician could draw to scale the existing elevations and plans of an existing building. The building surveyor's role in producing measured surveys is to ensure that they are accurate, can easily be understood by another person and contain sufficient detail and dimensions in order to reproduce a second detailed drawing.

## Dilapidation surveys

These apply to tenancy agreements as we shall see later. The building surveyor's role in this is one of diplomacy as they are checking a tenant's flat, house or maisonette for damage during their occupancy which may result in the loss of a deposit by the tenant. They must be fair and reasonable in their actions, and record carefully the level of wear and tear before a tenant moves in and out so a subjective assessment can be made. This may often result in a disagreement between landlord and tenant, so the surveyor must be sure of the facts to provide evidence for withholding deposits from tenants.

## Condition surveys

These may also relate to the condition of housing stock, for example. Once again, the building surveyor may have to enter premises or homes to carry out an inspection with the tenant in occupation.

The surveyor has to be accurate in assessing condition as the whole of the housing stock will require assessment as to how much money requires to be spent. Awareness of financial costs and details are therefore an essential requirement of this role.

## Production of survey reports

The building surveyor needs to produce accurate reports for two reasons:

- Many clients make large financial investments on properties based on the recommendation of a surveyor as to the properties' value. In addition, monies are being lent to the buyer on the condition of the property. Therefore, the communication within a survey report must be clear, concise and accurate, with no ambiguities.
- To enable the surveyor to take out **professional indemnity insurance** cover.

## Key Term

**Professional indemnity insurance** The insurance policy that building surveyors carry so that if they make an error which results in a loss for a client, then the surveyor and the company they work for are covered against legal proceedings.

## Production of schedules of maintenance and repair

This role involves assessing what maintenance is required on a building or structure and evaluating the financial costs involved in making repairs to an acceptable level. Many commercial buildings have a set standard to maintain, for example schools and hospitals where safety plays an important part.

# Interaction with other members of the building team

## Client

The client or employer would engage a building surveyor to look at their buildings or housing stock, to assess them for the level of repairs, for value and condition. A building surveyor may interact directly with a client, for example in a house valuation for a potential purchaser or through an agent such as a mortgage lender. The client is ultimately engaging the building surveyor for a fee or salary and so they must act professionally in all dealings with the client. **Approvals** and instructions should be backed up in writing, as would expenditure on a client's budget.

## Key Term

**Approvals** The approval of the cost for the survey and instruction to proceed.

## Building owner

A building owner would interact with a building surveyor on many points, including:

- the cost of repair works
- measured surveys in land purchasing
- drainage surveys
- condition surveys
- dilapidation surveys.

This interaction would involve the contractual engagement of the building surveyor to undertake these works on the building owner's behalf, and to obtain any necessary historical information, for example from a health and safety file. Building owners and clients are often one and the same person.

## Architect

A building surveyor may produce measured surveys for architects and designers. This is done to provide accurate details of the existing building and would be used for planning and building regulation controls. The architect would commission a building surveyor to take all the dimensions of an existing structure so that it could be drawn to scale and proportion. An architect may also engage a building surveyor in advising on **listed building consents**, structural and general building defects, damp surveys and timber surveys. These are specialisms that are outside the architect's area of expertise. Building surveyors who are employed by English Heritage would liaise with architects on aspects of **listed design approval** to enable the structure to be maintained for the community as a whole.

## Key Terms

**Listed building consent** This is when a building is graded and listed as a national heritage building which cannot be altered or demolished without consent.

**Listed design approval** All works on listed buildings must match their original character and materials.

## Quantity surveyor

Interaction here is on a financial basis. If a building surveyor is acting as a consultant on a refurbishment contract, then they would liaise with the client's quantity surveyor to ensure that estimates for the work fall within the client's budget. Monthly valuations of the level of works undertaken could also be the responsibility of a building surveyor.

## Structural engineer

The building surveyor may liaise with the structural engineer over structural surveys of buildings that have signs of structural problems. The building surveyor will then call the structural engineer who can then undertake a more detailed structural investigation, especially one that requires some calculations. The structural engineer will be able to guide the building surveyor on the best possible course of action for the client or building owner.

## Clerk of works

On large construction projects, a clerk of works may be employed. This person's duties are to ensure that the work produced is in accordance with the specification and drawings. A clerk of works would interact with the building surveyor on larger refurbishments run by the building surveyor, on quality, instructions required and record keeping.

## Main contractors and subcontractors

If the building surveyor has been engaged by the client to undertake, control and manage a construction project, especially refurbishment or adaptation work, then a great deal of interaction will be involved between the building surveyor and the main contractor. Not much interaction will take place between the subcontractors and there is no contract between them and the client, employer or building owner.

The building surveyor will interact on some common issues, such as:

- written instructions
- verbal instructions
- specification queries
- colour schedules
- variations
- drawn information.

Meetings are the economical way to coordinate and interact with all parties face to face and minutes are recorded.

## Local authorities

Building surveyors would have several interactions within different departments of local authorities. Examples of these, with reasons, might be:

- highways – to locate drainage details, runs and depths where drainage surveys are required

- tree and woodlands officer – to discuss **tree preservation orders**
- conservation officer – to discuss aesthetical matters of a building within a conservation area
- fire officer – to discuss escape provisions
- planning officer – to discuss planning applications
- building control – to discuss aspects of the Building Regulations.

## Key Term

**Tree preservation order (TPO)** Protects the tree from being cut down, damaged or altered without permission of the local authority.

## Health & Safety Executive

The interaction between the building surveyor and the Health & Safety Executive (HSE) would be on matters of health and safety relating to older structures, including:

- lead – in paints and water pipes
- asbestos – location and potential for harm.

The HSE would require to know from the contractor how they plan to deal safely with asbestos as this has a very high long-term risk. Both lead and asbestos have their own legislation. The building surveyor would have to notify the HSE via a specialist contractor to have these removed from a building before any refurbishment work could commence.

# Qualifications

## The qualification route to professional status

### ■ Secondary education

The qualification route starts here as each of the following stages builds from this foundation (see Figure 15.1). A good standard of GCSEs, particularly Maths and English, will be required to gain entry to the Nationals Scheme or A levels. Science and Design Technology would help to reinforce the progressive

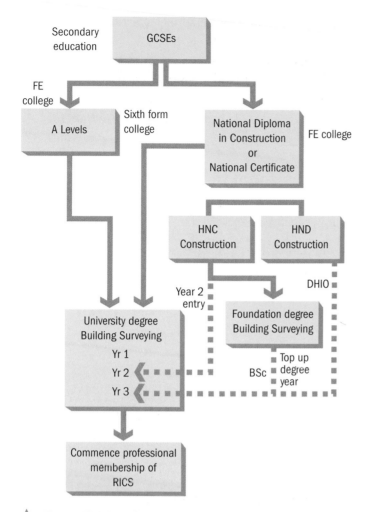

▲ **Figure 15.1 Qualification routes**

learning that is starting to take place. It is important at this stage for students to obtain detailed information on the progression routes that are possible. The flow chart illustrates the development from GCSE to university degree. Progression from GCSEs is to A levels either at sixth form college or a further education college where success provides an entry level qualification to a university degree.

## ■ National Certificate/Diploma

This is the alternative route to A levels. These are vocational qualifications providing detailed modules on construction relevant to this career pathway and which provide an accepted university degree entry route.

National Certificate is for the part-time learner who is employed and the Diploma is for the full-time FE

student. The certificate consists of 12 modules and the diploma 18 modules. Because the qualifications are vocationally specific they give the learners sound background knowledge of construction techniques for both domestic and commercial applications.

## ■ Higher National Certificate (HNC)/ Diploma (HND)

This is one progression route from the National Certificate and Diploma in Construction. It can also be accessed via A levels and by mature students with appropriate experience within the construction industry.

The HNC progression can be into several different areas as follows:

- a second-year degree course
- a foundation degree top-up year
- a final year top-up from HND to full degree.

Both qualifications extend the student into technical pathways and involve ten units for the HNC and 16 units for the HND.

## ■ Honours degree accredited by professional body

This type of degree is recognised by the professional body, the **RICS**, and narrows down the student's career path. Most professional associations such as the **CIOB** require a higher-level degree in order to attain full membership status. There is now a great deal of flexibility with degrees from full-time to part-time to distance learning through the Open University. Learners should check the status of their proposed degree against the list of accredited degrees that provide exemptions from professional institutions' exams.

## Key Terms

**RICS** Royal Institution of Chartered Surveyors – a professional association for surveyors.

**CIOB** Chartered Institute of Building – a professional association for construction personnel.

## ■ Professional membership of RICS

Membership of the RICS enables surveyors to obtain full indemnity insurance and provides a professional trademark for the chartered surveyor. All members follow a code of ethics in the way they conduct themselves and their businesses in dealing with clients, employers and building owners. Membership has several routes:

- three postgraduate routes after obtaining a first degree
- an academic route for tutors, lecturers and university teaching staff
- a senior professional route

- a technical route for personnel assisting the chartered surveyor.

The membership routes all involve some experience requirements before joining except for the direct graduate route 1. You should refer to the RICS website (www.rics.org.uk) for more detailed information on membership.

## ■ Professional membership of CIOB

This association provides a chartered status to its members, who are expected to act under a code of conduct. There are various levels of membership, along with qualifications, experience and training.

## Assessment practice

As the new recruit, the building surveying practice has asked you to help with marketing the building surveying posts it is currently trying to fill. You have been tasked with producing a promotional leaflet that needs to cover the following areas:

- Describe the role and responsibilities of a typical building surveyor
- What training and qualifications are required for a typical position?

- Which people within the design team will they interact with and how.

The manager of the practice thinks you have done a fantastic job on the marketing leaflet and has asked you to undertake the following for an advert that will go into the national press:

- Prepare a typical job description for a building surveyor
- Explain the building surveyor's interaction with other members of the building team.

# Types of building survey

## Measured surveys

These would be undertaken for the initial design stages of a refurbishment, remodelling, adaptation or extension of an existing building. Each elevation would be sketched free-hand and dimensions taken so that it could be reproduced to scale, either manually or using computer-aided design (see Figure 15.2). A similar approach is taken with the floor plan, with each floor sketched and room sizes measured so the plan can be drawn accurately to scale.

The height of a building and different features, for example windows, may sometimes present a problem if you do not have ladders. If the building is of brickwork, then you could count the courses of brickwork. As 75 mm is one course for metric and 85 mm one course for imperial brickwork, you will be able to establish the height. Alternatively, you could measure the floor to ceiling heights internally to establish the eaves' height at guttering level. The roof pitch is often another problem, but by using an adjustable set square and a spirit level you can often establish this. Access to the loft space will then confirm the roof pitch. It is often a good idea to take along a digital camera. You can use this to record all the elevations and details which you can then refer to when redrawing to scale.

## Bank or building society surveys

These are surveys undertaken by the financial lender to establish whether the property that is being purchased has a valuation that matches its market value. Such surveyors are almost entirely contracted to the financial institution lending the money to the purchaser. The purchaser pays for the valuation as part of the mortgage application process. The building surveyor will assess what the market value is by using recent transactions in the area and by visually inspecting the property for any substantial damage that would reduce the value of the loan to the purchaser.

The survey is very simple and often brief, no intrusive work is undertaken, only a brief visual inspection of the loft space and possibly some damp readings using a moisture meter. If the valuation report reduces the market value of the property and hence the amount

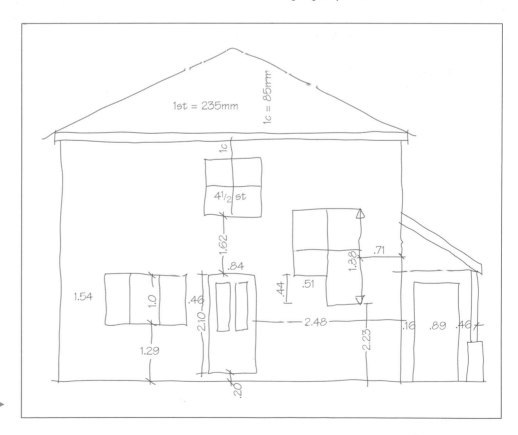

Figure 15.2 Free-hand sketch for a measured survey

of money that can be borrowed against it, then the prospective purchaser will have to increase the deposit or find the balance in order to proceed with the purchase. Many lenders require identified works within valuation reports to be undertaken before they will release the whole of the agreed loan, and retain a sum to cover this work, which is released on checking that it has been completed.

Both these surveys are commissioned by the purchaser. The only reason the seller may instruct a valuation is to borrow against the building as an asset. The lending institution would then require a valuation to confirm value.

## House buyer's reports and valuations

This is a survey that lies between a full structural survey and a valuation. It gives a valuation but also includes many other points about the property that the buyer is purchasing. It would be instructed by the buyer and will indicate to the buyer any faults or defects that have a high money value. It would contain sections under the following points:

- a general description of the property, type and age
- chimney stacks
- general joinery
- services connections, i.e. water, gas and electricity
- rainwater goods and pipes
- external decoration
- any evidence of subsidence or movement
- any evidence of woodwork infestation
- any obvious leaks from pipework
- state of electrical wiring
- evidence of damp course work
- evidence of damp to walls and ceilings
- internal decorations
- roof tile check
- loft space check
- outbuildings
- recommendations of further investigation – damp, sub-floor checks.

This type of report gives the intended purchaser sound building surveying advice on any work that may be required to be undertaken which can be used as a negotiation tool on the asking price of the seller's property.

If a purchaser is intending buying an older property, then a building surveyor may recommend that a full structural survey report is undertaken to provide evidence of any defects that have occurred over time.

## Dilapidation and condition surveys

### ■ Dilapidation survey

This type of survey is used before and after agreements such as the letting of a house or flat to a tenant or the commencement of construction works on existing sites.

Part of an agreement between a landlord and tenant will usually include a deposit on the flat or house or commercial premises for damage that may occur during the life of the tenancy agreement. This agreement will often state that any damage as a result of the tenant's occupancy will be recovered from the tenant, usually the cost being taken from the deposit held by the landlord. In order to provide evidence of damage, the landlord will undertake a **dilapidation** survey before a tenant moves in and again when the tenant moves out so the two can be compared for any changes. (See below for the methods involved in carrying out a dilapidation survey.)

## Key Term

**Dilapidation** Falling or causing to fall into ruin.

Tenants can also undertake a dilapidation survey to protect them against landlords who may falsely charge them for damage that was already there when they took over the tenancy, but unfortunately this is not in itself proof. It is advisable for both parties to agree at the beginning of a lease or rent agreement what state or condition the building is in. This avoids any disputes at the end of the agreement, but to some extent normal wear and tear should also be evaluated.

The second reason for undertaking a dilapidation survey is to protect other interested parties around a construction site who, as a consequence of the construction works, may suffer damage as a result.

This is often called a pre-construction survey, and it is advisable to have one undertaken in order to protect yourself against claims from people who might be affected by your work. Demolition works involving explosive are very worrying for adjacent residents and every precaution must be taken. For example, if you were undertaking a refurbishment of a middle terrace building which involves extensive alterations, you might ask each neighbour for access to undertake a dilapidation survey to establish the condition of the other side of the party walls before work starts and then recheck their condition after the work is completed. If these surveys are undertaken by a professional independent building surveyor, then there should be no disagreement as a result of damage sustained during the construction work. Typical damage could be as a result of:

- excavating close to a neighbour's foundation causing settlement and cracking to internal walls within their property
- demolition works
- piling foundation works
- working on an adjacent chimney causing soot to fall and damage to carpets and furnishings
- vibration causing structural cracks to walls
- excessive dust entering adjacent properties
- damage to water, electric and gas services by excavation
- road kerbs and tarmac surfaces to roadways
- the breaking of glass in windows.

If you are working near to something that is very valuable, for example a museum containing many important artefacts next to the construction site, the contractor's insurance company will need to be involved in the dilapidation survey in order to assess the risks associated to the valuable items. This may mean an increase on the insurance premium for the work being undertaken.

## ■ Condition surveys
### Stock

This is a global survey that would, for example, be undertaken by a local authority on the condition of its housing stock, schools and community buildings. It takes a snapshot in time, and tries to predict what future spending levels would be required on upgrades and repairs. Typical sections within a condition survey report would be:

- use of the housing stock, e.g. empty or let
- how many people on average are living in each
- type of dwelling, semi, detached, flat, maisonette
- how many have central heating
- how many have modern kitchens
- type of fuel used to heat
- age of housing stock
- repair costs per unit
- fitness standard
- health and safety
- energy efficiency ratings
- renovation grants (Source: headings taken from Dover District Council (2001) 'Private Sector House Condition Survey: Final Report', available at www.dover.gov.uk/privatesectorhousing/ps-house-condition-survey.pdf).

### Case study

The client you work for owns over 50 flats in the city centre. Part of your work involves landlord/tenant agreements and the release of deposits when each tenant vacates the property and a new tenant moves in. You therefore carry out regular dilapidation surveys.

Outline in detail the benefits of dilapidation surveys for your client.

# Purposes of, and processes involved in, surveys

## Measured survey to produce accurate plans prior to alteration

We have already established the purpose of undertaking a measured survey for initial feasibility design works.

The process involves visiting the property in order to draw a free-hand outline of each elevation on A4 sheets of plain paper attached to a clipboard. Horizontal and vertical dimensions are taken to enable a third party to interpret these either manually or digitally. A set of ladders can accurately establish the heights which are out of reach of a 5-metre tape measure. As we have seen, it is useful to photograph each elevation in order to provide any information that has been missed at the time of the measured survey, especially if a number of miles have been travelled to undertake the survey.

It does not matter where you commence the survey as long as the information that you record can be understood by the person who has to reproduce the accurate drawing to scale. Care should be taken to ensure a high degree of accuracy, otherwise this could lead to expensive mistakes. For example, if a surveyor in measuring the building next to the proposed one takes the wrong height, when the new building is installed with the new steelwork, it will not marry up with the adjoining properties.

## Remember!

Use a pencil to draw your free-hand sketches. It won't run in wet weather, cannot be washed off easily and does not smudge.

Digital tapes are acceptable, but you must not be reliant on the accuracy of an infra-red or optical beam that you cannot see or confirm from a taped dimension. They also must not be used on external dimensions, only between walls.

## Condition survey for prospective lenders and purchasers

This looks at housing on a smaller scale and takes a snapshot for the prospective buyer of the condition of the house at that moment in time. It is merely an analysis of what condition the building is in, and contains no reasons for defects or any structural or investigation works.

The basic process involves taking photographs and/or video to illustrate the condition on a digitally dated

image. The survey should be divided into external and internal items. Internally, it could be broken down into room-by-room surveys with the condition of each. A general section would cover services. This type of report is not as detailed as a house buyer's report.

## Advice on maintenance, repair and conservation

Clients may wish to know what it will cost to put right the defective parts of a building highlighted within a home buyer's survey report.

### ■ Maintenance

This involves looking after the building's fabric and structure to keep it maintained at a fit-for-use status. If you maintain your house in a very good condition, then when you come to sell it, it will look attractive to a potential purchaser and will add a premium to its market value. Typical maintenance items on a house include:

- ensuring guttering is clean of weeds and runs freely
- external painting is fresh and clean
- weeds removed from gardens, driveways and footpaths
- fences in good condition and painted
- attention to plumbing leaks from overflow pipes causing water staining on external faces of building
- cleaning glazed surfaces and replacing broken glass
- roof tiles and felt in good condition
- internal decorations (fill cracks and redecorate)
- areas of damp treated
- carpets and furnishings clean.

The better presented a property, the more saleable it is likely to be. A building surveyor can identify many of the above 'building' items and provide cost estimates which would enable some negotiation on the asking price of a property.

### ■ Repair

Repairs sometimes involve a specialist. Structural cracks will need a good builder to investigate and repair to a satisfactory level. Often older properties that have settlement may be required to have their foundations **underpinned**. A good building surveyor can produce a repair schedule for a client with accurate cost estimates so that informed decisions can be made on purchasing a property. Repairs carried out by the property owner can be cosmetic, and the services of a builder or a construction professional contractor should be sought in order to obtain some form of guarantee. One organisation with such members is the Federation of Master Builders.

## Key Term

**Underpinned** This is where the existing foundation is currently settling downwards, which causes structural cracks to the external and internal finishes. A new, deeper foundation is cast in sections below the old one.

Roof repairs are best left to a roofing contractor who will supply all the specialist equipment required to gain safe access to fix roof tiles or roofing felt problems. Window repairs should be undertaken by a glazier or upvc window company who can advise on replacements or repair to double-glazed units. As part of their report, a building surveyor will check the quality of the double-glazed units and whether they are still sealed units, as there is no guarantee with them.

### ■ Conservation

Many local authorities have areas which are designated as 'conservation areas'. These are areas that have historical significance, natural beauty or important architectural interest and as such have restricted planning permissions. Any tree within a conservation area is automatically protected and must have permission before any work is undertaken on it, for example pruning or felling.

Conservation also covers **listed building** consent, which is a grading given to a building that saves it for our heritage. Here any work has to be done to the approval of an inspector which can include having antique paint manufactured! Conservation of materials and the character of a building must often be undertaken by a specialist company, for example replacing a thatched roof – there are few companies left that can

undertake this old skill. A building surveyor will be able to recommend specialist companies to undertake the conservation work on old and antique materials.

## Key Term

**Listed building** This is a status given by English Heritage to buildings of architectural merit that need protecting. There are three grades, and any work to them requires like-for-like construction details.

### Assessment of dangerous structures

The first person who might be called to a dangerous structure is the building control officer because this forms part of their role and responsibility. The building can then be referred to a building surveyor by a client or building owner to take care of the dangerous structure. In some cases of imminent danger the local authority will undertake the work and charge the property owner for the cost of such work.

A building surveyor would be able to offer advice and guidance on dangerous structures such as:

- gable end wall tie failure
- general wall tie failure
- chimney collapse
- bowing of walls at first-floor level
- damage caused through a traffic crash to a structure
- roof tile fixing failure
- retaining walls
- tree root damage.

### Structural appraisal

This is the element of a survey that might require the services of a structural engineer or senior building surveyor. Typical elements of a building that would be investigated would be:

- foundation settlement
- roof spread
- wall tie failure

- external cracking
- internal cracking
- removal of any roof timbers
- sagging of roof ridge
- sagging of floors.

The techniques may require some investigation works. Sub-floors will require inspection through cutting access hatches into timber floors to inspect the floor joists below. Roof access and lighting will be required, including loft access ladders to inspect roof timbers. A theodolite, spirit level and plumb line can be used to check the verticality of a structure and to establish if it is leaning. A level can be used to establish horizontal control to see if any part of the building has settled over time and may be a cause of cracking in the structure. Visual checking of door heads will give a clue as to whether a building has moved; similarly, with sticking doors that have been planed to fit uneven openings. Roof spread can be observed by visual lining in of elements from a point at height or by physical measurement within the roof space. Wall tie investigation will involve drilling holes through the outer skin of brickwork and inserting a camera with a mirror to observe and record. Drain problems are best investigated using a specialist company that can drag and steer a mobile camera up a drain to locate a crack or obstruction or break in the drain.

## Detailed examination of the building's condition

To help you to understand the processes and equipment involved in surveying, we will now look at different ways in which a building can be examined using more specialised techniques and at the basic surveyor's tool kit.

### ■ General and specialised techniques and equipment

#### Thermal imaging camera

This is a very specialised survey that involves a camera that can detect heat and produce a thermal image. The red areas are where it is hottest and the blue where it is cold or equal to the background temperature. This allows a picture to be taken of any potential cold bridging across cavities and above lintels, and shows

▲ A thermal image

areas that are subject to excessive heat loss. Thermal images can also demonstrate if a cavity wall contains sufficient insulation to meet current regulations.

#### Drainage survey camera

This is used to survey the drainage system and allows a mobile, electrically powered camera to be run up small diameter drains to investigate drainage problems. Smoke bombs and fluid dyes also provide assistance in surveying the direction and runs of drains to establish how the network works. This type of equipment can equally be used to survey chimneys for defects in the flue system.

### Case study

You have been looking to buy a house close to the city centre and have at last found a property built in 1905 in the older part of the city. You have now to sort out a mortgage on the property from a lender. The lender has indicated that you can have a 90 per cent loan and you will have to find a 10 per cent deposit. This is your first step on the property ladder, and money is tight. The lender has asked if you would require any further surveys on this property.

Is it worth spending extra to have these surveys?

What would be the benefits of a structural survey?

Is a timber survey required?

**Radon gas detector survey**

This involves the use of a specific radon gas detector to analyse the sub-floor voids to detect this potentially carcinogenic (cancer forming) gas that can have a detrimental effect on human health.

▲ Steel tape

# Assessment practice

The potential buyer of a property has approached your building surveying company to seek advice on what type of survey to have undertaken on the property. The details from the commercial sales brochure sound less than convincing:

'This period property is over 150 years old and is constructed of a one brick walling with timber oak beams with a thatch roof structure, and is in keeping with the conservation area surroundings of the enclosed village. Its character and charm are worthy of the investment that would be required in refurbishing this property to an acceptable standard.'

From this, identify the reasons why you would survey the building, what procedures you would adopt and what techniques you would use in carrying out the survey. **P2**

The buyer in P2 above is still unsure after the advice you have given and is considering having the following surveys undertaken on the property:

▲ Fibre tape

- Structural survey
- Condition survey
- Valuation survey
- Timber survey

Discriminate (i.e. differentiate) between each, and explain the applications of the building surveys. **D3**

considered the normal length use. Both operate with a wind-up mechanism which folds the tape into the reel.

## Remember!

A fibre tape is less accurate than a steel tape because it tends to stretch when pulled and will therefore read short in any long dimension, but it is not affected by temperature, unlike the steel tape which expands.

# Surveying equipment

### Steel and fibre tape

These types of tape are useful when undertaking a measured survey where long external dimensions are required and where a 5-metre tape is not long enough. There are various sizes available; from 30 m to 100 m is

### Folding rule

A folding rule, as the name suggests, folds down into a convenient 300 mm length but extends to 2 m. This is useful where an ordinary tape would bend and collapse when taking a vital dimension, while the folding rule will remain rigid until folded back into itself. It can be used for a constant set of measurements that repeat over and over, thus making it easy simply to hold up the folding ruler. They are normally constructed of timber and graduated in metric.

## Electronic distance measurement device

This device uses a laser to bounce from a known surface – the machine – to an unknown surface – the other wall. The speed of light of a laser is constant and thus the distance between the two walls can be calculated and appears on the readout. You can see where you are pointing the laser by the red dot it projects on the adjacent wall. This has to be then

▲ Electronic distance measure device

recorded on the measured survey. Some newer machines have data loggers that enable the measurements to be downloaded back at the office.

These machines are good for internal dimensions but, externally, where you are not working between walls, a tape measure will be more effective, as it can be attached by the end clip to the outside angle of the wall.

## Moisture meter

The basic machine uses two metal probes and measures the electrical resistance across the probe pins. The wetter a material they are pushed into, the less resistance there is across the material due to the presence of moisture and the higher the reading given. A moisture meter is used to check the moisture content of timber and walls above and below the damp proof course to check that the damp course is working effectively. Several readings should be taken to ensure

that an accurate average is obtained. You should also make a visual check to ensure that a damp course is present within a building and take into account the age and construction of the building.

## Camera

The improvements to cameras in the last ten years have been phenomenal. Digital imaging has made the old film-based systems nearly obsolete. Time and date recorded photographs of properties and different aspects of the survey can be instantly captured, and used as a historical record, especially for dilapidation surveys. This technology enables images to be stored and emailed very easily, enabling a report to be compiled more quickly. A digital camera is very useful when conducting measured surveys as it enables you to take a second look at any aspect that you have missed, for example you can count brick courses from a photograph.

## Inspection chamber keys

These are used to lift inspection or manhole covers from their surrounding frames. Great care should be taken when lifting a manhole due to the weight and length of time that the lid has been down, as dirt and debris can cause the lid to lodge securely within the frame. Larger lids should only be lifted by two people.

Often, on major roads the health and safety implications are extensive and we shall look at this aspect later. There are various sizes of keys and manual handling lifting devices to help reduce the strain on the back.

### Safety tip

Never try to lift a large inspection or manhole cover on your own. You could damage your back.

## Binoculars

These extend your range of vision, especially in surveying roof work. Small defects can be spotted more easily by using binoculars to identify weaknesses within the structure. Binoculars are especially useful for high-rise buildings where your scope of view of the outer walls is limited from the inside. A set of $10 \times 8$ binoculars is all that would be required for a surveyor's tool kit and will help to reduce eye strain when surveying exteriors in strong sunlight.

## Boroscope

This is a very useful tool for gaining access into a structure with the minimum of disruption and damage to the fabric of the building. The boroscope consists of a telescope with a mirror at the end that diverts the line of sight by 90 degrees. This is especially useful when you need to inspect the cavity of a wall. A light within the equipment enables a good visual inspection of these inaccessible areas of a structure. Adding a camera to this process enables a record of the inspection to be made.

To use the equipment, a hole must be drilled through the outer part of the structure that you are trying to inspect. This must be oversized to allow the camera to slide through easily. Once the inspection has been carried out, the boroscope is withdrawn and the hole must be made good. Obviously, the larger the

inspection area, the more holes you will have to drill in order to make an evidenced judgement as to the defect.

## Thermal imaging equipment

As we have seen earlier, this is very complex equipment that requires specialist training to use. It is often better in smaller building surveying practices to obtain the services of a specialist subcontractor to undertake this work. A thermal camera with some form of recording media will be required along with a digital player to observe the findings.

## Sectional ladder

This is a typical surveyor's ladder. Built in sections, it can be easily disassembled and placed in a car boot. This avoids the need to hire ladders delivered to a survey job or the use of a car roof rack, which would mean a permanent fixture to the car. Sectional ladders are light weight and have a limited height use.

## Spirit level

This is available in a number of differing lengths and measures the horizontal and vertical positions of the surface it is placed upon. Care should be taken when measuring vertical walls as you obtain a better measurement when using a longer level.

## Electric torch

An essential item is a torch when entering the following conditions:

- a roof loft space that does not have a mains light installed
- a sub-floor inspection
- a cellar
- a boarded-up property.

A surveyor should always carry spare batteries, or if using a rechargeable torch, ensure that it is fully charged before leaving to undertake the survey. Use a torch of a good size so you can see everything that you need to on the survey.

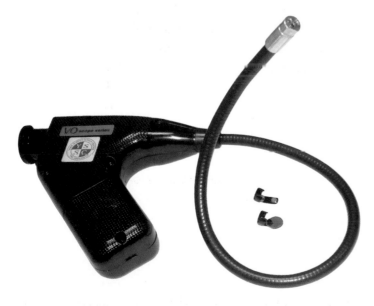

▲ **A boroscope**

## Optical levels

An optical or automatic level, as we can see from the photograph, is used with a staff to establish what the difference in level is across two or more points. This can be used to establish the settlement of a building, whether it is even or is dipping in one corner. Taking several levels over a period of time would provide a course of monitoring to establish if the building is continuing to settle. A known reference point away from the building must be established as a control point to establish if the building levels are moving.

## Basic land surveying equipment

Theodolites, ranging poles and optical reflectors can be used to survey large areas of land and buildings to quickly plot an area to scale. Modern surveying equipment uses global positioning equipment to measure electronically an area by using satellite navigation to triangulate a known point. All you have to do is locate a grid coordinate and then print out your survey.

▲ **A level and staff**

## Personal protective equipment

Typical personal protective equipment (PPE) that a surveyor should consider carrying and wearing includes:

- stout steel toecap boots or shoes
- gloves for handling manhole lifting keys and drainage inspections
- a high visibility jacket
- a safety helmet when climbing into and through loft spaces
- a mask to prevent inhalation of glass fibres from loft insulation
- safety glasses if cutting any material for testing
- specialist equipment, e.g. harnesses for abseiling inspections.

This equipment should always be used as a last resort as a risk assessment should in all cases be undertaken to try to design out the use of PPE.

### Safety tip

Always maintain your PPE in a working and clean condition.

## Assessment practice

You are the new graduate building surveyor who has been assigned as an assistant to the senior building surveyor in the local authority environment department. Part of your role as the assistant is to look after the survey equipment store and ensure that all survey equipment is kept clean, serviced and maintained. You have been asked to prepare some equipment for the following surveys:

- structural survey
- roof survey
- dilapidation survey.

In each case, identify what essential equipment would be required, and explain the uses of the surveying equipment required for each different survey task. **M2**

# Procedures

## Preliminary surveys

The first item on this list is to arrange with the client a date and time for a survey. This is normally done on the telephone through the client initially contacting the surveyor's office. The building surveyor should then contact the client to arrange a mutually convenient time when the survey could be undertaken. Due to the fact that many home owners are employed full-time, this may mean arranging for a time through the selling agent who will have access and keys.

It must be made clear to the client the terms and conditions of engagement that the building surveyor operates under and the client must be aware and have agreed the fee for the survey. Often this is done by acknowledging by letter and a fee deposit. Advice can be given over the phone to establish the client's knowledge of the different types of survey that are available with costs so that the client gets the correct survey for their potential purchase.

When a date and time has been established, you should turn up on time, suitably dressed to undertake the survey, which can take from one to two hours depending on the level of detail required. Photographs can be taken and any measurements established. It is professional not to discuss with a seller or leaser your client's position on the purchase or let.

Once the survey is complete, you should make sure that the property is left secure and safe and return to the office to have a survey report typed up. This should be checked by a second person before it is sent to a client to ensure accuracy of the information supplied, and to establish that nothing has been missed from the report.

## Site location

The distance from your office will affect how many surveys you can physically undertake in a working day. Obviously, the time of year will also have a bearing on the amount of light available for external surveys as in the winter the nights draw in rapidly. Urban locations are easy to undertake surveys within but care must be taken of the security of vehicles and equipment. Rural locations may require the use of a four-wheel drive vehicle to undertake a survey. Congested locations where ladders have to be placed across footpaths and roads to gain access to survey must be carefully considered before proceeding. Great care should be taken when undertaking survey work within factory site locations, and you should ensure that you attend an induction before starting and are aware of all the risks associated with that site.

## Building location

The building location sometimes has a bearing on the survey being undertaken, for example a third-floor flat is not easily surveyed from the outside. When access to a property is over another owner's land, you should seek permission to do so, otherwise you will be trespassing. Buildings next to water, railways, harbours and major trunk roads should be recorded as such due to the location regarding flood plain and vibration causing damage to the structure. This is also the case with buildings next to airports, but here the damage is merely excessive noise levels as a disturbance to the occupiers.

**Remember!**

Never trespass on adjoining property.

## Elemental surveys

### ■ External inspection

It is sometimes easier to commence the survey from the inside out. This is done for two reasons, the first to prevent damage if you forget to take your shoes off and, secondly, it disturbs the occupants less and reduces the time they need to secure the building before returning to work.

External surveys should be commenced at one corner and finish at the same point. While this is good practice on a detached building, it is not possible on a mid terrace or semi detached. It is often worthwhile looking at the defects on adjacent properties to give clues to any potential defect that might occur within the property you are surveying. Typical elements that will be inspected externally are:

- guttering and downpipes – blocked or damaged
- chimney stacks – condition of pointing; verticality
- roofs pitched – ridge and hip tile bedding; age of tiles
- roofs flat – life span of three layer felt; ponding on roof
- external high level joinery – fascias, soffits and barge boards
- external ventilation vents and airbricks – broken or blocked
- manhole covers and lids – broken
- surface water drainage – blocked
- fencing and property boundaries
- external brickwork – evidence of cracking
- external face of any exposed lintels over openings.

## ■ Internal inspection

This can be divided into two areas: those which are clearly visible and the others which are not, particularly the roof space. Internal inspection of visible areas would include:

- the condition of the internal decorations
- internal joinery – evidence of woodwork or rot
- windows and double-glazed units – are the seals intact?
- doors and frames – are they square?
- gas fittings – have they been checked and serviced?
- electrical services, fuse board and wiring and fittings – are they current or require updating?
- radiators, boiler and pipework –evidence of leaks
- flooring, solid or timber – evidence of bounce indicating soft wall plates
- ceilings and plaster finishes – evidence of cracking
- chimneys – leaning or condition of pointing.

Inspection of non-visible areas is mainly limited to those where access can be gained without causing damage to the fabric of the building, for example loft spaces are easily accessed through hatches. Roof void inspections would normally cover the following items:

- age of tiles and state of fixings
- if any underfelt is present
- state of fixing battens
- general condition of roof timbers
- ventilation to the roof space
- evidence of light passing through roof – slipped tiles
- infestation from wasps, woodworm and birds or bats
- amount of insulation utilised.

## ■ Building services

These are gas, water, electric and drainage. A telephone can be loosely called a service but is not essential to the serviceability of a building. Gas inspections must be undertaken by a registered heating and plumbing engineer and not an unqualified building surveyor. The surveyor can check the presence of a meter, the number of appliances attached to the pipework, isolation valves and visual observation of any pipework exposed. A qualified engineer would undertake two tests. The first would be to detect any leaks from the system; the second to check the flues from boilers and gas fires to check they are functioning correctly as carbon monoxide discharge into occupied areas can kill.

Water services should be checked for **cross bonding** beneath sinks and taps and for general leaks. The existence of old lead pipes should be noted to a potential buyer due to health risks associated with lead poisoning. Leaking overflows produce external staining of finishes and should be mentioned in the survey report.

Electricity inspections should check the condition of the existing wiring and whether an older property has been rewired. The consumer unit should be inspected to note the presence of **RCBs** or **MCBs** or old fuse wire. A basic

## Key Terms

**Cross bonding** In the event of an electrical fault, this prevents any metal service from becoming live with electricity.

**RCB** Residual current device acts as a fuse.

**MCB** A miniature circuit breaker which switches off power on an earth short.

plug-in test can give some diagnostics to the building surveyor, but again if there is any doubt, a certified inspection from a qualified electrician should be sought.

Drainage can be inspected by lifting manholes and observing the drainage run, whether it has standing water, and the condition of the manhole. Areas of flooding should be inspected to locate a cause. Surface and foul systems that are combined should be noted as against separate systems. Soakaways that allow water from surface drains to percolate into the ground should be noted. If the property is not connected to main drainage, septic tanks should be inspected to see if they have been maintained properly.

### ■ External works

An inspection of external works would cover items such as:

- footpaths and driveways – check for cracking and settlement
- external paving – age and condition; frost attack
- decking – age and treatment
- fences – condition of posts and panels
- gates – metal or timber and condition
- surface water drainage – working effectively
- trees – TPOs
- outbuildings – general condition
- garden – general condition of plants, bushes and maturity
- brick boundary walls
- retaining walls.

## Checklists for surveys

### Standardised checklists

Checklists are a very good idea to develop in a building surveying practice. They enable a standard methodology to be employed in surveying buildings and can be extended to form the basis of a building surveying report. The main advantage is that they ensure that no single item is missed as a box has to be checked against each one. They make the surveyor's job that much

easier to undertake and allow for the development of handheld electronic building surveying, especially on large housing stocks where repetition occurs. Figure 15.3 illustrates how a typical checklist can be built up and used by ticking the appropriate material used in construction, then checking condition with any comments. You can develop a checklist for any particular part or whole of a survey.

## Legislative considerations

### Health, safety and welfare

Health and safety is important in any work the surveyor undertakes. There are risks associated with carrying out surveys, including:

- electrocution from old, faulty wiring exposed during survey
- Weil's disease from rats' urine contaminating the water during drainage surveys
- disease from human waste during drainage inspections
- surveying old buildings frequented by homeless people with drug habits – needle stick injuries, Hepatitis B or C
- standing on unsafe timber floors and structures
- falling down manholes that are unprotected
- falling from height during inspections using ladders
- trips, slips and falls while surveying loft spaces
- injury to the head while gaining loft or sub-floor access
- risks associated with surveying near major roads
- asbestos presence in loose format that is inhaled.

You should be particularly careful when surveying very old and derelict properties as the structure can be weakened through timber decay and rot and can lead to collapse when you try to enter the building and walk over floors and stairs. Buildings that have been empty for some time may contain stale air which will need venting before inspection can take place.

Another aspect of survey work is dealing with tenants. They may be in dispute with a landlord and will try to obstruct a dilapidation survey for fear of losing a deposit on the property. Great diplomacy is required by the

Figure 15.3 A typical building surveying checklist

**External roof inspection checklist**

| Element | Description | Tick box | Condition | | Comment |
|---------|-------------|----------|-----------|---------|---------|
| | | | Good | Repair | |
| Roof tiles | Concrete | | | | |
| | Clay | | | | |
| | Slate | | | | |
| | Other – specify | | | | |
| Ridge and hip tiles | Concrete | | | | |
| | Clay | | | | |
| | Asbestos | | | | |
| | Other | | | | |
| Guttering | Cast iron | | | | |
| | upvc | | | | |
| | Timber | | | | |
| | Lead | | | | |
| | Asbestos | | | | |
| Fascias and soffit | Asbestos | | | | |
| | Timber | | | | |
| | Plywood | | | | |
| | upvc | | | | |

building surveyor in this often stressful situation and a great deal of trust can be gained by clearly explaining that you have to undertake this work. A sound professional approach at all times should be maintained.

All survey work must be undertaken in accordance with the employer/employees duties under the Health and Safety at Work Act 1974 with regard to the duty of care not only for employees but also the general public and building owners who might be affected by the building surveyor's actions.

The Management of Health and Safety at Work Regulations 1999 must also be considered with regard to the risk assessments that should be undertaken with all survey work. The electrical testing of any electrical survey equipment must conform to the Provision and Use of Work Equipment Regulations 1998 and have an annual PAT test – Portable Appliance Test for electrical safety. Any work at height should be conducted in accordance with the Work at Height Regulations 2005. Any design work must be undertaken in accordance with the Construction (Design and Management) Regulations 2007 with regard to design risk assessments and the duties of the parties involved within the contract. (See Chapter 1 Health, safety and welfare in construction and the built environment for more information on legislation.)

## Assessment practice

Your survey company has breached a regulation which has led to an inspection from the HSE. The managing director is very keen to ensure that all processes and procedures are current and within the legislative framework. Undertake a check for the director by explaining the implications of current health and safety legislation on the survey work the company typically carries out. **D1**

### Contractual obligations

Once an offer is made and accepted, then this is a legally binding contract. A building surveyor must ensure that their conditions of engagement are agreed and accepted by a client and contain all the terms of the contractual obligation between the two parties. Once a surveyor has accepted a contract, they are bound to complete their obligations and then receive payment for their services.

Confidentiality and data protection clauses should also be inserted into the agreement to ensure that a report is only used for the purpose that it was intended for. A clause on the concealed areas that cannot be surveyed should be included to limit the extent of the survey and not leave the surveyor open to legal action by a client.

If a building surveyor is running a contract on behalf of a client, say a refurbishment, then a typical **JCT** contract may be in place which states that the surveyor is the client's or employer's representative. This empowers them to act and run the contract on their behalf till completion. This role could be likened to that of the architect or designer.

## Key Term

**JCT** Joint Contracts Tribunal.

### Legal constraints

#### ■ Trespass

Contractually, you cannot enter a building unless you have the owner's permission to do so as this can technically be called a tort in law, which is trespass. A building surveyor could quite easily find that they place themselves in this position and should ensure that they are working with permission and instructions from clients. This is also a difficult position when a house has to be sold in a divorce settlement and is owned by one party, the other being obstructive. Again, diplomacy may win through in such cases.

#### ■ Breach of contract

If a building surveyor is commissioned to provide a survey report and accepts remittance for such services, or confirms intention to do so for an agreed fee and then fails to undertake the service, then they may be in breach of contract. A client, tenant or building owner can then take them to court and seek damages for failure to complete the work. Similarly, if a client fails to pay the surveyor, then they can in turn be taken to court to recover a debt due.

### Remember!

If the surveyor fails to notice an obvious defect which is not excluded by the report, they could be sued for damages. Reports must be written with care.

#### ■ Limited liability of reports

A survey report must be structured so it is quite clear what terms and conditions the report is issued under. If a surveyor cannot see a defect and the defect manifests itself within a short period, then the surveyor needs to indemnify themselves against legal proceedings for damages of negligence. The best way to do this is through professional indemnity insurance. This is paid by the surveyor to an insurance company who indemnifies the surveyor against any act of omission or negligence on their part which may result in legal claims for damages against the surveyor.

## Thinking points

Indemnity insurance has often to be paid for the life of the surveyor.

Survey reports, therefore, contain many disclaimers so that a client is left in no doubt as to the legal position of the survey.

### ■ Bankruptcy

If the client or the surveyor goes bankrupt, then an official receiver would undertake the winding up of the company and establish the liability of the debtors and sums to be paid to creditors.

## Assessment practice

As the newly qualified surveyor in the company, the managing director has asked you to take a look at the current company health and safety policy. The policy is an old one and will need updating. In order to do this you will need to do the following:

Evaluate the key surveying operations in terms of health, safety and welfare, identifying the hazards, the risks and the controls that will be necessary for the company when conducting its business. **D2**

# Measured survey

This approach to the content involves undertaking a measured survey of a building and producing the raw data that will need to be processed to form a completed scale drawing.

To undertake the survey, first select a case study building that involves the elevation of a building and conduct a measured survey of that elevation to produce the data in order to redraw the elevation to a scale of 1:100 (see Figure 15.4). You should pick an elevation of a building that contains sufficient detail and proportions to reproduce a good industrial standard drawing. Undertake a measured survey of this building using all or some of the following equipment:

- digital camera
- tape measure
- 30 m metal tape
- A4 paper and pencil.

Ensure that your measured survey contains sufficient detail and dimensions to enable you to redraw it successfully. With inaccessible heights, use the counting courses of brick method or carry out internal dimension heights to establish the elevation height. Reproduce this elevation on A3 paper to a scale of 1:100 ensuring that it fits onto the paper. If this is not the case, then cut down your elevation. Alternatively,

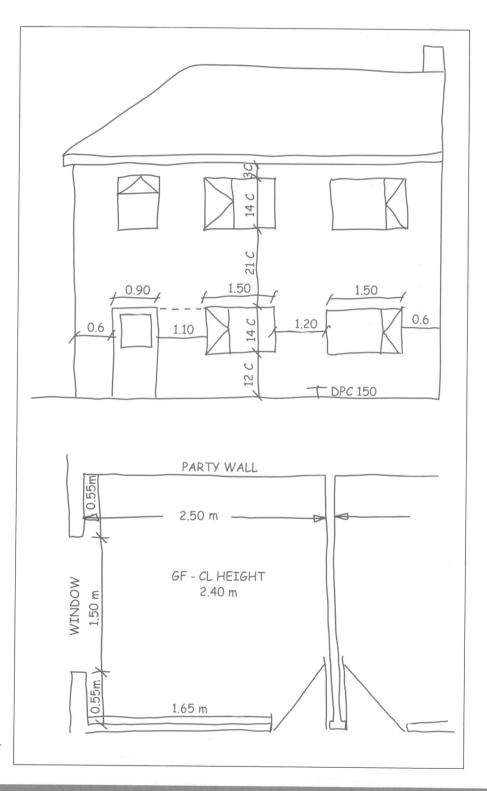

**Figure 15.4 A measured survey sketch of a room** ▶

you can reproduce the elevation using computer-aided design and a plotter.

# Dilapidation survey

As a surveyor, you must be able to apply your knowledge and understanding of this type of surveying and actually undertake a dilapidation survey. You must be aware that there is various legislation that protects a tenant and landlord and act professionally at all times. The equipment you could use would be:

- internal and external checklist
- dictaphone to record notes from survey
- loft ladders
- **PDA** with built in checklist
- digital camera
- previous survey to check against for deterioration.

## Key Term

**PDA** Personal digital assistant – a handheld computer.

Before commencing any dilapidation survey, you should confirm with the tenant or landlord (whichever one has instructed you) the agreed terms of engagement. It is also advisable to obtain copies of all relevant documentation between landlord and tenant including the lease agreement. This will indicate who is responsible for what aspect of the building. For example, the landlord may be responsible for the exterior of the building, and the tenant the internal decorations.

An itemised schedule divided initially into 'External' and 'Internal' should be constructed and subheadings listed under each, for example:

| External | Internal |
| --- | --- |
| Guttering | Room 1 decorations |
| Roof | Room 2 radiators |
| Walls | |

Once completed, the report should be handed to the person who appointed you for them to discuss and finalise any lease agreement to return deposits.

# Condition survey

We have already looked at condition surveys on pages 461–2.

## Assessment practice

This consists of three activities:

1   A measured survey: Select a small manageable building on your campus, or your house. Undertake a measured survey to produce fully dimensioned sketches. Hand these sketches to a colleague and ask them to produce one of the elevations in a scaled drawing. Ensure that you also have one from a colleague to undertake.

2   A dilapidation survey: Liaise with a local housing association or tenants association or the local authority housing office to gain access to an empty rental property so that you can carry out a dilapidation survey. Ensure that a risk assessment is undertaken before entering an unoccupied property.

3   A condition survey: Produce a condition survey on your home including all internal and external points that should be considered. **P3**

For all three activities in P3 produce final measured, dilapidation and condition survey reports for the low-rise domestic or commercial buildings surveyed. Ensure that you collect and compile your survey data using standard techniques and record and present the data in appropriate formats. **P4 M4**

In each of the measured, dilapidation and condition surveys you carried out in P4, identify and evaluate the different ways in which survey data can be recorded and presented. **M3**

## Preparing a final survey report from raw data

A survey report is the final document that a client, tenant or building owner receives for the payment agreed. It needs to be a professionally produced document, using clear technical language so the uninformed client can understand its content.

### Remember!

A survey report must look professional in the setting out and format as it is the final summary which may contain financial penalties for either party.

The initial data produced from the survey will be some or all of the following:

- digital photographs
- samples
- handwritten notes
- sketches and dimensions
- meter readings
- PDA checklists
- video surveys
- previous survey reports.

This then has to be reproduced into a report format. The outer covers should contain an image or company logo along with any professional membership logo, for example the RICS. Within the covers, the report should be secured so that the client can easily flick through its content. The report can follow a standard format and, indeed, many building society valuation reports follow a standard format with the society's logo at the top of the report.

Often reports contain a brief summary of findings on the first page. This is done to focus the client on the main findings, with the detail behind in the main body of the report. The report can then be divided into observations that are internal and external – it does not matter which comes first, but note the earlier comment on disturbing a tenant or client. The report should include a conclusion with any further recommendations which may be further investigations or surveys, for example a roof timber survey, and should be signed by the surveyor and a checker if required. An appendix can contain any further information such as limitations of the survey. In all aspects the survey report must be impartial and not favour any one party.

The building surveyor's practice may have developed a standard word processing package template that just requires that the boxes are filled to compile a finished report. It is often advisable not to release copies of the report until payment has been completed. The report can often then be emailed with a hard copy posted out that day.

The report format should initially contain an introduction explaining the purpose of the survey, its location address and the date it was undertaken.

## Preparing maintenance and repair schedules

### Maintenance schedule

Following any simple survey, it is quite easy to prepare a maintenance schedule that can be given to a landlord or a premises/facilities manager to organise future maintenance to keep the building in a fit standard and condition. This is done for several reasons, including:

- health and safety
- to avoid devaluation of a building
- to attract tenants.

**Simtop Ltd**

## Maintenance schedule

Building.......................................................................

Date schedule prepared.......................................

By whom....................................................................

Organisation...............................................................

| Item | Interval | Done | Comment |
|------|----------|------|---------|
| **Externals** | | | |
| Guttering | Annually | | Clean out guttering by hand and flush with water |
| Down-pipes | Annually | | Flush with water |
| Drainage traps | 2x year | | Remove grids and clear trap flush with water |
| Manholes | Annually | | Remove lid, regrease and flush out benching |
| Pathways | 3x year | | Remove weeds and spray with weed killer |
| upvc fascias | 2x year | | Wash down with warm water and mild detergent |
| External doors | 2x year | | Oil and lubricate hinges, check closers |
| upvc windows | 2x year | | Spray with silicone lubricant hinges |
| External vents | 3 x year | | Remove and clean external ventilation vents |
| Landscaping | Summer | | Weed and mulch beds and water |
| | Winter | | Prune back bushes and trees |

▲ Figure 15.5 A maintenance schedule

A repair schedule lists the repairs that need to be undertaken. These may be classified as follows:

- Urgent and immediate – liable to cause injury to occupiers.
- Action required within a week.
- Action required within a month.

A repair schedule for a landlord would contain a full specification on how to undertake the repair along with an associated cost estimate for the repair.

# Assessment practice

Locate a suitable building that can be easily accessed and that is safe to enter. Undertake a simple survey of the building externally and produce the following schedules:

**a** A maintenance schedule that can be handed to the estates manager to instruct the maintenance crew on what will be required over a one year period.

**b** On your survey, note any items that will require repairing and produce a repair schedule for three items covering the following:

  i full specification for the repair

  ii an estimated cost

iii timer interval when it should be done by.

# Preparation for assessment

Describe the various roles and responsibilities of a typical building surveyor. Identify what training and qualifications are required to work for a professional building survey practice. What members of the design team would a building surveyor interact with? **P1**

You have been asked to write some marketing materials for the surveying company you work for. Produce a short leaflet that explains the various reasons why buildings are surveyed and the procedures/techniques that you would adopt in each case. For each type of survey, identify the equipment you would use. **P2**

Select several suitable low-rise domestic or commercial buildings and undertake the following simple surveys: measured; dilapidation; condition. **P3**

For the work you have produced in P3, prepare final measured, dilapidation and condition survey reports for a low-rise domestic or commercial building. **P4**

Select several suitable low-rise domestic or commercial buildings and undertake the following simple schedules: a schedule of maintenance; a schedule of repairs. **P5**

You have been asked to prepare a job description for an advertisement to attract a building surveyor to your organisation which is currently undergoing an expansion.

Prepare a typical job description for a building surveyor to include what interactions this recruited person will have with other members of the design team. **M1**

From the following list of surveys:

- dilapidation
- structural
- drainage

identify the surveying equipment you would need and how you would use it. **M2**

Your manager wants to vary the ways in which data is recorded on surveys the company undertakes. Identify and evaluate the different ways in which survey data can be recorded and presented. **M3**

In undertaking the work for the P3 and P4 criteria, ensure that you use standard techniques to collect, record and compile this data and present the data in appropriate formats. These techniques could mean the use of some standard forms that you have devised to promote a professional impression with a potential client. **M4**

The chief surveyor is concerned that some of the survey work that the company has undertaken does not comply with current health and safety standards imposed through health and safety legislation. Identify several pieces of legislation and their application to surveying tasks. **D1**

You have been asked to evaluate the following surveying tasks in terms of health and safety and welfare:

- Inspection of manholes and drainage
- Inspection of chimney flue lining
- Inspection of unlit roof void

Produce your evaluation in a short report format. **D2**

From the following list of surveys:

- dilapidation
- structural
- drainage

discriminate between them, and explain the applications of the various types of building survey listed above. **D3**

## Grading tips

You could look through several websites that contain advertisements for a building surveyor in order to obtain the necessary titles that would go into a description. Take care not to cut and paste as this must be in your own words. You could reference it to local issues. This criterion contains two elements, the *job description* and the *interaction*. **M1**

Make sure that you contrast different equipment for each type of survey. **M2**

Outline a range of ways of obtaining survey data, how it can be recorded and presented in a final format for different surveys and uses. **M3**

Clear presentation to an industrial standard is required. Ensure that all your notes are clean, clear and concise. Utilise a word processing package to format the survey. **M4**

Explain the implications of health and safety legislation in the context of survey work. You need to identify some health and safety legislation and reference it to typical building survey work explaining what the implications are. **D1**

Identify some key hazards associated with survey work and the controls that will be required. **D2**

Discriminate between, and explain the applications of, the various types of building survey. Identify a number of different surveys and compare and contrast each so that a person who has limited knowledge can clearly see an explanation against each survey of their application to different purposes. **D3**

## Knowledge check

1 Name three members of a typical design team with whom a building surveyor would communicate and interact.

2 In what way would a member of the local authority interact with the building surveyor?

3 What is a TPO?

4 What do the RICS and the CIOB stand for?

5 What further qualifications and training would a graduate require who has just completed their degree to become a full member of the RICS?

6 Name six items contained in a valuation report?

7 What does a dilapidation survey look at and whom might it be carried out for?

8 What would you typically look for on a stock condition survey?

9 How would you undertake a measured survey and what equipment would you require?

10 What items would require maintenance on the external envelope of a building?

11 What should repair schedules contain?

12 Name a typical dangerous structure element.

13 What is radon gas?

14 How does a moisture meter work?

15 What essential PPE would be required for a roof void survey?

16 For what parts of a survey may a building surveyor obtain the services of a specialist contractor?

## Grading criteria: Unit 15

| To achieve a pass grade the evidence must show that the learner is able to: | To achieve a merit grade the evidence must show that, in addition to the pass criteria, the learner is able to: | To achieve a distinction grade the evidence must show that, in addition to the pass and merit criteria, the learner is able to: |
|---|---|---|
| **P1** describe the roles and responsibilities of the building surveyor, training and qualifications required, and identify the other members of the building team with whom the building surveyor interacts **Assessment practice pages 458, 479** | **M1** prepare a typical job description for a building surveyor and explain the building surveyor's interaction with other members of the building team **Assessment practice pages 458, 479** | |
| **P2** demonstrate basic understanding of the reasons for surveying buildings and identify the procedures, equipment and techniques used **Assessment practice pages 465, 479** | **M2** identify, and explain the uses of, the surveying equipment required for different surveying tasks **Assessment practice pages 468, 479** **M3** identify and evaluate the ways in which survey data is recorded and presented **Assessment practice pages 476, 479** | **D1** explain the implications of health and safety legislation, contractual obligations and legal constraints in the context of survey work **Assessment practice pages 473, 479** |
| **P3** execute simple measured, dilapidation and condition surveys for a low-rise domestic or commercial building **Assessment practice pages 476, 479** **P4** produce final measured, dilapidation and condition survey reports for a low-rise domestic or commercial building **Assessment practice pages 476, 479** **P5** produce schedules of maintenance and repair including planned maintenance **Assessment practice pages 478, 479** | **M4** collect and compile survey data using standard techniques and record and present the data in appropriate formats **Assessment practice pages 476, 479** | **D2** evaluate key surveying operations in terms of health, safety and welfare **Assessment practice pages 474, 479** **D3** discriminate between, and explain the applications of, the various types of building survey **Assessment practice pages 465, 479** |

# Index

structural appraisal 463–4
building technology 224
buyer 273

CAD 318–19, 330–6
  plotting 328–9
  red lining 334
  rendering and photo-realisation 332
  techniques 327–9
  walk-throughs 332–3
calculations 77–81
  addition and subtraction 83
  algebraic expressions 83–4
  binomial theorem 92–4
  BODMAS 77
  brackets and factors 83–4
  decimal places 80–1
  FOIL rule 84
  formulae and equations 84–91
  geometric techniques 112–17
  graphical techniques 126–33
  loading 82–3
  multiplication and division 83
  perimeters, areas and volumes 96–111
  significant figures 80, 81
  standard form 81–2, 83
  statistical techniques 133–9
  trigonometric techniques 118–24
  use of calculator 76, 77–8
CAWS 327
CDM Regulations (1994) 10, 13, 192–4, 202, 282
  health and safety 4–5, 6–7
  method statements 20
  risk assessments 14
cement 170, 177, 179, 265
cement mixers 265
cement plasters 255
centre line calculation 367
CESMM3 368
CFCs 44, 52–3
chalk-line marker 406–7
chemical/sulphate attack 177–8, 179
chemicals 31, 169, 262
CIAT 202
CIOB 286, 373, 394–5, 458
cladding 226

clerk of works 195, 456
client 4–5, 193, 198, 199, 455
  rights of 200–1
clothing and heat 147–8
coal industry 53–4, 59
cold bridging 256
collective means of protection 11
columns 159, 207
comfort disturbance see human
component drawings 342–3
component schedules 344–5
compression 161–2, 163
concrete 170–1, 174, 175–6, 205
  blocks 247
  efflorescence 178, 179
  embedded energy 260
  forms of construction 230
  foundations 380
  slump 171, 190
  sulphate attack 177, 179
concrete piles 240–1
condensation 150
condition surveys 454
cones and pyramids 101
confined access 305
confined space working 17, 30
construction drawings 208
  construction detailing 211–12
Construction (Health, Safety and Welfare) Regulations
  (1996) 12, 13, 14, 263
construction methods 205–7
  multiple modules 206
construction project 282–5, 305–6
  alterations 280
  design phase 278–9, 282
  maintenance phase 280
  management functions 292–7
  planning stage 278–9, 282, 288–91
  production phase 279–80, 298–306
  production planning 284
  resources required 286–8
contaminated ground 32, 57, 238–9
contract programme 289, 292–3, 304
  bar chart 307
contractors 189, 193–4
contracts 201, 284

environmental issues 202, 259–65
    construction techniques 67–70, 259–60
    energy consumption 67–8
    foundation construction 244–5
    legislation 61, 202
    and materials 68–9, 169, 259
    *see also* natural environment
equations 84–91, 130–3
estimating 360, 370–3
    area method 372
    CIOB code 373, 394–5
    costing data 385–6
    cubic methods 372
    elemental 372
    labour costs 375–6
    material costs 374
    net cost 370
    overheads 371
    plant costs 376–7
    and profit 370–1, 396
    tender price indices 386
    traditional cost modelling 383–4
    unit or number basis 372
    unit rates 377–81
    wastage allowance 291
    *see also* tendering
estimator 273, 277
excavations 32, 242–3
excavators 265, 287

F10 document 5, 6, 7
facilities managers 196, 200
factorisation 88–9
factors of safety 164–5
feasibility 186, 187, 278–9, 282, 384
final account 363
final certificate 279
financial side of project 292, 298
finishes 254–6
flat roofs 227
flood plains 45
floors 210, 216, 250
forces 159–60
    concurrent/non-concurrent 160
    coplanar 160
    parallelogram of 166

    triangle of 166
forecasting 298
forestry 47
forklift trucks 264–5, 287
forms of construction 225–7
    implications of 227–30
formulae and equations 84–91
    quadratic equations 88–91
    simultaneous equations 87–8, 90–1
    transposition of formulae 85–7
fossil fuels 53–4, 259
foundation design 236–42
    Building Regulations 243–5
    excavations 242–3
    influencing factors 236, 237–42
    loading of building 236, 237
    piling 239–41
    and soil conditions 237–9
    subsoil shrinkage 241–2
    and water in ground 241–2
foundations 215, 243–5
    pad and raft 245
    setting out 446–7
    unit rate example 380
frames 159
frost attack 177, 179
fungal attack 177, 179

GA drawings 339, 340, 341, 343
gangers 277, 295
Gantt chart 134, 306
general foreperson 273, 277
general operatives 273, 277
geometric techniques 112–17
    angles 112–14
    circles 117
    triangles 114–16, 123, 124
glass 174, 206
global warming 42, 43, 49, 51, 67, 202, 259
    and choice of materials 169
Glulam construction 206, 229
goods received sheets 309
GPS equipment 468
graphical detailing 314–54
    abbreviations 324
    CAD detailing 318–19

plastics 173, 175
point loads 161, 165
polar measurement 430
pollution 52, 62, 63, 259
   air 44
   industrial 56, 57
   noise 261–2
   water 49, 56
porosity of materials 174–5
portal frames 206, 207, 224, 225, 229–30, 247–8
PPE see Personal Protective Equipment
precast concrete 70, 230
prefabrication 226, 227–8, 260
price book 372
primary setting-out points 441, 442
principal contractor 5, 276, 277, 456
   and tendering 395
procurement of contractor 279, 283–4, 346
production drawings 339–42
production information documents 346
production phase of project 279–80
   management functions 298–306
   organisational aspects 299–304
profits and estimating 370–1, 396
programme of works 189, 304, 306
programming techniques 307–8
progress monitoring 302
project information systems 326–7
project planning see planning
published price books 386
Pythagoras' rule 115, 116, 117, 437
quadratic equations 88–91, 131–3
quantity surveyor 196, 214, 273, 455

radiation of heat 147
radon gas 235, 465
raft foundations 245
ranging poles 406
raw materials extraction 59
reasonably practicable concept 25, 193, 287
recycling 57, 69–70, 169, 260
refurbishment 280, 285
Register of Drawings 349
repair schedule 454, 462–3, 478
requisitioning materials 294, 302
resident engineer 196

resource depletion 259
resources for construction 286–8
   controlling 298
   documentation 302–3, 309–10
   labour 286
   role of planner 272–3
retail outlets 224–5
RIBA
   and disputes 201
   Plan of Work 185, 186–91, 384, 385
RICS 458
RIDDOR (1995) 34, 35, 36
risk 207
   matrix 14–15
   see also hazards
risk assessment 5, 10, 12, 13, 299
   5 steps 11, 25–6
   forms 26–7
   IDERR 25
   surveying 407, 472
roles and responsibilities 272–7
   and accountability 277
   team working 274–7
roofs 216–17, 227
   construction of 250–3
   flat and pitched 227, 251
   green planted 169
   insulation and ventilation 251–4
   trussed rafters 251–2
room temperatures 148–9

safety inspections 20–1
safety policies 28
scaffolding 17, 264
schedule of work 353
schedules 344–6, 392
   component 344–5
section drawings 210–11, 235
security on site 301
setting out 402, 441–7
   corners of building 442–4
   equipment 442, 444–5
   levels 444–7
   preparation 441–2
sewers levelling survey 427–8
shear force 162, 163

SI units 78–9
sick building syndrome 60
Simpson's rule 107, 108, 109
simultaneous equations 87–8, 90–1
  graphical techniques 130
sine rule 120, 121, 123
single-storey buildings 226
site accommodation 300–1
site diary 189, 190
site documentation 309–10
site investigation 231–6
  ground investigation 233–5
  radon gas 235
site management 31, 64–6
site manager 272, 277
site meetings 31, 302
site plans 210
  layout plan 292, 299, 441
  survey drawing 337
site supervisor 273
sketch plans 187, 198, 208
slump test 190
SMM7 327, 361, 362, 366, 368, 372
soil 44–5, 232, 237–9
  compressibility 238
  contaminated 238–9
  and drainage 45
  profile 232
sound 153–5
  nature of hearing 154
specifications 214, 314, 326–7, 392–3
  descriptions and quantities 366–7
  information 346
  sample specification 215–17
  written information 353–4
staffs, surveying 417, 418, 419, 421, 445, 447
stairs 254
standard deviation 136–8
statistical techniques 133–9
  cumulative frequency 135–6
  mean 135, 136
steel piles 240
steelwork 174, 345
  steel frames 230
strain 162–3
stress fatigue 178, 179

stresses 161–5
  factors of safety 164–5
structural engineer 195–6, 200, 455–6
structural steel 205, 206, 226
structures, forces acting upon 158–66
  loadings 159, 161
  stresses 161–5
struts and ties 158
subcontract labour 286
subcontractors 5, 288, 295, 456
  liaison 302
  and tendering 395–6
subsoil investigation 231–6
subsoil shrinkage 241–2
substructure 207, 231–45
superstructure 207, 247–54
suppliers and tendering 396
surface resistances 151–2
survey reports 454, 477–8
surveying 402
  angular measurement 430–9
  geometric 402
  levelling survey 416–28
  reconnaissance 407–9
  *see also* building survey; levelling; linear
sustainability issues 67, 260, 261
  design 192
  materials 64, 169
symbols 323–4, 325
  line 322, 323
  map 414

take-off list 364–5
  cut and shuffle 366
team working 185, 274–7
temperature and comfort 146–50
  humidity and ventilation 149–50
Temporary Bench Mark 416, 441, 442, 444
temporary facilities 284, 292
tender price indices 386, 387–8
tendering 273, 360, 363, 389, 395
  activity schedules 393–4
  codes of procedure 394–5
  documentation 188, 391–5, 396–7
  factors affecting level 395–7
  methods 389–91